GW00579831

GROUNDWATER: OCCURRENCE, DEVELOPMENT AND PROTECTION

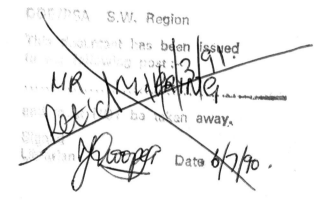

WATER PRACTICE MANUALS

GROUNDWATER: OCCURRENCE, DEVELOPMENT AND PROTECTION

EDITOR
Thomas W. Brandon, BSc, FRSC, Hon.FIWES

Compiled and Published by
The Institution of Water Engineers and Scientists,
London, England.

©Published by The Institution of Water Engineers and Scientists,
31-33 High Holborn, London WC1V 6AX,
England.

ISBN 0 901427 14 4

First published, 1986

Text photoset in 9/10pt. Times

*Printed in Great Britain
at The Lavenham Press Ltd., Lavenham, Suffolk, England.*

PREFACE

Both the former Institution of Water Engineers and the Society for Water Treatment and Examination held a well-earned reputation as learned societies responsible for the publication of authoritative works on water technology and science. In 1975 the common interests of these bodies led to their amalgamation and The Institution of Water Engineers and Scientists was formed. The new Institution has a continuing involvement in the book-publishing field with this wide-ranging series under the general title *Water Practice Manuals*.

The books will appear, over a period of several years, as a series of separate volumes and will deal mainly with the engineering and scientific elements concerned with the water cycle. They will also focus attention on more general subjects which, in England and Wales, have now become the responsibility of the Regional Water Authorities which were set up by the Water Act 1973. In recording what has become, or is likely to become, accepted current practice the books will not be confined entirely to British experience. Where relevant, references will be made to overseas practice and, in particular, to thinking and developments within the EEC. In due course the whole series will form a basic library for those concerned with the technology and science of water.

With this volume, five books in the series have now been published:

Book 1: The structure and management of the British water industry
Book 2: Recreation: water and land
Book 3: Water supply and sanitation in developing countries
Book 4: Water distribution systems
Book 5: Groundwater: occurrence, development and protection.

Groundwater projects now demand a knowledge not only of drilling and construction methods, pumps and pumping costs, contractual procedures and specifications, but *inter alia* of hydrogeology, surface and downhole geophysics, hydrogeochemistry (including tracer studies), and mathematical modelling. The aim of this volume is to describe all of these—and many other, including pollution control—techniques and to lead the reader to an understanding of the best modern practices.

In Britain groundwater provides about 25 per cent of the total public water supply but the proportion is higher in many European countries. Over the last 20 years attention has been increasingly directed to the conjunctive use of groundwater and surface water rather than using groundwater for direct supply only. Schemes are described employing groundwater for conjunctive use and for river regulation, and for using surplus surface water to recharge groundwater resources.

Although a relatively small country, Britain has a very diverse geology. Many permeable rocks are exploited as groundwater sources, ranging from hard but fractured granites, yielding small supplies, to highly porous river sands and gravels yielding substantial supplies from riverside infiltration galleries. Between these extremes lie many aquifers, including the Chalk and the Permo-Triassic sandstones—the two principal British water-bearing formations.

So, whilst this book has concentrated on British groundwater sources, the geology here is so diverse that the techniques described will be applicable to groundwater studies in many parts of the World.

NOTE ON THE INSTITUTION OF WATER ENGINEERS AND SCIENTISTS

The Institution was established as The British Association of Waterworks Engineers in 1896 and was incorporated in 1911 as The Institution of Water Engineers. On 2nd January 1975 its name was changed to The Institution of Water Engineers and Scientists preliminary to the Institution and the Society for Water Treatment and Examination amalgamating on 1st September 1975. The combined Institution now has a membership of over 5900. In 1987 the Institution will join with The Institution of Public Health Engineers and The Institute of Water Pollution Control to form a new body, to be called The Institution of Water and Environmental Management.

The *objects* of the Institution are set out in its Memorandum of Association. In summary these are:

1. To advance water engineering and science and education therein.
2. To promote study and research work in water engineering and science and to publish the results thereof for the public benefit.

"Water engineering and science" means the application of engineering or scientific knowledge or skill to the treatment and supply of water, the management of rivers, the treatment of sewage and its disposal, and the control of pollution in relation to water.

The corporate membership of the Institution comprises engineers and scientists, including chemists, bacteriologists, geologists, hydrologists and others concerned with the water cycle. Corporate members must be holders of approved first degrees in engineering or science and must satisfy the Council as to their practical knowledge and experience of water engineering and science. Persons in other disciplines who occupy senior positions in the water industry or who are engaged in support services can be admitted to non-corporate membership.

Most members of the Institution in the United Kingdom work for public or quasi-public authorities. In England and Wales, these are the ten Regional Water Authorities and the statutory water companies; in Scotland, the nine Regional and three Islands Councils together with the Central Scotland Water Development Board; and in Northern Ireland, the Department of the Environment for Northern Ireland (Water Services Branch).

Other members work in central government, research and teaching establishments, or as consulting engineers. Some members are concerned with the construction of civil engineering works as contractors, or as manufacturers of equipment such as pumps or treatment plant.

Nearly 20 per cent of the members of the Institution are overseas (spread in more than 80 countries throughout the world), either because they are citizens of overseas countries or because they are working there on secondment from the United Kingdom. In addition, a substantial number of members, in particular many of those employed by consultants, are extensively engaged on overseas projects even though they are United Kingdom based. The Institution has a number of Correspondents spread throughout the world, who act as focal points for the members in their areas.

The main function of the Institution is the provision of learned society activities, i.e. the sharing of experience and the dissemination of knowledge through meetings and publications. In the United Kingdom and the Republic of Ireland there are seven Local and two Specialist Sections, each with its own programme of papers and visits to works.

The publications of the Institution, besides this range of Water Practice Manuals, include a Journal (published six times a year), Handbook, proceedings of symposia, and various reports.

ACKNOWLEDGEMENTS

The Council of The Institution of Water Engineers and Scientists acknowledges the help given in the preparation of this book by those serving the many bodies and organizations involved in the water industry and related activities.

Acknowledgements for permission to reproduce extracts from published works are included, where appropriate, in the text.

The Council also acknowledges with gratitude the work of the Manuals Subcommittee, which was set up for the planning of this series of Water Practice Manuals. The members of the Subcommittee are: H. Speight (Chairman); R. A. Bailey; T. W. Brandon; R. W. Hemphill; J. D. Jepson; B. H. Rofe; K. H. Tattersall; and B. J. Dangerfield (Subcommittee Secretary).

CONTRIBUTORS

The Council of The Institution of Water Engineers and Scientists acknowledges the considerable debt of gratitude which is due to the following who have contributed to the writing of this book.

Book Co-ordinator

W. B. Wilkinson

BSc (Eng), BSc(Geol), PhD, FICE, MIGeol, FGS, FIWES, Professor of Civil Engineering, Royal Military College of Science.

Chapter Contributors and Helpers

Chapter 1: General Introduction

Contributed by: W. B. Wilkinson   (see "Book Co-ordinator" above).

Chapter 2: The Occurrence of Groundwater in the United Kingdom

Contributed by: J. B. W. Day

BSc, FGS, (retired) lately Chief Hydro-geologist, British Geological Survey.

Chapter 3: Groundwater Chemistry

Contributed by: W. M. Edmunds

BSc, PhD, FGS, Head of Hydro-geochemistry Section, Hydrogeology Research Unit, British Geological Survey.

Chapter 4: Theory of Groundwater Flow

Contributed by: D. B. Oakes

BSc, MIWES, Head of Strategic Studies, Water Research Centre (Environment).

Chapter 5: Well Tests

Contributed by: M. J. Reeves

BSc, PhD, MCGS, FGS, Professor of Geological Engineering, University of Saskatchewan.

Chapter 6: Groundwater Modelling

Contributed by: K. R. Rushton

DSc, MICE, MIWES, Professor of Civil Engineering, University of Birmingham.

Chapter 7: Hydrogeological Investigations

Contributed by: H. G. Headworth

BSc, DIC, MIGeol, IWES, Chief Hydro-Geologist, Southern Water Authority.

A. C. Skinner

BSc, PhD, MIGeol, FGS, MIWES, Principal Resources Officer (Groundwater), Severn-Trent Water Authority.

Chapter 8: Surface Geophysical Techniques

Contributed by: R. D. Barker   MSc, PhD, MIGeol, FGS, Lecturer in Groundwater Geophysics, University of Birmingham.

Chapter 9: Downhole Geophysics

Contributed by: K. Beesley   MSc, SPWLA, EAEG, Assistant Geologging Manager, Robertson Research (formerly Geophysicist, Water Research Centre).

Chapter 10: Tracing Techniques

Contributed by: K. E. White   FInstP, Consultant (formerly Manager, Radiochemistry Department, Water Research Centre).

Chapter 11: Design of Boreholes and Wells

Contributed by: W. B. Wilkinson   (see "Book Co-ordinator", p. viii).

Chapter 12: Borehole and Well Drilling Contractual Procedures

Contributed by: A. N. Charalam-   MSc, FGS, Associate, Howard
bous   Humphreys & Partners.
R. W. Simpson   BSc, FICE, MASCE, MIGeol, FGS, FIWES, Director of Water Resources, Howard Humphreys & Partners.

Assisted by: J. D. Williams   MEng, FICE, FIWES, Consultant.
M. Simpson   BSc, FIStructE, FIHE, Consultant.

Chapter 13: Drilling and Construction Methods

Contributed by: P. K. Cruse   TD, FGS, UK Contracts Engineer and Overseas Supervisor, George Stow & Co, and Director, Stow Engineering.

Chapter 14: Development of Groundwater

Contributed by: R. A. Downing   DSc, MIGeol, MIWES, Manager, Geothermal Energy Programme, British Geological Survey.

Chapter 15: Groundwater Pollution and Protection

Contributed by: R. J. Aldrick   MSc, PhD, FGS, MIGeol, Hydrogeologist, Yorkshire Water Authority.
K. J. Edworthy   BSc, FGS, MIGeol, MIWES, Senior Hydrogeologist, Binnie and Partners.
C. P. Young   BSc, FGS, Manager, Waste Disposal to Land Group, Water Research Centre (Environment).

Chapter 16: The Law Relating to Groundwater in the United Kingdom

Contributed by: D. S. Akroyd   LLB, Solicitor, (retired) lately Assistant
                                  Director, Legal Services, Anglian Water
                                  Authority.

Assisted by: Officials of the Scottish Development
                                  Department and of the Department for the
                                  Environment for Northern Ireland (for
                                  relevant Statute Law).

CONTENTS

LIST OF ILLUSTRATIONS
(not related to specific chapters)

Chapter 1

GENERAL INTRODUCTION

BRITAIN is a small country but has a very diverse geology and a plethora of permeable rocks that can be exploited for water supply. At one extreme are the hard but fractured granites which, with careful exploration, may yield enough water for domestic, farm or small industrial supplies. At the other are the highly porous river sands and gravels which may give substantial supplies from riverside infiltration galleries. Between these there lie many aquifers including the Chalk, a fine-grained limestone, and the Permo-Triassic sandstones which are the two principal water bearing formations. The geology of UK aquifers is often complex and the intersection of the coastline by many aquifers and the prospect of saline intrusion means that a wide range of development techniques have been employed. Therefore, while this volume has focused on groundwater development in the UK the approaches described will be applicable to either groundwater resource development or to water quality or pollution problems elsewhere in the World. A detailed description of the aquifers in the UK, their water bearing properties, yields and degree of exploitation is given in Chapter 2. The quality of the water in these aquifers and the way in which changes in that quality can be used to assess the hydrochemistry, recharge, and resource potential are described in Chapter 3.

The growth and prosperity of many of the industrial cities in the UK owe much to the availability of a plentiful supply of good quality groundwater. In the late 19th and early 20th century many thousands of deep wells were constructed below London, Birmingham, Nottingham, Manchester and elsewhere. The pumped water was used for public and industrial supply. The use has increased steadily over the years and although for the country as a whole groundwater supplies only about a quarter of that supplied from surface water rivers and reservoirs, it still meets the needs of about 16 million people.

In the UK the proportion of groundwater to surface water is smaller than that of many other countries in Europe. Before the middle of the 19th century the advantages of groundwater in terms of public health were unknown and it was only following the cholera epidemics of the late 19th and early 20th centuries that the benefits were fully recognised. In Hamburg, Germany, the cholera epidemic of 1897 affected 20000 people and caused the deaths of 8000 as a result of drinking contaminated surface water. Following these disasters the maritime nations in Europe accepted the need for the treatment and disinfection of all surface water while many of the continental countries rejected surface water completely and used only groundwater. The use of treated surface water has only been relatively recently reintroduced into some European countries.

As indicated above, groundwater now makes up about 25 per cent of the total water supply demand in the UK (excluding that used for cooling by CEGB). Two-thirds goes to public supply and most of the rest to industry. UK agriculture makes little demand on groundwater. Up to 20 years ago groundwater was developed on a local basis, water being pumped directly into supply. This method of abstraction is not without its problems. In some areas withdrawal over many years exceeded natural recharge and led to a fall in water levels, a reduction in river or spring flow and a deterioration in quality as poor quality water was drawn from deep in the aquifer or, for coastal aquifers, from the sea. However, the occurrence of such problems and a search for solutions led to improved methods of development and to a more basic understanding of the physical processes governing groundwater flow and a mathematical description of these (Chapter 4).

Over the last 20 years considerable attention has been given to the regional development of groundwater in conjunction with surface water rather than, as was formerly the case, using groundwater only for direct supply. This regional approach would have been very difficult, if not impossible, without the introduction of the Water Resources Act 1963. The Act established an administrative structure for the planning and management of water resources on a catchment basis. During the decade 1964-74 many regional schemes were investigated and these included the use of groundwater for river regulation, conjunctive use, and artificial recharge of surplus surface water. The water authorities, set up under the Water Act 1973, have now implemented a number of these regional schemes. The range of options available for the development of groundwater is described in Chapter 14. The many investigations which commenced in the 1960s gave a tremendous boost to the knowledge and understanding of the hydrogeology of the UK, groundwater engineering and the regional management of water resources. Many new techniques were developed. For example, advanced analytical techniques of the type described in Chapter 5 were used to determine the hydraulic properties of aquifers from single and group pump tests. Mathematical modelling of groundwater systems was introduced.

Fifteen years ago the application of modelling techniques was relatively new. They are now widely used but unfortunately there is a tendency to believe that these models will provide the solution of all groundwater and operational management problems. This is not so. To be of value for quantitative predictions, indeed so as not to be positively misleading, models must be based on reliable data. They must be subject to calibration and adjustment during the project development or operational stage as new data become available. The advantages and pitfalls of mathematical modelling are described in Chapter 6.

The impetus to groundwater development given by the investigations of the late 1960s and early 1970s led to the expansion of surface (Chapter 8) and downhole (Chapter 9) geophysics. They are now in routine use in all groundwater projects.

A philosophy was developed to cover groundwater investigations from the preliminary desk study stage through to the introduction of the project in a regional policy. This encompassed not only the technical aspects of hydrogeology, well engineering and operational management, but also examined the impact that a scheme would have on the overall environment, including the lives of the people who live and work in the development areas. Such considerations are examined in Chapter 7.

Multi-disciplinary teams are now needed to work on regional projects and these may include a hydrogeologist, groundwater engineer, mathematician, chemist, economist, environmental botanist and others. The strong divisions which existed between the geologist and the groundwater engineer have been broken down. It is now necessary for the groundwater engineer to have an understanding of the geology of the aquifers in which he is working, the physics of groundwater flow, groundwater chemistry, geophysics and modelling. The hydrogeologist or geologist for his part must have a working knowledge of well and borehole drilling and construction methods, pumps and pumping costs, contractual procedures and specifications. These latter topics are covered in Chapters 11, 12 and 13.

Groundwater in the UK is generally of good quality. However in recent years an increasing number of cases of deterioration in quality have been reported. There are many reasons for this decline but common causes are badly located domestic and industrial waste disposal sites, certain modern agricultural practices, saline intrusion and over-pumping of resources. Growing awareness of these problems has led to an increasing number of field investigations and research studies into both natural and man-made changes that can occur in the quality of groundwater. Attention has particularly focused on man's activities that have caused, or are likely to cause, pollution and on the ways in which these can be controlled. Means of investigating groundwater pollution and possible solutions are described in Chapter 15.

Groundwater tracing techniques using either natural or artificial tracers have made major advances over the last decade. These are principally used in groundwater quality or pollution studies but in some cases have been applied to resource evaluation projects. The range of techniques available and guidance on the choice of the most appropriate tracer for any given situation are described in Chapter 10.

The Water Act 1945, Water Resources Act 1963, Water Act 1973 and Control of Pollution Act 1974 have all had a profound impact in establishing a legal and administrative framework in which the water resources in the UK can be developed in a controlled way to meet the needs of present and future generations. However, in addition to these statutory requirements there is a large body of case law relating to groundwater. It is important that groundwater practitioners should have an insight into this as well as the statutory requirements so Chapter 16 deals with legislative aspects of groundwater.

The aim of this volume is to describe the accepted principles and to lead the reader to an understanding of the best modern practice in groundwater engineering and hydrogeology. It is not its purpose to describe current research. However it is useful to be able to call upon specialist advice when problems arise and a brief description of those bodies in the UK who have specialist teams looking at some of the more fundamental research issues is given below.

Regional Water Authorities. A substantial contribution is made to hydrogeological research by the regional water authorities in England and Wales. Several of the authorities, relying on groundwater as their principal source of water supply, employ teams of hydrogeologists and groundwater engineers to ensure that present resources are properly managed and, where available, subsurface resources are developed. They are also concerned with groundwater quality, waste disposal and groundwater pollution. The authorities have become involved in research either directly by using their own staff or in cooperation with central research organizations or university departments.

British Geological Survey—Hydrogeology Unit. The Hydrogeology Unit of BGS is concerned with fundamental and applied research into the occurrence and behaviour of groundwater. The fundamental research is directed towards the quantitative and qualitative evaluation of the roles of groundwater in the hydrological cycle and as a geological agent. Applied research undertaken at home and overseas covers the full range of hydrogeology from water resource development to geothermal energy. BGS is responsible for the National Well Record Collection, collected for more than a century and continuously maintained.

Institute of Hydrology. The Institute is responsible for a broad programme of basic research into hydrology and also undertakes projects of an applied nature at home and overseas. Part of the programme involves some sub-surface studies, particularly related to sub-surface processes, while some of the overseas projects include groundwater applications.

Water Research Centre. This industrial research association was formed particularly to meet the research needs of the water industry and of Central Government. The centre has an extensive programme of applied hydrological, hydrogeological and groundwater engineering research which has essentially been concerned, from both a quantity and quality viewpoint, with the optimal management of existing resources and the development of new water resources. Over the last few years much more stress has been placed on groundwater pollution problems. Work has been undertaken both within the UK and overseas.

Universities. Funds are made available from the Natural Environment Research Council and from the Scientific Engineering Research Council to support university research in hydrogeology and groundwater engineering. There is no separate department in these disciplines although there are sub-departments of hydrology and hydrogeology within the Department of Environmental Studies at Lancaster. Postgraduate hydrogeology courses leading to higher degrees are offered at University College, London, and at Birmingham University in the Geology Department. Hydrogeological and groundwater engineering research is carried out by university staff and their postgraduate students in Civil Engineering, Geology, Geography and Environmental Science Departments at several universities.

The active nature of hydrogeological and groundwater engineering research in the UK is reflected in the programmes of the scientific and engineering societies. The Hydrogeological Group and the Engineering Geology Group of the Geological Society of London have formed the principal forum but meetings are often held under the auspices of the Institution of Water Engineers and Scientists and the Institution of Civil Engineers. The Water Research Centre has held several international conferences over the last few years on different aspects of groundwater. In 1977 the General Assembly of the International Association of Hydrogeologists was held in Birmingham and a further meeting was held in 1985 in Cambridge. Both have been organized in association with the Hydrogeology Sub-Committee of the Royal Society's National Committee for Geology.

No volume of this type would be complete without some reference to safety. Indeed everyone engaged on work associated with wells or boreholes should be aware and able to identify hazards arising from gases or other causes. **In the past deaths have occurred through ignorance.** Measures should be taken to prevent accidents but these do occur and personnel should be trained in the appropriate emergency procedures[1,2]. Recently a number of investigations of landfill sites containing hazardous waste have been undertaken to assess the impact that leachate from these will have on groundwater quality. Boreholes have been drilled through these waste materials into underlying aquifers and a safety procedure for working in such conditions has been developed[3]. It cannot be emphasised too strongly that all personnel concerned with groundwater works should study the references quoted.

REFERENCES

1. British Drilling Association 1980 "Surface drilling—Part 1 of Code of safe drilling practice", BDA, Brentwood, Essex.
2. The Institution of Civil Engineers 1972 "Safety in wells and boreholes".
3. Naylor, J. A., Rowland, C. D. and Barber, C. 1978 "The investigation of landfill sites", Technical Report No. 91, Water Research Centre, Medmenham.

Chapter 2

GROUNDWATER SOURCES IN THE UNITED KINGDOM

1. PRINCIPLES OF WATER FLOW UNDERGROUND

MAIN DEFINITIONS

THE definitions of groundwater adopted in this chapter are largely those of Pfannkuch[1] but other definitions, such as those of Lohman *et al*[2] may sometimes be preferred. However, following Pfannkuch, 'underground water' is considered to be all water below the surface of the ground and includes 'vadose water' (this term includes soil water)—water suspended in the unsaturated zone of aeration between the ground surface and the water table—and finally 'groundwater' itself, contained within the zone of saturation below the water table. A proper consideration of saturated zone processes cannot hope to be comprehensive without some examination of the processes operating within the unsaturated or vadose zone through which almost all groundwater has first to pass after leaving the surface sector of the hydrological cycle.

SOIL ZONE

Water in the soil zone is commonly considered not to lie within the province of the hydrogeologist, but within that of the agricultural hydrologist. In the UK rarely has the soil not been worked and reworked continually so that its physical state is constantly changed; the complexity which such changes impart to flow mechanisms is further compounded by continual wetting and drying cycles through the action of rainfall and direct evaporation and yet further complexed by the evaporative action of plants ('transpiration'). The term 'evapo-transpiration' has been coined to cover the combined physical processes of evaporation, transpiration and sublimation, but by common usage 'evaporation' is also now considered—albeit loosely—to refer to the combined effects of these processes.

The physical boundary between 'soil' and 'rock' is sometimes sharp, sometimes gradual. On hill slopes gravitational soil 'creep' can give rise to natural sharp division and in cultivated areas the presence of a 'plough pan' can provide a sharp but wholly artificial boundary. Conversely, smooth gradation from soil to weathered rock ('subsoil' is a commonly used convenient term which in practice is almost impossible to define precisely) tends to occur in flattish or gently sloping areas not subject to repeated tillage.

Soil mapping within the United Kingdom is carried out by the Soil Survey but is by no means complete; an up-to-date picture of the situation may be obtained by reference to this Survey's various maps and publications. Many different soil series and associations have been described; two typical classifications are those of Russell[3] and Taylor[4], the latter with particular reference to Welsh soils. However, the criteria commonly used are not for the most part relevant to soil hydrology where consideration of the soil's drainage characteristics is more appropriate. Interpretation of accepted soil classifications by the Soil Survey for the United Kingdom Flood Study[5] enabled production of a generalised map showing infiltration characteristics related to flood runoff; five "winter rain acceptance

TABLE 2.I. **Winter Rain Acceptance Indices**
(after Rodda et al[6] and NERC[5])

Drainage group	Depth to impermeable layer (mm)	Slope classes								
		0–2°			2–8°			>8°		
		Permeability rates above impermeable layer								
		Rapid	Medium	Slow	Rapid	Medium	Slow	Rapid	Medium	Slow
Rarely waterlogged within 600 mm at any time	800		1		1	2		1	2	3
	400–800	2	1		1	2		3	2	4
	400	3						—	—	—
Commonly waterlogged within 600 mm during winter	800	2		3		2	4			
	400–800							—		—
	400	3								
Commonly waterlogged within 600 mm winter and summer	800					5		—	—	—
	400–800									
	400									

Notes: **1** = very high; **2** = high; **3** = moderate; **4** = low; **5** = very low. Upland peat and peaty soils are in Class **5**; urban soils are unclassified.

indices" ranging from very high, through high, moderate, low to very low (see Table 2.I) were derived mainly by relating depth and frequency of waterlogging above an impermeable layer to surface slope.

With the exception of peat, few detailed hydrogeological studies of soil types have been made. Peat and peaty soil associations, however, are common in moorland areas suitable for afforestation, and the effects of artificial drainage on stream flows—and hence bank erosion—have been marked in many cases. In a typical study of peat hydrology[7] in four small catchments at Moor House in the northern Pennines, significant differences were found in the runoff characteristics as between drained and eroded catchments and those still in a natural state.

There is much confusion in the literature between 'infiltration' and 'percolation', but in this chapter infiltration, following Pfannkuch[1] and Rodda et al[6], is considered to relate to water flowing through the surface, under gravitational and capillary forces. 'Percolation', on the other hand, is the downward movement through the normally unsaturated profile to the saturated zone and thus follows the definition of Rodda et al[6]. "Interflow" (subsurface runoff) occurs as lateral movement of water within the soil zone whilst temporarily saturated, commonly on sloping ground.

Perhaps the soil zone's main interest to the hydrogeologist is its ability to soak up rainfall during much of the year when the upwards cumulative flux of evapotranspiration is greater than the downward input from rainfall so that percolation of water below the base of the soil layer—and hence recharge to underlying aquifers—does not occur. The soil acts to some extent as a reservoir which can within certain limits balance the moisture demands of vegetation against available rainfall. When evaporation exceeds infiltration over a given period a soil moisture deficit (defined as the amount of water required to restore the soil to field capacity) results, the magnitude of which depends largely on the nature and thickness of the soil. This deficit has to be made good by an excess of rainfall over evaporation before percolation can occur. In Britain recharge to aquifers occurs mainly during the winter months October to March; during the summer months significant recharge, although by no means unknown locally, is rare on a regional basis. Nevertheless it has frequently been observed that recharge can occur, as evidenced by rising water levels in wells, before soil moisture deficits have been fully satisfied; thus it appears that under certain conditions of heavy rainfall more than one mechanism of downward movement can operate.

THE UNSATURATED ZONE BELOW THE BASE OF THE SOIL

This zone extends from the base of the soil to the water table which forms the upper surface of the saturated zone. Neither the upper nor the lower limits of the zone are necessarily capable of simple or permanent definition; at the top it may be difficult to determine precisely where soil or sub-soil ends and weathered rock begins; the bottom of the zone will fluctuate vertically in response to ratio changes in the components of the percolation/recharge/drainage flux.

Water enters the unsaturated zone from the base of the overlying soil. Unsaturated flow may occur under the influence of both capillary and gravitational forces. Water moves from areas of high to low energy potential and the total energy potential at any point is the sum of these two components. Movement will be downward only when gravity dominates and it is frequently upward—although it can be in any direction—in response to evaporative tensions, at least within two or three metres below the ground surface. As within the soil, water exists throughout the unsaturated zone both in liquid and vapour form so that when percolation is not actually occurring much of the liquid is held by capillary forces within the rock. The speed of movement of water is largely governed by the size of voids and pore spaces and, most importantly, the degree of communication between these voids. The presence of an impermeable band may also limit downward movement.

Once the rock voids are filled with water the mechanism of downward movement in a homogeneous porous medium is usually one of piston-like displacement so that a quantity of water entering the surface displaces a like quantity at the base of the zone. However, these flow mechanisms are still subject to debate and research at the present time.

In limestone country—Britain's major aquifer, the Chalk, is a type of limestone—the presence of a subsurface fossil drainage system consisting of a series of vertical or sub-vertical 'pipes' is much more common than generally supposed. The tops of these pipes are more or less funnel-shaped and act as collectors for interflow whenever rainfall exceeds the infiltration capacity of the soil and local moisture deficits are satisfied. Within a few metres of the surface, weathering influences the degree of 'openness' of naturally-occurring joints and fissures; it is arguable whether surplus interflow reaches the water table directly via such voids or, more probably in most cases, whether the void network tends to channel much of the water more or less laterally to pipes and thus rapidly downwards to the water table. These pipes were formed under peri-glacial conditions towards the end of the glacial period when periodic, probably seasonal, melting of local icecaps gave rise to large quantities of melt water. Away from Chalk valleys (now dry in many cases) the only escape route for the melt water was via the pipes which were dissolved out of the Chalk by the action of the weakly-acidic water. The horizontal spacing of the pipes varies considerably, but their centres can be as little apart as 15-20 metres and where exposed may be seen to extend 10-15 metres below the surface. Pipes are commonly associated with thin overlying semi-permeable material such as the peri-glacial geological superficial deposit known as Clay-with-flints, which now more or less fills most of the pipes to their full depth. Close examination of exposed pipes usually reveals evidence of occasional modern water movement, and sudden subsidences within Chalk outcrops almost invariably involve 'pipes' which have either been enlarged or have had their superficial infilling washed away by the introduction of artificial drainage (land drains, roof drainage to soakaways, etc). In built-up areas such subsidences are not uncommon and sufficiently dramatic to attract media attention.

The presence of fissures and pipes explains the phenomenon of "bypass flow" which causes rises in the water table before soil moisture deficits are fully satisfied. Further evidence is provided by isotope (tritium, ^{3}H) studies of unsaturated Chalk porewater and groundwater (see Chapter 10).

Smith et al[8] first demonstrated the use of ^{3}H (artificially derived from testing atomic fusion weapons) as a tracer for the elucidation of water movement through Chalk unsaturated zones at a site in Berkshire. A ^{3}H concentration peak at 4 m depth was considered to indicate slow downwards piston-flow at a rate of about 0.8 m per year. The ^{3}H values in the peak (about 600 TU*) must have been derived from precipitation during the springs of 1963 and 1964. Furthermore the proportion of percolation following the 'slow' (piston-flow) route was estimated at 85 per cent with the balance gaining rapid access to the saturated zone via fissures and pipes.

More recent research, mostly in connection with investigations into groundwater nitrate pollution, has revealed similar pronounced peaks—always more than 200 TU− at depths between 5 and 14 m in a number of Middle/Upper Chalk profiles (Foster and Young[9])—see Table 2.II. After allowance for local factors and the

---

*One TU (tritium unit) = One tritium atom in 10^{18} hydrogen atoms

TABLE 2.II.   Depths Below Ground Level to Peak Tritium Concentrations in the Chalk
(after Foster and Young[9])

Location	Number of boreholes	Sampling date	Depth to peak (m)	Long-term average effective rainfall (mm) assuming 75 mm root constant
Cambridgeshire	1	1976	5	130
West Norfolk	5	1976/7	9–12	160
Isle of Thanet	1	1975	7.5	200
Oxfordshire	1	1975	7.5	210
Surrey	2	1975/7	8–11	240
Hampshire	1	1975	8–11	315
Sussex	1	1977	12.5	330

half-life of ^{3}H, each peak is consistent with the passage of time since 1963/64 and with a steady downward intergranular movement less than 1 m per year.

The precise mechanism of Chalk unsaturated flow remains controversial. Unfissured Chalk even above the water table remains virtually saturated because of its minute pore throat diameters (typically, 1μm, Price et al[10]) which must severely restrict physical movement under gravity alone. Foster[11] has proposed a 'mixing' of relatively static pore water with more mobile fissure water whereby molecular (^{3}H and other solutes) diffusion and exchange processes may be dominant. Other authors[12,13] have extended and broadened the concept but the situation for the Chalk and other UK aquifers is complex and likely to involve a number of mechanisms.

THE SATURATED ZONE

The zone of saturation ("zone of phreatic water", Davis and De Wiest[14]) of a geological formation is that part of the rock, below the water table or pressure surface, in which all voids are filled with water at or above atmospheric pressure. The base of the zone is commonly indeterminate but may be defined by the occurrence of totally impermeable rock (aquifuge); the top is either the water table or, in the case of confined aquifers, the base of the confining stratum. Since a water table commonly fluctuates seasonally, the top of the saturated zone of an unconfined aquifer is not fixed and the zone within which the water table moves vertically is known as the 'zone of fluctuation'. In Britain, the water table is normally lowest in autumn (October to November) and highest in early spring (February to March). Immediately above the water table is a thin capillary zone, in which the voids are water-filled and which varies from a few millimetres thick in gravel through about 6-40 cm in various grades of sand to a metre or more in silt (Todd[15]).

Water within the saturated zone is truly groundwater which no longer moves in response to gravity drainage but sub-horizontally in response to an energy gradient. The water movement occurs from areas of high to low pressure. The velocity of flow is governed by the aquifer's permeability and porosity and the hydraulic gradient expressed through Darcy's Law (see Chapter 4).

All groundwater in its natural state is dynamic, however slowly, and the appropriate physical laws apply. From its point of entry into the saturated zone the water tends to move normal to the equipotential lines in the direction of the natural discharge point—a spring or seepage—which serves the particular catchment.

Most British aquifers have a high degree of heterogeneity and anisotropy and water tends to move along preferred pathways in the saturated aquifer, many of which are within the present day, or previous, zones of fluctuation. For it is within this regularly-resaturated zone that most potential is offered for solution of the rock, particularly if it is calcareous, and it is here that primary cracks and joints become opened out to form secondary fissures and other discontinuities within the rock. The term fissure is commonly, but not necessarily, held to relate to vertical or highly inclined planar open cracks, but horizontal planar voids often associated with bedding planes (or in the case of the Chalk, tabular flints) are not uncommon. Networks of inter-communicating tabular voids also occur.

Fissuring, of course, extends below the minimum level of the water table but it has been established by downhole geophysical surveys, including CCTV observations, and by pump tests in boreholes (see Chapters 5 and 9) that the frequency and degree of openness of fissures decreases markedly with depth below this level.

Since groundwater flows from higher to lower elevations, linear concentrations of fissure flows can occur beneath topographic valleys, wet or dry, and such flow concentrations with relatively high velocities in which turbulent flow may be dominant still further increase potential for solution; in limestone aquifers the distinction between fissure and karstic flow (where "underground rivers" are a reality) is difficult to define. It is probable that karstic flow paths radially approach all large limestone springs, but in Britain true regional karstic conditions are rare and virtually confined to the Carboniferous Limestone rocks of the Mendip Hills in Somerset and of the Derbyshire Dome.

Artificial abstraction by wells distorts the regional patterns of groundwater movement so that some groundwater which would otherwise have eventually reached a natural outlet is diverted to and enters the well. Thus all artificial abstraction of groundwater is, in the long term, at the expense of the natural discharge.

2.   AQUIFERS—CHARACTERISTICS AND DISTRIBUTION

MAIN DEFINITIONS

An *aquifer* is a permeable geological stratum capable of containing and transmitting groundwater under natural field conditions. Implicit in this definition is an aquifer's ability to yield significant quantities of water to wells penetrating its saturated zone.

By contrast, and in descending order of permeability, are *aquitards* which although containing water and able to transmit it at very slow rates, will not readily yield water to wells (they are thus significant in studies of the regional movement of groundwater between aquifers), *aquicludes* which will store water but not transmit it (such as clay) and *aquifuges*, which will neither store nor transport water, for instance an unweathered, unfissured, crystalline granite. The above terms cannot be precisely defined in terms of their measurable physical properties. For instance, a formation in a desert area, which yields a few m^3/day, might be considered a good aquifer, whereas in more favoured areas where much higher yielding rocks occur the same formation could be considered an aquitard. Despite their qualitative nature, it is felt that such descriptive terms, because of their familiarity, continue to be useful under many circumstances and they have been retained here. However Lohman et al[2] have proposed that they should be supplanted by the term 'confining bed', qualified by a suitable modifer such as 'slightly permeable' or 'moderately permeable'.

Lithologically an aquifer can consist of almost any consolidated or unconsolidated sedimentary formation with primary or secondary permeability. An aquifer is *homogeneous* if its properties are the same at every point and *isotropic* if its properties at any point are the same in all directions.

HYDRAULIC CHARACTERISTICS OF AQUIFERS; FORMATION CONSTANTS

In order to quantify the potential of an aquifer to store and to yield water it is necessary to determine experimentally its relevant physical characteristics. The *porosity* of consolidated media depends on cementation, solution and fracturing of rock; in unconsolidated media it depends on the size, shape and packing of the grains. The porosity of a rock or soil is a measure of the contained interstices or voids expressed as the ratio (percentage) of the volume of interstices to the total volume[15] (and see Table 2.III).

TABLE 2.III. **Representative Values of Porosity**
(after Morris and Johnson[16])

Material		Porosity (per cent)	Material	Porosity (per cent)
Coarse gravel	} Repacked samples	28	Loess	49
Medium gravel		32	Peat	92
Fine gravel		34	Schist	38
Coarse sand		39	Siltstone	35
Medium sand		39	Claystone	43
Fine sand		43	Shale	6
Silt		46	Till, mostly silt	34
Clay		42	Till, mostly sand	31
Fine-grained sandstone		33	Tuff	41
Medium-grained sandstone		37	Basalt	17
Limestone		30	Weathered Gabbro	43
Dolomite		26	Weathered Granite	45
Dune sand		45		

Specific yield, S_y, of rock or soil is the ratio (percentage) of the volume of water which, after saturation, will drain from it under gravity to its own volume.

Specific retention, S_r, of a rock or soil, is the ratio of the volume of water which the rock or soil, after saturation, will retain against the pull of gravity to the volume of the rock or soil. The definition requires that gravity drainage should be complete, a state rarely achieved in nature because of the numerous variables involved, ie particle size, time of drainage, distance above water table.

Intrinsic permeability, k, is a measure of the ease of flow through porous media under a potential gradient. It is a property of the medium alone and depends on the degree of interconnection between pores.

Hydraulic conductivity, K, often known as the coefficient of permeability, is the proportionality constant in Darcy's Law which takes into account the properties of the fluid (ie viscosity) as well as those of the medium.

The constant K has the dimensions of velocity and is expressed in a variety of units, differing as between disciplines. Petroleum engineers use the darcy unit which is really a measure of intrinsic permeabilty because Darcy's Law has failed to take into account the characteristics of the fluid (ie varying viscosities) as well as those of the medium. In soil mechanics cgs units are used. In the United States, the contribution to groundwater hydraulics of the late O. E. Meinzer is reflected in the use of the meinzer unit (flow in gallons per day through a cross-sectional area of 1 sq ft under a hydraulic gradient of 1 at a temperature of 60°F) to express hydraulic conductivity, but Americans also use a field coefficient of hydraulic conductivity, defined as flow in gallons per day through a cross-section of aquifer 1 ft thick and 1 mile wide under a hydraulic gradient of 1 ft per mile at field temperature (Wenzel[17]). European usage formerly favoured cm/sec, now more commonly m/day.

Transmissivity and *storage coefficient* are known as formation constants. Transmissivity *(T)*, essentially an index of permeability, takes into account the saturated thickness of the aquifer and is the product of that thickness and the hydraulic conductivity expressed in m^2/day.

The coefficient of storage *(S)*, for an unconfined aquifer, almost synonymous with specific yield, is dimensionless and defined as the amount of water in storage released from a column of aquifer of unit cross-sectional area under unit decline of head. Values of *S* for most confined aquifers are of the order of 5×10^{-5}/m, several orders of magnitude lower than the corresponding values for some aquifers under unconfined conditions.

DETERMINATION OF AQUIFER CHARACTERISTICS AND FORMATION CONSTANTS

Porosity is determined by a number of laboratory methods which measure the ratio of void space to bulk volume. The sample must be gently but completely dried before testing either by resaturating with liquid and determining porosity using Archimedes' principle, or using a gas expansion technique.

In the laboratory, intrinsic permeability *(k)* is derived by means of *falling head* (mainly for low permeability materials) or *constant head* permeameters (for high permeability materials). In either case, a test fluid is passed through an accurately dimensioned sample of material at a measured rate. However, because small samples suitable for laboratory testing are seldom truly representative of field conditions (the effects of fissures and voids cannot be thus measured) values for *S* and *K* determined by laboratory methods are usually minimal, and more general values can be determined only by field methods. Values of *S* and *K* (and hence *T* through a knowledge of saturated aquifer thickness) can be obtained by observing the behaviour of water levels in the aquifer, by means of a pumped well and preferably (essentially in the case of *S*) one or more observation wells.

Such field pumping test methods, described in detail in Chapter 5, give bulk values for aquifer characteristics which tend to be more representative of true conditions than values obtained by laboratory measurements; the former take into account naturally-occurring fissures and cracks, the effects of which are generally impossible to simulate in the laboratory.

AQUIFER STATE: CONFINED AND UNCONFINED CONDITIONS; PERCHING

An aquifer is said to be *unconfined* when the upper surface of its saturated zone is formed by the water table which is free to fluctuate vertically (and thus reflect changes in storage) under atmospheric pressure in response to drainage/recharge conditions. It may also be said to be phreatic, or free, or non-artesian. The slope and form of a water table are determined by local aquifer characteristics and conditions, such as permeability, the positions of discharge points (springs) in relation to recharge as well as by the shape of the surface topography of which the water table tends to form a subdued representation. In an unconfined aquifer the level of the water table is approximately the same as the undisturbed level of the water in a well at that point; thus observations of water levels in a number of wells enable contours on a water table to be plotted, in turn enabling their graphic two-dimensional representation. A *confined* aquifer is overlain by impermeable, or relatively impermeable strata (aquitards) which confine the groundwater under greater than atmospheric pressure, the extent of which is related to the elevation of the outcrop or recharge area at the point where the aquifer becomes unconfined. When a well penetrates the aquifer through the overlying confining bed, the water in the well will rise to a level above the top of the aquifer, and if the pressure head is sufficient, may rise above ground surface in which case it will overflow and be truly artesian. Wells in which the water level is above the bottom of the confining bed but below ground surface are commonly known as *sub-artesian*, or *artesian, non-flowing*. The level to which the water will rise in the well or, if overflowing, the level to which the water will rise in a pipe extended above the surface is known as the piezometric, or pressure, surface although nowadays the term "potentiometric surface" is commonly used, although it may also denote an unconfined water table. Just as the level of a water table can be plotted areally by measuring water levels in unconfined wells, so can a piezometric surface be represented by contours, point levels for which can be obtained either by measuring water levels in sub-artesian wells or in extended pipes or by pressure gauges in artesian, flowing wells. It is worth noting that a measurement of artesian flow combined with a well-head pressure reading (or rest level in an extended pipe) can represent the first stage in a simple step-drawdown test without the necessity for pumping.

Fluctuations in piezometric levels result mainly from pressure differences rather than changes in storage. Abstraction from a confined aquifer lowers pressures in the vicinity of the well and these pressure effects are transmitted to much greater distances, and much more rapidly than the effects of well dewatering in the upper part of the saturated zone under unconfined conditions. The water abstracted is mainly derived from changes in storage caused by the elastic properties of the aquifer, much more marked in the case of an unconsolidated, confined aquifer, and only partly from transverse flow within the aquifer. On the other hand, water abstracted from an unconfined aquifer (before equilibrium between yield and level is reached) comes partly from vertical drainage from the well's cone of depression and, after steady state is reached (theoretically, steady state will not be reached unless a boundary is intersected or there is recharge from above or below), wholly from transverse (radial) flow within the aquifer in response to the hydraulic gradients induced around the well by pumping. In general, confined aquifers at depth are much less likely to carry significant proportions of fissure flow than their unconfined counterparts, although shallower confined water-bearing formations may acquire a degree of secondary permeability if acting as conduits between recharge area and discharge point.

Many confining strata are not wholly impermeable and some leakage from the aquifer through the confining beds to other (usually overlying) permeable strata may occur. The leakage when quantified over a wide area may form a significant and not always obvious source of recharge to a neighbouring aquifer with a lower hydraulic head. In a multi-layered aquifer differential pressures between individual aquifers may lead to a number of such water transfers simultaneously within the system, estimable only given a detailed knowledge of the differences of hydraulic head and the characteristics of both aquifers and aquitards.

It follows that there can be marked differences in degree of the ranges in values for aquifer characteristics, such as transmissivity and storage coefficient, as between confined and unconfined conditions. Abstraction can lower the potentiometric surface below the base of a confining bed so that the aquifer in the vicinity of the well becomes unconfined and partially drained.

When a well penetrates a confined aquifer, the water in it, as opposed to the water in the surrounding aquifer, is exposed to atmospheric pressure. Changes in atmospheric pressure cause the column of water in the well to act as a primitive barometer and measurement of actual fluctuations in level will enable the well's barometric efficiency to be derived. Wells with high barometric efficiencies are sometimes sensitive to other atmospheric pressure pulses, such as those caused by nuclear test explosions; a few wells are known to respond to ground pressure waves caused by major underground nuclear tests or natural earthquakes.

Groundwater, and the portion of the aquifer in which it occurs, is said to be *perched* if it occurs above the main zone of saturation by reason of a local impermeable, or semi-impermeable bed intercalated between more permeable strata. The bed impedes or retards the downward passage of water percolating through the unsaturated zone so that the strata immediately above the bed become locally saturated. This perched groundwater tends to drain at the margins of the impeding bed which, if cut by the topography (for instance, along the sides of a valley), causes the emergence of temporary springs. If sufficiently large, perched groundwater bodies may be permanent; conversely they may be seasonal, or short-lived.

DISTRIBUTION OF AQUIFERS IN ENGLAND AND WALES

Hydrogeological Maps

The hydrogeological map of England and Wales[18] at a scale of 1:625000 gives a good overall indication of aquifer distribution and groundwater potential. The format of this map was based on, and closely resembles, that adopted for the various sheets (scaled at 1:1500000) of the International Hydrogeological Map of Europe, of which Sheet B4 London[19] is relevant. The national map had brief notes printed on its face, but the International Sheet B4 was accompanied by separate and more comprehensive explanatory notes[20], which have formed the basis for this account of English and Welsh aquifers. Both national and international maps adopted an essentially three-fold classification of aquifers:

(1) those in which fissure flow dominates;
(2) those characterised mainly by intergranular flow; and
(3) minor aquifers.

Each of the first two categories is further sub-divided into 'extensive and productive' aquifers, and those of more local importance. Although there are differences between maps as to the precise definition of categories, the definitions are basically similar; the differences arise mainly from already internationally-agreed terminology in the case of the smaller-scale map.

Both maps denote predominantly fissure flow aquifers in two shades of green, predominantly intergranular flow aquifers in two shades of blue; in each case the darker shade denotes greater, or more extensive, aquifer potential. Pale brown denotes minor or local aquifers, or aquifers (unspecified) at depth beneath others. Dark brown denotes areas underlain mainly by non-aquifers, but the possibility of small-scale supplies (e.g. from superficial deposits) is not excluded. Aquifer lithology is indicated by stylised ornament overprinted in dark grey.

Because of the limitations of scale and the need to preserve clarity, the map cannot specifically show the underground extensions of aquifers where they become confined. It does however show a variety of other surface and groundwater information including major springs and wells, dams, aqueducts and river gauging stations.

In addition to the relatively small-scale sheets described above, a series of regional hydrogeological maps, mainly at scales of 1:100000 or 1:125000 has also been published (by the end of 1984 fourteen such maps had been produced) by the British Geological Survey.

Table 2.IV lists the main aquifers of England and Wales and the categories into which they fall.

TABLE 2.IV.   Categories of the Main Aquifers in England and Wales

Extensive and productive aquifers	Aquifers with local potential	Approximate locations	Age
	Alluvial and terrace sands and gravels	River valleys	Recent
	Crag Glacial sands	Eastern England North of approximate line joining River Thames and Severn Estuaries	Quaternary
	Sands within Woolwich, Bagshot, Bracklesham and Barton beds; Thanet Beds	Southern England; London Basin ('Lower London Tertiaries')	Tertiary
Upper Chalk Middle Chalk Lower Chalk		} Northeastern, eastern and southern England	Upper Cretaceous
Lower Greensand (Folkestone and Hythe Beds, Sandringham Sands, Spilsby Sandstone)	Upper Greensand Red Chalk Ashdown Beds Tunbridge Wells Sands	Eastern and southern England Eastern England Southern England Southern England Southern and eastern England Southern England Eastern England Lincolnshire	Lower Cretaceous
Great Oolite } Inferior Oolite } Lincolnshire Limestone	Marlstone Rock Bed Bridport Sands, Yeovil Sands Midford Sands, Cotteswold Sands Cornbrash Great Oolite Limestone }	Lincolnshire, Northants Southwest and south central England North Midlands South-central England Lincolnshire	Jurassic
Sherwood Sandstone (includes the former Bunter Series, the Bunter Pebble Beds, and the Keuper Sandstone) } St Bees Sandstone } Kirklinton Sandstone }		East and West Midlands; South-west England Northern England Northern England	Permo-Triassic
Magnesian Limestone	Penrith Sandstone Collyhurst Sandstone Yellow Sands	Northern England South Lancashire Northern England Northern England	Permian
	Coal Measures sandstones Pennant Sandstone Halesowen Group Millstone Grit Series	English and Welsh coalfields South Wales Midlands Cumbria, Northern England	Upper Carbon-iferous
	Carboniferous Limestone Series (thicker sandstones and limestones)	South Wales, Mendips Derbyshire, Northern England	Lower Carbon-iferous

EXTENSIVE AND PRODUCTIVE AQUIFERS OF ENGLAND AND WALES

Magnesian Limestone

Distribution and Development

This Permian formation extends slightly west of north from the Nottingham area in a belt up to 17 km wide, through Yorkshire as far as the north-east coast between Hartlepool and South Shields. It extends eastwards, confined beneath younger rocks, for several tens of kilometres. At outcrop in the Durham area the formation attains a thickness of 210 m and consists of Lower, Middle and Upper, massive, commonly dolomitic reef limestones and breccias with intercalated thinner beds of marl. At the base of the formation a thin Marl Slate overlies a highly permeable formation of very variable thickness known as the Yellow Sands.

Aquifer Characteristics and Well Yields

The commonly massive, compact limestones are nevertheless locally cellular and brecciated. Their low primary and interstitial permeability has been secondarily enhanced by the development of solution fissures resulting in very high permeabilities within certain vertical limits set by pre-existing base drainage levels.

An average transmissivity for Magnesian Limestone is about 300 m²/d but maximum values of 1 500 m²/d are recorded. Wells typically yield about 50 l/s. Major towns in north-east England supplied by Magnesian Limestone groundwater include Hartlepool, Sunderland and South Shields.

Fissure yields from the formation can be very high indeed; a group of fissures encountered at Easington Colliery during shaft sinking yielded 600 l/s.

The limestones become generally more compact and less fissured southwards from Durham and typical well yields decline to about 10 l/s within Yorkshire and Nottinghamshire.

Chemical Quality

The quality of Magnesian Limestone groundwaters is variable but all are hard or extremely hard; noncarbonate (sulphate) hardness commonly, but not necessarily, predominates. Total hardness values at or near outcrop are typically within the range 300-600 mg/l for the Upper Magnesian Limestone, but generally less (150-400 mg/l) within the Lower Limestone. Such high values have tended to restrict development of these groundwaters.

The Triassic ('Sherwood') Sandstones

There has been difficulty in establishing the dividing line between Permian and Triassic rocks within England and Wales as the temporal boundary tends to transgress the major lithological change from the more marine (or lagoonal) conditions of the Permian to the arid, desertic and detrital conditions of the Trias. In this chapter, however, the collective term 'Triassic' Sandstones has been used, because of its familiarity to the water industry; it includes the Bunter series (Upper and Lower Mottled Sandstones), Bunter Pebble Beds and the overlying Keuper Sandstones which include the Waterstones: most of these formations are now more correctly termed the Sherwood Sandstone Group. These arenaceous deposits form a single massive unit of immense hydrogeological significance in the English Midlands and elsewhere; in Lancashire these measures are up to 600 m thick. Generally the sandstones of the 'Keuper' are finer textured than those of the 'Bunter', which include coarse-grained and detrital beds. In north-west England sandstones of Permian age form the base of the unit and these beds are still commonly referred to as 'Permo-Trias', together with their intercalated shales and evaporites.

In the Midlands the sandstones crop out round the edges of structural basins such as those of Cheshire, Stafford and Needwood. Around the northern edge of the Cheshire Basin they approach 1 000 m in thickness. The centres of the basins are occupied by the overlying argillaceous Mercia Mudstones (formerly known as Keuper Marl) which are relatively impermeable and may confine the groundwater in the sandstones below. A number of large Midland towns obtain their water supplies at least partly from the Sherwood Sandstones, among them Manchester, Liverpool and Birmingham; over-abstraction may have led to falls in water levels. Around Merseyside levels have fallen by about 30 m in this century—with consequent saline water intrusion from the coast. In the Birmingham area levels have fallen between 40-75 m during the last 50 years. Around Burton-on-Trent wells drilled for the brewing industry originally overflowed, but abstraction has caused levels to fall so that not only do these wells now have to be pumped but in some cases where wells penetrate near the base of the aquifer up-coning of residual saline water has occurred.

In south Nottinghamshire the Sherwood Sandstone is about 90 m thick but further north in Nottinghamshire about 180 m of pebble beds occur. In north Nottinghamshire and south Yorkshire the Sherwood Sandstones provide supplies for Nottingham, Mansfield, Worksop and Doncaster. More northerly still, in the Vale of Eden and along the Cumbrian coast, the St. Bees and Kirklinton sandstones reach combined thicknesses of more than 900 m, but do not include significant pebble beds.

In south-western England beds of 'Bunter' age form an important aquifer in the valley of the River Otter east of Exeter. In central Somerset and Gloucestershire, 'Bunter' beds do not crop out at the surface but Keuper Sandstones at the base of the Mercia Mudstones reach a maximum thickness of about 70 m west of Gloucester and are tapped by several wells.

Aquifer Characteristics and Well Yields

There is now a considerable body of evidence that fissure flow plays a significant, if not dominant, role in saturated groundwater flow through sandstone aquifers such as the Triassic Sandstone. However, the degree and incidence of fissures are highly variable and for convenience the formation has been shown on the national hydrogeological map as a 'mainly intergranular flow' aquifer. Triassic sandstones vary also in their degree of cementation; the generally higher permeabilities of the 'Bunter' beds reflect the differences in cementation as between the 'Bunter' and 'Keuper' sandstones. Porosities of about 30 per cent and specific yields within the range 20-25 per cent are typical of the 'Bunter' Sandstone of the English Midlands. Such high porosities lead to relatively low (a few metres only) seasonal fluctuations in water levels.

Transmissivities may be high where fissures are well developed and contribute to flows. In Nottinghamshire field values for transmissivity of 1 500 m^2/d have been obtained, contrasting with laboratory values of 300 m^2/d.

In the Midlands bulk transmissivities lie within the range 350-750 m^2/d, but where the sandstones are less fissured and better cemented values are more likely to approach 150 m^2/d. Typical yields from wells in the Midland 'Bunter' may be 5-10 Ml/d with groups of wells and individual public supply stations yielding up to

20 Ml/d. In Lancashire and Cheshire transmissivities between 20 and 2000 m^2/d are recorded; here yields are typically 2-4 Ml/d. In the south-west and particularly in Somerset the 'Keuper' sandstones tend to be hard and relatively well cemented; they are also much thinner than their Midland counterparts so that transmissivities as low as 15-20 m^2/d result. In Devon the 'Bunter' sandstones are more permeable with well yields around 2 Ml/d which contrast with lower yields (0.5 Ml/d) from the Upper Sand of western Somerset.

Chemical Quality

Groundwater from the 'Bunter' sandstones is usually of good quality and only moderately hard; carbonate hardness predominates. In the 'Keuper' Sandstones, however, hardness varies from moderate to excessive with a much higher proportion of non-carbonate hardness. Down the stratal dip beneath cover of Mercia Mudstones, cationic exchange processes operate and water quality eventually deteriorates to a strong, impotable sodium chloride type. In Nottinghamshire this change occurs within 30 km of the outcrop, whilst in the vale of Mowbray, Yorkshire, the change occurs within much shorter distances. In the Worcester area ionic concentrations tend to decrease with distance south from outcrop, and groundwaters at depth around Stratford-upon-Avon (about 20 km down gradient from Warwick) are of the soft sodium sulphate type and quite potable.

Natural brines occur within the Staffordshire and Cheshire basins as a result of the dissolution by circulating waters of beds of rock salt near the base of the Mercia Mudstones. Elsewhere sandstones may carry brines not derived from local dissolution.

The Great and Inferior Oolites (Jurassic)

Distribution and Development

These two formations form distinct hydraulic units over much of their outcrop but in the area between Gloucester and Oxford, where they form the Cotswold Hills, they combine to form a single major aquifer. North of Peterborough the Lincolnshire Limestone forms the later equivalent of the Inferior Oolite Limestone of the area to the south-west. In Dorset the local representatives of both the Inferior and Great Oolite Limestones are thin with little aquifer potential, but they thicken to the north. Near Bath the Inferior Oolite is about 80 m thick but reaches a maximum thickness of 90 m near Cheltenham. Beyond Oxford as far to the north-east as Peterborough both formations thin and are largely replaced by water-bearing sands (Northampton Sands), marls or clays. North of the River Welland the Lincolnshire Limestone consists of massive beds of hard, well-jointed, sometimes oolitic limestone, and forms an important aquifer which extends as far north as the Humber Estuary. Near Grantham the limestone is 40 m thick, thinning to 30 m at Lincoln and only 9 m or less near the River Humber. Downdip to the east, the limestone is confined beneath younger clays; in the low ground around the Wash between Peterborough and Lincoln overflowing artesian conditions pertain.

Aquifer Characteristics and Well Yields

In the Cotswold Hills the limestones tend to be deeply dissected and well fissured. They may have high or very high transmissivities (1500 m^2/d is common, ranging up to 4000 m^2/d) so that they are easily drained. During prolonged dry weather, storage within thin saturated zones may be limited. Well hydrographs are very sensitive to recharge and drainage and present a characteristic jagged trace (see Fig. 2.1). Values for porosity are typically between 15 and 20 per cent with low specific yields (around 5 per cent).

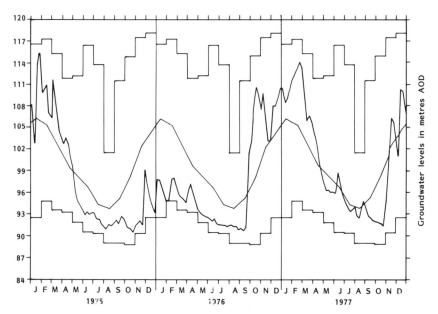

Fig. 2.1.　Well hydrograph in the Great Oolite Limestone at Westonbirt School, Tetbury, Glos. (ST 89/32) ST 8640 9030
(Maxima, minima and means calculated for 1932 to 1973; surface level 120.4 m AOD)

Well and spring yields are very variable. Around the Cotswold Hills in the outcrop areas, where dry weather storage may be limited, yields may be disappointing, but under confined and fully saturated conditions yields generally improve. Under favourable hydrogeological conditions (a thick, well-fissured saturated zone) properly constructed wells in the Inferior and Great Oolites of the Cotswolds may yield 50-100 l/s, more rarely as much as 200 l/s.

Within the artesian overflow area of south Lincolnshire, flows of more than 20 Ml/d have been recorded from springs. In north Lincolnshire well yields, which commonly range from 20-30 l/s, may be affected by the greater proportion of marls in the aquifer.

Chemical Quality

Groundwaters from the Great and Inferior Oolites at outcrop and for some distance downdip beneath cover of younger rocks are generally of good chemical quality but very hard, most of this hardness being due to carbonates. However, in the Lincolnshire Limestone, cationic exchange occurs downdip towards the east and initial softening is followed by increasing sodium chloride concentrations. South and west of Boston (Lincolnshire) natural fluoride concentrations vary from less than 1 to several mg/l.

The Lower Cretaceous Sands

Distribution and Development

Sands of the Lower Cretaceous are generically referred to as 'Lower Greensand' but in East Anglia and Lincolnshire are more specifically termed 'Carstone', 'Sandringham Sands' (partly of Upper Jurassic age) and 'Spilsby Sandstone'. True Lower Greensand crops out around the edges of the Wealden Anticline, where Upper Folkestone Beds (sands) are separated from Lower Hythe Beds (sand and sandy limestone) by clays and silts of the Sandgate Beds; in the Isle of Wight (where the formation attains a maximum thickness of 240 m); and intermittently from Dorset through Bedfordshire into Cambridgeshire. Erosion has removed the formation from the centre of the Wealden Anticline and it is absent beneath much of the London Basin, where it has been overlapped by the Gault, which then rests directly on Jurassic strata or the much older Palaeozoic rocks of the London platform. Around the northern and western edges of the Weald, the Folkestone and Hythe beds attain maximum thicknesses at outcrop of about 65 and 55 m respectively; along the northern edge, the Folkestone Beds extend beneath cover northwards to around Gravesend and the Isle of Sheppey, where they are less than 25 m thick. However, the Hythe Beds generally do not extend much more than 10-15 km northwards of their outcrop in this area. Further to the east between Ashford and Folkestone, the beds die out beneath cover within 5 km of outcrop.

Along the southern limb of the Weald, the Lower Greensand as a whole thins eastward from about 115 m in eastern Hampshire to less than 10 m north of Eastbourne. On the northern side of the London Basin in Bedfordshire there are substantial outcrops where the whole formation is represented by about 75 m of coarse sands which extend south-eastwards beneath younger rocks to the Luton area; however, it again dies out south of an approximate line from St. Albans to Bury St. Edmunds. Sands are also present at depth beneath Chalk and Gault around Cambridge. West of London, confined Lower Greensand is present beneath Slough at a depth of 300 m, and extends southwards into the areas of Egham, Staines and Ascot. In northern East Anglia up to about 20 m of Carstone (a ferruginous, jointed, medium to coarse sandstone) is underlain by up to 30 m of Snettisham Clay, which is in turn underlain by up to 40 m of Sandringham Sands. The latter consists of iron-rich, fine-grained sands which pass downwards to glauconitic sands and sandy clay. Northwards across the Wash into Lincolnshire, the succession is more complex but the Carstone, represented by up to 14 m of hard iron-rich, well-cemented sand, is separated by a considerable, but variable, sequence of marls and clays from the important Spilsby Sandstone at the base of the Lower Cretaceous. The Spilsby Sandstone reaches a maximum thickness of about 20 m near Louth, but thins and eventually dies out to the north.

Aquifer Characteristics and Well Yields

Around the edge of the Weald in southern England the aquifer characteristics of Folkestone and Hythe sands differ. At outcrop, both divisions form important aquifers hydraulically separated by the Sandgate clays and silts.

In central and east Kent the Hythe Beds are varyingly calcareous (they may be limestone in some areas) so that fissure flow is dominant. Further west the beds are less calcareous and intergranular flow predominates. The Folkestone Beds, by contrast, comprise coarse to fine sands which may be fairly friable and poorly cemented, so that fissuring is relatively rare. Within the Dorset, Bedfordshire and Cambridge sand facies, saturated flow is again mainly intergranular as it is in the

Spilsby Sandstone of Lincolnshire. Where the sands are less well cemented, porosities may be typically within the range of 20-30 per cent with specific yields ranging from 10-12 per cent. Transmissivities vary widely (as does the saturated thickness); values for hydraulic conductivity ("permeability") are typically 5-20 m/d.

South of the Thames, well yields from the Lower Greensand average 1.0-2.5 Ml/d. Larger yields may be obtained from Hythe Beds, more than 6 Ml/d being recorded from wells near Maidstone and Sevenoaks. Around Dorking, large yields are obtained from wells which penetrate both the Chalk and Lower Greensand. Within the wide outcrops of Hythe and Folkestone beds southwest of Guildford, yields of between 2 and 4 Ml/d are usual. North of London, near Luton and Cambridge, yields of 2 Ml/d are typical. Yields from the Sandringham Sands are variable but typically small. Exceptionally, 4 Ml/d has been obtained from properly constructed wells in this formation. In Lincolnshire yields from the Spilsby Sandstone around Louth reach 2-3 Ml/d but 1-2 Ml/d is more typical.

Chemical Quality

Lower Greensand groundwaters at outcrop are generally of good chemical quality with a hardness that varies with the degree of carbonate cementation. Between Sevenoaks and Dover along the northern edge of the Weald, total hardness of Folkestone Beds groundwaters varies from less than 20 mg/l to more than 350 mg/l. Downdip and beneath cover to the north, ion exchange again takes place and hardness generally decreases. At Gravesend total hardness, all carbonate, is only 50 mg/l. Within the Hythe Beds of the same general area, between Sevenoaks and Folkestone, an easterly increase in hardness can be correlated with an increasing development of calcareous cement within the Sandstones, until near Folkestone values for total hardness exceed 100 mg/l. Chlorides in the outcrop areas of both divisions are commonly less than 20 mg/l, but generally increase northwards beneath cover of younger beds. Water from the Folkestone Beds can be very rich in dissolved iron.

In East Anglia water from the Sandringham Sands is generally soft with low chlorides and may also be ferruginous. In Lincolnshire, Spilsby Sandstone groundwaters have hardness values at outcrop between 150 and 300 mg/l but soften progressively eastwards beneath cover. Chlorides are about 20 mg/l at outcrop, but exceed 250 mg/l at depth beneath Skegness on the coast.

The Chalk

Distribution and Development

The Chalk is Britain's most important aquifer. It sweeps in a broad outcrop from Flamborough Head on the north coast of England southwards and south-westwards to the Dorset coast around Weymouth. In the south of England it is present in the major structural basins of Hampshire and London and in both cases the centres of the basins are occupied by poorly permeable Tertiary silt and clay cover which confines groundwaters in the underlying Chalk. The asymmetric Hampshire basin (syncline) has its southern limb, which passes through the Isles of Purbeck and Wight, steeply inclined or vertical; to the south of the London (synclinal) basin lies the great complementary anticlinal structure of the Weald, from which the original Chalk cover has been eroded (see Fig. 2.2). The outcrops of Chalk on the north and south limbs are known as the North and South Downs respectively. North of

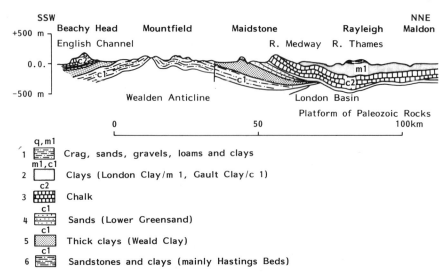

Fig. 2.2.   Geological cross-section SSW-NNE from Beachy Head to Maldon (after Cradock-Hartopp et al[18])

Southampton, in the area of the general westerly extension of the Wealden axis, a broad expanse of Chalk outcrop forms high 'downland' over much of Hampshire and parts of Dorset and Wiltshire.

In East Anglia much of the outcrop is covered by varying thicknesses of superficial glacial deposits, mainly sands and boulder clays; downdip towards the east coast Chalk is present at depth beneath the Tertiary clay and Pleistocene 'crag' cover.

The Chalk is divided into upper, middle and lower divisions which can be traced throughout the country although there are considerable variations in thickness as well as some in lithology. The Chalk probably attains its greatest thickness (nearly 500 m) beneath the Tertiary in East Anglia and in the Isle of Wight, but in Yorkshire and Lincolnshire it reaches thicknesses of 430 m and about 100 m respectively. Beneath the London basin the total thickness is about 200 m, along the North Downs about 300 m, but in the west of England in Dorset only about 90 m is present. Thickness variations within the Upper Chalk (when fully developed about 400 m thick) at outcrop are usually due to erosion, but primary sedimentational differences account in some measure for the variations in thickness within the two lower divisions. Lithologically, the Chalk consists of a fine white, generally soft, microporous limestone mainly of organic origin in which the grain-size of the finer, planktonic coccolith debris may be less than 1 μm. There is also a high proportion of coarse shelly detrital material the size of which is commonly within the range 10-100 μm. Much of the minute exoskeletal material has escaped secondary infilling and thus imparts to the Chalk a considerable degree of its porosity. Upper Chalk is commonly more than 95 per cent pure calcium carbonate, as is the Middle Chalk, but the two divisions differ substantially in that flint in the form of random nodules or more persistent tabular bands is present in significant amounts only within the Upper division. Within the Lower Chalk there is a much higher proportion of clay minerals (kaolinite, smectite or illite) which may reach as much as 60 per cent but is more commonly within the range 20-35 per cent. The presence of a substantial clay fraction influences both the permeability of the Chalk and the chemistry of its groundwaters.

Aquifer Characteristics and Well Yields

The porosity of the Chalk is relatively high although it is extremely fine-grained. The porosity falls below 20 per cent only in the very marly (Lower) Chalk or harder, partially cemented bands such as the Melbourn Rock and the Chalk Rock, which over much of the country separate Lower Chalk from Middle Chalk, and Middle Chalk from Upper Chalk, respectively. Normally values for the porosity of the Upper and Middle Chalk lie within the range 40-50 per cent, whilst values for the Lower Chalk are somewhat lower, between 20 and 30 per cent. Despite these high values, however, and the very fine-grained nature of the rock and its primary interstices (which results in a very high degree of capillary retention), interstitial permeabilities are low and rarely exceed 5 per cent, values of 1-3 per cent over the greater part of the country being common. However, the Chalk's value as an aquifer is derived from the development of secondary permeability along joints and fissures which are widened mainly through dissolution by undersaturated acidic groundwaters within the zone of circulation. Chalk may be more or less closely fissured—but solution and widening of the fissures are selective and become cumulative once started. The fissures may be near-horizontal and related to bedding features or to tabular layers of flint (inclined at almost any angle, planar or arcuate) and may occasionally occur as serpentine pipes, particularly where the water table is shallow and surface infiltration may have been concentrated via funnel-shaped 'sink holes'. There is little doubt that glacial or late glacial permafrost conditions have played a significant part in the development of superficial permeabilty. Characteristic of the Chalk Downs (these are, of course, really uplands) is the lack of surface rivers and the occurrence of 'dry valleys', which have obviously been eroded at some time by flowing water, probably during late glacial times when superficial, impermanent thin icecaps may have melted seasonally or periodically. The extensive and almost equally characteristic thin sheets of superficial, residual flinty clays which cover much of the higher interfluve areas were also probably formed at about the same time. Evidently many of these dry valleys and their lower, now wet, extensions were initiated by erosion along incipient fissure systems so that at the present time when the widening process has extended downwards they may be regarded as narrow zones of higher permeability, as evidenced by statistics of borehole yields. Resulting directly from the Chalk's low specific yield and high capillary moisture retention is the extremely high range of the seasonal fluctuation of the water table in outcrop areas remote from natural discharges; fluctuations of more than 30 m are commonly recorded (see Fig. 2.3).

Because the development of fissures within outcrop areas is largely a surface-related feature it follows that Chalk permeability decreases with depth. Borehole logging has shown that it is unusual for significant inflows from fissures to occur at depths greater than about 60 m below the water table. Under confined conditions, solution along fissures appears to have been more diffuse and penetration by wells of the top 75 m of the Chalk is generally worthwhile, although there is a marked decrease of permeability associated with increase in the thickness of impermeable covering rocks. The enhancement of fissure permeability along the axes of valleys in Chalk at outcrop has led to high transmissivities, typically within the range 1 500-3 000 m^2/d. However, in parts of east Yorkshire, Lincolnshire and East Anglia which are remote from valleys, high transmissivities are recorded.

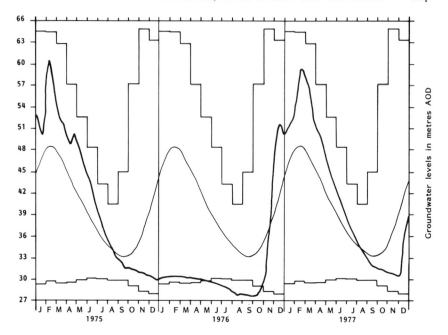

Fig. 2.3.   Well hydrograph in the Chalk at Compton (SU 71/23) SU 7755
1490
(Maxima, minima and means calculated for 1894 to 1973; surface level 81.4 m AOD)

Large areas of the confined Chalk of the London basin have transmissivities less than 15 m²/d, mainly because of restricted groundwater circulation which is related to lack of natural outlets at sufficiently low levels and aquifer compaction by the thickness and weight of overburden.

The wide range of Chalk transmissivities is reflected in an equally wide range of well yields. The yield of a well in Chalk which does not encounter fissures within the saturated zone is negligible. On the other hand wells which encounter extensive fissure systems at several levels below the water table have yields commonly in the range 5-10 Ml/d; pumping stations with mulitiple wells within restricted sites may yield as much as 20-30 Ml/d. Two boreholes in the valley of the River Ems at Walderton in Sussex were individually tested at 28 Ml/d and a group of wells at another valley site at Lavant a few miles east yields about 30 Ml/d for the supply of Chichester. Elsewhere the Chalk provides groundwater supplies for the major towns of Grimsby, Hull, Norwich, Cambridge, Ipswich, Reading, Salisbury, Southampton, Winchester, Brighton, Dover and Maidstone, to name but a few. Portsmouth also obtains much of its public supply from the Chalk but in this case abstraction is from a group of high yielding springs at Bedhampton, augmented by boreholes within the Chalk outcrop area further inland. The Bedhampton Springs have an average yield of about 100 Ml/d and even under extreme drought conditions the recorded flow of this group of springs has never been less than 56 Ml/d.

Chemical Quality

Chalk waters from the saturated zone at outcrop are commonly very hard, with a high proportion of carbonate hardness. Typical values for total hardness lie within the range 200-300 mg/l, and for non-carbonate hardness 20-60 mg/l. Downdip and down hydraulic gradient beneath Tertiary clay cover, cationic exchange processes operate. Changes in chemical composition of Chalk groundwaters with distance from outcrop have been delineated, for example, in north Kent (see Fig. 2.4) for various parts of the UK Chalk outcrop. In East Anglia the quality of Chalk groundwaters is affected by the presence of thick superficial glacial deposits, mainly boulder clay, and total hardnesses of 500 mg/l are not uncommon. Also in East Anglia, as in some other areas, the quality of Chalk groundwaters deteriorates with depth; remote from the coast the chloride concentrations in groundwaters below about 80 m below sea level exceed 1000 mg/l. In some coastal situations saline intrusion has occurred either naturally (East Anglia and East Kent) or as a result of over-abstraction (Lincolnshire coast around Grimsby). Within the London basin over-abstraction from the Chalk and the associated severe lowering of water levels has resulted in significant saline intrusion of the aquifer from the tidal Thames. On the north bank of the river, within London itself, there are now large areas where chlorides exceed 500 mg/l, and values exceeding 1000 mg/l occur within a belt from the mouth of the River Lee east to West Thurrock and, on the south bank, in the Deptford and Northfleet areas.

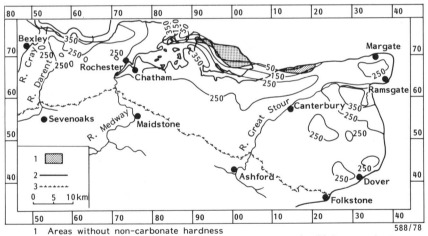

1 Areas without non-carbonate hardness
2 Contour lines of areas with equal carbonate hardness (mg/l) in groundwater
3 Base of the Chalk

588/78

Fig. 2.4. Hardness of groundwater in the Chalk of Kent (after Day *et al*[21])

AQUIFERS WITH LOCAL POTENTIAL IN ENGLAND AND WALES

Although few formations are completely impermeable, especially in their weathered shallow zones, in England and Wales most of the igneous, metamorphic and sedimentary rocks older than the Lower Carboniferous have limited value as aquifers. Because of their indurated nature, and sometimes their structural complexity, the rare permeable horizons are difficult to predict or to locate, so that development by springs is commonly preferred to highly speculative drilling. For local supplies it may be possible by carefully selecting sites to obtain yields of the order of 0.25-5.0 l/s; rarely, larger yields are obtainable, for instance wells about 20 m deep into weathered granite in south-west England have yielded about 10000 m^3/d. However, the failure rate of boreholes into hard or metamorphosed sediments or into igneous rocks is relatively high.

Carboniferous Limestone, Sandstones etc

The Carboniferous Limestone, where massively developed, as in the Mendip Hills of south-west England, around the edges of the South Wales coalfields and in the Peak District, is a hard well-bedded limestone in which primary joint patterns have been secondarily enlarged by solution giving rise to 'karstic' conditions. Springs are common, as are drainage adits of old mine workings in the mineralised areas. At Buxton in Derbyshire thermo-mineral springs occur. Farther north in the Bowland and Shap areas, the Lower Carboniferous sequence contains not only limestones but also shales and sandstones in varying proportions. When so constituted the formation may be regarded as a multi-layered aquifer in which vertical permeabilities vary greatly; the eventual rest water level in a borehole is the resultant of all the different piezometric heads encountered.

There is considerable variation in well yields from these measures (up to about 20 l/s) but wells which penetrate the more massive limestone sequences may yield up to about 175 l/s.

Carboniferous Limestone water is commonly very hard with a high proportion of carbonate hardness. Measures in the Upper Carboniferous include a lower Millstone Grit 60-900 m thick and vary lithologically from shales to massive sandstones, waters from which may be very soft.

The overlying economically important Coal Measures form a rhythmic sequence of fireclays, coals, shales and sandstone; these measures attain a maximum thickness of more than 200 m in South Wales. The sandstones have both intergranular and fissure permeability, but in mined areas the natural hydraulic regime has been greatly modified by subsidence. In terms of total abstraction, the Coal Measures are almost equal in importance to the Triassic sandstones, but by far the greater proportion of Coal Measures groundwater is pumped as mine drainage into rivers. Individual sandstone formations, locally important as aquifers, are the Pennant Sandstone in South Wales and the Halesowen Beds of Warwickshire.

The quality of Coal Measures groundwater varies considerably but many are rich in iron, particularly in mined areas. They may also be rich in chlorides, especially at depth, but in South Wales groundwaters from the Coal Measures are exceptional in that their chloride concentrations are generally low.

Permian and Other Sandstones

In south-west England sandstones and breccias of Permian age attain a maximum thickness of 150 m and yield supplies of up to 12.5 l/s. In northern England the Penrith Sandstone of the Vale of Eden comprises poorly-cemented round-grained sandstones of aeolian origin from which yields up to about 30 l/s have been reported. The Collyhurst Sandstone of Lancashire provides good yields where it forms a discrete aquifer separated from the higher Triassic sandstones by the Manchester Marls. In north-eastern England basal Yellow Sands, up to 50 m thick, are developed beneath the Permian Magnesian Limestone. These sands are very permeable and poorly consolidated. As they overlie the productive Coal Measures of the Durham Coalfield, they frequently pose problems to mine sinkers. The variable thickness of the sands gives rise to variable well yields; a maximum recorded yield of 125 l/s was obtained from a small diameter colliery boring later used for supply. The Triassic Mercia Mudstones, largely impermeable, reach great thicknesses, particularly in the Midlands (Cheshire and Worcestershire) and in south-west England (Somerset). The formation is mainly important as a confining bed for the groundwater within the thick sandstone sequences beneath, but thin sandstones may sometimes be developed within the Marl and may yield small supplies of sulphate-rich groundwater.

Jurassic Limestones, Sandstones etc

The Jurassic System includes a number of major, minor and non-aquifers. It varies in thickness and lithology and forms a wide outcrop from the north coast between Flamborough Head and Middlesbrough, where the Great and Inferior Oolites form the Cleveland Hills, to Lyme Bay on the south coast. The Penarth Group and Lower Lias comprise an alternating series of thin limestones and shales with poor aquifer potential at the base of the Jurassic. The small supplies which may be available are commonly of poor chemical quality. Higher in the sequence, the Marlstone Rock Bed (Middle Lias) of Lincolnshire forms a thin, well-jointed aquifer which yields local supplies. In south-west England, the Bridport, Yeovil, Midford and Cotteswold Sands of the Upper Lias form a diachronous sandy development up to 75 m thick which extends from the Cotswold Hills to the Dorset coast. Wells in the Midford Sands supply the City of Bath. The Yeovil Sands, where in hydraulic continuity with the overlying Inferior Oolite Limestone, yield up to 40 l/s.

In the Northern Midlands, between the Humber Estuary and Peterborough, the Great Oolite Limestone and the overlying Cornbrash reach a combined thickness of 25 m. Because the important Lincolnshire Limestone aquifer immediately underlies these beds, their limited aquifer potential is little used. The Great Oolite is again present in the Cleveland Hills, together with the overlying Corallian Limestones, which in this area reach a thickness of 110 m and from which yields of up to 15 l/s have been recorded. To the south, however, the Corallian measures become progressively more argillaceous. In the south of England, limestones and sandstones of the Portland and Purbeck formations provide little aquifer potential. In Wessex, however, locally significant yields may be obtained from these beds.

Lower Cretaceous Clays, Sands etc

The Lower Cretaceous, like the underlying Jurassic, includes many widely-differing lithologies. In the Weald of southern England the Ashdown Sands of the basal Cretaceous, up to 210 m thick, provide a useful aquifer with yields up to 60 l/s; they are separated from the Upper Tunbridge Wells Sand, up to 150 m of fine sandstone and silts (which yield up to 10 l/s) by 55 m of Wadhurst Clay. Groundwater from these sands is usually of good chemical quality but soft and commonly ferruginous.

Within the great Wealden anticline of southern England the thick, largely impermeable, Weald Clay separates the Tunbridge Wells Sand from the major aquifer of the Lower Greensand, higher in the sequence. The Lower Greensand and its regional equivalents form major aquifers already described in a previous section. The impermeable Gault (clay) up to about 100 m thick immediately overlies the Lower Greensand and provides an effective aquiclude between that formation and the Upper Greensand above the Gault, but the Gault wedges out in northern East Anglia and is hardly represented within the sequence in Lincolnshire and Yorkshire. The Upper Greensand is a glauconitic calcareous sand commonly in hydraulic continuity with the overlying Chalk but may be a discrete aquifer in areas where it crops out extensively. Around the western edge of the Wealden anticline, the vale of Wiltshire, parts of Dorset and in the Thames valley south of Oxford, yields of up to 25 l/s have been recorded; Upper Greensand which crops out at the base of steep Chalk scarps produces many powerful springs with relatively constant flows; the water is thrown out along the formation's contact with the underlying impermeable Gault.

Tertiary, Quaternary and Recent Silts, Clays, Sands and Gravels

Above the Upper Greensand lies the Chalk and above the Chalk a series of silts and clays of Tertiary age. West and south-west of London thick basal silts and clays of the Reading Beds and London Clay are overlain by Bagshot, Bracklesham and Barton sands and silts, which are particularly well developed within the Hampshire basin. In these beds wells must be correctly screened and may then yield, typically, 5-10 l/s. In eastern England widespread Quaternary sands ("crags") may yield more than this, but wells penetrating these very fine sands need careful screening. In the past the efficiency of wells in crags has been limited by poor design. In England and Wales, by contrast with much of the rest of the world, glacial and recent unconsolidated sands, silts and gravels do not form important aquifers. However, many of the principal rivers such as the Thames, Trent, Severn and Great Ouse, are flanked by Alluvial and Terrace gravels and, particularly in the north of England, there may be spreads of late-glacial melt-water sands and gravel. Yields of up to 50 l/s can be obtained from such superficial deposits from properly constructed wells which are commonly of large diameter and may have added horizontal pipes. In the low rainfall areas of eastern England glacial sands and gravels are particularly important for local irrigation water supplies.

In the vale of York in northern England the '25 ft drifts' offer limited shallow aquifer potential.

There are few significant areas of coastal dune sands in England and Wales. They offer little aquifer potential; some local supplies may be obtained, but the water in many cases is brackish or saline.

DISTRIBUTION OF AQUIFERS IN SCOTLAND AND NORTHERN IRELAND

Hydrogeological Maps

Scotland and Northern Ireland are covered by Sheet B3 of the International Hydrogeological Map of Europe[22] scaled at 1 : 1 500 000. Larger-scale national maps have not yet been published. The format of Sheet B3 follows international practice and an Explanatory Note has been produced[23] on which the following accounts are largely based.

Hydrogeology of Scotland

Scotland may be divided into three geographical areas:

(a) the Highlands and Islands;
(b) the Midland Valley; and
(c) the Southern Uplands.

The Highlands and Islands includes the western and northern islands of the Inner and Outer Hebrides, together with Orkney and Shetland; these islands range widely in geological complexity and in age from the Lewisian of the Outer Hebrides through the Lower Palaeozoic Sandstones of Orkney to the Tertiary Volcanic strata of the Inner Hebrides. The Highlands form that part of the mainland north of the Highland Boundary Fault which runs from the coast near Stonehaven south-west to the estuary of the Clyde via a chain of small islands in Loch Lomond. Mostly high moorland, the region consists geologically of Precambrian metamorphic schists and gneisses with Old Red Sandstone sediments forming a coastal belt of relatively low relief on the East from Aberdeen to Inverness and thence northwards to Thurso.

The Midland Valley lies between the great sub-parallel Highland Boundary and Southern Uplands faults. The area contains much mining and other heavy industry and is densely populated by comparison with other regions; it is underlain mainly by sediments of Old Red Sandstone and Carboniferous age associated with volcanic suites. Glacial (superficial) deposits frequently mask the underlying solid rocks. The topography is variable.

The Southern Uplands lie between the Southern Upland Fault and the English border. Ordovician and Silurian indurated sediments predominate, overlain by Old Red Sandstone and Lower Carboniferous strata along the eastern coast and border area. Near Dumfries are two basin-like outliers of Permian sandstones locally important as aquifers. The area has moderate relief and has been subjected to extensive glaciation.

Most of Scotland's water supplies have traditionally been derived from surface sources of which there is no shortage; high topographic relief, high rainfall and preponderance of impermeable rocks have all contributed to a superabundance of large and small lakes (lochs) many of which are utilised either for water supply or for hydropower. Only in recent years has serious thought, prompted mainly by economic considerations, been given to the development of groundwater resources. Under the Scottish legal system, which differs in several respects from that of England, a number of River Purification Boards are responsible for controlling surface waters, but groundwater abstraction is not controlled in Scotland so that relevant data are scattered and difficult to obtain. Nevertheless it has been estimated[23] that groundwater provides up to 10 per cent of the total public water supply. Groundwater use is therefore not negligible and, bearing in mind the absence of major aquifers in Scotland, is significant locally.

In the Highlands and Islands area, significant use of groundwater is limited to the area north and east of Inverness underlain by Old Red Sandstones, to raised beach deposits ("Machair") mainly along the western seaboard, and to the alluvial spreads of valleys. The distillery industry is a traditional user of shallow groundwaters in the highlands and, more recently, fish hatcheries have also made use of similar sources.

In the Midland Valley there is considerable groundwater abstraction from Carboniferous and Old Red Sandstone strata. The latter comprise sandstones, siltstones and mudstones; interbedded lavas are common. Most sandstones are well cemented so that fissure flow is dominant, with transmissivities commonly in the order of 50 m^2/d. In Fife the Knox Pulpit Formation (Upper Old Red Sandstone) has been developed for public supply and a number of wells have yielded up to about 40 l/s.

Within the Carboniferous—lithologically a rhythmic sequence of sandstones, shales, seatearths and coals, with limestones in the lower part of the sequence— groundwater occurs mainly within the thicker sandstone units. However, the natural flow regime has in many areas been modified by mining and large quantities

TABLE 2.V.   Abstraction of Groundwater from Scottish Aquifers
(after Harrison[24])

Purpose of abstraction	Ml/d
Public supply	46
Industry and agriculture	118
Mine drainage	640
Total abstraction	804

of water are pumped as mine drainage, perhaps as much as 80 per cent of the total groundwater pumped in Scotland[24] (Table 2.V).

Typical well yields for Carboniferous sandstones are of the order of 10 l/s, but from some of the thicker sandstones in the Edinburgh area yields of up to 75 l/s have been recorded.

Glacial outwash sands are widely distributed throughout the Midland Valley and give rise to numerous springs, many formerly used for public or private supply.

In the Southern Uplands, comprising mostly impermeable Lower Paleozoic formations, groundwater development is concentrated in a small number of Carboniferous and Permian outliers of which the Dumfries basin is the largest. Here permeable Permian sandstones are more than 200 m thick and support significant abstractions. Well yields up to 67 l/s have been recorded[23] for drawdowns of about 30 m. In this area also, glacial and fluvial deposits are widespread and have some potential for water supply.

Hydrogeology of Northern Ireland

Although a relatively small province, Northern Ireland is underlain by a wide variety of rocks from the Pre-Cambrian to the Quaternary. Many of these rocks are permeable but because of extensive cover by superficial deposits—mostly impermeable glacial tills—have limited potential as aquifers. The boulder clay tends to inhibit both recharge to, and discharge from, the solid rocks[23] although the more permeable beds remain saturated. Abundance of surface supplies has tended to inhibit groundwater exploitation; Manning[25] assessed groundwater usage (other than springs) at 9 Ml/d in 1964, a figure which by 1977 had risen to 28 Ml/d. The more important aquifers comprise rocks of Carboniferous age or younger but are extensively masked by drift so that their detailed hydrogeology is poorly understood[23].

Particularly in the northeast and northwest, crystalline basement rocks of the Dalradian and Moine series contain little or no groundwater. Similarly, the Ordovician and Silurian greywackes to the southeast are without significant groundwater potential.

Old Red Sandstones occupy a considerable area between Loughs Neagh and Erne; mostly these comprise indurated conglomerates although there may be local intercalations of sandstone. Groundwater flow is through fissures; wells encountering broken or jointed rocks may yield small supplies, generally of good chemical quality.

Carboniferous strata (up to 2000 m thick) provide extensive, but little known, aquifers. The measures comprise in downward succession:

(i) Coal Measures and Millstone Grit, very largely arenaceous but occupying small areas and not developed as aquifers. At the base of the Millstone Grit the Slieve Beagh Clastics are poorly permeable but occupy moorland tracts so that their limited potential has not been realised.

(ii) An Upper Limestone which may be fissured and is karstified in upland areas. In County Fermanagh a karstic spring near Marble Arch yields more than 3 Ml/d for public supply, but in general the limited storage restricts the formation's usefulness as an aquifer.

(iii) Calp limestones and shales, where fissured, yield moderate supplies up to about 1 Ml/d.

(iv) The Lower Limestone contains evaporite minerals which, on solution, result in increased secondary fissure permeability, where sulphates, iron and manganese often result in poor groundwater qualities. Well yields are up to 3.5 Ml/d[23].

(v) Basal clastics, comprising sandstones, grits and conglomerates, are mainly indurated with poor yields. Near Armagh, a 100 m thick sandstone yielded 0.7 Ml/d per day with a transmissivity of 30 m^2/d.

Variable groundwater quality is the hallmark of all Carboniferous aquifers in Northern Ireland. Since limestones are ubiquitous, water is usually hard although it is in most cases potable. Locally (i.e. Clogher, County Tyrone), however, mineralised groundwaters occur[23].

Permo-Triassic sandstones underlie the Antrim Basin in the Lough Neagh area at a depth of about 2000 m. The sandstones crop out around the edges of the Basin, towards the centre of which they are overlain by a total thickness of up to 2000 m of Triassic and Jurassic marls and mudstones, Cretaceous Chalk, Tertiary plateau basalts and clays. The potential for obtaining potable groundwater supplies from Permo-Triassic sandstones thus exists essentially only at the outcrops. The aquifer has been extensively developed within the Lagan Valley for the supply of Belfast; here Permian sandstones and conglomerates up to 150 m thick rest on impermeable Lower Palaeozoic basement rocks and are confined by 100 m of Permian marls and mudstones, all beneath considerable but varying thicknesses of glacial drift. Transmissivities are typically of the order of 110 m^2/d. Conformably above the Permian marls lies a Triassic ('Bunter') sandstone sequence, which includes some mudstone bands, to a total thickness of 300 m. This sequence floors much of the Lagan Valley but is intruded by numerous Tertiary basalt dykes trending NNW-SSE, and up to 30 m wide. Inevitably such dykes may affect individual borehole yields, but groundwater usage from the Permo-Triassic aquifers of the Lagan Valley and Newtownards-Comber areas total 30 Ml/d, from 22 boreholes[23] with individual yields within the range 0.5-2.5 Ml/d.

Bennett[26] has estimated that further reserves amounting to a possible 4 Ml/d could be available in the area between Lisburn and Belfast.

The Triassic sandstone is overstepped by Tertiary basalts at the south-west end of the Lagan Valley, but it again crops out south-west of Lough Neagh where it is finer-grained than elsewhere and borehole yields are relatively poor.

In County Londonderry three public supply boreholes have been developed in a narrow strip of sandstones at the base of a steep escarpment of younger rocks. Transmissivities of around 100 m^2/d have been recorded hereabouts with storage coefficients around 0.001.

Groundwaters from the Triassic sandstones are of good chemical quality but moderately hard. Total hardness commonly lies between 35 and 200 mg/l, with Cl^- and SO_4^{2-} concentrations up to 35 mg/l and 150 mg/l respectively[23].

Neither the Upper Jurassic nor the Lower Cretaceous are represented in Northern Ireland. However, Upper Cretaceous Hibernian Greensand underlies the Chalk (also known as the White Limestone) throughout much of County Antrim but these formations, which form a single aquifer, mainly crop out around the periphery of the great spreads of basalt lava which occupy much of the surface of the Antrim Basin. This Chalk differs considerably from its English equivalent in that it is much thinner (maximum thickness 50 m), harder and more dense, with much of the available pore-space infilled by secondary calcitic cement. Nevertheless its well-jointed nature has endowed the Northern Irish Chalk with significant but variable secondary permeability and the formation is a useful aquifer. Recharge appears to be mainly from leakage from the overlying basalt; vertical leakage from the Chalk is prevented by a series of underlying impervious clays, marls or schists of widely varying ages, so that for the most part the formation is fully saturated. Natural drainage is from springs many of which form public sources supplying, or partly supplying, by gravity, such towns as Limavady, Larne, Ballycastle and Stewartstown. The largest springs, at Sallagh, supply Larne with 2.8 Ml/d. At Ballymullock an 81 m deep borehole yields 2.3 Ml/d; pumping test data[23] indicated a transmissivity of 360 m^2/d. Drilling into the Chalk through basalt cover reputedly met with very limited success, probably due to restricted fissuring in areas remote from outcrops.

Groundwater from the Chalk has normally a satisfactory chemical quality although, predictably, it is hard.

Tertiary Plateau Basalts underlie almost 4000 km^2 of Northern Ireland, attaining a thickness of about 800 m. The presence of weathered zones at the tops of individual lava flows which vary from 1 to more than 40 m thick, suggests that some at least of these flows may constitute aquifers with primary horizontal permeability as well as secondary permeability through joints and fissures. A maximum yield from two boreholes 91 m and 122 m deep north of Belfast of 1.7 Ml/d is quoted [23].

Glacial sands and gravels are fairly widespread in Northern Ireland and have been investigated in some detail locally[27,28]. The deposits mainly comprise river valley gravels or spreads of outwash on higher ground—sometimes the two may be associated as a single aquifer. The combined thickness of the deposits rarely exceeds 20 m although single wells may yield up to 3.5 Ml/d and yields of 1.5 Ml/d are sustainable by saturated gravel thicknesses of around 5 m in certain areas.

Glaciofluvial aquifers are commonly unconfined, but rarely may be confined by fluvial silts, glacial till or peat. Gravel aquifer properties are shown in Table 2.VI.

Chemically the quality of gravel groundwaters is generally satisfactory although

TABLE 2.VI. Gravel Aquifer Properties from Pumping Tests in Northern Ireland
(after Bennett and Harrison[23] and Price and Foster[28])

Aquifer name	Type	Transmissivity (m^2/d)	Storage coefficient or specific yield
Culmore	F	350	—
Roe	A	65	0.0002
Glarryford	F	4,750	0.0003
Braid	F	2,000	0.050
Braid	A	300–2,300	0.050–0.110
Killyfaddy	F	180	0.028
Augher	F	400	—
Oona Water	F,A	4,700	—
Derrylin	F	2,200	—
Enler	F,A	315–650	0.001–0.002

F = glaciofluvial   A = alluvial

such shallow aquifers are frequently at risk from surface pollution. Most of these groundwaters are hard, with Cl^- concentrations not exceeding 25 mg/l. Recorded NO_3^- levels have amounted to 7.4 mg/l (as N), possibly reflecting a significant degree of pollution from fertilisers.

3. METEOROLOGICAL FACTORS RELEVANT TO BRITISH AQUIFERS

The Hydrological Cycle

No hydrological treatise is complete without at least some reference to the 'hydrological cycle' which has been described variously from 'what happens to

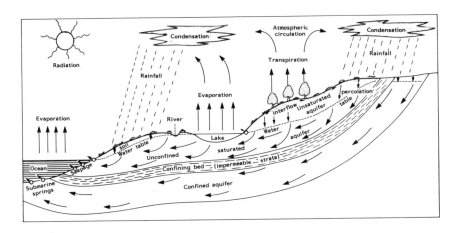

Fig. 2.5. The hydrological cycle

rainfall' to a more scientifically comprehensive 'global study of atmospheric and lithospheric water in all its forms, their distribution and circulation below ground, and their environmental and anthropomorphic interactions'. Rodda et al[6] drew attention to the wide scope of hydrological science implied by the cycle and its interaction with other sciences but this chapter and Chapter 3 will be concerned with the relevant land-based parts of the cycle, namely with atmospheric precipitation and evaporation (above ground) and, below ground, percolation and aquifer response.

The hydrological cycle can be represented graphically either pictorially (Fig. 2.5) or as a system (Fig. 2.6). Variations and refinements of the cycle are almost infinite; in particular the regime underground is dependent on geological structure and lithology; in practice no two localities are precisely alike. Freshwater is a mineral unique in that it is indestructible; changes of phase (solid/liquid/vapour) within the cycle are reversible and its chemical quality is almost infinitely variable. Saline water can be evaporated to become freshwater and freshwater can become saline by mineral solution. Although man can make use of water, can contaminate or purify it, he does not irreversibly consume it in the same way that he consumes other mineral resources.

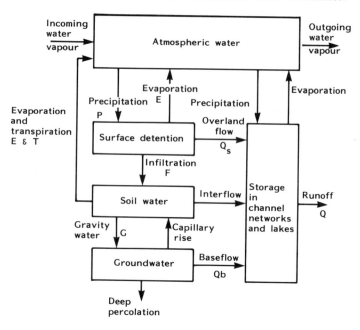

Simplified catchment model

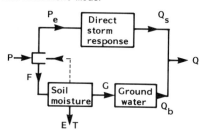

Fig. 2.6.   A systems representation of a basin water balance (after Dooge[29])

CLIMATE

Long-term predictability is the outstanding characteristic of the British climate: the relative rarity of extremes of drought, flood and temperature is reflected in water supply planning policy which commonly allows for meteorological conditions likely to occur on average during 98 out of 100 years. Nevertheless over short periods there can be, within certain limits, quite startling changes in almost all climatic variables. It is rare, for instance, for ground frosts to occur during the period June to October in the south of England, although the diurnal range in temperature can exceed 20°C during the same period. The British Isles are situated almost mid-way between equatorial and polar regions, whilst flanked by the Atlantic Ocean to the west and the European continent to the east. Westerly-drifting sequences of variable atmospheric disturbances (areas of high and low barometric pressure), whose precise nature is determined by route, cross the Atlantic to be modified by proximity to other continentally-derived disturbances; the associated 'fronts' result in rapid weather changes regardless of season. Within the British Isles, however, there is considerable climatic variation due to local influences such as maritime amelioration particularly along the western seaboard, although in the more mountainous areas the effect tends to be balanced by altitude. Latitude (which controls hours of daylight), aspect, exposure, soil type and vegetative cover are other modifying factors.

The prevailing westerly, moisture-bearing winds interact with the western uplands of Cornwall, Devon, Wales, Cumbria and the Scottish Highlands to produce areas of high rainfall; conversely the areas of lowest rainfall lie on the eastern side of England and Scotland. On the other hand evaporation is highest in the east so that generally on the western side of the country (including Northern Ireland) rainfall considerably exceeds evaporation whilst in several eastern areas—particularly for instance in East Anglia—the balance between rainfall and evaporation is more tenuous, although the former always exceeds, albeit marginally, the latter in these relatively dry areas.

PRECIPITATION

Precipitation is the generic name of all forms of atmospheric moisture reaching the ground and includes (most importantly) rainfall, snow, hail, condensative drips and dew. Of these, only rainfall can be measured with any accuracy; although snowfall can be considerable it is the melting phase which is of most significance to water supplies. Systematic rainfall records have been kept since 1727 but long continuous sequences are rare and records have commonly to be adjusted. The estimated general annual rainfall over England and Wales from 1901 to 1975 is shown in Table 2.VII.

TABLE 2.VII.   Estimates of General Annual Rainfall over England and Wales, 1901–1975
(prepared by averaging annual totals measured at selected stations—after Wales-Smith[30])

Year	mm	Year	mm	Year	mm	Year	mm	Year	mm
1901	790	1916	1019	1931	975	1946	1057	1961	874
1902	752	1917	876	1932	922	1947	823	1962	790
1903	1146	1918	958	1933	726	1948	953	1963	851
1904	798	1919	940	1934	851	1949	785	1964	706
1905	770	1920	975	1935	1011	1950	1021	1965	993
1906	904	1921	627	1936	975	1951	1110	1966	1024
1907	886	1922	942	1937	986	1952	902	1967	983
1908	813	1923	1011	1938	886	1953	757	1968	980
1909	940	1924	1074	1939	1013	1954	1085	1969	909
1910	1011	1925	947	1940	904	1955	785	1970	912
1911	841	1926	912	1941	859	1956	869	1971	798
1912	1118	1927	1100	1942	841	1957	899	1972	848
1913	876	1928	1026	1943	833	1958	1029	1973	739
1914	968	1929	894	1944	897	1959	805	1974	991
1915	986	1930	1052	1945	833	1960	1171	1975	752

The British Meteorological Office periodically publishes countrywide rainfall maps at various scales and reference should be made to that organization to find out what is currently available. Maps for the standard periods 1881-1915 and 1916-1950 as well as for non-standard periods 1901-1930 and 1931-1960 are available[31,32]. Although the general pattern of distribution is similar, there has been, over the country as a whole, an approximately 6 per cent increase of estimated general rainfall during the more recent 35-year standard period. In England and Wales average annual rainfall ranges from about 500 mm in parts of East Anglia and the London area to almost 5000 mm in the highest parts of North Wales and the Cumbrian massif. Only marginally less wet are the north-west Highlands of Scotland[23] with up to 4000 mm and, in Northern Ireland, the mountains of the western seaboard with up to 3000 mm. Nevertheless in parts of these mountainous areas local ameliorating factors may operate; in Scotland along the coast of the Western Highlands, for instance, the influence of the Gulf Stream is strong and maritime amelioration can cause wide variations in rainfall as well as in other climatic factors.

In Northern Ireland the low-lying area immediately south of Lough Neagh is relatively dry (annual average 600 to 700 mm); in Scotland rainfall is generally less than 800 mm along the northern shore of the Moray Firth and the eastern coasts of Aberdeen, Fife and East Lothian.

Seasonally, rainfall is almost equally distributed between summer (April-September) and winter (October-March). Table 2.VIII shows monthly rainfall averaged for England, Wales and Scotland (British standard period 1916-1950).

Limited data are available for short duration high intensity rainfall and the shortest period for which such data can be obtained is generally one day. Information can be gleaned from the various volumes of 'British Rainfall' but Rodda et al[6], by comparing British and world maxima, have shown that the heaviest rains recorded in the UK were only about one quarter of the amounts recorded elsewhere for comparable periods.

In Britain the most intense falls do not necessarily occur in recognised areas of highest rainfall, although there is in general an association with mountainous areas of the north and west, where frontal activity is exacerbated by orographic effects.

TABLE 2.VIII.   Average Monthly Rainfall Distribution

	England mm	Wales mm	Scotland mm	United Kingdom mm
January	86	150	145	112
February	64	104	102	79
March	56	86	84	69
April	58	81	84	71
May	64	86	81	71
June	53	79	81	66
July	79	107	107	91
August	79	117	114	94
September	74	114	122	94
October	86	147	150	114
November	91	145	135	112
December	84	142	135	107
Year	874	1358	1340	1080

EVAPORATION

'Evaporation' is possibly the most complex meteorological parameter and its direct measurement is commonly held to be almost impossible. It is necessary to define evaporation for the purposes of this section; the term is usually held to apply to the process by which liquid water is converted to vapour by the application of energy, whereas 'transpiration' is the term applied to the transfer of moisture in the soil to the atmosphere via living plants, mostly through stomatal tissue. However, the hydrogeologist and the water supply engineer are mainly concerned with the net effect of both processes and the term 'evaporation' will here refer to the sum of these evapotranspirative processes, unless the stricter usage is indicated. Only a brief outline of 'evaporation' will be given here; for a comprehensive account of the theory, physics and systematics of evaporative processes see Rodda et al[6].

There is also a distinction to be made between actual and potential evaporation. *Actual evaporation* from water surfaces can be measured from instruments such as:

(1) the British Standard Evaporation Tank (610 mm deep with a square cross-section having sides 1.8 m long, with a rim 76 mm above ground surface); water is removed or added when changes in water level exceed 30 mm;
(2) the US Weather Bureau Class A pan; or
(3) GGI-3000 pans of the Russian Meteorological Service.

Measurements derived from lysimeters have the added advantage that if they are properly constructed the effects of soil moisture deficits are allowed for, although the results are true only for surface conditions similar to those of the lysimeter. However, lysimeters (which are primarily intended to measure infiltration) can be criticised on the grounds that they are necessarily too small (edge effects may be disproportionate) or too shallow to be accurately representative or that, in the case of repacked lysimeters, their contents do not necessarily represent the natural structure of the soil or sub-soils. However, a more detailed description of lysimetric methods will be given later.

Potential evaporation can be determined theoretically by a number of methods, but the most reliable make use either of the energy budget or the aerodynamic (vapour flow) approach. The Thornthwaite[33] method, based on mean air temperatures, is suitable where climatic data are sparse but in Britian where fairly comprehensive long-period data are available, the energy-budget method of Penman[34-40], later refined by Monteith[41-43], is generally favoured. The values for potential evaporation in England and Wales shown in Fig. 2.7 have been derived[44] from the Penman method adjusted for the mean county height above sea level. Those for Scotland are based on Monkhouse and Richards[45].

Although only those factors, e.g. energy supply, vapour fluxes, which concern the transfer of water to the atmosphere are involved in the determination of potential evaporation, the theoretical determination of actual evaporation must allow for soil moisture conditions. Whilst the soil is at field capacity, actual equals potential evaporation, but once soil moisture deficits arise, actual evaporation starts to fall below potential evaporation.

Opinion differs as to exactly at what stage in the soil drying process moisture deficiency occurs and whether plants transpire at constant rates between field capacity and wilting point. The concept of the 'root constant' invokes ranges of values for different vegetative covers. In British catchment studies root constants for short pasture between 12.5 mm and 75 mm have been used, rising to 140 mm for cereals and 200 mm for woodland.

Soil moisture deficits are commonly highest in the east and south east of England

and can exceed 100 mm towards the end of summer in an average year. During the 1975-1976 drought, estimated deficits in many parts of southern and eastern England particularly, were, by the end of June 1976, the highest recorded since records began in 1941. By the end of July 1976 estimated deficits south-east of a line joining the coast of North Yorkshire with the Severn Estuary everywhere exceeded 125 mm and in several areas, 138 mm (Doornkamp et al[46] and Aldwell et al[20]). Around Cambridge a maximum value of 148 mm was estimated.

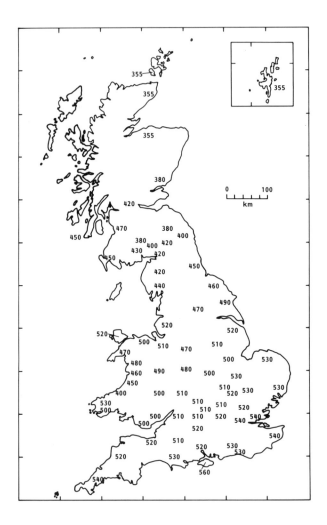

Fig. 2.7. Potential annual evaporation (mm) in Great Britain (after Smith[44])

PERCOLATION

The use of this term here follows the definition of Rodda *et al*[6] and covers the downward movement of water through the unsaturated zone, between the base of the soil layer (to which water "infiltrates" from the surface) and the water table. Percolation thus constitutes the bulk of aquifer recharge, which to many hydrogeologists is a preferable term, although strictly recharge can occur from sources other than rainfall. However, many authors fail to distinguish clearly the two terms. Unconfined aquifer recharge therefore occurs when surface infiltration from rainfall satisfies and exceeds soil moisture deficits.

Percolation to an unconfined aquifer from which there is no surface run-off (e.g. upland Chalk) may be estimated by subtracting the mean annual evaporation over the aquifer outcrop from the mean annual rainfall. The presence of superficial deposits complicates the situation and lack of data may necessitate somewhat arbitrary reduction in the estimated infiltration rate, the amount depending upon the nature and permeability of the deposit.

In areas such as the Chalk of eastern England, where the difference between actual evaporation and rainfall is small, it is desirable to minimise error, otherwise recharge may be unnecessarily underestimated and important reserves overlooked. Thus the measurement of percolation becomes important and can act as a useful spot check on theoretical estimations. The main problem in achieving accurate measurements is to produce, at model or instrumental scale, as nearly as possible natural undisturbed soil and sub-soil conditions and it is of course important to establish vegetative cover representative of the area.

Although the use of lysimeters is not new, until recent years the scale and method of construction of such instruments has left much to be desired and results have been unreliable. For instance many of the older types of lysimeter have had cross-sectional areas of about 1 m^2 and depths of less than 1 m; furthermore it was common practice to repack them with soil, rock, or both. Nowadays large (up to 100 m^2) and deep (several metres) undisturbed blocks of permeable strata (sandstone or chalk) have been enclosed on site by sheet steel piling or by trenches into which have been inserted sheet (clay or membrane) seals with their bases penetrating impermeable underlying strata. The level of the water table within the lysimeter is maintained (by pumping) at a level similar to that outside the instrument so that measurements of throughput indicate values for percolation from which actual evaporation can be derived.

The newest type of lysimeter (at the Cambridge Water Company's Fleam Dyke Pumping Station) consists of an undisturbed 5 m cube of Middle Chalk and topsoil with sheet piled sides and similar base. The latter was driven, at a few degrees to the horizontal, from two opposite sides towards the centre where there is a collecting trough. The base is welded to the lower edges of the sides and suitable underground access to sides and trough provided; the bottom of the instrument is drained so that the entire cube, the contents of which are as 'undisturbed' as engineering techniques allow, remains unsaturated at all times. The drainage is collected in the central trough and automatically measured by means of a tipping bucket mechanism. At Fleam Dyke results so far indicate that the conventional adoption of a 75 mm root constant for short grass and pasture is too great and that therefore actual measured percolation here is significantly greater than the amount estimated by modified Penman methods.

The 'zero flux plane' (or level at which downward movement of moisture under gravity is balanced by the upward suction exerted by capillarity and evaporation) method for determining percolation depends on observations of the pattern of soil moisture behaviour and in particular the vertical fluctuation of the plane of zero moisture flux. Tensiometers in boreholes are used to determine the position of the zero flux plane which descends in autumn in response to rainfall and infiltration and subsequently ascends in summer in response to evaporation. In winter however when evaporation is small and infiltration at its greatest, the flux plane is obliterated so that the method on its own can only be used at certain times of the year and not those most critical to the determination of percolation. Although the use of large undisturbed lysimeters would appear to offer a reliable method of determining percolation and recharge to unconfined aquifers, they are unquestionably expensive to construct and replicate, although cheap to maintain and measure. However, the perfection of soil moisture flux methods would imply a much cheaper methodology. The problem of instrument automation on which the economics of soil moisture methods largely depend, has so far proved intransigent; necessarily frequent manual measurements raise considerably the maintenance costs of a network. Research into these problems continues.

Whilst 'undisturbed' lysimeters can be criticised because of a degree of disturbance around their edges during construction, these edge effects decrease as the size of the lysimeter increases. Unfortunately costs increase, so that huge, artificially enclosed lysimeters are not practical, although 'outlier' lysimeters (consisting of a permeable geological outlier on an impermeable basal stratum surrounded by a ring drain leading to a suitable measuring device) have been proposed but not implemented, again on grounds of cost.

WATER BALANCES

In theory, water balance studies of permeable catchments should produce an ideal result but in practice the difficulties inherent in accurately delineating a permeable groundwater catchment effectively prevent their use in most cases.

Positions of groundwater divides must be accurately known at all times of the year. For example, the groundwater catchment of the River Itchen (downstream to Allbrook) is 35 per cent larger than its surface equivalent[6,47]. Similarly, some groundwater from the River Lee surface catchment (part of the London basin) drains into the adjacent River Great Ouse catchment[48]. Rodda et al[6] point out that a catchment water balance can be expressed in the form:

$$P = E + S_R + G_R \pm U \pm S$$

where P = precipitation
E = actual evaporation
S_R = direct run-off (including overflow)
G_R = groundwater discharge
U = net groundwater flow through aquifer (i.e. inflow less outflow)
S = change in storage of groundwater and soil moisture.

The equation is usually solved over a long period, so that the effect of changes in storage, for which information may not be available, can be minimised. Over a long period, groundwater discharge (if known) is of course equal to percolation and thus to recharge, assuming that there is no leakage to or from adjacent aquifers.

Day[49] derived a water balance for the permeable groundwater catchment to the Bedhampton group of springs which at that time formed the main basis of Portsmouth's water supply. In this case the flows of all springs were gauged, or could be estimated, with reasonable accuracy; significant leakage from the catchment could be ruled out on geological structural grounds. The size of the catchment was also known as numerous observation wells enabled water table contours to be drawn and groundwater divides plotted. Representative water levels in wells had been measured for many years; changes in storage at the limits of the 90-year period, for which the balance equation was solved, were minimal and could be quantified. Occasional surface run-off via ephemeral streams could also be calculated. Using the available Penman figure for evaporation the long period average groundwater discharge for the 40 mile^2 (104 km^2) catchment was estimated at 19.1 mgd (1.004 m^3/s) compared with the measured average discharge of 19.8 mgd (1.042 m^3/s).

GROUNDWATER DISCHARGE

Groundwater discharge (in the long term equal to recharge) takes place from points as springs or from areas or lines as seepages. The discharge is commonly called a spring if it results in surface flow in a defined channel. Historically, many springs have had magical or religious associations; such 'holy wells' are common-place in most countries. The classification of springs is difficult and complex; because of the main parameters involved, e.g. temperature, chemical composition, rate of flow and seasonal variation, geological or topograpical reason for discharge, it can be said with some force that no really satisfactory classification exists. As long ago as 1923, Meinzer[50] attempted a classification on mean discharge, evoking eight 'magnitudes'—the first having flows greater than 100 ft^3/sec (2.83 m^3/sec) ranging to the eighth with less than one pint/minute (less than 7.9 ml/sec).

Perennial springs have long been used for water supply and to them many towns and villages owe their origin. London's piped supplies originally came from the Chadwell spring in the Hertfordshire Lee valley; before over-abstraction lowered groundwater levels in the Chalk of the London basin, this spring had an average flow of 9-13 Ml/d. The largest spring, or rather group of springs, in the British Isles, issues from the Chalk at Bedhampton (Hants) where the mean annual flow of 19.8 mgd (90.01 Ml/d) is used for the supply of Portsmouth. Recorded flows of these springs have ranged from about 14 mgd (63.64 Ml/d) to more than 36 mgd (163.66 Ml/d).

The three principal variables which determine spring discharge are aquifer permeability, contributing catchment area and amount of groundwater recharge (Davis and De Wiest[14]). A high permeability permits concentration of large volumes of water in a small area, and there are dramatic increases in permeability of aquifers (development of fissured permeability) as discharge points are approached. If aquifers were completely homogeneous, groundwater discharge would all be in the form of diffuse seepage over large areas.

The location of springs is frequently determined by variation in vertical or horizontal permeability commonly associated with layered rocks. Unconfined aquifers normally drain to the lowest point that their geological structure permits; the control may then be a fault or fold, or junction with a less permeable formation. 'Pressure' springs may arise under confined conditions which create a manometer effect. Submarine discharges are not uncommon and several are known around the coasts of Britain. Some typical instances of spring discharge are shown in Fig. 2.8 but these illustrations are far from comprehensive.

Mineral and thermal springs commonly involve deep or long pathways for the groundwater they discharge. The high temperatures encountered at depth plus long residence time enables solution of minerals and there has been less opportunity for soluble minerals to have been flushed from the aquifer. According to Andrews *et*

al^{51} groundwater discharge from the well-known thermal springs at Bath has its origin, and derives its head, from the Carboniferous Limestone outcrops some 20 km distant in the Mendip hills.

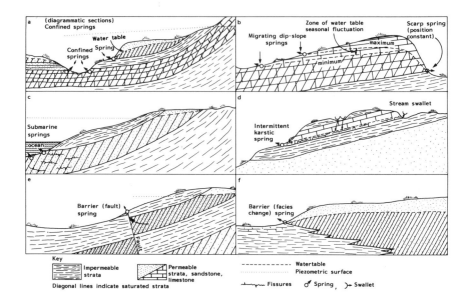

Fig. 2.8.   Some typical instances of spring discharge in relation to geology and topography

BASEFLOW OF RIVERS

Baseflow is defined by Pfannkuch[1] as 'sustained fair weather run-off', but this is only part of the story. In effect, river base flow under such conditions is spring flow and rivers which receive no discharge from aquifers will dry up when surface run-off and interflow cease.

Groundwater discharge to rivers may not be entirely from definable point spring sources, although the heads of some rivers are so determined. Where a river crosses permeable strata it either loses water to the aquifer or receives water from the aquifer along its bed as line discharge. The alluvial banks of the river form minor aquifers and may contribute diffuse discharge—some of it 'bank storage' acquired during periods of high flow—which also contributes to baseflow.

Dry weather baseflow can be measured by gauging (care must be taken in siting such gauges to ensure no underflow or, if underflow is suspected, due allowance made for it); at times of higher flows the groundwater component of flow can be determined by careful analysis of hydrographs.

RELATIONSHIP OF GROUNDWATER TO SURFACE FLOW

To some extent, this has been covered earlier. In the natural state the hydrological cycle is in dynamic equilibrium so that interference by man with any component requires the system as a whole to readjust. All abstraction of groundwater from wells is ultimately at the expense of natural discharge, but the great storage capacity of most aquifers damps down the effect, which may be spread over a period of time. Another ameliorating effect in practice is that most, perhaps as much as 90 per cent, of the water pumped from wells for public supply finds its way back into a river system as effluent, so that this water bypasses natural pathways and in dry weather may actually enhance flow of a river or stream. However, the groundwater pumped for efficient irrigation evaporates and is therefore a total loss to the landbased part of the hydrological cycle.

The relationship between groundwater abstraction, reduction in spring flow and thus of surface flow, and the augmentation of streamflow by effluent discharge is complex in space and time. The factors involved are utilised to good effect in schemes to augment river flow in dry periods by pumping from wells in unconfined aquifers in remote parts of the catchment and piping the water to the nearest perennial tributary for intake further down stream (see Chapter 14). Augmentation wells are sited remotely from natural discharges so as to delay effects on them for several months and preferably until the winter when higher flows in the rivers have been restored. Groundwater for river augmentation can also be pumped from a confined aquifer to a nearby stream without the need for long pipelines; in this case the stream is 'insulated' from the aquifer in the neighbourhood of the well and the time-lag is obtained by siting the well remotely from the outcrop of (and intake to) the aquifer.

Most augmentation schemes are largely dependent upon winter recharge to replenish the areas of aquifer dewatered around the wells. The lowered hydraulic gradient results in less groundwater being discharged from the springs during the winter period so that, in effect, the hydrograph of groundwater discharge is smoothed to an extent depending upon the quantities pumped and the volume of aquifer dewatered.

4.   GROUNDWATER STORAGE AND AQUIFER ABSTRACTION

GLOBAL AVAILABILITY OF GROUNDWATER

According to Huisman[52] the global availability of fresh liquid water is 8.2 MKm^3, or 0.6 per cent of the total amount of water on earth. Of this stock, 1.2 per cent comprises surface water in lakes and rivers and of the remainder, which is groundwater, half occurs below 800 m depth and can be regarded as unavailable. Soil moisture, also unavailable, accounts for a further 0.6 per cent of the total quantity.

GROUNDWATER STORED IN BRITISH AQUIFERS

The groundwater storage capacity of British aquifers, such as the thick and extensive Chalk and Triassic sandstones, is very great indeed. Estimates vary of the total long-term utilisable groundwater storage within English and Welsh aquifers, but Richards and Downing[53] quote a figure of almost 10 000 Mm³/a. This figure is broken down in Table 2.IX, together with abstraction figures which relate to the year 1975.

TABLE 2.IX.   Groundwater Resources of England and Wales
(after Richards and Downing[53])

	Groundwater resources* 10^6m³/a	Abstraction 1975 10^6m³/a	Balance 10^6m³/a	Abstraction as percentage of resources	Abstraction as percentage of total abstraction
Chalk and Upper Greensand	3938	1152	2786	29	57
Permo-Triassic Sandstones	1410	359	1051	25	18
Coal Measures	1178#	81**	1097	7	4
Carboniferous Limestone	1128#	81	1047	7	4
Middle Jurassic Limestones	875	109	766	12	5
Millstone Grit	608#	20	588	3	1
Magnesian Limestone	335	83	252	25	4
Lower Greensand	181	102	79	56	5
Hastings Beds	47	13	34	28	<1
Upper Jurassic	44	Nil	44	—	—
Lias	35	2	33	6	<1
Pleistocene Crag	29	14	15	48	<1
TOTALS	9808	2016	7792	21	100

Notes: * Does not include resources of river gravels
** Does not include abstraction for mine-drainage purposes
# The high value for the resources of Carboniferous rocks gives a false impression of their total potential. Their aquifer properties limit economic large-scale development.

These resources are renewable by percolation and take no account of the much larger (although less easily defined) quantities stored below the base drainage levels of aquifers, commonly referred to as 'permanent' or more accurately perhaps (and following Rodda et al[6]) 'storage' resources. To estimate such storage it is necessary to know not only the extent and effective thickness (saturated thickness) of the aquifer but also its storage coefficient. The Chalk, which may exceed 300 m in thickness and crops out, or is overlain by relatively thin drift deposits, over about 17 000 km² of eastern and southern England, may have an average effective aquifer thickness considerably less than 100 m and has a storage coefficient typically less than 2 per cent. By contrast the Triassic sandstones have an outcrop, or subcrop below thin drift, of about half that of the Chalk, an average effective aquifer thickness greater than that of the Chalk and a storage coefficient (in the unconfined condition) commonly of the order of 20 per cent, ten times that of the Chalk.

Richards and Downing[53] quote figures for storage resources in parts of English aquifers. Some 200 km² of Chalk forming the South Downs of the Brighton area contain 500 Mm³; 3500 to 5000 Mm³ are stored in the Chalk of the East Anglian Ely Ouse catchment and 10 000 Mm³ reposes in the top 50 m of saturated Sherwood (formerly 'Bunter') Sandstone of Nottinghamshire. These figures should be compared with the total available volume of surface water stored for supply in British reservoirs of 2000 Mm³.

By contrast, the groundwater resources of Scotland and Northern Ireland, although locally important, are not of regional significance. Few major aquifers are present and the relative lack of groundwater reflects the greater abundance of ancient, hard and impermeable rocks, particularly in Scotland. Although much of Northern Ireland is underlain by permeable Carboniferous Limestone, this formation's usefulness as an aquifer is inevitably limited by the extensive blanket of impermeable, or at best poorly permeable, glacial clays.

ABSTRACTION OF GROUNDWATER FROM BRITISH AQUIFERS

Groundwater abstraction in England and Wales is, since the 1963 Water Resources Act, everywhere licensable except for minor domestic use and temporary dewatering in connection with constructional works. Returns of abstraction are made by licensees to Regional Water Authorities and effective records of groundwater abstraction are no longer kept centrally. However, between 1948 and 1963 central records were kept under Section 6 of the Water Act 1945. From this information, which may be taken as roughly indicative of the present situation, the Chalk and Triassic sandstones accounted for some 60 per cent of total abstraction, with 20 per cent derived (mainly as mine drainage) from the Coal Measures. Excluding mine drainage, these two major aquifers accounted for about 75 per cent of the groundwater pumped for supplies. Of the remaining aquifers the Permian Magnesian Limestone, the Jurassic Inferior Oolite and the Cretaceous Lower Greensand each provided about 3.5 per cent with the superficial deposits (mostly glacial, not riverine) contributing a like amount.

TABLE 2.X. Groundwater Abstraction and Uses in England and Wales, 1948–63 and 1973–77
(in 10⁶/m³ per annum)

Year	Total abstraction	Used for public supply	Used in industry	Other uses, including agriculture & horticulture
1948	1475	986	431	58
1949	1522	995	461	66
1950	1554	1002	484	68
1951	1570	1006	487	77
1952	1592	1046	484	62
1953	1636	1063	503	70
1954	1702	1099	531	72
1955	1749	1136	538	75
1956	1782	1173	534	75
1957	1801	1191	533	77
1958	1753	1182	503	68
1959	1852	1252	526	74
1960	1902	1288	539	75
1961	1976	1361	539	76
1962	2002	1404	523	75
1963	2058	1459	526	73
1973	2462	1874	530	58
1974	2509	1953	501	55
1975	2391	1830	501	60
1976	2325	1770	514	41
1977	2280	1739	497	44

Monkhouse and Richards[45] provide much useful statistical information on British groundwater abstraction, in the context of the aquifers from which it was abstracted. Both licensed (these figures usually provide a maximum) and actual abstraction are given as well as supplementary data, such as the estimated mean annual replenishment. Groundwater abstraction is tabulated for Northern Ireland, Scotland and the 10 Water Authority areas of England and Wales. These areas are further subdivided into units, defined in consultation with the authorities concerned. These units are referred to in the text and are shown in a series of 8 accompanying maps at a scale of 1:500000 which cover the whole of the United Kingdom. This major work was carried out under the auspices of the former Central Water Planning Unit.

Table 2.X summarises groundwater abstraction in England and Wales between the years 1948 and 1977 (including a 9-year gap from 1964 to 1972 when reliable records were not kept). Total abstraction is divided into 'public supply', 'industrial' and 'other uses', which include agricultural and horticultural use. The figures do not include mine waters for which, regrettably, no data are available after 1963. In that year mine drainage was believed to amount to 0.4×10^9 m^3 per annum[54].

Until 1974 there was a steady increase in abstraction, accounted for by a steady growth of 2 per cent per year in groundwater pumped for public supply. The falls in abstraction evident after 1975 are attributed by Monkhouse and Richards[45] to the effects of the 1975-76 drought and the success of the measures then adopted to restrict demand.

5. REFERENCES

1. Pfannkuch H. O. 1969 "Elsevier's dictionary of hydrogeology", Elsevier, Amsterdam/London/New York.
2. Lohman, S. W. *et al* 1972 Wat. Supply Pap. 1988, US Geol. Surv., "Definitions of selected groundwater terms—revisions and conceptual refinements".
3. Russell, Sir E. J. 1957 "The world of the soil", Collins, London.
4. Taylor, J. A. 1957 "Soils and vegetation in Wales; a physical, historical and regional geography", Bowen, E. G. (Ed.), Methuen, London.
5. Natural Environment Research Council 1975 "Flood studies report", Vol. 1, Ch. 4.
6. Rodda, J. C., Downing, R. A. and Law, F. M. 1976 "Systematic hydrology", Newnes-Butterworth, London/Boston.
7. Conway, V. M. and Miller, A. 1960 *J. IWE*, 14, 415, The hydrology of some small peat-covered catchments in the northern Pennines.
8. Smith, D. B. *et al* 1970 Proc. Symp. Isotope Hydrol., IAEA, Vienna, "Water movement in the unsaturated zone of high and low permeability strata using natural tritium".
9. Foster, S. S. D. and Young, C. P. 1980 'Effects of agricultural land-use on groundwater quality with special reference to nitrate' in "A survey of British hydrogeology", The Royal Society, London.
10. Price, M., Bird, M. J. and Foster, S. S. D. 1976 *Wat. Services*, 968, 596, Chalk pore size measurements and their significance.
11. Foster, S. S. D. 1975 *J. Hydrol.*, 25, 159, The Chalk groundwater tritium anomaly—a possible explanation.
12. Young, C. P., Oakes, D. B. and Wilkinson, W. B. 1976 *Groundwater*, 14, 426, Prediction of future nitrate concentrations in groundwater.
13. Oakes, D. B. 1977 Proc. 3rd Int. Symp. on Hydrology, Univ. Colorado, Fort Collins, USA "The movement of water and solutes through the unsaturated zone of the Chalk in the United Kingdom".
14. Davis, S. N. and De Wiest, R. J. M. 1966 "Hydrogeology", John Wiley and Sons, New York.
15. Todd, D. K. 1980 "Ground water hydrology", John Wiley and Sons, New York.
16. Morris, D. A. and Johnson, A. I. 1967 Wat. Supply Pap. 1839-D, US Geol. Surv., "Summary of hydrologic and physical properties of rock and soil materials, as analysed by the hydrologic laboratory of the US Geological Survey, 1948-1960".

17. Wenzel, L. K. 1942 Wat. Supply Pap. 887, US Geol. Surv., "Methods for determining permeability of water-bearing materials with special reference to discharging-well methods".

18. Cradock-Hartopp, M. A. *et al* 1977 "Hydrogeological map of England and Wales 1:625000", Institute of Geological Sciences, London.

19. Karrenberg, H., Buchan, S. and Day, J. B. W. 1976 "International hydrogeological map of Europe; Sheet B4 (London)", Bundesanstalt für Geowissenschaften und Rohstoffe, Hannover and UNESCO, Paris.

20. Aldwell, C. R., Day, J. B. W. and Struckmeier, W. 1978 "Explanatory notes for the international hydrogeological map of Europe; Sheet B4 (London)", *ibid.*

21. Day, J. B. W. *et al* 1970 "Hydrogeological map of the Chalk and Lower Greensand of Kent, Sheet 1", Institute of Geological Sciences, London.

22. Karrenberg, H., Moseley, R. and Day, J. B. W. 1980 "International hydrogeological map of Europe, Sheet B3, Edinburgh", Bundensanstalt für Geowissenschaften und Rohstoffe, Hannover and UNESCO, Paris.

23. Bennett, J. R. P. and Harrison, I. B. 1980 "Explanatory notes for the international hydrogeological map of Europe, Sheet B3, Edinburgh". *ibid.*

24. Harrison, I. B. 1982 "Groundwater in Scotland—a hidden asset", Report No. ARD 11, Scottish Development Department, Edinburgh.

25. Manning, P. I. 1972 *Instn. Civ. Engrs, N. Irel. Assn*, 1, 31, The development of the groundwater resources of Northern Ireland.

26. Bennett, J. R. P. 1976 "The Lagan Valley hydrogeological study", Open File Report No. 23, Geological Survey, Northern Ireland, Belfast.

27. Foster, S. S. D. 1969 "Final report on groundwater investigation at the projected Michelin plant, Ballymena, Co. Antrim, Northern Ireland," *ibid.*

28. Price, M. and Foster, S. S. D. 1974 *Proc. ICE*, 57, 451, Water supplies from Ulster valley gravels.

29. Dooge, J. C. I. 1974 *Hydro. Sci. Bull.*, 19, 279, The development of hydrological concepts in Britain and Ireland between 1674 and 1874.

30. Wales-Smith, B. G. 1971 *Met. Mag.*, 100, 345, Monthly and mean totals of rainfall representative of Kew, Surrey, from 1967 to 1970.

31. Anon 1953 "Climatic atlas of the British Isles", HMSO, London.

32. Anon 1971 "Climatic atlas of Europe, Vol. 1, maps of mean temperature and precipitation", WMO, UNESCO and Cartographia.

33. Thornthwaite, C. W. and Hare, F. K. 1965 'The loss of water to the air' in "Agricultural meteorology", Am. Met. Soc. Monograph No. 28.

34. Penman, H. L. 1948 *Proc. Royal Soc. A*, 193, 120, Natural evaporation from open water, bare soil and grass.

35. Penman, H. L. 1950 *Q. J. Royal Met. Soc.*, 76, 372, Evaporation over the British Isles.

36. Penman, H. L. 1950 *J. IWE*, 4, 457, The water balance of the Stour catchment.

37. Penman, H. L. 1954 Proc. IASH General Assembly, Rome, Pub. No. 38, "Evaporation over parts of Europe".

38. Penman, H. L. 1955 *Q. J. Royal Met. Soc.*, 81, 280, Components in the water balance of a catchment area.

39. Penman, H. L. 1956 *Trans. Am. Geophys. Union*, 37, 43, Estimating evaporation.

40. Penman, H. L. 1956 *Netherlands J. Agric. Sci.*, 4, 29, Evaporation; an introductory survey.

41. Monteith, J. L. 1959 *Q. J. Royal Met. Soc.*, 85, 386, The reflection of shortwave radiation by vegetation.

42. Monteith, J. L. 1965 *Symp. Soc. Exp. Biol.*, 19, 205, Evaporation and environment.

43. Monteith, J. L. 1966 *Exper. Agric. Rev.*, 2, 1, The photosynthesis and transpiration of crops.

44. Smith, L. P. 1967 Min. Agric. Fish and Food, Tech. Bull. No. 16, "Potential transpiration".

45. Monkhouse, R. A. and Richards, H. J. 1982 "Groundwater resources of the United Kingdom", Directorate-general for the environment, consumer protection and nuclear safety, CEC, Brussels.

46. Doornkamp, J. C., Gregory, K. J. and Burn, A. S. 1980 "Atlas of drought", Inst. of Brit. Geographers, London.

47. Ineson, J. and Downing, R. A. 1965 *J. IWE*, 19, 59, Some hydrogeological factors in permeable catchment studies.

48. Water Resources Board 1972 "The hydrogeology of the London Basin", Publication No. 139, WRB, Reading.

49. Day, J. B. W. 1964 "Infiltration into a groundwater catchment and the derivation of evaporation", Research Report No. 2, Geol. Surv. Gt. Brit., London.

50. Meinzer, O. E. 1923. Wat. Supply Pap. 494, US Geol. Surv., "Outline of groundwater hydrology (with definitions)".

51. Andrews, J. N. *et al* 1982 *Nature, London*, 298, 339, The thermal springs of Bath.

52. Huisman, L. 1972 "Groundwater recovery", Macmillan, London and Basingstoke.

53. Richards, H. J. and Downing, R. A. Mem. IAH 13th Congress, Birmingham, G30 and 46, "Aquifer management in England and Wales".
54. Jones, G. P. 1977 'Utilization of groundwater in Britain' in "Proc. Conf. on groundwater quality, measurement, prediction and protection", Water Research Centre, Medmenham.

Chapter 3

GROUNDWATER CHEMISTRY

1. INTRODUCTION

"WATER takes on the properties of the rocks through which it has passed" wrote
Pliny nineteen centuries ago. This statement still adequately defines the subject
area of hydrogeochemistry. Modern exploitation of groundwater and the management of resources require a detailed understanding of these properties as well as
the processes by which they are attained. Groundwater, traditionally regarded as
pure and wholesome, has also become threatened by man's polluting activities, so
that there are very few areas of Britain and other developed countries where water
can be found without traces of substances derived from intensive agricultural or
industrial activities.

With this background it is important that the natural processes by which
groundwater gains its intrinsic properties can be identified and understood and
used as a basis for measuring the encroachment of pollution and protecting water
supplies. Most of the chemical properties of groundwater are attained rapidly,
during movement through the soil and unsaturated zone, and an understanding of
reactions taking place here is of special importance in groundwater protection.
Although there may be very little change in total mineralisation in the saturated
zone it is here that exchange reactions and other processes can slowly modify
groundwater chemistry. There is also scope for removal or modification of harmful
substances by adsorption, precipitation or oxidation/reduction reactions. Therefore
it is in the deeper aquifer sections that valuable resources of potable groundwater
unaffected by man's activities may be found.

To understand the distribution and variations in groundwater chemistry, the
nature of reactions between water and rock, the residence time of water, and the
rate by which reactions proceed, it is necessary to combine chemical, geological and
hydrogeological principles. In this chapter, an outline is given of the main
principles of hydrogeochemistry using examples mainly from UK aquifers. This
chapter begins with an outline of the principal processes which control groundwater
composition. The hydrogeochemical characteristics of groundwaters from the main
British aquifers are then described, with special emphasis on alluvial formations,
Chalk and Triassic Sandstones. A major section deals with the philosophy and
criteria required for successful hydrogeochemical investigations and a review of the
main parameters which should be measured. The chapter concludes with sections
on the interpretation of hydrogeochemical data and on water quality and use.

2. PROCESSES CONTROLLING GROUNDWATER COMPOSITION

PHYSICAL PROCESSES

Dilution, dispersion, filtration, mixing and related physical processes may be
important, either on their own or coupled with other geochemical or biochemical
processes, in modifying the chemical composition of groundwater. To assess their
relative significance it is helpful first to consider various solute transport
mechanisms and then the particle sizes of solutes and suspended material in

relation to aquifer porosities.

Dispersion is a collective term describing both flow and diffusion. Groundwater flow may either be rapid (via fissures) or slower via intergranular pore spaces; in any event it is the flow component which is primarily responsible for the reactivity of the hydrogeochemical system, bringing in new reactants and removing reaction products. In the context of groundwater protection the magnitude of the flow component will be of greatest significance in determining the rate of travel of any contaminant. In porous intergranular materials, molecular diffusion becomes important in considering longer term compositional change. Self-diffusion of a solute in pure water (values often reported in the literature) should be distinguished from matrix diffusion where the mobility of the solute is reduced by the rock porosity, water content and flow path tortuosity, as well as by interaction with the solids.

Matrix diffusion coefficients have been determined using labelled tracers for a number of solutes in Chalk[1]. The non-interactive solutes, Cl^- and NO_3^-, move at roughly the same rate as each other but slower than tritiated water (HTO) (Table 3.I). Sulphate diffusion is less than half the rate of the other two anions due to surface impedance.

Fissure flow is quantitatively more important than intergranular flow in the majority of aquifers. Fissure storage, on the other hand, is commonly only a small fraction of the total storage in most sedimentary aquifers. Additionally the rates of solute transport in the intergranular pore space may be several orders of magnitude lower than in fissures. Thus a compositional disequilibrium may exist between water in rapid transit via fissures and relatively immobile interstitial fluids within the bulk of the rock. This is illustrated schematically in Fig. 3.1 for two situations:

(1) induced flow of groundwater into a brackish aquifer;
(2) contamination of an aquifer by a pollutant.

These probably occur in various permutations in most British aquifers and are of fundamental importance to the interpretation of groundwater quality. The large volumes of intergranular storage may continue to exert a long term influence on the fissure water chemistry either by intergranular flow or molecular diffusion—as for example in the Lincolnshire Limestone. Equilibration may take a long time, especially if solute movement is diffusion controlled; supply of reactants and products to and from interstitial sites will be slowed down as equilibration proceeds, thereby limiting the rates of geochemical reactions.

This heterogeneity may be expressed in different ways. In the Chalk of Berkshire a difference in ionic composition between fresh fissure-derived and slightly saline interstitial water has been described[3]. A difference in chemical composition need not necessarily exist, however, and the distinction may be one of groundwater age between waters with similar chemistries; examples of this are also found in the Chalk, where a difference may exist in levels of tritium between fissure drainage

TABLE 3.I.   Values of Matrix (Restricted)
Diffusion Coefficents in Chalk (after Hill[1])

Labelled tracer	Diffusion Coefficient (cm^2/s)
Cl^-	$0.52 - 3.23 \times 10^6$
NO_3^-	$0.53 - 3.20 \times 10^6$
HTO	$0.60 - 3.51 \times 10^6$
SO_4^{2-}	$0.28 - 1.47 \times 10^6$

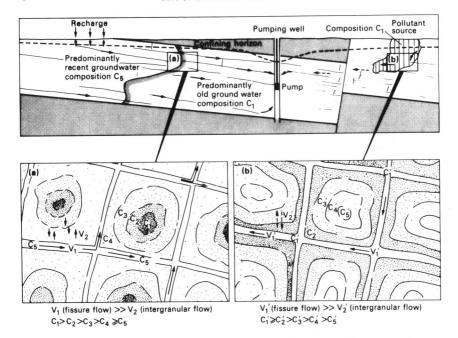

V₁ (fissure flow) ≫ V₂ (intergranular flow)
$C_1 > C_2 > C_3 > C_4 \geqslant C_5$

V₁' (fissure flow) ≫ V₂' (intergranular flow)
$C_1' \geqslant C_2' > C_3' > C_4' > C_5'$

Fig. 3.1. Compositional differences between fissure and intergranular water during (a) downgradient flow and (b) aquifer contamination (after Edmunds[2])

(high ^{3}H) and intergranular storage (low ^{3}H). In this example there is progressive exchange between the low tritium intergranular reservoir and recent water percolating through fissures, especially in the unsaturated zone[4]. A further example is provided by cores from the Lincolnshire Limestone, where there is visual evidence of the oxidation reaction which has taken place during the flux between intergranular and fissure water over a long time scale; redox gradients must therefore exist over distances of centimetres in the aquifer framework.

The physical size of solutes and suspended matter relative to the rock framework can have an important influence: notably upon filtration but also upon coprecipitation, surface and biochemical reactions. The particle size fractions of possible particulate matter derived from surface waters, soil and groundwaters in relation to pore diameters of principal British aquifers are shown in Fig. 3.2. The larger microorganisms, clay grade material and amorphous oxyhydroxides such as limonite, will not be transported within the finer intergranular pore spaces although there is scope for movement through fissures. Bacteria would be excluded from pore spaces of Chalk and Jurassic Limestones and limit the sites of microbiological reactions to the margins of the intergranular space. Biological processes have been reviewed by Matthes[5].

PARENT-ROCK GEOCHEMISTRY

The chemical composition of groundwater is dependent primarily upon the type (e.g. carbonate, granite, sandstone) and geochemistry of the parent rock. Two concepts are important—geochemical abundance and geochemical mobility. Those

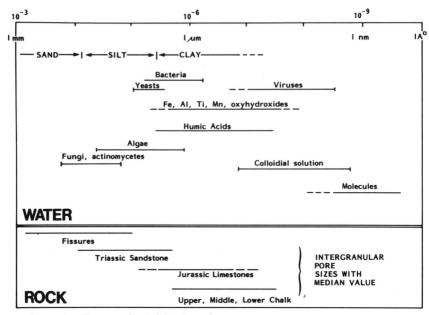

Fig. 3.2. Range of particle size of suspended and dissolved matter in groundwaters in relation to aquifer geometry

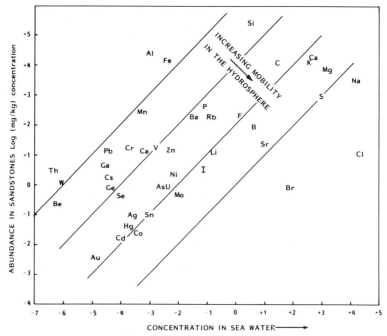

Fig. 3.3. Geochemical mobility of the elements, based on their abundance in sandstone compared with sea water

elements most abundant in the earth's crust, e.g. Si, Al and Fe are typically not those most mobile in the hydrosphere, e.g. Na, Cl and Br. Taking one rock type—average sandstone composition, which is itself a good sample of crustal material—and comparing elemental abundance with that in sea water (Fig. 3.3) gives an approximate summary of geochemical mobility for the most important elements. Many solutes in groundwater are involved in cycling processes. The overall geochemical cycle can be conveniently expressed as the residence time in the ocean[6], which is the mean period between element release via rivers and incorporation back into ocean sediments. Thus, sodium has a residence time of 10^8 years but aluminium only 10^2 years. However, the various processes that occur within groundwater systems (e.g. solution-precipitation, adsorption-desorption, discussed later) ensure that, within the overall cycle, elements may be involved in a whole series of water-rock reactions that change both the nature of groundwater chemistry as well as the parent rock.

The mineralogy of each aquifer lithology must be established before the details of geochemical reactions are considered. During diagenesis the primary rock framework materials are likely to control the main solute characteristics and groundwater is likely to be in equilibrium with the secondary cementing phases. As well as mineral solubility the grain size and specific surface area are important controls on the reactivity of the rock. The mineralogical controls can be illustrated with representative samples from UK aquifer lithologies.

The stability of rock-forming minerals should be taken into account when considering their reactivity. Many are formed in high temperature environments and may be unstable or metastable at the present day; reaction should proceed to produce minerals stable at low temperatures, e.g. biotite could break down to give kaolinite or chlorite and silica. Perhaps it is more important to realise that some new minerals will form only under limiting conditions of solute concentration and temperature or under favourable kinetic conditions. For example, strontianite ($SrCO_3$), which has a lower solubility than celestite ($SrSO_4$), (K_s 1.6×10^{-9} against 2.8×10^{-7}) does not appear to limit strontium in low temperature groundwaters because a limiting, high Sr/Ca ratio is probably required[7] before strontianite can form. In contrast, the aqueous levels of some minor elements, such as Sr^{2+}, may be controlled by the formation of other stable minerals, such as calcites, which require some impurities in their structures.

IONIC STRENGTH AND COMPLEXATION

As the total mineralisation of groundwater increases, so, in general, the apparent solubility of minerals tends to increase. In dilute solution nearly 'ideal' behaviour, as described by the Mass Action Law, is maintained. As salinity increases, however, the solute activity (the chemically effective concentration) becomes lower than the total ionic concentration expressed by the analysis. This is partly because of the weak interactions of the charged ions and partly because ion pairs are formed between simple ionic species, e.g. $Ca^{2+} + SO_4^{2-} = CaSO_4^\circ$ and the solubility of gypsum shows an apparent increase with increasing salinity.

The departure from ideal behaviour can be expressed in terms of *ionic strength* *(I)* and the *activity coefficient* *(γ)*. The ionic strength expresses the total mineralisation, taking account of the ionic charges and molar concentrations, whilst the activity coefficient expresses the ratio of activity of an ion to its concentration. For a detailed discussion see Stumm and Morgan[8], Hem[9] or Matthes[5]. The concept is summarised in Fig. 3.4, which can be used for determining γ if I is known for the principal single ions in natural waters. Only at values of ionic strength less than

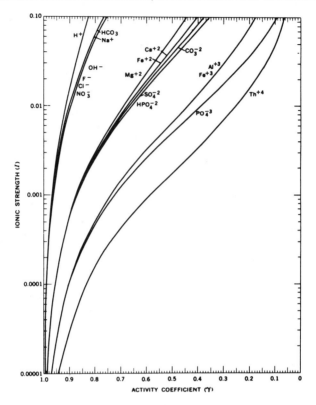

**Fig. 3.4.   Relationship between activity coefficients for some single and
complex ions and ionic strength of solution** (after Hem[9])

10^{-4} (roughly 50 mg/l total mineralisation) is the concentration approximately
equal to activity, within the limits of analytical error. Therefore, for practical
purposes, and especially for hydrogeochemical interpretation, the activity of single
· ions, complex ions and of ion pairs should be taken into account. For practical
purposes the calculations may be handled by several computer programs, for
example WATEQF[10], MINEQL[11] or SOLMNEQ[12].

The effects of ionic strength and activity are shown in Table 3.II. Free
monovalent ions predominate in dilute groundwaters and are only slightly
associated in sea water. Divalent ion concentrations are significantly reduced,
however, mainly by the formation of complex ions. The most important ion pairs in
natural waters are $CaCO_3^0$ and $CaSO_4^0$ but many other charged or uncharged
species such as $MgHCO_3^+$, $CaHCO_3^+$, $MgSO_4^0$, KSO_4^-, $Fe(OH_2)^+$, may influence
solubility. In dilute groundwater at pH 7 and 25°C the equilibrium Ca^{2+}
concentration will be around 80 mg/l in the absence of sulphate. If 500 mg/l SO_4^{2-}
are added, the equilibrium Ca^{2+} will roughly double due to formation of the
$CaSO_4^0$ ion pair[13].

The solubility and stability of many minor and trace elements in solution is

TABLE 3.II. Ionic Concentrations (mg/l) and Free Ions in Selected UK Groundwaters Relative to Sea Water

Parameter	Sea water		Bunter Sandstone Copley, Salop		Lincolnshire Limestone, Billingborough		Lincolnshire Limestone, Crowland	
	Ionic conc^n	Free ions (per cent)	Ionic conc^n	Free ions (per cent)	Ionic conc^n	Free ions (per cent)	Ionic conc^n	Free ions (per cent)
Ca^{2+}	401	91	71	96.4	134	90.7	10	89.7
Mg^{2+}	1312	87	19	94.7	6.3	90.4	16.4	91.2
Na^+	11030	99	115	100	14	100	1150	100
K^+	391	99	5.6	100	2.4	100	7.4	100
Cl^-	19852	100	200	100	22	100	1480	100
HCO_3^-	146	69	232	98.2	279	—	719	—
SO_4^{2-}	2688	54	46	89.0	124.7	79.3	87	92.8
CO_3^{2-}	16.2	9	0.57	51.9	0.42	39.2	10	91.8
pH	8.15		7.45		7.12		8.36	
Ionic strength	0.7		0.013		0.011		0.055	
Total mineralization	35836		689		582		3477	

increased considerably by formation of complex ions, giving solute concentrations considerably in excess of those indicated by the solubility products. The geochemical mobility of uranium provides a good illustration[14]. In the absence of carbonate, the solubility of uranium as the uranyl species (UO_2^{2+}) is probably controlled by the hydroxide $UO_2(OH)_2H_2O$ and the solubility of uranium should be negligible above pH 6. In the presence of carbonate species, and therefore in most groundwaters, uranium forms two soluble complex ions, $[UO_2(CO_3)_2H_2O]^{2-}$ and $[UO_2(CO_3)_3]^{4-}$, which effectively remove the hydroxide solubility control and ensure uranium mobility in neutral and slightly alkaline oxidising conditions.

SOLUTION-PRECIPITATION

Mineral dissolution accounts for the primary geochemical characteristics of groundwater. All minerals are soluble to a greater or lesser extent but the bulk characteristics will be accounted for by the solubility of only a few minerals— calcite, dolomite, gypsum, plagioclase, K-feldspar for example. Some minerals formed at high temperature will be unstable or metastable and reactive in the low temperature environment. Additionally, most minerals in nature are impure and may dissolve congruently, completely breaking down into ionic reaction products and/or secondary minerals, or incongruently, where a solid phase is left behind, usually purer and of higher stability than the original mineral. These slight differences in mineral purity are often important in determining the geochemical characteristics of groundwater. Dissolution reactions may also be reversible or irreversible. For instance, gypsum dissolution:

$$CaSO_4 \cdot 2H_2O \overset{K_s}{\rightleftharpoons} Ca^{2+} + SO_4^{2-} + 2H_2O \quad \dots \qquad \dots \qquad \dots \qquad \dots \quad (1)$$

is a reversible reaction which can be described by the law of mass action, the equilibrium constant of which (K_s) is well known from experiment. Albite dissolution on the other hand is irreversible and relatively slow:

$$2NaAl_3Si_3O_8 + 2H^+ + 9H_2O \rightarrow 2Na^+ + H_4Al_2Si_2O_5 + 4Si(OH)_4 \quad (2)$$
$$\text{albite} \qquad\qquad\qquad\qquad\qquad \text{kaolinite}$$

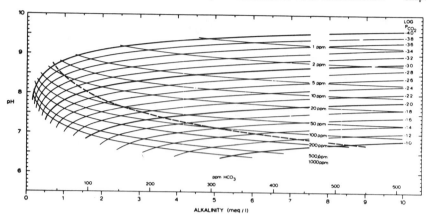

Fig. 3.5. Relationship between pH, HCO$_3$, pCO$_2$ and Ca^{2+} in waters saturated with respect to calcite at 25°C (after Drever[17])

and cannot be described in equilibrium terms; insoluble reaction products are formed but this and similar silicate weathering reactions are important in the primary release of cations and silica to groundwaters.

The initial pH and partial pressure of carbon dioxide (pCO$_2$) are the most important parameters influencing solubility. The pH of rain is normally 5.0 to 6.0 but may be as low as 3.5 in areas with acid industrial emissions of SO$_2$ and NO$_x$. Rain is therefore highly reactive and H$^+$ is important directly in mineral solution (Eqn. (2)). The pCO$_2$ of the atmosphere is low (equivalent to around 5 ppm) but microbiological action in the soil increases this by up to two orders of magnitude. Subsequent reaction of minerals takes place by the combined effect of H$^+$ and/or CO$_2$ (H$_2$CO$_3$), especially in the soil zone and upper unsaturated zone. This is usually under *open* system conditions, where the reaction is continuously in contact with the gas phase. However, on entering the saturated zone most groundwater reactions take place under *closed* system conditions, denying fresh access to the 'gas' reservoir as reaction proceeds[15,16]. Thus, progressive mineral dissolution will take place along groundwater flow paths until equilibrium is reached. The relationship between pH, HCO$_3^-$, pCO$_2$ and Ca^{2+} concentrations in waters saturated with respect to calcite at 25°C is shown in Fig. 3.5.

The dissolution of calcite illustrates how to determine whether a groundwater has reached equilibrium and also demonstrates how good field data combined with well established thermodynamic values can be used in hydrogeochemical interpretation.

For the reaction:

$$CaCO_3 \xrightarrow{K_{calcite}} Ca^{2+} + CO_3^{2-} \qquad \dots \qquad \dots \qquad \dots \qquad \dots \qquad \dots \qquad \dots \qquad (3)$$

$$K_{calcite} = \frac{[Ca^{2+}]\ [CO_3^{2-}]}{[CaCO_3]} = 10^{-8.3} \text{ at } 25°C$$

$K_{calcite}$ is the predicted value for equilibrium, determined experimentally; [CaCO$_3$], being the activity of the pure solid, equals 1. Determination of the field value of the ion activity product, K_{IAP}, permits comparison with the experimental value:

$$K_{IAP} = [Ca^{2+}] \, [CO_3^{2-}]$$

$$[Ca^{2+}] = m_{Ca^{2+}} \cdot \gamma_{Ca^{2+}}$$

The activity coefficient $\gamma_{Ca^{2+}}$ at the field conditions is known and $[Ca^{2+}]$ is therefore the product of $\gamma_{Ca^{2+}}$ and the analysed molar concentration of calcium $m_{Ca^{2+}}$. In the calculations, conveniently by computer[10] or by programmable calculator, allowance is made for complex ions, e.g. $CaHCO_3^+$, $CaSO_4^0$, $MgSO_4^0$, which effectively enhance the solubility. $[CO_3^{2-}]$ is then obtained from the reaction:

$$HCO_3^- = H^+ + CO_3^{2-} \quad \dots \quad \dots \quad \dots \quad \dots \quad \dots \quad \dots \quad (4)$$

for which the equilibrium constant is given by:

$$K_{HCO_3} = \frac{[H^+] \cdot [CO_3^{2-}]}{[HCO_3]} = 10^{-10.3} \text{ at } 25°C$$

or:

$$[CO_3^{2-}] = \frac{K_{HCO_3} \cdot [HCO_3]}{H^+}$$

K_{HCO_3} is known experimentally for pure calcite and

$$[HCO_3^-] = m_{HCO_3^-} \cdot \gamma_{HCO_3^-}$$

and $-\log_{10} [H]^+ = pH$

Therefore the value for $[CO_3^{2-}]$ can be calculated and substituted in Eqn. (3) to determine K_{IAP}. By comparing $K_{mineral}$ and K_{IAP}, saturation indices can be derived, e.g.

$$SI_{calcite} = \frac{\log K_{IAP}}{\log K_{calcite}} \text{ i.e. } \frac{\text{measured}}{\text{predicted}}$$

The SI value is an important parameter in groundwater chemistry for determining the progress of dissolution of many minerals and measuring the tendency of a groundwater to dissolve or precipitate solids. Good examples of the use of SI in groundwater studies may be found in Hanshaw et al[18], Langmuir[15] and, for the UK, in Edmunds[19], Pitman[20] and Edmunds et al[21]. For most UK aquifers the reaction of carbonate minerals dominates the hydrogeochemistry, even in relatively pure sandstones and in some igneous rocks.

For calcite and several other minerals, equilibrium is reached within a short time, days rather than years. In karstic regions however undersaturated groundwaters may occur, notably where CO_2 loss takes place under continuing open system conditions (e.g. in caves) and re-equilibration to the new pCO_2 does not take place. This is observed, for example, in the Derbyshire Carboniferous Limestone[19]. In the karstic Floridan aquifer[22] calcite saturation during downgradient flow is established only after 40000 years and, for dolomite, after around 15000 years.

ACID-BASE REACTIONS

The supply of hydrogen (H^+) and hydroxyl (OH^-) ions, expressed as $pH(-\log_{10} H^+)$, is one of the main factors limiting the availability and mobility of groundwater solutes. Only Na^+, Ca^{2+}, NO_3^- and Cl^- can be present in normal groundwaters over the whole pH range of natural waters. It has already been noted that H^+ is important in the hydrolysis of minerals such as feldspars and other silicates and in restricting the mobility of silica which is only significantly soluble in groundwater above pH 9. Most groundwaters are effectively buffered in the pH range 5.0-8.0 by the carbonate/carbon dioxide system (Fig. 3.5). However, in the absence of carbonate material, low pH, buffered mainly by silicate mineral reactions, may persist into the saturated aquifer and the mobility of Fe^{3+}, Al^{3+} and other metal ions may be enhanced. A good example of this occurs in the Sherwood Sandstone of SW England[23].

Most metals are soluble at low pH but will form insoluble hydroxides as the pH increases, limiting their mobility. At constant E_H the solubility of iron (Fe^{2+}) may decrease by two orders of magnitude as pH rises from 4.5 to 5.5, demonstrating the necessity for accurate pH measurement for the characterisation of natural waters.

REDOX PROCESSES

Oxidation and reduction reactions play an important role in controlling the groundwater chemistry of iron and other transition elements and subsurface biochemical reactions involving C, N, O and S. Oxidation involves loss of an electron and subsequent increase in charge (e.g. $Fe^{2+} \rightarrow Fe^{3+} + e$) whereas reduction involves gain of an electron and increase in charge (e.g. $Fe^{3+} + e^- \rightarrow Fe^{2+}$). In natural waters it is usual for several redox reactions to contribute to the state of the oxidising conditions and the contribution of individual redox reactions may be difficult to identify. However, it is convenient to use the redox potential (E_H) as a working parameter in field investigations to summarise the redox status:

$$E_H = E^O + \frac{2.303\ RT}{nF} \log \frac{[ox]}{[red]}$$

where E_H is the redox potential in volts;
         E^0 the standard potential of the reaction;
         R the gas constant;
         T the absolute temperature;
         n the number of electrons transferred in the reaction;
         F the Faraday constant; and
         $[ox]$ and $[red]$ the activities of the oxidised and reduced species involved at equilibrium.

In most groundwaters the reaction sequence (Fig. 3.6) follows that predicted thermodynamically. In a closed system, such as a flowline in a confined aquifer, dissolved oxygen will first be removed by reaction with organic matter, followed by denitrification ($NO_3^- + N^+ + e^- \rightarrow N_2$ (gas) $+ H_2O$). Reduction of MnO_2 should precede NO_3^- reduction ($NO_3 + H^+ + e^- \rightarrow NH_4 + H_2O$) and so forth. When sufficiently low E_H values are reached CO_2 and SO_4 reduction and fermentation reactions may proceed simultaneously. For a review of the actual sequence of redox reactions in UK aquifers see Edmunds et al[24].

A complementary redox sequence can be constructed to account for the sequence of reactions that should occur in reduced groundwaters which become open to dissolved oxygen, for example during spring discharge or during weathering of sulphide minerals.

In practice, many redox reactions are microbiologically mediated. In most groundwater flow systems, the requisite bacteria are likely to be present, although exact conditions for their active participation may not exist. Therefore, some of the reactions may proceed very slowly, especially during reduction; sulphate reduction, for example, may be sluggish at low SO_4^{2-} concentrations.

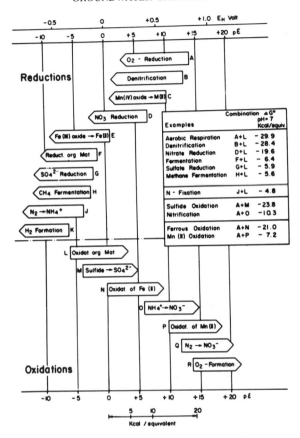

Fig. 3.6. Sequence of microbially mediated redox processes (after Stumm and Morgan[8])

The E_H therefore serves as a useful parameter in groundwater studies, defining the physico-chemical environment in which certain reactions might occur. Conversely the detection of key indicator reaction products, e.g. NH_4^+, Fe^{2+}, CH_4, H_2 should define the limiting E_H of a groundwater system. In practice, measurements of dissolved oxygen and E_H should be considered complementary, since detection of trace oxygen is difficult but a large redox change usually accompanies the complete disappearance of O_2 (and some other species, e.g. NO_3^-, SO_4^{2-}). Good examples of redox processes in groundwater systems are found in Back and Barnes[25], Langmuir[26], Edmunds[27] and Champ et al[28].

SURFACE REACTIONS

Porous aquifer materials present a very large surface area for water–rock contact; for example, the Cretaceous Chalk has a specific surface area of 6×10^4 cm^2/cm^3 (Edmunds et al[3]). This large surface area results from the presence of clay minerals or other colloidal material. Colloid size particles have adsorption

TABLE 3.III.   Cation Exchange
Capacities (meq/100 g at pH 7)
(after Carroll[29] and Rosler and Lange[30])

Mineral or colloid	CEC
Kaolinite	3- 15
Montmorillonite	50-150
Montronite	75- 80
Illite	10- 70
Vermiculite	100-150
Chlorite	10- 40
Glauconite	11- 20
Ferrihydrite	80-100
'Humic acids'	100-500
Organic matter	up to 300

capacities of various magnitudes due to unbalanced electrical charges on the surface and/or within the colloid that become neutralised by adsorption from solution of ions of opposite charge.

It is conventional to consider the charge relationship between solute and colloid in terms of the electrical double layer theory. Two types of double layer may be recognised:

(a) imperfections or substitutions within a crystal lattice, giving a 'fixed layer' charged surface on to which is bonded a mobile layer;
(b) preferentially adsorbed specific ions which provide the fixed layer.

Most clay minerals are of the first type and give rise to a generally constant charge independent of the chemistry (for example, the pH) of the solution. Silica, organic colloids and hydrous metal oxides provide examples of the second type and in such cases the surface charge is variable; this means for example that a change in solution pH would affect the adsorption capacity of the colloid.

The adsorption capacity of a colloid can be measured in terms of its cation exchange capacity (CEC) (Table 3.III). Nearly all minerals have small but measurable exchange capacities as a result of crystal imperfections or impurities which may affect the mobility of solutes.

For most conditions in groundwaters an affinity series may be defined where an ion with a larger hydrated radius will tend to become displaced from the adsorption site by an ion with smaller hydrated radius:

$$Cs^+ > Rb^+ > K^+ > Na^+ > NH_4^+ > Li^+$$
$$Ba^{2+} > Sr^{2+} > Ca^{2+} > Mg^+$$

Thus, K^+ has a tendency to displace Li^+ from adsorption sites and so on.

MICROBIOLOGICAL PROCESSES

Microorganisms are commonly present in subsurface environments. Under conditions favourable for their growth they may play either a direct or an indirect role in the modification of groundwater composition (Matthes[5]).

Bacteria have adapted to the groundwater environment: they may extract directly dissolved or particulate material and release to the water products of their metabolism; indirectly they may increase the solute concentration by breakdown of insoluble substances and influence CO_2 production in the soil zone. They are responsible by their catalytical action for many important geological processes

TABLE 3.IV.   Conditions Considered Favourable for Growth of *Desulphovibrio desulphuricans*

1. E_H 0-100 mV
2. pH 5.5-8.5
3. Temperature below 85°C
4. Salt tolerance up to 30°/$_{oo}$ NaCl
5. Heterotrophic bacteria present to produce smaller organic substrates (as hydrogen donor and energy sources) from larger molecules
6. SO_4^{2-} levels relatively high
7. Nutrients, e.g. HPO_4^{2-}, Ca^{2+}, Mg^{2+}, Cl^- and NO_3^-, for cell development
8. Water flux to carry reactants and products
9. Toxic substances, e.g. Cu^{2+}, Ni^{2+}, Zn^{2+} and Hg^{2+}, below lethal levels

including the biogenic accumulation of oil and natural gas, and some sulphide mineralisation. Principally, microorganisms will influence the mobility and reaction of carbon, nitrogen and oxygen in the groundwater environment; they are probably of lesser importance in controlling reactions involving iron and manganese. Microorganisms will not affect the thermodynamic limits of geochemical reactions but will generally affect their rates; reactions such as those involving sulphur which can proceed inorganically are considerably enhanced[31]. However, bacterial activity may also be limited unless certain optimum conditions are met. For *Desulphovibrio desulphuricans*, for example, the conditions in Table 3.IV are considered necessary for growth. To demonstrate the presence of sulphate-reducing bacteria is one thing but to show they are actively reducing sulphate is another.

3.   GEOCHEMISTRY OF THE PRINCIPAL UK AQUIFERS

GENERAL SETTING

The principal geochemical characteristics of groundwater in the UK can best be introduced by reference to the ten-mile geological map, or to the hydrogeological maps of the country. The main resources are found in sedimentary rocks of Mesozoic age of marine, fluviatile or continental origin. The chemistry of water in an impure marine limestone (e.g. Inferior Oolite) might, for example, be considerably different from that evolved in a rather pure sandstone (e.g. Sherwood Sandstone) of desert origin. Significant facies changes also take place within these formations. Thus, lateral changes in a hydrogeological unit may influence significantly groundwater quality. The position of the aquifers in respect to the coastline is important because:

(i)   the maritime 'input' of solutes will vary from place to place, mainly with distance from the coast;

(ii) the hydrodynamic development of the aquifer and thus the rate of movement and residence time of the water are controlled by the difference in piezometric surface from that of mean sea level. This in turn affects the hydrogeochemical evolution from place to place;

(iii) the susceptibility to coastal, saline intrusion (both historic, in response to sea level changes, and present day).

Since the main UK aquifers occur within a series of gently dipping sedimentary basins, it is convenient to consider the principal geochemical changes as they evolve spatially and in time along hydraulic gradients.

Significant groundwater resources are also found in the older Palaeozoic rocks notably of Carboniferous age which have undergone deformation, secondary

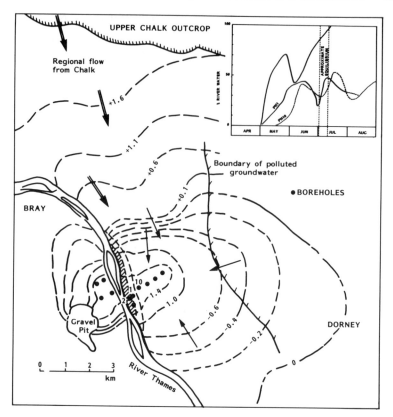

Fig. 3.7.   Configuration of groundwater contours and river inflow into alluvial aquifer at Dorney at maximum drawdown (after Ridings *et al*[32])
Extent of 100 and 50 per cent river inflow shown. Inset shows development of river inflow at three boreholes (PH 1, 2 and 10) with approximate steady state conditions developing during June

mineralisation and fabric changes. In these rocks, the amount of intergranular movement is usually insignificant and the geochemistry of the groundwater is controlled by the secondary mineralogy, for example by minerals on fracture surfaces, as well as by the parent lithology. This also applies to the locally important, limited supplies of groundwater derived from igneous rocks. Finally the importance of drift deposits must be recognised. Alluvial aquifers are important in their own right but glacial drift, overlying the main aquifers, especially in the northern half of Britain, may be significant in determining the geochemical character of the groundwater, especially since the main acquisition of solutes is taking place in the uppermost levels of the unsaturated zone.

QUATERNARY FORMATIONS

By far the most important Quaternary water resources in Britain are found in alluvial deposits. Their distribution and significance may be assessed by reference to the Hydrogeological Map of the UK (see Chapter 2). The main drainage systems of the Trent, Severn and Thames for example traverse many of the important solid aquifer systems and the alluvial aquifers developed in these basins are important in their own right or as an adjunct of the solid formation. They are also important in many valleys and coastal regions outside the main ground-water provinces. Conflict over the abstraction of aggregates, landfill siting and pollution generally, heightens the need for understanding groundwater quality as well as quantity.

The main characteristics of alluvial aquifers important in relation to groundwater chemistry are summarised below:

(1) The aquifer lithology usually bears some resemblance to the local solid geology. In the UK the aquifers do not exceed 20 m saturated thickness and are usually less than 10 m.

(2) Water table conditions usually prevail. High transmissivities are common, although these may be highly directional, parallel with the river channel. Semi-confining layers of silt may also be present.

(3) Recharge may occur by artesian leakage from underlying solid formations, by lateral flow from adjacent formations, or by direct recharge from rainfall. Interaction with the river may also result in recharge either by flooding or by effluent flow. The river may also receive influent water from the alluvial aquifer and interact with it by means of throughflow and underflow.

(4) Residence times are short. The groundwater resource is therefore especially vulnerable to pollution.

Information on water quality in alluvial aquifers is very scattered and much of it unpublished. To illustrate the principal characteristics of such systems, a case study from the Thames Valley is chosen, which demonstrates many of the problems both of the geochemistry of the resource and problems associated with its development.

An evaluation of the water resources in the Thames flood plain at Bray and Dorney was completed in 1976. The poorly sorted flint gravel and sand is about 6 m thick and overlies mottled sands and sandy clay (Reading Beds). The gravels abut on to Reading Beds and Upper Chalk in the north of the test area. Four large diameter abstraction boreholes were constructed on the western bank of the river and six on the eastern bank (Fig. 3.7). A regional and local network of 28 150 mm observation wells and over 120 50 mm tubewells were installed over the area to monitor the progress of the testing, designed principally to establish the extent of any recharge induced from the river, in relation to the total resource[32]. As part of the very thorough evaluation of the site, hydraulic analysis, geophysical logging and hydrochemical studies were carried out to quantify the recharge from the river and to further characterise the movement and quality of the resource, along the lines established for an analogous site on Chalk, some 3 km to the north[33].

Representative analyses (Table 3.V) of the alluvial groundwater, in relationship to the river and surrounding sources of water prior to any development pumping, are compared with the final alluvial water produced when equilibrium conditions were established. The alluvial groundwater near the river (PH1, PH2) had a fairly homogeneous initial composition with low Mg/Ca ratio and moderate NO_3^- and SO_4^{2-} content. The chemistry is quite distinct from that of the adjacent river and the underlying Chalk and Reading Beds, implying that there is no leakage under natural conditions. A relatively polluted groundwater (with 20-40 mg/l NO_3^-N) was identified to the east of the site which coincided with an area on which sewage sludge had been spread. The initial geochemical results suggested that:

(a) there was no evidence of river water anywhere in the aquifer (except locally at Bray Lock where an artificially high head was maintained);

(b) there was no local upward leakage from the chalk;

(c) lateral flow, parallel with the river from north to south, was occurring under the hydraulic gradient from the higher ground formed by Upper Chalk.

This last feature may account for some similarity between the alluvial and regional Chalk groundwater (although that derived from beneath the site was much more geochemically evolved than at outcrop). The boundary of the high nitrate water with that in the gravels remained distinct.

A complex programme of pumping involving sets of boreholes on both river banks took place between April and September 1976, culminating in a maximum drawdown in August at a combined extraction rate of 35 Ml/d (8 mgd); this also coincided with the period of severe drought. The aquifer condition at this time is illustrated in Fig. 3.7. The geochemical differences between the river and groundwater were used to estimate the percentage induced recharge at this time at each of the pumping boreholes. K^+, Sr^{2+} and HPO_4^{2-} were monitored over the whole period of the test at several sites to check both lateral and upward (Chalk) leakage[33]. No increase in Sr^{2+} was detected anywhere, indicating that even under dynamic conditions artesian flow from underlying Chalk was undetectable. Phosphate, in high concentration in the river water, was strongly attenuated during recharge. Although this limited its value as a quantitative tracer, it is still of qualitative value, demonstrating the natural capacity of the aquifer to improve the quality for supply purposes.

Potassium was the best tracer of river water movement into the aquifer, the River Thames containing approximately 3 mg/l excess (double) over that of the groundwater (Table 3.V). Using the potassium concentrations monitored during the test, the limits for 100 per cent and for 50 per cent migration of river water—at steady state conditions—are shown in Fig. 3.7. The steady state condition was reached in June 1976 (see inset) in boreholes 1 and 10. The overall conclusion was that 36 per cent river water (13.2 Ml/d, 2.9 mgd) was being induced at the steady

TABLE 3.V.   Representative Analyses of Groundwater in Alluvial Gravels near Dorney, Thames Valley

	Alluvial Gravels Aquifer Initial Chemistry			PH I Steady State Chemistry	River Thames	Reading Beds	Chalk	
Analysis No.	1	2	3	4	5	6	7	8
Borehole No	(a)	(b)	(c)	1	—	(d)	(e)	
Date	26.2.78	26.2.76	26.2.76	8.7.76	1.7.76	26.2.76	5.2.76	
pH	7.8	7.8	7.83	—	—	8.2	8.07	
Ca	149	136	149	—	113	65	91	
Mg	5.8	5.1	5.6	—	5.5	10.7	32	
Na	27.2	23	26	—	35.6	18	80	
K	4.0	3.2	3.4	6.4	7.3	6	10	
HCO_3	245	246	270	—	271	218	364	
SO_4	91.6	84	106	—	71	29	138	
Cl	43	35	45	—	42	18	73	
NO_3	58	47	47	—	36	1.6	4.8	
Sr	0.48	0.43	0.50	0.43	0.34	1.3	4.3	
Li	0.007	0.008	0.008	—	0.01	0.022	0.063	
F	0.15	0.11	0.15	—	0.17	0.33	1.2	
HPO_4	0.006	0.006	0.008	0.001	3.07	0.006	0.01	
Total mineralisation	773	580	653	—	584	368	798	

state period on the basis of chemistry. An identical value was obtained from hydraulic analysis, but a slightly higher value (53 per cent) was obtained on the basis of geophysical (temperature) logging.

The prolonged pumping of this aquifer demonstrated that the available resource was derived from three sources—lateral recharge, rainfall and induced abstraction from the river. The geochemistry of groundwater in alluvial aquifers may therefore be rather variable and the natural recharge may be modified by river water and by anthropogenic pollution.

THE CHALK

More water is pumped from the Chalk than from any other UK aquifer and controversy still exists over its hydrogeological and geochemical behaviour. The debate over the mechanism of water movement through the unsaturated zone in particular has a bearing upon the chemistry of its groundwater. Smith et al[34] demonstrated through the use of tritium profiles that movement of water in the unsaturated zone occurred predominantly by piston-type displacement. Further studies[4,35] demonstrated that the more likely model involves fissure seepage combined with lateral dispersion of tritiated water into the Chalk matrix. Foster and Smith-Carington[36] have shown that this model must also apply to solutes, e.g. nitrate and sulphate, which are therefore retarded in a quasi-piston flow movement in transit to the water table. Therefore, in describing the geochemistry of groundwater in the Chalk, the thickness of the unsaturated zone must be considered since this strongly controls inputs to the saturated aquifer by dispersion. Studies[37] dealing mainly with percolation of agrichemical leachates demonstrate the nature of solute migration towards the water table. Soil type and thickness as well as vegetation cover are important in controlling the solute fluxes into the aquifer. Detailed studies of the evolution of Chalk groundwaters have been carried out in East Yorkshire by Pitman[20] who investigated the relationships between precipitation, soil and spring water quality in small outliers during a one-year period. It was found that the thickness of the unsaturated zone is a critical factor in determining whether groundwater evolves under open or closed conditions with respect to pCO_2 (Deines et al[38]). This study confirmed the general view that closed system evolution is the rule rather than the exception for carbonate groundwaters. Chalk soil waters evolved under open system conditions and were markedly undersaturated with calcite (log $SI_{calcite}$ <0.5) during the winter recharge period. Summer leachates on the other hand were supersaturated due to CO_2 outgassing and longer soil residence times. It was also found that the calcite equilibration rate for a closed system was slower than for an open system.

The water quality distribution and evolution in the thick, saturated zones of the Chalk in southern England are strongly dependent upon storage and movement in and reaction with the intergranular matrix. Water abstracted from production boreholes (or from depth samples) represents the most rapidly moving component of the groundwater. However, this water is likely to be less than one per cent of the total storage of the Chalk and the slow exchange of water between that in fissures and in the matrix (pore water) may be one of the most important factors controlling the gradual hydrochemical changes at depth. Under natural, geological development of the aquifer there has probably been sufficient time for the fissure water to equilibrate with the pore water, but under the dynamic conditions of groundwater development this steady-state condition will have been disturbed. The three-dimensional distribution of the hydrochemistry in the Chalk can be illustrated from

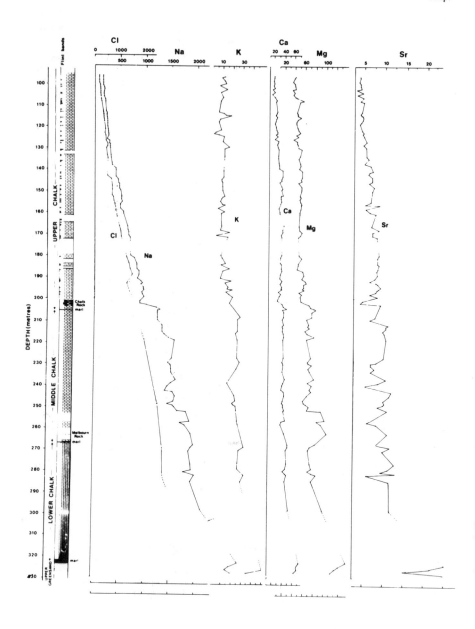

Fig. 3.8.   Interstitial water profile through the confined sequence of the Chalk at Faircross, south of Reading (based on unpublished BGS data).
(Results in mg/l)

studies by the British Geological Survey in the London Basin, where fully cored profiles through the Chalk sequence have been obtained, serving as accurate 'depth samples' of the interstitial water component of the aquifer. Radioisotope and stable isotope analyses also provide information on the residence time of the groundwater.

The chemical depth profile through the full sequence of the confined Chalk at Faircross, 8 km south of Reading, based on unpublished BGS data, is shown in Fig. 3.8. Minor changes in the geochemistry of the Chalk are important in considering groundwater evolution over a long time scale. However, the Chalk can be regarded as a fairly homogeneous lithology when considering its groundwater chemistry. The water profile, as illustrated for Na^+, Cl^-, K^+, Mg^{2+}, Ca^{2+} and Sr^{2+}, shows a progressive increase in total mineralisation with depth, illustrated by Na^+, with a range of 100–2 000 mg/l; there is a sharp increase in salinity at the Chalk Rock horizon. At the base of the Chalk the salinity is approximately one-fifth that of sea water. This profile shape and chemistry indicate that there has been progressive dilution, mainly by molecular diffusion of an original 'connate' marine fluid, aided by slow flow through tight fissures. In fact, elsewhere in the Chalk in north East Anglia, an almost unmodified original marine composition can be identified at depth[39].

Slightly saline groundwater can also be found at depth in the unconfined aquifer of the western London basin[3]. Water supply boreholes drilled in this region often penetrate the full Chalk sequence but Owen and Robinson[40] found that the majority of the abstraction is taking place only from the upper saturated 60 m of the aquifer where fissures are strongly developed. Slightly saline waters are preserved in the pore spaces of the Chalk.

The regional hydrochemical distribution, using data from pumped boreholes, can be illustrated using a cross-section through the aquifer which includes the position of the Faircross borehole referred to earlier. The parameters chosen for illustrating the chemical variations are the major elements (Na^+. Cl^-, Ca^{2+} and Mg^{2+} (Fig. 3.9a) and E_H, NO_3^- and O_2 (Fig. 3.9b), indicating the main changes in redox conditions in the aquifer. The highest salinities (120 mg/l Cl^-) found in pumped samples are of the same order as those in interstitial waters at the top of the cored profile (Fig. 3.8). Thus there is steady-state development between fissure and interstitial water chemistry. The levels of Cl^- (and Na^+) in the unconfined aquifer (10-32 mg/l) are predominantly controlled by input conditions; these values can be explained largely by evapotranspiration of atmospheric input, modified to a much lesser extent by pollutant (e.g. agrichemical) input or by pore fluid exchange. It is noted that Na^+ closely follows Cl^- and the increased Na^+ source at depth is also likely to be of original marine origin. The decrease in Ca^{2+} towards the centre of the basin is mirrored by an equivalent increase in Mg^{2+} indicating a progressive reaction with the Chalk; the Chalk tends to recrystallise with time releasing impurities such as Mg^{2+} to the groundwater. Ion exchange is therefore not considered important in controlling the major element chemistry[41]. When the carbonate reaction is investigated carefully (using the pH, HCO_3^-, Ca^{2+}, Mg^{2+} and subtracting $SO_4^{2-} \equiv Ca^{2+}$) it can be shown that the bicarbonate is all derived from dissolution of calcite, reaching saturation very early in its flow history, probably in the unsaturated zone; this is also supported by the $\delta^{13}C$ evidence. Sulphate, at levels above input values, is either derived from oxidation of pyrite or from dissolution of gypsum frequently found in massive horizons like the Chalk rock[42].

In addition to the mineral solution-precipitation reactions which dominate the hydrogeochemistry of the Chalk, redox reactions are also important. The relationships illustrated in Fig. 3.9 (b) show that in the unconfined aquifer dissolved oxygen levels are uniformly high, maintaining high E_H values. There appears

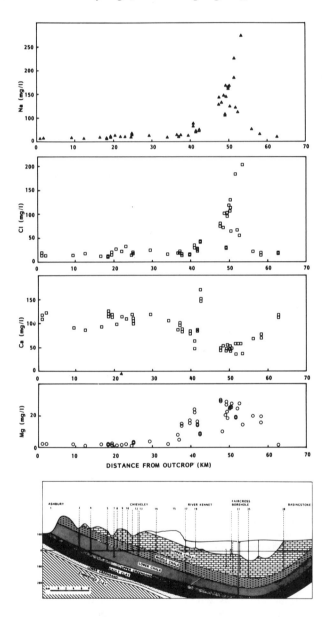

Fig. 3.9(a).   Hydrogeochemical changes across the Berkshire syncline (for Na^+, Cl^-, Ca^{2+} and Mg^{2+}) (based on unpublished BGS data)

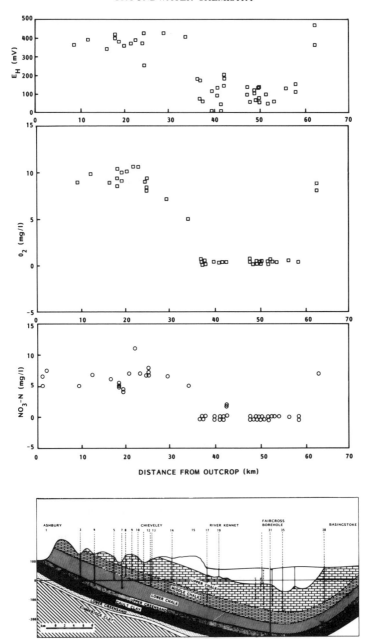

Fig. 3.9(b).   Hydrogeochemical changes across the Berkshire syncline (for E_H, NO_3^- and O_2) (based on BGS unpublished data)

therefore to be little loss of oxygen during percolation and flow, over a timescale of tens of years[24], reflecting both the unimportance of oxygen-using bacteria in the aquifer as well as the organic and inorganic purity of the rock. The onset of reducing conditions, shown by the removal of all oxygen in the aquifer and a fall in E_H of around 300 mV, is considered mainly to be controlled by oxidation of traces of pyrite in the aquifer, shown by the sulphate increase. The redox boundary also controls the hydrogeochemistry of iron; in the oxidising zone Fe_T remains around 1 $\mu g/l$ but rises to near 1 mg/l under reducing conditions. Nitrate levels remain fairly uniform (20-30 mg/l NO_3^-) in the oxidising zone, probably reflecting input conditions. In the reducing aquifer, NO_3^- is below detection limit; this may indicate an efficient *in situ* nitrate reduction as demonstrated using nitrogen isotopes plus N_2/Ar ratios[43] or merely indicate that the older groundwaters never had significant input levels of nitrate. At present, the former explanation is preferred although further evidence is required.

Further information on processes taking place in the Chalk and its trace element and isotope geochemistry are given by Bath and Edmunds[39]. In the deeper London Basin, the classic study of the chemistry of groundwaters by Ineson and Downing[41] has been followed by more detailed work (Water Resources Board[44]) and on the age of groundwater by Smith *et al*[45], which includes a discussion on the problems of using ^{14}C. Groundwater of at least Pleistocene age must exist in the centre of the basin on the basis of lighter $\delta^{18}O$, δD values. Regional studies of the chemistry of Chalk groundwaters include Sussex[46], East Yorkshire[47,48] and East Anglia[49].

LOWER GREENSAND

The Lower Greensand forms an important aquifer to the north and south of the London Basin, in the Weald and in parts of central southern England. The hydrochemical characteristics can be considered with reference to the area south of London[50].

The aquifer is divided into an upper half (Folkestone Beds) and a lower half (Hythe Beds) by an aquiclude (Sandgate and Bargate Beds). The principal distinction between the two aquifers is their carbonate content, the Folkestone Beds being mainly non-calcareous. The Hythe Beds are marked by considerable lateral change from a mainly calcareous lithology in Kent to loamy sands and sandstones in West Sussex and Surrey.

The aquifer is hydraulically continuous from the south crop to the north crop of the London Basin and 1978 tritium measurements indicated that there had been significant down-dip movement of water probably from south to north compared with data from 1965 (Mather *et al*[51]).

The unconfined groundwaters in both the Hythe and Folkestone Beds are of low total mineralisation and undersaturated with respect to calcite, on account of the very low frequency of carbonate minerals. A redox boundary is found in the confined parts of the two aquifers and the intensity of redox changes is comparable to that in other UK sandstone aquifers; the absence of oxygen corresponds with E_H values near +100 mV and the lowest redox potential recorded is −280 mV. Total iron concentrations up to 3.7 mg/l are recorded in the confined aquifer; the range of iron concentrations in the Folkestone Beds is much larger than in the Hythe Beds.

With the generally rather low mineralisation of the Lower Greensand groundwaters, the natural hydrogeochemical characteristics are masked by anthropogenic influence, including enhanced Na^+ and Cl^- from winter road salting, agricultural activity (high NO_3^-) and some septic tank discharge. Nevertheless, in the confined aquifer, residual saline water can be identified in the Folkestone Beds of Kent and natural softening at depth gives an enrichment of Na^+ and HCO_3^-.

JURASSIC LIMESTONES

Several impure limestones and interbedded sands in the Upper and Middle Jurassic form locally important aquifer systems in the United Kingdom. Because of the diachronous nature of the Jurassic sedimentation, the lateral extent of the aquifers is usually limited, resulting in very variable saturated aquifer thicknesses. In the Lower Jurassic, the Bridport (Yeovil) Sands form an important arenaceous aquifer group in Wessex; however the presence of carbonates in most of the succession ensures that geochemically their groundwater often resembles that in adjacent limestones. Because of the impurity of the limestones—they contain a higher content of organic material and the carbonate contains a higher percentage of minor elements such as Fe^{2+}, Sr^{2+}, Mg^{2+} and Mn^{2+}—they are more reactive (than Chalk, for example) and this is reflected in their groundwater chemistry.

The most detailed account of the geochemical evolution of Jurassic groundwaters is found for the Lincolnshire Limestone (Inferior Oolitic Limestone) of the Middle Jurassic; the Great Oolitic Limestone of the Cotswolds here is reduced to a minor aquifer only a few metres thick. The Lincolnshire Limestone reaches a maximum thickness of about 40 m in south Lincolnshire but is attenuated both eastwards, down-dip and northwards towards the Humber, north of which it is insignificant as an aquifer. The main hydrogeological study of this aquifer[52] has served as the basis for the detailed geochemical work. The aquifer is confined beneath argillaceous rocks and is underlain also by clays or siltstones. Groundwater movement occurs predominantly by fissure flow from west to east and there is an artesian zone commencing some 10 km east of the onset of confined conditions. The overall hydrochemical zonation in the aquifer has been described by Lamont[53], Downing and Williams[52] and, in more detail, by Edmunds[27,54] who made particular reference to redox processes and geochemical controls over minor and trace element distribution. Changes in the aquifer over the period 1969-1983 have been described[55,24].

The main hydrogeochemical changes taking place as the groundwater evolves across the aquifer are summarised in Fig. 3.10. Most early reaction takes place during groundwater recharge and the water quickly reaches saturation with respect to calcite, probably in the unsaturated zone. Over the next 10 km there is very little reaction affecting the major element characteristics of the aquifer. Within this zone, oxygen persists and nitrate remains stable in the presence of oxygen.

There is an abrupt change in the chemistry at the 'redox barrier' so called because of the fall in E_H of $\sim$250 mV which is effective in removing all dissolved oxygen and nitrate. This zone of reduction corresponds with a change in the rock from grey limestone (containing Fe^{2+} and organic matter) to a buff coloured limestone characterised by iron oxides and hydroxides. This rock alteration took place mainly on a geological timescale but is still effective today in controlling the redox chemistry, despite large fluxes of groundwater across it. Most importantly it acts as a means for denitrification, shown by the absence of NO_3^- in this zone despite progress across the 'barrier' of tritium, and SO_4^{2-} derived from agrichemicals.

Iron (Fe^{2+}) concentrations rise to levels near to 1 mg/l at the lower E_H values and dominate the redox system for at least 2 km east of the 'barrier'. At this point, sulphide (as HS^-) is detectable as a product of sulphate reduction although ≤ 0.2 mg/l; its solubility is kept low by the appearance of amorphous FeS, noticeable as black particles in the groundwater:

$$SO_4^{2-} + CH_2O + H^+ \rightarrow HS^- + 2CO_2 + 2H_2O$$
$$HS^- + Fe^{2+} \rightarrow FeS_{(amorphous)} + H^+$$

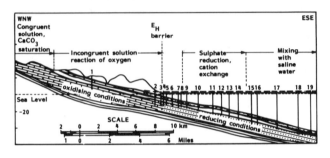

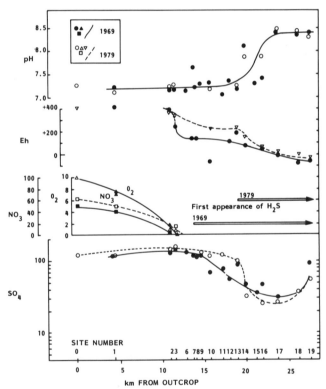

**Fig. 3.10(a).   Downgradient profile of the Lincolnshire Limestone
illustrating the principal hydrogeochemical changes in redox parameters**
(after Edmunds and Walton[55])
Note: Changes in the system from 1969 to 1979 are indicated

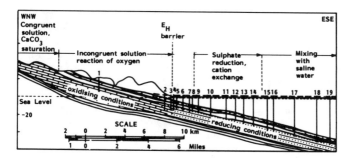

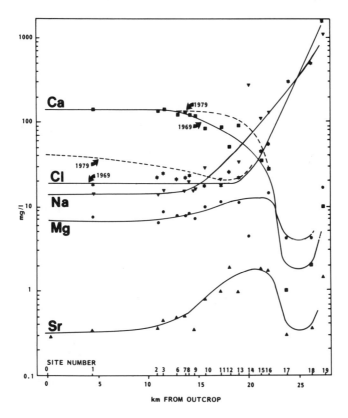

**Fig. 3.10(b).   Downgradient profile of the Lincolnshire Limestone
illustrating the principal hydrogeochemical changes in Ca^{2+}, Na^+, Cl^-, Mg^{2+}
and Sr^{2+}** (after Edmunds and Walton[55])
Note: Changes in the system from 1969 to 1979 are indicated

The progress of the groundwater downgradient is marked by an increase in pH which marks also the decrease of calcium and increase in HCO_3^- and Na^+. Some 12 km from outcrop, cation exchange reactions ($Ca^{2+} \rightleftharpoons 2Na^+$) can be detected which only become significant east of the redox boundary, suggesting a link with the mineralogy of the aquifer. Calcium decreases to 4 mg/l, bicarbonate increases to over 700 mg/l and the pH to > 9.0 yet it can be shown that equilibrium with calcite is still maintained.

The increase in bicarbonate is partially at the expense of organic matter on reduction of sulphide, but since the carbon isotope ratio ($\delta^{13}C$) becomes more positive this means that most bicarbonate is derived from carbonate minerals.

With the rise in pH, and E_H values below 0 mV, iron concentrations are also controlled by $Fe(OH)_3$ which may also appear as precipitates in the groundwater. The gradual fall in redox potential downgradient, from $+100$ to -100 mV, is mainly the results of changes in Fe^{2+} and HS^- concentrations. However methane and hydrogen gas in trace amounts may give rise to highly reducing groundwaters (-200 to -400 mV).

Saline groundwaters found in the extreme downgradient section of the Jurassic aquifer are shown from isotopic and inert gas studies[56] to be at least of Pleistocene age and possibly much older.

It is possible to follow and explain the behaviour of minor elements across the aquifer in relation to the principal hydrogeochemical processes. The behaviour of fluoride has been known for a long time. Lamont[53] showed how zonation in the aquifer might be used to exploit water of different types including both hard and soft waters and also waters with F^- concentrations optimal for dental care. The rise in fluoride is coincident with the onset of reducing conditions and it appears that oxidation of the rock probably also releases fluoride from organic matter. Iodide also follows the behaviour of fluoride. The upper limits of F^- solubility are mainly controlled by the decrease of Ca^{2+} yet the equilibrium with solid CaF_2 (fluorite) is maintained. Bromide and chloride increase *pari passu* but do not follow the trend of the other halogens; in this case the control is the residual saline water with a fixed Br^-/Cl^- ratio. The behaviour of other minor elements has been described[27].

A very similar pattern of hydrogeochemistry has been described for the Jurassic limestone aquifers of the Cotswolds[57]. It is possible to recognise two distinct aquifers—the Great Oolite and the Inferior Oolite with more strongly reducing conditions occurring in the deeper aquifer at the same site.

TRIASSIC SANDSTONES

Important groundwater resources occur in sandstones of Triassic age throughout the UK, but especially in northern and central England, where the Sherwood Sandstone is the most important aquifer. In some parts of Britain, the West Midlands for example, Upper Carboniferous sandstones may be hydraulically continuous with the Trias. Locally important aquifer units may be found in Sandstones within the Mercia Mudstone. These may be in hydraulic continuity with the Upper Sherwood sequence where it may have a significant influence on the groundwater chemistry due to interbedded evaporites. The presence or absence of evaporites in the Mercia Mudstone as well as other facies changes in the Triassic sandstones across the country are important in controlling the regional hydrogeochemistry. The Trias lithostratigraphy is summarised by Audley-Charles[58] and the diachronous nature of several aquifer units previously thought to have been deposited at similar times is discussed. The other important lithological feature of the Triassic sandstones, which dominates the chemistry, is the strongly oxidised character of the rock.

The extent and nature of Pleistocene Drift cover are important in determining groundwater quality. South of a line between Bristol and southern East Anglia, ice transported material is largely absent although fluvial deposits may be present. The effect of this may be noticed in comparing the drift-free Triassic aquifer of Devon with those further north[23]. The influence of drift deposits on the quality of ground-water in the Trias of the Vale of York has been discussed by Spears and Reeves[59]. They concluded that the recharge taking place through the drift can be readily recognised by the relatively high Mg^{2+} and SO_4^{2-} contents derived from pore waters, relative to other areas. In the area of the Fylde in Lancashire[60], Pleistocene sand deposits, related to lines of river channels overlying the sandstone, act as zones of preferential recharge, sometimes near present day rivers. The zones of recharge can be identified chemically by their relatively low bicarbonate concentrations.

The differences in chemistry across the country can be discussed using three contrasting areas:

(i)   an area of mainly unconfined sandstone (Shropshire)[61];
(ii) a confined sequence (East Midlands)[61,62,63];
(iii) a drift-free area (Otter Valley, Devon)[23].

East Shropshire Area

The Triassic aquifer comprises several well-recognised aquifer units, sometimes in hydraulic continuity (Fig. 3.11). Semi-confined conditions may exist within formations due to variable cementation and/or discontinuous siltstones or marls. The main lithological units, however, contain groundwaters with recognisable hydrochemical differences. The essential geochemical features of the groundwater may be summarised:

(1) The contribution of post-1953 groundwater to pumping boreholes is frequently less than 50 per cent and sometimes much less. This implies that recent groundwater occurs in a thin surface layer which may be drawn down under the influence of pumping.

(2) Aerobic conditions exist in the sandstones to considerable depths, at least 100 m, and reducing lithologies must therefore be virtually absent. From consideration of tritium 'ages', dissolved O_2 can persist naturally in the groundwater for at least 20 years and probably much longer.

(3) Carbonate saturation is encountered in almost all waters from the Keuper Sandstone and the Lower Mottled Sandstone; in the intervening units, groundwater is usually undersaturated, probably reflecting an absence of any calcareous lithology or cement.

(4) Waters from the Keuper, and to a lesser extent, the Upper Mottled Sandstone, may be distinguished from other units by their higher Mg^{2+}/Ca^{2+} ratios. This is thought to indicate the presence of a dolomitic cement near the top and base of the sandstones.

(5) Saline water probably occurs extensively in the aquifer below a depth of 200 m. This may be due to several factors, including lateral (or vertical) leakage from Carboniferous strata or the much longer residence time of the water at depth with the saline/freshwater interface representing the base of the present day, naturally active hydraulic system.

(6) High nitrate levels clearly relate to recent groundwaters, as defined by tritium.

(7) Minor and trace element levels in the groundwater are controlled by impurities in the Mercia Mudstone iron oxide cements and the predominantly oxidising conditions. 21 trace elements (< 1 mg/l) were detected in the groundwaters.

East Midlands Area

The Sherwood Sandstone here comprises a thick sandstone overlain by Mercia Mudstone with a gradational claystone/sandstone confining layer. Parts of the area

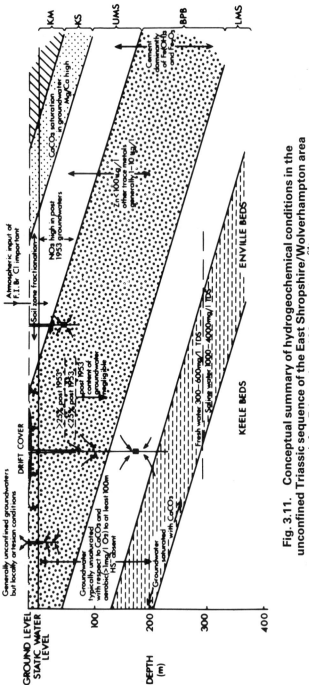

Fig. 3.11. Conceptual summary of hydrogeochemical conditions in the unconfined Triassic sequence of the East Shropshire/Wolverhampton area
(after Edmunds and Morgan-Jones[61])

(*Note*: KS = Keuper Sandstone; UMS = Upper Mottled Sandstone; BPB = Bunter Pebble Beds; LMS = Lower Mottled Sandstone)

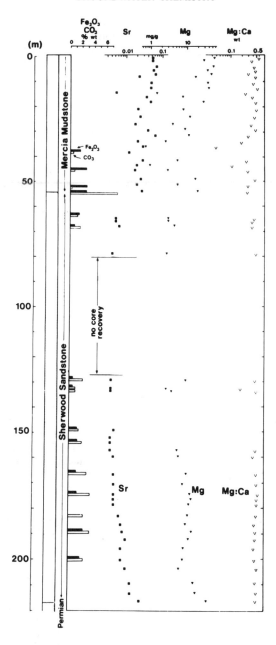

Fig. 3.12. Geochemistry of the Sherwood Sandstone and Mercia Mudstone, Nottinghamshire (based on BGS unpublished data)

are overlain by mainly sandy drift. The sandstone is a typical red-bed lithology almost devoid of reducing horizons. The groundwater evolution is dominated by reactions with a freshwater carbonate cement, detrital dolomite and sulphate minerals, and redox reactions. The stratigraphic sequence and the main geo-chemical characteristics of the Sherwood Sandstone are summarised in Fig. 3.12 where the low percentage of carbonate should be noted. Despite clearly being an arenaceous formation, it is the very small amount of carbonate present which dominates the hydrogeochemistry.

The groundwater is entirely fresh throughout the aquifer so far exploited for public supply. The very low salinity (Cl^- often below 10 mg/l) is attributed to recharge by meltwaters from ice-sheets and subsequently from rainfall derived from continental rather than maritime air masses. In contrast, the present day recharge has Cl^- values 3-5 times higher, derived not only from a maritime source but also from industrial fallout and other anthropogenic sources.

Three 'zones', or types, can be recognised in the aquifer on the basis of geochemical indices:

(a) Recent groundwater (mainly < 100 years old); oxidising; chemistry dominated by congruent dissolution of dolomite with the inputs of anions (SO_4^{2-}, NO_3^-, Cl^-) derived largely from anthropogenic sources.

(b) Groundwater age 10^3-10^4 yr; mostly reducing; dominated by incongruent dissolution of dolomite. Very low levels of chloride (<10 mg/l) and sulphate (<25 mg/l) characterise the groundwater chemistry which is entirely non-polluted.

(c) Groundwater age $>10^4$ yr; reducing; there is an approach to isotopic and chemical equilibrium in the carbonate water–rock system and gypsum dissolution becomes important; pollution absent.

This section of the Trias illustrates several interesting hydrogeochemical features. The absence of any saline groundwater has been mentioned, but additionally the Cl^-, SO_4^{2-} and other ions *decrease* along the profile as the pre-industrial, unpolluted water is reached. Also important is the concomitant persistence, for several thousands of years[21], of oxygen and nitrate. This and other redox features are illustrated in Fig. 3.13. Note that sulphate increases in the deeper confined zone (III) due to gypsum dissolution. Although sulphide is present, reduction of sulphate is considered quantitatively unimportant. This can be demonstrated by the isotopic ratios of carbon. If significant reaction were occurring, then from the reaction:

$$15CH_2O + 2Fe_2O_3 + 8SO_4^{2-} + H_2CO_3 \rightarrow 4FeS_2 + 16HCO_3^- + 8H_2O$$

twice as many equivalents of bicarbonate would be produced compared with sulphate and this bicarbonate should be isotopically light (more negative). In fact the $\delta^{13}C_{HCO_3}$ becomes heavier downgradient, showing that sulphate reduction is negligible and the carbon isotope compositions are dominated by the carbonate reactions.

Other features illustrated in this aquifer are the various reactions of carbonate minerals. The pH, Ca^{2+} and Mg^{2+} for groundwater in each of the three zones are plotted against HCO_3^- in Fig. 3.14. Sulphate equivalent to calcium is first subtracted to remove the effect of gypsum solution. The pH is seen to decrease across the aquifer and is inversely related to bicarbonate due to the carbonate mineral reactions. Three main reactions are possible which have different stoichiometries:

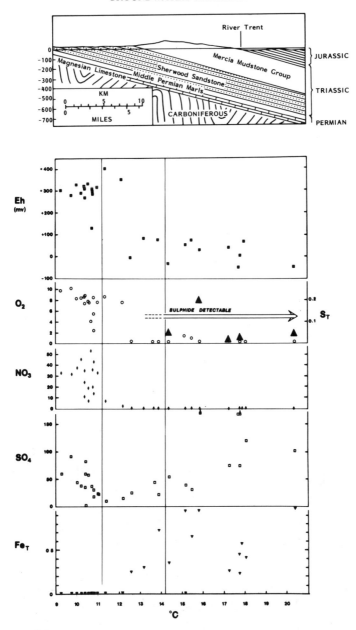

Fig. 3.13. Downgradient trends in redox related parameters (E_H, O_2, NO_3^-, HS^-, SO_4^{2-} and Fe_T) in the Triassic (Sherwood) Sandstone of the East Midlands (after Edmunds et al[21])

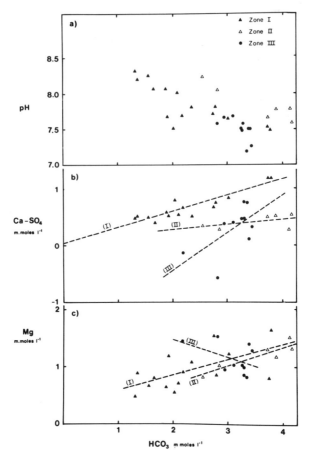

Fig. 3.14.   Relationships between pH, Ca^{2+}, SO_4^{2-}, Mg^{2+} and HCO_3^- in the three zones of the Sherwood Sandstone groundwaters of Nottinghamshire
(after Edmunds *et al*[21])

(i)   congruent dissolution of calcite

$$CaCO_3 + H_2CO_3 \rightleftharpoons Ca^{2+} + 2HCO_3^-$$

(ii)   congruent dissolution of dolomite

$$CaMg(CO_3)_2 + 2H_2CO_3 \rightleftharpoons Ca^{2+} + Mg^{2+} + 4HCO_3^-$$

(iii)   incongruent dissolution of dolomite

$$CaMg(CO_3)_2 + H_2CO_3 \rightleftharpoons CaCO_3 \downarrow + Mg^{2+} + 2HCO_3^-$$

In (i), the ratio $Ca^{2+}/HCO_3^- = 1:2$ and in (ii) and (iii) the proportions are $Ca^{2+}/Mg^{2+}/HCO_3^- = 1:1:4$ and $0:1:2$ respectively. Therefore congruent dolomite reaction is the dominant reaction in Zone I (Fig. 3.14). In Zone II, the Mg^{2+}/HCO_3^- ratio is nearer $1:3$ and a shift towards incongruent solution of dolomite is favoured, whilst in Zone III the influx of calcium from gypsum causes some calcite to be precipitated.

These relationships are explained in more detail in Edmunds *et al*[21], where the behaviour of strontium, barium and other minor and trace elements is also described in relation to the hydrogeochemical framework.

South Devon Area

The Triassic (Sherwood Sandstone) aquifer in Devon comprises the Otter Sandstone and underlying Budleigh Salterton Pebble Beds formation, confined beneath mudstones of the Mercia Mudstone Group. A degree of hydraulic continuity between both units of the aquifer is enhanced by faulting. The aquifer differs from other areas of the Trias, being completely drift free. The southern outcrop areas of the aquifer are strongly weathered and decalcified to considerable depth giving more acidic groundwaters, especially in the Pebble Beds. In the north, the aquifer is less permeable and contains more calcareous material.

Groundwater from the Mercia Mudstone Group is characterised by higher total mineralisation (>1000 mg/l) caused mainly by gypsum dissolution. Groundwaters in the Pebble Beds are of low total mineralisation (<150 mg/l) and low alkalinity (<25 mg/l) with pH generally between 5 and 6. The Otter Sandstone groundwaters are typically carbonate saturated. The principal hydrochemical features of each aquifer unit are summarised in Table 3.VI.

The main point of hydrochemical interest in this aquifer is the behaviour of iron (Fig. 3.15). In theory the acidic groundwaters in the Pebble Beds are capable of dissolving considerable amounts of iron, yet they contain low Fe^{2+} and remain well undersaturated with respect to common iron minerals at the prevailing E_H and pH. This is because readily available iron has already been leached from the rock (containing <0.5 per cent Fe_2O_3 by weight). By constrast the overlying Otter Sandstone waters show apparent oversaturation with respect to amorphous $Fe(OH)_3$. As upward leakage occurs, naturally or induced by pumping, the Pebble Beds water dissolves more iron, giving rise to ferruginous waters, and thus to a corrosion problem in public supply boreholes. This problem and its remedy and control have been discussed[64].

CARBONIFEROUS LIMESTONE

The Carboniferous Limestone has been developed for groundwater resources in several areas of Great Britain—the Pennines, North Wales, the Mendips, South Wales, Scotland and Northern Ireland. It is the only true karstic limestone in Britain and much of the understanding of the hydrochemistry of the various areas has been provided by speleologists and others[65,66,67].

The most comprehensive study of the Carboniferous Limestone is that of the Derbyshire Dome[19], in which the carbonate hydrogeochemistry and minor and trace element occurrence were described. Eight discharges of thermal water (including those at Buxton and Matlock) are also described, indicating that meteoric waters have circulated to depths down to 600 m.

The vast majority of groundwaters are saturated with respect to calcite but some undersaturated waters are recognised near the margins where infiltration of acidic Millstone Grit drainage enters the system, or where degassing in cave systems has occurred. It is also possible that low pCO_2 values are attained during infiltration in bare limestone areas resulting in undersaturated groundwaters.

The minor and trace element geochemistry can be used to distinguish water from mineralised and non-mineralised areas of the limestone as well as thermal groundwaters having a longer residence time. Sr^{2+} and F^- are particularly sensitive indicators of base metal (Cu, Pb and Zn) mineralisation in the region. This

TABLE 3.VI.   Principal Differences in Trias Hydrochemistry with Geological Formation (from Walton[23])

	Mercia Mudstone Group (MMG)		Otter Sandstone Formation (OSF)		Budleigh Salterton Pebble Bed Formation (PBF)	
Water Type	$Mg(Ca)HCO_3(SO_4)$		$CaHCO_3$		No dominant type	
Sp.elec. conductance (µS/cm @ 25°C)	*High 900*		*Moderate 500 (350-550)*		*Low 200 (160-230)*	
Mineral saturation	Calcite, dolomite and ± gypsum		Calcite only		Grossly undersaturated	
pH	Just alkaline	7.5 (7.3-8.1)	Neutral	7.2 (6.8-7.5)	*Acidic*	*5.0 (4.4-5.8)*
HCO_3^- (mg/l)	High	400 (200-500)	Mod. high	240 (200-260)	*Very low*	*6 (0-23)*
Ca (mg/l)	High	90 (80-400)	Moderate	70 (50-90)	*Very low*	*10 (9-13)*
Mg (mg/l)	*Very high*	*70 (65-90)*	Low	10 (7-15)	*Very low*	*4 (5-7)*
SO_4^{2-} (mg/l)	*Very high*	*240 (100-1200)*	Moderate	28 (23-34)	Moderate	22 (15-28)
Sr, Li, U, SiO_2 (mg/l)	Significantly elevated values		Generally low levels		Generally very low levels	

Note: Principal distinguishing parameters are italicised

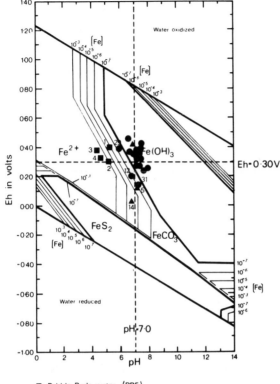

Fig. 3.15. E_H/pH stability field diagram for aqueous iron species in the Triassic aquifers of South Devon (after Hem[9])

information can in turn be used to indicate the groundwater provenance within the limestone.

4. WATER QUALITY INVESTIGATIONS

Any water quality investigation is likely to have several clearly defined stages:

(1) problem or project definition;
(2) sampling;
(3) analysis;
(4) interpretation of data;
(5) reporting.

Groundwater quality investigations may be carried out for a variety of reasons and two general points may be made:

(a) There are many chemical and geochemical tools available and it is necessary to select the right ones to solve the particular problem.

(b) The precise fraction(s) of the groundwater relevant to the investigation (Fig. 3.2) must be considered and whether, for example, total sample, dissolved and/or particulate samples and/or dissolved gases should be collected.

In this section some of the main parameters that may be used in hydrogeochemical investigations are considered, with some discussion of their applications.

SAMPLING CRITERIA

Systematic or random errors using modern analytical techniques are likely to be small and unimportant in hydrochemical studies in comparison with those introduced by sampling. This raises such conflicting issues as the cost and time needed to collect rather than analyse samples and the use of the data for quality control alone or as part of a permanent data base for hydrogeochemistry. Measurement of each additional parameter may require a different investment in terms of sampling cost and effort. Establishing the scale of sampling is therefore paramount in groundwater quality studies and the subject can be considered under six topics:

(i) the aquifer framework;
(ii) pumping and flow regimes;
(iii) geographical constraints;
(iv) size fraction and filtration;
(v) stability and storage;
(vi) contamination.

Aquifer Framework

Fissure flow and intergranular flow will occur in the majority of aquifers. Whilst fissure flow may be quantitatively more important than intergranular flow, fissure storage is often small in comparison to intergranular storage. Rates of movement of water by flow and diffusion will vary considerably in both components and chemical gradients may exist within the aquifer. Two examples may be envisaged (see Fig. 3.1):

(1) induced flow of 'fresh' water into an area with older and/or saline water;
(2) migration of a polluting front into a freshwater aquifer.

The large volumes of stored interstitial fluids will exert an influence on water quality over a long period. Thus, it is important to consider the sampling implications—that is, whether the rapidly moving water (fresh water front or pollution front) alone should be sampled, or whether the matrix should also be sampled (to establish the nature of older pore fluids or the extent of contaminant invasion respectively). In the former case sampling from existing boreholes may be sufficient: in the latter case special drilling may be required.

Various drilling techniques (Chapter 13) can be used to recover uncontaminated core material for investigation, including augering, percussion drilling, air-flush or water-flush rotary drilling. If water-flush drilling is used, a suitable tracer (Li^+, Cl^-, NH_4^+, NO_3^-, etc) may be added to quantify formation invasion; otherwise, air-flush 'dry' sampling is to be preferred.

Extraction of interstitial fluids may be carried out by centrifugation, squeezing, gas or fluid displacement, or in certain cases, by elutriation. Squeezing methods are applicable only to unconsolidated material[68]. Centrifuge drainage methods have been described[69]. There is a development of this method, using immiscible liquid displacement[70] and a displacement method for relatively dry samples[71].

Pumping and Flow Regimes

For detailed investigation, interstitial fluid sampling is considered by far the best means of examining the water profile with depth. However, for most surveys pumped samples from wells or boreholes or spring discharge, representing integrated discharge, are the only samples readily available.

Although pumped samples are the most important from a water supply viewpoint, these samples are inevitably mixtures of water of different quality and age, penetrated by the borehole and drawn into the pump as a function of its depth and the relative contribution from different horizons. A change in the pumping régime (rate of pumping, depth of pump, etc.) is likely to change the chemistry.

The relative contribution from each depth can be established by flowmeter survey or temperature conductivity surveys as described in Chapter 9 and by Tate *et al*[72]. In view of differential heads within the aquifer, intervals of the borehole may be stagnant, while in others vertical flow may predominate. Depth sampling may be used to sample components of the flow following hydrogeophysical survey. Uncontrolled depth sampling is not advisable.

Accurate information on vertical stratification is important for groundwater management. Mixing of oxygenated and reducing waters may precipitate iron within the rising main/distribution system and control of this boundary will be critical. Near-surface polluted groundwater must be identified and kept under control; upconing of saline water must also be controlled. Individual samples of such mixed groundwaters are unlikely to be unique and frequent monitoring is essential during abstraction.

Geographical Constraints

Groundwater quality variations are rarely homogeneous yet mapping such variations is heavily restricted by the network of existing boreholes and other sources. Borehole sampling points vary in depth, method of construction, diameter and discharge characteristics. Considerable skill is required in interpreting both the two- and three-dimensional nature of the quality distribution and in comparing sets of regional data over periods of time.

Size Fraction and Filtration

Natural waters, including groundwaters, contain various components, summarised in Fig. 3.2. Some form of filtration is necessary, unless a total sample is required, including particulate, colloidal, biological and dissolved fractions. A total sample may be required for studies of element fluxes (for example, for geochemical prospecting) and often in water supply control where the total supplied/ingested water sample is relevant; in such cases, some form of stabilisation is needed.

Filtration through 0.45 μm cellulose acetate filters is fairly standard practice in water quality investigations. This is valuable in regional or monitoring studies where all data can be compared to a common reference point, and randomly introduced particulate matter from abrasion in the well, from fine-grained material in the aquifer, corrosion products etc. can be excluded. Fig. 3.2 shows that not all particulate matter is excluded by 0.45 μm filtration[73]. For studies of aluminium and iron chemistry the use of 0.1 μm or even smaller pore-size membrane filters may be desirable.

Stability and Storage

A groundwater chemical analysis (raw water) should represent as closely as possible the *in situ* aquifer conditions. Some species, especially those involved in carbonate and redox reactions, will undergo changes on reaching atmospheric conditions and particular care is needed to measure or stabilise the sample at the sampling point; field determinations of pH, oxygen and other variables are necessary in most investigations and are described below. For certain elements, for example aluminium, some field treatment may be needed to ensure that only reactive rather than polymerised forms are determined[74].

In general, stabilisation of the total sample and/or the filtered sample in the field to pH $\leqslant 1.5$ with HCl or other strong ultrapure mineral acid is sufficient for most work. Standard major and trace element samples stored in this way for up to two years have given reproducible results in BGS laboratories.

Contamination

From the point at which the groundwater leaves the aquifer, it is likely to undergo some contamination, mainly by metals. This contamination by casing, headworks or distribution system will be included in the raw water analysis giving the 'correct' result, for example, if potability is being tested. It is virtually impossible to sample groundwaters from boreholes with metal installations without some slight contamination.

Contamination from containers is also likely. For geochemical analysis of groundwaters polyethylene bottles should be used. New bottles should be acid-washed to remove any chemicals used during manufacture and subsequently acid-washed prior to re-use to remove carbonate and other precipitates and adsorbed metals. Special care should be exercised for trace element work and all equipment should be metal-free. For further discussion on contamination problems, see Robertson[75] and Wagemann and Graham[76].

MAIN PARAMETERS

The total range of constituents that could be determined for groundwater quality investigations is very large. Each constituent may give some information about the nature of the aquifer, residence time, amount of contamination, and so on. It will generally be necessary for reasons of economy to restrict the number of parameters measured. Historically, the type of chemical analysis carried out by the water industry has often not been adequate for geochemical or hydrogeological analysis, giving only potability criteria. Since the 1973 Water Act and, more recently the Harmonised Monitoring Scheme and CEC* Directives, more data useful for purposes other than potability assessment are being collected. The minimum set of data useful for geochemical study is the mineral analysis for the major ions—Ca^{2+}, Mg^{2+}, Na^+, K^+, SO_4^{2-} Cl^-, HCO_3^- and NO_3^-—and pH value. Using only these parameters together with temperature, it is possible to infer a lot about the history of the groundwater and the rocks through which it has passed. This should form the basic unit of analysis and interpretation: minor element, trace element, certain field measurements and isotopic studies can provide useful additional information. Each constituent is briefly reviewed.

Chloride

The bulk of chloride in groundwaters is derived from atmospheric inputs. Input values are likely to vary regionally away from coasts and the amount of chloride

CEC = Commission of the European Communities

entering the closed aquifer system will also have been modified by evapotranspiration, also varying regionally. Chloride can generally be regarded as a 'conservative' parameter, being neither gained nor lost by chemical reaction in the soil or rock. It can be used to obtain an estimation of recharge[77] if the rainfall chemistry and amount is known, using the equation:

$$R_d = P \cdot \frac{Cl_p + Cl_d}{Cl_g}$$

where R_d is direct recharge (simplified to ignore surface run off);
$\quad P$ precipitation;
$\quad Cl_p$ chloride in rainfall;
$\quad Cl_d$ chloride in dry deposition;
$\quad Cl_g$ chloride in groundwater.

The chloride concentration in UK rainfall has been increasing generally—firstly, due to increasing industrial fallout since the industrial revolution and secondly, since the last ice age (late Pleistocene) when air masses were less maritime. Evidence for lower Cl^- values associated with late Pleistocene groundwaters may be found in the East Midlands Triassic sandstone aquifer described earlier[62]; low chloride values (below 12 mg/l) may indicate late Pleistocene waters. There is evidence in the same aquifer that present day chloride values may be higher than those that could be explained by normal rainfall, suggesting contamination by agrichemicals, road salt or industrial emissions.

Increase in salinity in many aquifers is observed either at depth or down gradient. These saline waters are likely to represent a residual either of an original (connate) marine water as has been demonstrated for the Chalk[39] or of a saline water that has replenished the aquifer at some time in its geological history. This saline water may exist in pore fluids adjacent to fresh water in fissures[3] and is gradually released by diffusion into the groundwater.

Another source of chloride may be leakage or diffusion from evaporite (halite) horizons above or below the aquifer. Such is the case for saline waters in some of the Permo-Trias (Sherwood Sandstone) and this can be further characterised by low Br^-/Cl^- ratios. Intrusion of sea water may also be responsible in coastal areas for increases in chloride and this may be an active or a fossil process. The use of $\delta^{18}O$ combined with Cl^- is a useful diagnostic tool for such water.

Sulphate

Some sulphate is derived from the atmosphere as marine aerosol, as dust or as an oxidation product of SO_2 gas. Some will also be derived from mineralisation processes in soils but the majority will come from dissolution of gypsum $(CaSO_4 \cdot 2H_2O)$ or the oxidation of sulphide minerals.

Input levels to the aquifer from the rain and soil zone should seldom amount to more than 20-50 mg/l and amounts in excess of this mainly reflect inputs from agrichemicals—for example, $(NH_4)_2SO_4$ (Foster et al[37]) although dissolution of fine grained sulphate minerals in Drift deposits may contribute. The behaviour of sulphur is shown in Fig. 3.16 for the three main British aquifers. In the Sherwood Sandstone, low sulphate values down-gradient of the redox boundary are explained by lower input values during the pre-industrial era over a period of several thousand years. Sulphate increase due to gypsum solution can be seen in the older groundwaters. The low sulphate groundwaters in the downgradient Lincolnshire Limestone probably have a similar origin to the Trias and sulphate reduction is considered quantitatively unimportant. Sulphate is also produced in the Limestone and other aquifers by oxidation of fine grained pyrite (FeS_2):

$$FeS_2 + 8H_2O \rightarrow 2SO_4^{2-} + Fe^{2+} + 16H^+.$$

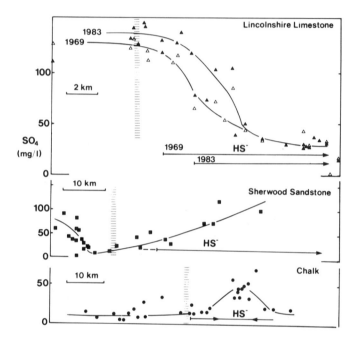

Fig. 3.16.   Comparison of downgradient profiles for sulphur (SO_4^{2-}, HS^-) in relation to the redox boundaries in the Lincolnshire Limestone, Sherwood Sandstone and Chalk aquifers

Alkalinity

Alkalinity, measured by titration with acid to a fixed end-point (pH 4.5 as a rule) or to the inflection point on the titration curve, is a measure of the acid neutralising capacity. In groundwaters and most natural waters, the carbonate equilibria predominate and the end-point essentially measures the HCO_3^- concentration. In some waters, other weak acids—borate, silicate, organic acids and dissolved aluminium and iron species—may contribute to the alkalinity and must be subtracted for more accurate interpretation of the carbonate system; computer programs can be used to perform this function.

The alkalinity of a groundwater is probably the single most useful measured constituent. The gain in alkalinity of water passing through soil and rock records the reactions of H^+, either of strong acids (H_2SO_4) or weak acids (H_2CO_3). The production of CO_2 in the soil zone is important for most geochemical reactions of carbonate and other minerals. Direct infiltration of water low in CO_2 (e.g. in some karstic systems) may give rise to low alkalinity groundwaters. In addition, infiltration of water into carbonate-deficient sandstones and similar lithologies may give rise to low alkalinity groundwater even through the partial pressure of CO_2 (pCO_2) derived from soils, may be quite high.

In most groundwaters the alkalinity should reach a value buffered by calcite or other carbonate minerals after sufficient time and the mineral saturation index (Table 3.VII (b)) can be used to determine the state of the reaction. The alkalinity may change during migration downgradient under closed system conditions (with respect to the atmosphere). This may occur, for example, if calcium is removed by cation exchange; the equilibrium with carbonate is maintained by an increase in alkalinity and/or pH. For example, in the Lincolnshire Limestone, an alkalinity of 750 mg/l is reached, when Ca^{2+} is reduced to around 2 mg/l; pH rises to about 9.0 yet the water is still in equilibrium with respect to calcite.

Alkalinity is unaffected by gains or losses of gaseous CO_2. The pH will change; it will increase with $CO_2(g)$ loss and decrease with $CO_2(g)$ gain. If pH and temperature are measured in the field and alkalinity measured in the laboratory, then the pCO_2 in the original water may be calculated without error.

Nitrate

Nitrate levels in groundwaters may be naturally enhanced in certain terrains due to leguminous plants, but on the whole the levels observed in UK aquifers at the present day are mainly the result of anthropogenic factors[37]. Arable farming increases biological activity of the soil, and nitrogen-fixing bacteria plus artificial additions of nitrogen fertilisers combine to give excess NO_3^- in many drainage waters and in the unsaturated zone.

The fate of nitrate once in the unsaturated zone is primarily a function of the redox conditions. In line with theoretical considerations it is generally found that nitrate is quite stable in the presence of oxygen[24]. In fact, nitrate at levels of 2-10 mg/l NO_3^-, can be shown to have persisted in the Triassic Sherwood Sandstone for over 2000 years.

The distribution of nitrate-free groundwater in the main UK aquifers is almost precisely coincident with the complete reaction of oxygen and the redox boundaries. It is clear from this circumstantial evidence (see Figs. 3.9(b), 3.10(a) and 3.13) that *in situ* denitrification is taking place almost immediately after oxygen has reacted. The evidence for denitrification is also borne out in the Lincolnshire Limestone by the presence of tritium and agrichemical indicators other than nitrate (e.g. SO_4^{2-}) well downgradient of the redox boundary.

Calcium

Calcium is the predominant cation in most freshwaters. The amount in rainfall is generally below 2 mg/l but calcium is readily dissolved during infiltration by reactions of carbonate or silicate minerals. The dissolution of Ca^{2+} is strongly dependent upon concentrations of dissolved CO_2. Distilled water can dissolve only 5.6 mg/l Ca^{2+} (Garrels and Christ[14]) but increase in CO_2 from microbiological activity in the soil zone (up to two orders of magnitude above that of the atmosphere) produces carbonic acid which greatly accelerates calcium solubility.

Calcium at equilibrium with respect to calcite ($SI_{calcite} = 0.0$) may still have a wide range of concentrations, depending on the accompanying pH and HCO_3^- (see Alkalinity earlier). However, values exceeding 100 mg/l are not common in fresh, potable groundwaters. Solution of gypsum may give rise to higher calcium values and subtraction of $Ca^{2+} \equiv |SO_4^{2-}$ can be used to estimate this contribution. The $CaHCO_3^+$ complex ion may constitute up to 10 per cent of dissolved calcium in some waters and $CaSO_4^0$ is also an important species (Table 3.VII).

TABLE 3.VII. **Analysis of a Groundwater from the Confined Chalk near Reading**
(a) Information on Speciation and Related Parameters

Ion	mg/l	meq/l	m mol/l	% free ion	Speciation (decreasing order of importance)
Ca^{2+}	52	2.59	1.30	95.1	$CaSO_4^0$, $CaHCO_3^+$, $CaCO_3^0$, CaF^+
Mg^{2+}	10.3	0.85	0.43	94.7	$MgSO_4^0$, $MgHCO_3^+$, $MgCO_3^0$, MgF^+
Na^+	80	3.48	3.48	99.8	$NaHCO_3^0$
K^+	5.1	0.13	0.13	99.9	KSO_4^-
HCO_3^-	268	4.39	4.39	98.4	$H_2CO_3^0$, CO_3^{2-}, $CaHCO_3^+$
Cl^-	72	2.03	2.03	100	Cl^-
SO_4^{2-}	34.4	0.72	0.36	87.7	$CaSO_4^0$, $MgSO_4^0$
NO_3^-	<2.0	<0.03	—	100	NO_3^-
Fe^{2+}	0.072	—	0.13×10^{-2}	97.2	$FeSO_4^0$, $FeOH^+$
Mn^{2+}	0.003	—	0.5×10^{-7}	85.3	$MnHCO_3^+$, $MnSO_4^0$
Sr^{2+}	2.05	—	0.23	100	Sr^{2+}
Ba^{2+}	0.056	—	0.4×10^{-3}	99.8	$BaOH^+$
F^-	10.40	—	0.068	98.1	CaF^+, MgF^+

(b) Further Hydrogeochemical Data Derived from the Analysis

Σ cations	7.06	$^*SI_{calcite}$	−0.08
Σ anions	7.11	$SI_{dolomite}$	−0.62
Charge balance	−0.035%	SI_{gypsum}	−1.88
Ionic strength	0.00895	SI_{barite}	−0.27
Log pCO_2	−2.15	$SI_{fluorite}$	−0.37
Total hardness	172	$SI_{celestite}$	−2.52
Na/Cl (molar ratio)	1.72	SI_{quartz}	0.75
Na/K ,, ,,	26.7		
Na/Mg ,, ,,	3.05		
Sodium adsorption ratio (SAR)	1.88		

Note: $^*SI$ = Saturation Index

In non-carbonate terrain calcium may be dissolved as a result of silicate mineral weathering. Alteration of plagioclase feldspars will produce calcium, although sodium will also be released, as a rule, during feldspar weathering. Calcium may be removed from solution by two main processes—precipitation and cation exchange. If the $SI_{calcite}$ is exceeded for any reason (e.g. evaporation, mixing, loss of CO_2) calcite should precipitate; calcite precipitation may also occur if gypsum dissolves in a water otherwise saturated with respect to calcite. Calcium is likely to be preferentially exchanged on clay mineral or colloid surfaces. Apart from the greater affinity of exchange sites for divalent relative to monovalent ions, it is also necessary for the ratio in solution of Ca^{2+}/Mg^{2+} to be relatively high for significant exchange to take place.

Magnesium

The principal sources of magnesium in groundwaters are carbonate minerals, either dolomite or calcite. Consequently the dominant reaction producing Mg^{2+} in solution is the congruent solution of these minerals during infiltration. Dolomite generally contains Mg^{2+}/Ca^{2+} in the ratio 1:1 whilst calcite may contain up to a few per cent Mg^{2+} in its structure. High-Mg^{2+} calcites may be found especially in modern sediments with up to 20 per cent Mg^{2+} substitution.

Congruent reaction of Chalk and other pure limestones will typically give rise to 2 mg/l Mg^{2+} in solution. In the Sherwood Sandstone of the East Midlands it has been shown[21] that congruent solution of dolomite occurs during infiltration (Fig. 3.14) and initial Mg^{2+}/Ca^{2+} ratios are relatively high. An increase in Mg^{2+}/Ca^{2+} can often occur during groundwater evolution by incongruent solution of either calcite or dolomite and good examples of this can be found in these two aquifers. The Mg^{2+}/Ca^{2+} ratio rises to nearly 1:1 in the confined Chalk as a result of continuous reaction of carbonate even though in the rock Ca^{2+} exceeds Mg^{2+} by a factor of 20. These waters seldom have Mg^{2+}/Ca^{2+} ratios greatly in excess of 1:1 and dolomite solubility probably exerts the control. The increase in Mg^{2+}/Ca^{2+} ratio is probably one of the most useful diagnostic tools in groundwater chemistry and enables the maturity and evolution of groundwater to be followed.

Other sources of Mg^{2+} may include soluble salts such as epsomite ($MgSO_4 . 7H_2O$) or carnallite ($KMgCl_3 . 6H_2O$). These may be found in marine or terrestrial evaporite deposits and are locally important in certain lithologies, such as the Tertiary and Jurassic formations, where they may account for groundwaters with higher than average Mg^{2+}/Ca^{2+} ratios. High Mg^{2+}/Ca^{2+} ratios may also arise from weathering of basic igneous rocks.

Magnesium may also be removed from solution by formation of clay minerals and by cation exchange, but these are not considered important processes at most groundwater Mg^{2+}/Ca^{2+} ratios, although they may be important in removing Mg^{2+} from sea water entering some aquifers. Dolomite precipitation is likely to be the main process removing Mg^{2+} from solution, although relatively little evidence is available for new formation of dolomite in aquifers.

Sodium

The concentration of Na^+ in groundwaters is initially controlled by atmospheric input and comments made about Cl^- also apply for many groundwaters. However, there is generally an excess of sodium over chloride in rainwater and rather variable Cl^-/Na^+ ratios are typical of shallow groundwaters, reflecting this variable input. In the saturated zone these variations have usually been smoothed out and Na^+/Cl^- ratios are nearer to 1.0.

Increases in sodium in deeper groundwaters generally follow chloride and result from incorporation of saline formation waters. This is a common phenomenon in many areas of Britain. These formation waters may be true connate waters[39] or marine or brackish water which has replaced the connate water during the geological history. In the Chalk, elevated sodium at depth can be traced to dilution of connate water, mainly contained in interstitial waters, which is then slowly released by diffusion and flow to the circulating groundwater.

An excess of Na^+ over Cl^- in some aquifers may occur as a result. In the Lincolnshire Limestone, cation exchange allows Na^+ increase at the expense of Ca^{2+}. The same effect is also seen in the Chalk, where waters of $NaHCO_3$ type are found[41]. In granitic and other hard rock terrains, weathering of feldspars may give rise to groundwaters with enhanced Na^+/Cl^- ratio.

Temperature

All geochemical reactions are temperature dependent so that knowledge of groundwater temperature is essential for assessing the extent to which equilibrium has been achieved. The solubility of many minerals—for example, quartz and gypsum—increases with increasing temperature but that of calcite, for example, does not. The measurement of temperature at source is also important in characterising the nature of groundwater recharge and separating waters from different depths.

pH Value

The pH of a natural water represents the combined expression of a number of chemical reactions. Most groundwaters lie in the pH range 6-8, within which the hydrogen ion (H^+) is a trace constituent. At pH values below 5, H^+ should be accounted for in the ionic balance. The measurement of pH in the field is essential for correct interpretation of groundwater chemistry. The pH is likely to change due to loss (or gain) of dissolved CO_2, redox and other reactions and laboratory measured values are of no use for calculating *in situ* conditions, representing only the conditions in the sampling bottle at the time the determination is made. Historical pH data should therefore be treated with caution, since it has been common practice in the water industry and elsewhere to measure pH only in the laboratory; with CO_2 loss in transit these values may be up to one pH unit too high.

Field measurement of pH requires both reliable equipment and techniques[78,79,80]. Modern pH equipment with a readability to $\pm$ 0.02 pH unit should be used in conjunction with a good quality glass-calomel dual electrode, with toughened glass tip. It should be possible to obtain precise readings of most groundwaters with the same system and with different operators. Buffer solutions (pH 4.00 and pH 7.00 for most groundwaters) should be fresh and allowed to reach thermal equilibrium with electrodes at the groundwater temperature; otherwise drift will occur. Stable readings should be obtained within 1-2 minutes with good equipment in well-buffered groundwaters under isothermal conditions. Badly maintained electrodes are generally the main cause of unstable pH readings. At low pH (<5.5) and in very dilute solutions difficulty in pH measurement may be experienced due to poor buffering of the system and extra precautions and/or a different electrode system may be necessary[81].

Whilst it is relatively easy to achieve good precision in field pH measurement, achievement of accuracy may be more of a problem. One source of inaccuracy is the response of different batches of pH electrodes. This problem has been highlighted by Neal and Thomas[82], who found that many commercial electrodes give a Nernst response below 100 per cent and pH measured with different electrodes in the same water can give rise to pH differences up to 1 pH unit. It is important therefore to check out pH electrodes fully in the laboratory before going in the field, to discard bad electrodes and carefully maintain 'good' electrodes.

Specific Electrical Conductance (SEC$_{25}$)

Specific electrical conductance of groundwater (referred to 25°C) is a valuable yet simple method for estimation of total mineralisation, and for a more detailed discussion of theory, Hem[9] is a good source. The routine measurement of SEC_{25} in the field is recommended for three reasons:

(a) to provide an instant reference of total mineralisation of one water relative to another during field survey,

(b) to monitor changes in quality with time during discharge; to this end, automated conductivity monitoring is recommended with precision of better than 2 µS/cm.

(c) to establish vertical gradients in water quality of boreholes, either under natural or flowing conditions.

Redox Potential (E_H)

A consideration of E_H as well as pH of natural waters provides a convenient theoretical means of studying the limiting conditions of element speciation and mobility in the natural environment. E_H–pH diagrams[14,26] offer a convenient means of summarising the occurrence of many species in aqueous solution relative to solid mineral phases.

Measurement of redox potential in the field does not generally provide information on the specific behaviour of a single redox couple or on the reducing or oxidising condition of that water. It is a useful operational parameter[83] and in natural waters can usually be used to monitor the onset of reducing conditions more readily than the oxygen electrode. In the presence of oxygen, the potential developed at the platinum electrode surface does not reflect the concentrations of oxygen but behaves mainly as a Pt-O electrode and responds more readily to pH. Thus, relatively high redox potentials are developed in oxygenated acid waters. The measurement of E_H in well oxygenated waters is not generally worthwhile. E_H measurement should, however, be carried out routinely in reducing waters, or where there are low or fluctuating levels of oxygen. A stable potential may be reached rapidly in well buffered groundwaters, but elsewhere up to one hour may be needed to achieve a stable reading. In reducing groundwaters there will be a mixture of redox reactions involving iron, sulphur, nitrogen and manganese species, for example, as well as organic matter. The redox potential obtained will generally be a mixed potential, but along the groundwater flowpath a sequence of changes is generally observed and the redox potential should decrease as new reactions become dominant[24,84].

Environmental Isotopes

Environmental isotope data may give information about the groundwater system, complementary to that given by elemental analysis. The stable isotope ratios of oxygen and hydrogen ($\delta^{18}O$, δ^2H) and the radioisotope concentration of tritium (^3H) give information on the behaviour of the water molecule, in contrast to all other hydrochemical information which refers to solutes in the water. Stable carbon isotopic ratios ($\delta^{13}C$) and radiocarbon (^{14}C) are of value in detailed studies of groundwater carbonate systems and under favourable circumstances can provide information on groundwater residence time. Other radio and stable isotope ratios may be useful for special purposes. For example studies of uranium isotope series disequilibrium ($^{238}U/^{234}U$) can also provide information on groundwater evolution and age[56,63]. Good reviews of the applications of a 'cocktail' of isotopic inert gas and other techniques in hydrogeological studies have been provided for the East Midlands Triassic aquifer[62,85] and for the thermal springs at Bath[86]. Sulphur $^{34}S/^{32}S$ (Krouse[87]) and nitrogen $^{15}N/^{14}N$ (Létolle[88]) isotope ratios may also be of value in certain hydrogeochemical investigations. For a more detailed discussion of isotope applications in groundwater studies and in environmental studies generally see Fritz and Fontes[89] and Chapter 10.

Oxygen and Hydrogen Stable Isotope Ratios

The isotope ratios $^{18}O/^{16}O$ and $^2H/^1H$ can be used in hydrochemical studies to provide information on climatic processes, recharge conditions, groundwater origin, and the identification of palaeogroundwater. The enrichment in the heavier isotopes (here in the case of oxygen) is conventionally expressed as

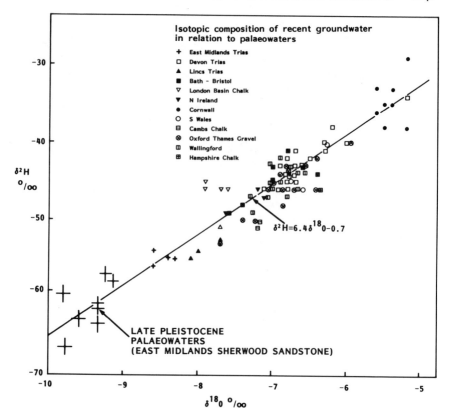

Fig. 3.17. Oxygen and hydrogen stable isotope compositions for groundwaters in various parts of the UK (after Bath[62,91])

$$\delta^{18}O \; ^o\!/_{oo} = \left(\frac{^{18}O/^{16}O_{sample}}{^{18}O/^{16}O_{standard}} - 1 \right) \times 10^3$$

Thus a greater concentration of ^{18}O is reflected by a more positive value of $\delta^{18}O$. The reference standard for most groundwater studies is Standard Mean Ocean Water (SMOW). The other parameter commonly used, especially to indicate climatic conditions is the deuterium-excess (d), defined by $d = \delta^2H - 8\delta^{18}O$, (Dansgaard[90]).

The geographical variation of isotopic composition of some recently recharged UK groundwaters (Fig. 3.17) is based on data from Bath[91] and Bath et al[62]. The slope represented by these samples is similar to that for other UK studies[92]. However, the slope for most UK data is generally below 8 which is that given by Dansgaard for weighted mean annual precipitation at continental stations in the northern hemisphere. In addition, the range of values in groundwater (here 4‰) is considerably less than that seen in rainfall from a given station which may be as much as 12 per ‰ $\delta^{18}O$. The groundwater compositions reflect the average rainfall

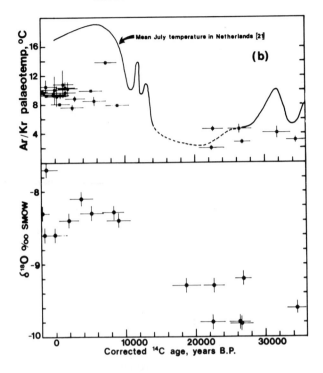

Fig. 3.18. **Oxygen isotopes as indicators of palaeowaters in the East Midlands Triassic aquifer** (after Bath *et al*[62])

(Ar/Kr palaeotemperatures are shown for comparison)

conditions in a given area. The heaviest isotopic compositions are found in the south-west and the lightest in the north-east, although the detailed pattern of variation is not straightforward. At the local level the isotopic composition may also reflect longer term climatic fluctuations.

The isotopic compositions of groundwaters from the confined Sherwood Sandstone in the East Midlands are lighter than −8 ‰ (Bath *et al*[62]) and represent palaeogroundwaters recharged during colder climatic conditions prior to the last glacial maximum. This is borne out by the supporting hydrochemical evidence of inert gas ratios and radiocarbon analysis. The shift in isotopic composition can be used to calculate a likely temperature difference of up to 7°C using the temperature coefficient given by Evans *et al*[92].

The most practical use of oxygen and hydrogen stable isotopic variations in the UK context is in identifying or confirming the presence of palaeowaters (Fig. 3.18). Investigations of recharge phenomena, groundwater mixing and similar studies clearly require a detailed knowledge of secular variations in the area of interest (see Chapter 10).

Tritium

Tritium occurs naturally in the atmosphere at around 12 TU* as a result of cosmic ray bombardment of nitrogen nuclei. It decays with a half-life of 12.35 yr. Since 1952, atmospheric tritium has been much higher than this due to thermonuclear testing, reaching a peak in 1963. Present-day levels in the atmosphere are only slightly above the natural background. In hydrogeological investigations, tritium has been used extensively between the 1960s and the present day to measure the rate of movement in the unsaturated zone[34] and the processes whereby water is transmitted to the water table[36].

In hydrogeochemical studies, tritium serves to monitor the rate of movement of water compared with solutes and various references have been made to this use elsewhere in this chapter and in Chapter 10. In the unsaturated zone, tritium provides a useful marker for monitoring the progress of pollutants such as nitrate towards the water table. In saturated zone studies tritium can best be used as an indicator of the presence or absence of 'current' recharge or as a tracer for the extent of downgradient movement.

In the 1980s and beyond, tritium should still be a valuable tracer in hydrogeochemical studies, despite lower input levels. However, the analysis of tritium at the lower environmental levels, to produce results of high precision and accuracy, will increase the costs and may restrict its use to only the most urgent problems or to fundamental studies.

Carbon Isotopes

Radiocarbon (^{14}C) is continually being produced from nitrogen in the earth's atmosphere and, through a series of exchange, assimilation and other processes of carbon fixation, is incorporated into all living matter. The carbon cycle is illustrated in Fig. 3.19. As a result of geochemical reactions ^{14}C is dissolved in groundwater, where it occurs mainly as HCO_3^-. Theoretically, it should then be possible to use ^{14}C (half-life 5730 ± 40 yr) to establish groundwater age. However, the geoche-

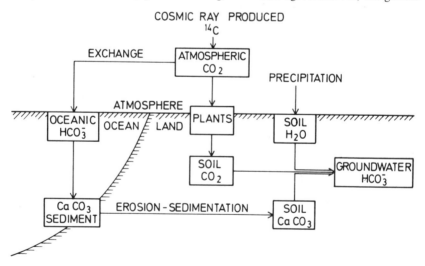

Fig. 3.19.   Part of the natural carbon cycle (after Mook[93])

*One TU (tritium unit) = One tritium atom in 10^{18} hydrogen atoms

mical complexities of the carbon cycle mean that there is unlikely to be a simple interpretation of a groundwater ^{14}C activity. For further discussion of groundwater dating using ^{14}C see Mook[93].

The carbonate system can be investigated further using stable carbon isotope ratios, either as an additional means of correcting ^{14}C ages or as a method of studying carbonate reactions. Various models have been proposed for using carbon-isotope ratios for age correction[94,95] and these have been applied to UK studies[62,85]. In most groundwater studies, the difficulties and ambiguities associated with ^{14}C dating restrict its use to fundamental studies, rather than as a readily applied tool (see Chapter 10).

Stable carbon isotope ratios ($\delta^{13}C$) are, however, of value in their own right in hydrogeochemical studies to identify both the *source* of dissolved carbon and the *extent* of chemical reaction with parent rock. Marine limestones have $\delta^{13}C$ values enriched in the heavier ^{13}C isotope and therefore have more positive delta values (generally $+3$ to 0 $^o/_{oo}$). Freshwater limestones and soil carbonates are usually lighter than this (-5 to -10 $^o/_{oo}$). Soil carbon dioxide, derived from organic matter has much lighter (more negative) $\delta^{13}C$ values, generally near to -25 $^o/_{oo}$.

The ideal reaction:

$$CaCO_3 + CO_2 + H_2O \rightarrow 2HCO_3^- + Ca^{2+}$$

results in a 1:1 ratio of carbonate to CO_2 so that the groundwater HCO_3^- will have an intermediate value. The $\delta^{13}C_{HCO_3}$ can therefore be used to study reaction pathways, sources of pollution and the ageing of deep, confined groundwater, if the carbon isotope compositions of starting materials are known.

INTERPRETATION OF HYDROCHEMICAL DATA

Introduction

Modern chemical analysis is capable of producing large amounts of good quality data on groundwaters. In addition, there are huge archives of chemical data of variable quality in many public and private organizations. This information forms an important data base for water quality studies, especially for examination of historical trends and much is now stored on computer by Regional Water Authorities and other large organizations making it much more accessible than before. Generally speaking, data have mainly been collected for quality control. The reliability of many historical data sets may be difficult to assess due to changes in analytical techniques, and possibly inaccurate analysis and inadequate reporting.

It is the purpose of this section to outline an approach to data collection, storage and interpretation. For the future, water quality trends must be watched even more closely and more specialised information, on trace elements and organic species for example, will be required. More sensitive instrumentation combined with automation should mean that more data will be produced quite rapidly. However, more rigorous standards of analytical accuracy and data registration and interpretation will be required.

Data Organization

The criteria for sampling and for planning hydrochemical studies have been dealt with earlier. Methods for conducting chemical analysis have been described[96,97,98]. For proper interpretation and organization of the data it is assumed that field data have been obtained where necessary, that all relevant qualifying data have been recorded (e.g. site coordinates, date of sampling) and that chemical analysis has been sufficiently comprehensive for the objectives of the investigation.

Data should be quoted to significant figures rounded off according to the precision of the method used. The completed data should be verified for major ion analytical balance and generally accepted once they are within ± 3 per cent expressed as:

$$\text{Balance (per cent)} = \frac{\Sigma(\text{cations, meq/l}) - \Sigma(\text{anions, meq/l})}{\Sigma(\text{cations, meq/l}) + \Sigma(\text{anions, meq/l})} \times 100$$

The units chosen are mg/l, equivalent in dilute waters to parts per million (ppm) or mg/kg. Above concentrations of about 7000 mg/l, however, solution density must be taken into account and values converted according to the equation:

$$\text{mg/kg} = \frac{\text{mg/l}}{\text{solution density}}$$

From the analysis in mg/l all other relevant parameters may be computed (Table 3.VII). Whilst the analysis in mg/l is most readily understood, analyses expressed in millimoles per litre (m mol/l) or in milliequivalents per litre (meq/l) are generally more useful in geochemical interpretation, where chemical equivalent quantities involved in reaction must be compared. Table 3.VIII gives conversion factors from mg/l to m mol/l and meq/l.

The individual analysis can then be treated to reveal a large amount of additional information using a variety of software, including one or more large computer programs[10,94,12]. A typical analytical summary is given in Table 3.VII from the data in Fig. 3.8. This includes information on speciation, per cent free ions, ionic balance, ionic strength, ionic ratios and the extent of saturation with respect to various minerals. Other parameters used in the water industry and elsewhere are

TABLE 3.VIII.   Conversion Factors from mg/l to (a) meq/l and (b) m mol/l

Element and species	Conversion Factors		Element and species	Conversion Factors	
	(a)	(b)		(a)	(b)
Aluminium (Al^{3+})	0.11119	0.03715	Lead (Pb)	—	0.00483
Ammonium (NH_4^+)	0.05544	0.05544	Lithium (Li^+)	0.14411	0.14411
Barium (Ba^{2+})	0.01456	0.00728	Magnesium (Mg^{2+})	0.08226	0.04113
Beryllium (Be^{3+})	0.33288	0.11096	Manganese (Mn^{2+})	0.03640	0.01820
Bicarbonate (HCO_3^-)	0.01639	0.01639	Molybdenum (Mo)	—	0.01042
Boron (B)	—	0.09250	Nickel (Ni^{2+})	—	0.01703
Bromide (Br^-)	0.01251	0.01251	Nitrate (NO_3^-)	0.01613	0.01613
Cadmium (Cd^{2+})	0.01779	0.00890	Nitrite (NO_2^-)	0.02174	0.02174
Calcium (Ca^{2+})	0.04990	0.02495	Phosphate (HPO_4^{2-})	0.02084	0.01042
Carbonate (CO_3^{2-})	0.03333	0.01666	Potassium (K^+)	0.02557	0.02557
Caesium (Cs^+)	0.00752	0.00752	Rubidium (Rb^+)	0.01170	0.01170
Chloride (Cl^-)	0.02821	0.02821	Silica (SiO_2)	—	0.01664
Cobalt (Co^{2+})	0.03394	0.01697	Silver (Ag^{2+})	—	0.00927
Fluoride (F^-)	0.05264	0.05264	Sodium (Na^+)	0.04350	0.04350
Hydrogen (H^+)	0.99209	0.99209	Strontium (Sr^{2+})	0.02283	0.01141
Hydroxide (OH^-)	0.05880	0.05880	Sulphate (SO_4^{2-})	0.02082	0.01041
Iodide (I^-)	0.00788	0.00788	Sulphide (S^{2-})	0.06238	0.03119
Iron (Fe^{2+})	0.03581	0.01791	Zinc (Zn^{2+})	0.03060	0.01530
Iron (Fe^{3+})	0.05372	0.01791			

Note: Multiply concentration in mg/l by conversion factor

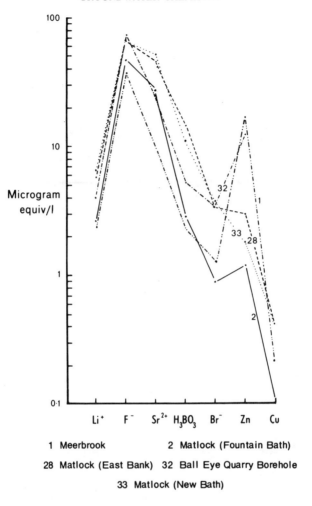

1 Meerbrook   2 Matlock (Fountain Bath)

28 Matlock (East Bank)   32 Ball Eye Quarry Borehole

33 Matlock (New Bath)

Fig. 3.20.   Variation diagram for minor elements—data from Derbyshire thermal springs (after Edmunds[19])

derived from the ionic analysis. The concentrations of important minor species, e.g. CO_3^{2-} and H^+, not measured directly during analysis are also computed. A number of other computations are possible using the larger computer programs—for example the calculation of the theoretical E_H values from measured species, such as SO_4^{2-} and HS^-.

The individual analyses stored in this form can therefore be used to provide a wealth of information about the water which can be interpreted further in relation to potability, potential for corrosion, scaling etc. In addition they can be used to assess similarities to other groundwaters in space or time.

Representation of Groundwater Analyses

Groundwater data may require interpretation as single analyses, as groups of analyses representing time series, or as groups representing some spatial or regional grouping. Data sets from different periods of time or locations may need comparison. For a detailed discussion of methods of presentation see Matthes[5] or Hem[9].

For small groups of waters, especially of different total mineralisations, differences and similarities in chemistry may be recorded using vertical scale diagrams (Schoeller diagrams); characteristic patterns are formed for water with a certain chemistry. These are mainly used for presentation of major element patterns but may also be used for minor or trace element patterns (Fig. 3.20) where differences in thermal waters in the Matlock area are distinguished.

By far the most useful plot for comparison of larger numbers of groundwaters is the cation trilinear plot, which can be used to compare changes in major cation ratios (e.g. Mg^{2+}/Ca^{2+}, Na^+/Ca^{2+}) for large numbers of waters. The present day analytical accuracy and precision of cation measurements mean that the resolution of data plotting can be refined and, if needed, an area of the diagram expanded. The trilinear diagram is useful in representing groundwater evolution, e.g. with depth or along flow paths as in the example from the Chalk (Fig. 3.21). It can also be used to superimpose mineral compositions or other data concerned with the solid phase.

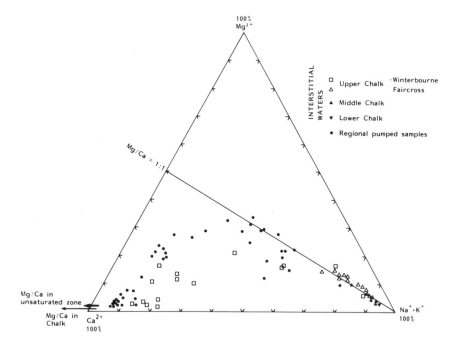

Fig. 3.21.   Trilinear diagram (Na^+ and K^+, Mg^{2+} and Ca^{2+}) of groundwaters from the Chalk

Projected trilinear diagrams (Piper diagrams, Durov diagrams, etc.—see Table 7.III) may also be used to represent combined changes in cations and anions. However their interpretation is often confusing, especially at higher salinities. They are limited because the projection of a ratio obscures much valuable information, e.g. SO_4^{2-}/Cl^-, Mg^{2+}/Ca^{2+}, and because of the limitation placed on HCO_3^- concentrations by carbonate solubilities.

The use of ionic ratios in hydrogeochemical interpretation is to be encouraged over consideration of single ionic values. For example, consideration of Cl^- alone as an index of rainfall origin may be misleading and a study of the Cl^-/Na^+ ratio may give more information as to whether a marine source or an industrial source is contributing.

5.   WATER QUALITY AND USE

Hydrogeochemical investigations have as their ultimate objective the better understanding of distributions and processes in aquifer systems. This can assist in development and utilisation of the groundwater resource. As a basis for any groundwater development, therefore, certain hydrogeochemical characteristics need to be understood, including:

  (i)   the natural baseline conditions;
 (ii)   the origin of the water(s);
(iii)   the residence time(s) of the water(s);
 (iv)   the ability of the aquifer to withstand contamination.

Some of these factors have been referred to earlier but before considering water quality and use it is worthwhile to consider further the natural baseline conditions in the aquifer.

Natural Baseline Conditions

Each aquifer will have a characteristic chemistry determined by interaction between recharging groundwater, soil and rock. Due to intensive land use in recharge areas, point-source and diffuse pollution, artificial recharge, etc., the baseline chemistry is often masked, and it is in fact difficult at the present day to find any aquifer where the influence of man is still undetectable.

However much pollution an aquifer may receive, certain geochemical characteristics of the water will still be overwhelmingly determined by reaction with the rock. Thus the Ca^{2+}/Mg^{2+} ratio, and levels of Sr^{2+}, Al^{3+}, Si^{4+} and other constituents will be geochemically controlled. Other elements such as Cl^- and F^-, may be dominated by atmospheric inputs. Many other elements, including SO_4^{2-}, NO_3^- and Zn^{2+}, may be influenced more by anthropogenic activity.

As a basis for monitoring water quality, therefore, an attempt should be made to determine the baseline chemistry. Otherwise many anomalies that may be entirely natural (e.g. changes in metal concentrations due to changes in redox conditions) may be mistaken for the onset of pollution.

The natural baseline chemistry will also vary across the aquifer due to sequential hydrochemical changes, lithological facies changes and changes in hydrogeological conditions. Natural fluctuations in the baseline are also likely to occur seasonally in shallow unconfined aquifers.

It is recommended that for major aquifer systems, a representative hydrochemical cross section or type area is used as a reference. This section should be thoroughly investigated by hydrogeochemical methods as outlined earlier, not least

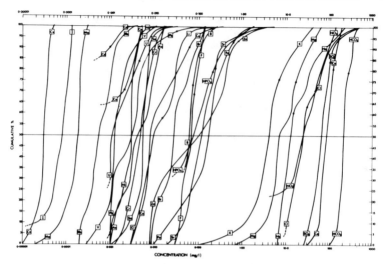

Fig. 3.22.   Cumulative frequency diagram showing major, minor and trace element occurrence in the outcrop Sherwood Sandstone of the East Shropshire area (after Edmunds and Morgan-Jones[61])

with reference to the geochemistry and mineralogy of the aquifer. This reference aquifer section can then be used for comparison with data from adjacent samples from boreholes along the strike, and as a basis for understanding changes with time.

Cumulative frequency diagrams are useful for summarizing the chemistry of groundwater within a single aquifer or for comparing chemistry between aquifers. They are of more value than single histograms since the distribution of several elements may be compared. The example shown in Fig. 3.22 is for major, minor and trace elements in the unconfined Sherwood Sandstone of East Shropshire[61]. The diagram summarizes the abundances of the elements relative to each other as well as individual distributions. The median (50 per cent) value is a good approximation to the likely baseline concentration for each element in the aquifer. The top 10 per cent of groundwaters in the distribution are likely to represent pollution from natural or anthropogenic sources. The lower concentrations may represent young groundwaters which have not reacted significantly with the rock or may indicate values where an element has been removed by adsorption, oxidation or reduction, or by some other process. Bimodal distributions for some elements may indicate that more than one process may be controlling the occurrence of the element.

POTABILITY

Water supplied for drinking must be wholesome; in other words it must meet high standards of physical, chemical and biological purity. It must be free from undesirable physical properties such as colour, turbidity, and objectionable odours and tastes. The latter properties are rather subjective and many undesirable substances, e.g. free Cl_2, H_2S and phenols, are detectable at or below levels at which they might become toxic. Other substances, e.g. Cl^-, cannot be distinguished readily until they reach several hundred mg/l. There are now statutory

TABLE 3.IX. Shortened Version of CEC Standards for Potable Water

Parameter		Guide Level	MAC†	Parameter		Guide Level	MAC†
Temperature °C		12	25	B	µg/l	1000	—
Conductivity		400	—	Fe^{2+}	„	50	200
µS/cm, 20°C				Mn^{2+}	„	20	50
Cl^-	mg/l	25	—	Cu^{2+}	„	100*	—
SO_4^{2-}	„	25	250	Zn^{2+}	„	100*	—
Ca^{2+}	„	100	—	$P_2O_5^{2-}$	„	400	5000
Mg^{2+}	„	30	50	F^-	„	—	1500*
Na^+	„	20	150*	Ba^{2+}	„	100	—
K^+	„	10	12	Ag^{2+}	„	—	10
Al^{3+}	„	0.05	0.2	As	„	—	50
NO_3^-	„	25	50	Cd^{2+}	„	—	5
NO_2^-	„	—	0.1	CN^-	„	—	50
NH_4^+	„	0.05	0.5	Cr	„	—	50
Kjeldahl N	„	—	1	Hg	„	—	1
				Ni	„	—	50
				Pb^{2+}	„	—	50*
				Sb	„	—	10
				Se	„	—	10

Notes: †MAC = Maximum Admissible Concentration
*Na – 150 mg/l from 1987; possibly as low as 120 mg/l as suggested by WHO.
*Cu – 100 µg/l at outlets from pumping stations; 3000 µg/l at the tap, after standing for 12 hours.
*F – 1500 µg/l at 8–12°C average temperatures; 700 µg/l at 25–30°C.
*Zn – 100 µg/l at outlets from pumping stations; 5000 µg/l at the tap, after standing for 12 hours.
*Pb – 50 µg/l in running water. Should not exceed 100 µg/l in any circumstances after flushing.

requirements in Europe[99,100] for the quality of water intended for human consumption which largely supersede WHO standards[101]. A shortened version of the CEC requirements is given in Table 3.IX where the 'Guide Level' is the level to be fixed where possible by each of the member states and the 'Maximum Admissible Concentration' is 'The concentration in water below which a substance is not expected, in the course of regular ingestion, to cause or indirectly result in an identifiable effect harmful to health in a statistically representative sample of the population concerned'.

Water should also be bacteriologically pure and for the purposes of the directive the count (per 100 ml) of coliform bacteria (as indicators of faecal pollution) should be zero. Although coliform bacteria are not themselves harmful they are likely to indicate the presence of pathogenic organisms and viruses. Methods for the treatment of bacteriologically impure water have been described[102,103].

The occurrence of radionuclides in groundwater and the maximum permissible levels in drinking water have been discussed by Matthes[5] who gives a table of elements with hydrogeologically significant natural and artificial radionuclides and the maximum permissible limits. These limits are rather arbitrary as, ideally, water for drinking should not contain any radioactive material. However, due both to natural occurrence (e.g. ^{40}K, ^{14}C) and weapons testing (e.g. ^3H) a certain background is inevitable. The 'maximum permitted dose' rates are based upon a daily water intake of 2.2 litres over 50 years, within which time the maximum permitted radiation would not be exceeded. The unit of radioactivity is the becquerel (Bq) replacing the curie (1 Ci = 3.7×10^{10} Bq). Differences in the physical and radiobiological behaviour of the individual nuclides account for deviations of several orders of magnitude between values; for example, the maximum permissible concentration for tritium is 11.1×10^8 Bq/l and that for ^{90}Sr is 14.8×10^4 Bq/l, because after a few weeks most of the tritium has left the body (the biological half-life is low) whereas ^{90}Sr is stored in the bones.

AGRICULTURAL USE

In temperate climates water used for agriculture and for livestock is often mains water, of the same standard as domestic supply. There is however a growing demand for groundwater for seasonal irrigation in some regions (in eastern Britain in particular) and many boreholes now exist solely for this purpose. The main difference is the absence of the pretreatment required for domestic supplies; thus anaerobic waters, waters high in iron, and polluted supplies (e.g. nitrate-rich), may be suitable for direct irrigation.

For livestock, many of the quality standards for domestic supplies also apply. However, animals are generally able to tolerate higher total solids concentrations than humans (up to 10000 mg/l in the case of beef cattle, for example) although levels well below this are clearly desirable.

For irrigation, the main concerns are the build-up of salinity levels and presence of elements toxic to plants. In the former case geochemical evaluation can be useful in predicting minerals likely to precipitate following irrigation. The drainage characteristics of the soil are equally as important as the water chemistry. It may be possible to irrigate with quite saline water on well drained sandy soils but on clayey soils saline build-up and the formation of gypsum or other minerals may occur during irrigation with reasonably fresh groundwater. Although some plants, like cotton and sugar beet, are relatively resistant to Cl^-, some fruits are sensitive to as little as 350 mg/l Cl^- (Unesco[104]).

An excess of sodium in irrigation water may be damaging to soil structure due to the replacement by sodium of calcium and magnesium. The sodium adsorption ratio (SAR) is commonly used to express the tendency for these cation exchange reactions to occur:

$$SAR = \frac{Na^+}{\sqrt{(Ca^{2+} + Mg^{2+})/2}}$$

The low value for SAR in Table 3.VII(b) (1.88, due to a large excess of Ca^{2+} and Mg^{2+}) indicates no hazard, but SAR values exceeding 8 may pose problems in irrigation.

6.   REFERENCES

1. Hill, D. 1984 *J. Soil Sci.*, 35, 27, Relative rates of diffusion of nitrate, chloride, sulphate and water in cracked and uncracked chalk.
2. Edmunds, W. M. 1983 'Hydrogeochemical investigations'; Ch. 6 in "Case studies in groundwater resource evaluation", J. W. Lloyd (Ed.), Oxford University Press.
3. Edmunds, W. M., Lovelock, P. E. R. and Gray, D. A. 1973 *J. Hydrol.*, 19, 21, Interstitial water chemistry and aquifer properties in the Upper and Middle Chalk of Berkshire, England.
4. Foster, S. S. D. 1974 *ibid*, 25, 159, The Chalk groundwater tritium anomaly—a possible explanation.
5. Matthes, G. 1982 "The properties of groundwater", John Wiley and Sons, New York.
6. Goldberg, E. D. 1961 *Ann. Rev. Phys. Chem.*, 12, 29, Marine geochemistry.
7. Helz, G. R. and Holland, H. D. 1965 *Geochim. Cosmochim. Acta*, 29, 1303, The solubility and geologic occurrence of strontianite.
8. Stumm, W. and Morgan, J. J. 1981 "Aquatic chemistry", Wiley Interscience, New York.
9. Hem, J. D. 1970 Wat. Supply Pap. 1473, US Geol. Surv., Washington, "Study and interpretation of the chemical characteristics of natural water".

10. Plummer, L. N., Jones, B. F. and Truesdell, A. H. 1976 US Geol. Surv. Water Resources Investigations 76-31 "A Fortran IV version of WATEQF, a computer program for calculating chemical equilibrium of natural waters".
11. Westall, J. C., Zachary, J. L. and Morel, F. M. M. 1976 Tech. Note 18, Dept. Civil Eng., Mass. Inst. Tech., Cambridge, Mass., "MINEQL, a computer program for the calculation of chemical equilibrium composition of aqueous systems".
12. Kharaka, Y. K. and Barnes, I. 1973 NTIS Tech. Rept. PB 214-899, Springfield, Va, "SOLMNEQ: solution–mineral equilibrium computations".
13. Langmuir, D. 1972 *Earth Mineral Sci.*, 42, 13, Controls on the amount of pollutants in subsurface waters.
14. Garrels, R. M. and Christ, C. L. 1965 "Solutions, minerals and equilibria", Harper and Row, New York.
15. Langmuir, D. 1971 *Geochim. Cosmochim. Acta*, 35, 1023, The geochemistry of some carbonate groundwaters in Central Pennsylvania.
16. Drake, J. J. and Harmon, R. S. 1973 *Wat. Res. Res.*, 9, 249, Hydrochemical environments of carbonate terrains.
17. Drever, J. I. 1982 "The geochemistry of natural waters", Prentice-Hall, Englewood Cliffs, USA.
18. Hanshaw, B. B., Back, W. and Rubin, M. 1965 Int. Ass. sci., Hydrol., Dubrovnik Symp., "Carbonate equilibria and radiocarbon distribution related to groundwater flow in the Floridan limestone aquifer".
19. Edmunds, W. M. 1971 Rep. Ser. Inst. Geol. Sci., 71/7 "Hydrogeochemistry of groundwaters in the Derbyshire Dome with special reference to trace constituents", HMSO, London.
20. Pitman, J. I. 1978 *Geochim. Cosmochim. Acta*, 42, 1885, Carbonate chemistry of groundwater from Chalk, Givendale, East Yorkshire.
21. Edmunds, W. M., Bath, A. H. and Miles, D. L. 1982 *ibid*, 46, 2069, Hydrochemical evolution of the East Midlands Triassic Sandstone aquifer, England.
22. Back, W. and Hanshaw, B. B. 1971 *Am. Chem. Soc. Publ.*, 106, 77, "Non-equilibrium systems in natural water chemistry; rates of physical and chemical processes in a carbonate aquifer".
23. Walton, N. R. G. 1981 Rep. Ser. Inst. Geol. Sci., 81/5, "A detailed hydrogeochemical study of groundwaters from the Triassic Sandstone aquifer of S. W. England".
24. Edmunds, W. M., Miles, D. L. and Cook, J. M. 1984 IASH Publ. No. 150, Proc. Symp. Uppsala, "A comparative study of sequential redox processes in three British aquifers".
25. Back, W. and Barnes, I. 1965 Prof. Pap. US geol. Surv., 498-C, "Relationship of electrochemical potentials and iron content to groundwater flow pattern".
26. Langmuir, D. 1969 Prof. Pap. US Geol. Surv., 650-C, "Geochemistry of iron in a coastal plain groundwater of the Camden, New Jersey area".
27. Edmunds, W. M. 1973 Proc. Tokyo Symp. Hydrogeochem. and Biogeochem., Vol. 1, "Trace element variations across an oxidation–reduction barrier in a limestone aquifer", Clarke, Washington, DC.
28. Champ, D. R., Gulens, J. and Jackson, R. E. 1979 *Can. J. Earth Sci.*, 16, 12, Oxidation–reduction sequences in groundwater flow systems.
29. Carroll, D. 1959 *Bull. Geol. Soc. Am.*, 70, 754, Ion exchange in clays and other minerals.
30. Rosler, H. J. and Lange, H. 1972 "Geochemical tables", Elsevier, Amsterdam.
31. Postgate, J. R. and Kelly, D. P. 1982 "Sulphur bacteria", The Royal Society, London.
32. Ridings, J., Robinson, V. K. and Eggboro, M. D. 1977 Unpubl. Rept. Thames Water, Reading "Groundwater investigations in the river gravels at Dorney and Bray".
33. Edmunds, W. M., Owen, M. and Tate, T. K. 1976 Rep. Ser. Inst. Geol. Sci., 76/5, "Estimation of induced recharge of river water into Chalk boreholes at Taplow using hydraulic analysis, geophysical logging and geochemical methods", HMSO, London.
34. Smith, D. B. *et al* 1970 Proc. Int. Symp. Isotope Hydrol, IAEA, Vienna, "Water movement in the unsaturated zone of high and low permeability strata using natural tritium".
35. Young, C. P., Oakes, D. B. and Wilkinson, W. B. 1976 *Groundwater*, 14, 426, Nitrate in groundwater studies on the Chalk near Winchester, Hampshire.
36. Foster, S. S. D. and Smith-Carington, A. K. 1980 *J. Hydrol.*, 46, 343, The interpretation of tritium in the Chalk unsaturated zone.
37. Foster, S. S. D., Cripps, A. C. and Smith-Carington, A. K. 1982 *Phil. Trans. Roy. Soc., Lond.*, 296, 477, Nitrate leaching to groundwater.
38. Deines, P., Langmuir, D. and Harmon, R. S. 1974 *Geochim. Cosmochim. Acta*, 38, 1147, Stable carbon isotope ratios and the existence of a gas phase in the evolution of carbonate groundwaters.
39. Bath, A. H. and Edmunds, W. M. 1981 *ibid*, 45, 1449, Identification of connate water in interstitial solution of chalk sediment.
40. Owen, M. and Robinson, V. K. 1978 'Characteristics and yield of the fissured Chalk' in "Thames groundwater scheme", Institution of Civil Engineers, London.
41. Ineson, J. and Downing, R. A. 1963 *Bull. Geol. Surv. Gt. Brit.*, 20, 176, Changes in the chemistry of groundwaters of the Chalk passing beneath argillaceous strata.

42. Morgan-Jones, M. 1977 *Clay Miner*, 12, 331, Mineralogy of the non-carbonate material from the Chalk of Berkshire and Oxfordshire, England.
43. Towler, P. A. 1982 "The geochemistry of nitrogen species in groundwaters", Ph.D. thesis, University of Bath.
44. Water Resources Board 1972 "The hydrogeology of the London Basin: with special reference to artificial recharge", WRB, Reading.
45. Smith, D. B. *et al* 1976 *Wat. Res. Res.*, 12, 392, The age of groundwater in the Chalk of the London Basin.
46. Downing, R. A., Smith, D. B. and Warren, S. C. 1978 *J. IWES*, 32, 123, Seasonal variations in tritium and other constituents in groundwater in the Chalk near Brighton, England.
47. Foster, S. S. D. and Crease, V. A. 1974 *J. IWE*, 28, 178, Nitrate pollution of Chalk groundwater in East Yorkshire in a hydrogeological appraisal.
48. Howard, K. W. F. and Lloyd, J. W. 1978 Proc. Int. Symp. Hydrogeochem. of Mineralised Waters, Cieplice, Poland, "Iodide enrichment in the groundwaters of the Chalk aquifer, Lincolnshire, England".
49. Heathcote, J. A. and Lloyd, J. W. 1984 *J. Hydrol.*, 75, 143, Groundwater chemistry in south-east Suffolk (UK) and its relationship to quaternary geology.
50. Morgan-Jones, M. 1985 *Q. J. eng. Geol.*, 18, 443, The hydrogeochemistry of the Lower Greensand aquifers south of London.
51. Mather, J. D. *et al* 1973 *ibid*, 6, 141 Groundwater recharge in the Lower Greensand of the London Basin—results of tritium and ^{14}C determinations.
52. Downing, R. A. and Williams, B. P. 1969 "The groundwater hydrology of the Lincolnshire Limestone with special reference to groundwater resources", Water Resources Board, Reading.
53. Lamont, P. 1959 *J. Brit. Watwks. Assoc.*, 41, 48, A soft water zone in the Lincolnshire Limestone.
54. Edmunds, W. M. 1976 'Groundwater geochemistry—controls and processes' in "Groundwater quality, measurement, prediction and protection", Water Research Centre, Medmenham.
55. Edmunds, W. M. and Walton, N. R. G. 1983 *J. Hydrol.*, 61, 201, The Lincolnshire Limestone—hydrogeochemical evolution over a ten-year period.
56. Andrews, J. N. and Kay, R. L. F. 1983 *Earth and Planet Sci. Lett.*, 57, 139, $^{234}U/^{238}U$ activity ratios of dissolved uranium in groundwaters from a Jurassic Limestone aquifer in England.
57. Morgan-Jones, M. and Eggboro, M. D. 1981 *Q. J. eng. Geol.*, 14, 25, The hydrogeochemistry of the Jurassic Limestones in Gloucestershire, England.
58. Audley-Charles, M. G. 1970 *Q. J. geol. Soc. Lond.*, 126, 19, Stratigraphic correlation of the Triassic rocks of the British Isles.
59. Spears, D. A. and Reeves, M. J. 1975 *Q. J. eng. Geol.*, 8, 255, The influence of superficial deposits on groundwater quality in the Vale of York.
60. Sage, R. C. and Lloyd, J. W. 1978 *ibid*, 11, 209, Drift deposit influences in the Triassic Sandstone aquifer of N.W. Lancashire as inferred by hydrochemistry.
61. Edmunds, W. M. and Morgan-Jones, M. 1976 *ibid*, 9, 73, Geochemistry of groundwaters in the British Triassic Sandstones: 1 The Wolverhampton–East Shropshire area.
62. Bath, A. H., Edmunds, W. M. and Andrews, J. N. 1979 'Palaeoclimatic trends deduced from the hydrochemistry of a Triassic Sandstone aquifer, United Kingdom' in "Isotope Hydrology (Proc. Symp. Vienna 1978, Vol. II)", IAEA, Vienna.
63. Andrews, J. N. and Kay, R. L. F. 1983 *Isotope Geoscience*, 1, 101, The U contents and $^{234}U/^{238}U$ activity ratios of dissolved uranium in groundwaters from some Triassic Sandstones in England.
64. Walton, N. R. G. 1982 *J. IWES*, 36, 63, The origin of high iron concentrations in groundwater from the Triassic aquifer in East Devon.
65. Atkinson, T. C. 1977 'Carbon dioxide in the atmosphere of the unsaturated zone: an important control of groundwater hardness in Limestones' in "Proc. 12th Int. Ass. Hydrogeologists Cong.", Huntsville, Alabama, USA.
66. Pitty, A. F. 1968 *Nature, Lond.*, 217, 939, Calcium carbonate content of Karst water in relation to flow through time.
67. Smith, D. I., Atkinson, T. C. and Drew, D. P. 1976 'The hydrology of limestone terrains' in "The science of speleology", Ford, T. D. and Cullingford, C. H. D. (Eds.), Academic Press, London.
68. Presley, B. J., Brooks, R. R. and Kaplan, I. R. 1967, *J. Marine Res.*, 25, 355, A simple squeezer for removal of interstitial water from ocean sediments.
69. Edmunds, W. M. and Bath, A. H. 1976 *Environ. Sci. Technol.*, 10, 467, Centrifuge extraction and chemical analysis of interstitial waters.
70. Kinniburgh, D. G. and Miles, D. L. 1983 *ibid*, 17, 362, Extraction and chemical analysis of interstitial water from soils and rocks.
71. Patterson, R. J. *et al* 1977 *Can. J. Earth Sci.*, 15, 162, A coring and squeezing technique for the detailed study of subsurface water chemistry.
72. Tate, T. K., Robertson, A. S. and Gray, D. A. 1971 Wat. Supply Pap. No. 5, Inst. geol. Sci., London

"Borehole logging investigations in the Chalk of the Lambourne and Winterbourne valleys of Berkshire".

73. Kennedy, V. C. and Zellweger, G. W. 1974 *Wat. Res. Res.*, 10, 785, Filter pore size effects on the analysis of Al, Fe, Mn and Ti in water.

74. Barnes, R. A. 1975 *Chem. Geol.*, 15, 177, The determination of specific forms of aluminium in natural water.

75. Robertson, D. E. 1968 *Anal. Chim. Acta*, 42, 533, The adsorption of trace elements in sea water on various container surfaces.

76. Wagemann, R. and Graham, B. 1974 *Wat. Res.* 8, 407, Membrane and glass fibre filter contamination in chemical analysis of fresh water.

77. Edmunds, W. M. and Walton, N. R. G. 1980 'A geochemical and isotopic approach to recharge evaluation in semi-arid zones, past and present' in "Arid zone hydrology: investigation with isotope techniques", IAEA, Vienna.

78. Barnes, I. 1964 Wat. Supply Pap. US geol. Surv., No. 1535-H, "Field measurement of alkalinity and pH".

79. Whitfield, M. 1971 "Ion selective electrodes for the analysis of natural waters", Australian Marine Sciences Association, Sydney.

80. Bates, R. G. 1973 "Determination of pH; the theory and practice", John Wiley & Sons, New York.

81. Covington, A. K., Whalley, P. D. and Davison, W. 1983 *Analyst*, 108, 1528, Procedures for the measurement of pH in low ionic strength solutions, including freshwater.

82. Neal, C. and Thomas, A. G. 1985 *J. Hydrol.*, 79, 319, Field and laboratory measurement of pH in low conductivity natural waters.

83. Whitfield, M. 1974 *Limnol. Oceanogr.*, 19, 857, Thermodynamic limitations in the use of the platinum electrode in E_H measurements.

84. Jackson, R. E. and Patterson, R. J. 1982 *Wat. Res. Res.*, 18, 1255, Interpretation of pH and E_H trends in a fluvial–sand aquifer system.

85. Andrews, J. N. *et al* 1984 'Environmental isotope studies in two aquifer systems; a comparison of groundwater dating methods' in "Proc. Symp. Isotope Hydrology in Water Resources Development", IAEA, Vienna.

86. Andrews, J. N. *et al* 1982 *Nature, London*, 298, 339, The thermal springs of Bath.

87. Krouse, H. R. 1980 'Sulphur isotopes in our environment', Ch. 11 in "Handbook of environmental isotope geochemistry", Fritz, P. and Fontes, J-Ch. (Eds.), Elsevier, Amsterdam.

88. Létolle, R. 1980 'Nitrogen-15 in the natural environment', Ch. 10 in "Handbook of environmental isotope geochemistry", *ibid.*

89. Fritz, P. and Fontes, J-Ch. (Eds.) "Handbook of environmental isotope geochemistry", Elsevier, Amsterdam.

90. Dansgaard, W. 1964 *Tellus*, 16, 436, Stable isotopes in precipitation.

91. Bath, A. H. 1983 'Stable isotopic evidence for palaeo-recharge conditions of groundwater' in "Palaeoclimates and palaeowaters: a collection of environmental isotope studies", IAEA, Vienna.

92. Evans, G. V. *et al* 1979 'Some problems in the interpretation of isotopic measurements in United Kingdom aquifers' in "Isotope Hydrology (1978), Vol. 2", IAEA, Vienna.

93. Mook, W. G. 1980 'Carbon-14 in hydrogeological studies' in "Handbook of environmental geochemistry", Fritz, P. and Fontes, J-Ch. (Eds.), Elsevier, Amsterdam.

94. Reardon, E. J. and Fritz, P. 1978 *J. Hydrol.*, 36, 201, Computer modelling of groundwater ^{13}C and ^{14}C isotope compositions.

95. Fontes, J-Ch. and Garnier, J. M. 1979 *Wat. Res. Res.*, 15, 399, Determination of the initial ^{14}C activity of the total dissolved carbon; a review of existing models and a new approach.

96. Brown, E., Skougstad, M. W. and Fishman, M. J. 1970 'Methods for collection and analysis of water samples for dissolved minerals and gases' Ch. A1 in "Techniques of water resources investigations of the United States Geological Survey", US Dept. of the Interior, Washington, DC.

97. US Dept. of the Interior 1977 "National handbook of recommended methods for water data acquisition, US Dept. of the Interior, Reston, Virginia.

98. Cook, J. M. and Miles, D. L. 1980 Rep. Ser. Inst. Geol. Sci., 80/5 "Methods for the chemical analysis of groundwater", HMSO, London.

99. Commission of the European Communities 1980 "EC directive relating to the quality of water intended for human consumption (80/778/EEC)", CEC, Brussels.

100. UK Dept. of the Environment 1982 "EC directive relating to the quality of water intended for human consumption", Circular 20/82, DoE, London.

101. World Health Organization 1971 "International standards for drinking water, 3rd edition", WHO, Geneva.

102. Holden, W. S. (Ed.) 1970 "Water treatment and examination", Churchill, London.

103. Rubin, A. J. 1974 "Chemistry of water supply, treatment and distribution", Ann Arbor, Michigan.

104. Unesco/WHO 1978 "Water quality surveys: a guide for the collection and interpretation of water quality data; Studies and reports in hydrology No. 23", Unesco, Paris.

Foam/air circulation drilling in the Middle East

48 inch composite rock bit used for drilling in granites (Singapore)

Large hammer bit used for drilling hard rocks in West Africa

(All by courtesy of George Stow & Co Ltd)

Chapter 4

THEORY OF GROUNDWATER FLOW

1. INTRODUCTION

TO optimise the development of groundwater resources requires a quantitative understanding of the processes controlling the flow of water and the transport of pollutants in aquifers. This understanding is described by physical laws and mathematical analyses and is generally called the theory of groundwater flow. Groundwater flow theory is combined with geological and chemical sciences to form the framework of hydrogeological science.

2. HYDRAULIC CONDUCTIVITY

Experimental investigations of the flow of water through a porous medium were first reported in 1856 by Henri Darcy[1] and from his experiments the law of groundwater flow which bears his name was propounded. Darcy investigated the vertical flow of water through filter beds but for illustrative purposes it is more instructive to consider the flows in the apparatus of Fig. 4.1.

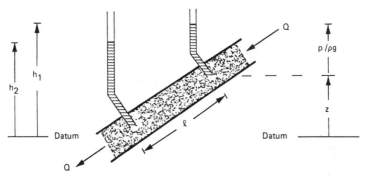

Fig. 4.1.   Darcy's law apparatus

Darcy's law may be written:

$$Q = K.A.\frac{h_1 - h_2}{l} \qquad \ldots \quad \ldots \quad \ldots \quad \ldots \quad \ldots \quad \ldots \quad \ldots \quad (1)$$

where Q is the rate of flow, A the cross-sectional area of the tube and K is a constant of proportionality, commonly called the hydraulic conductivity or permeability. It is a measure of the ease with which water can flow through a porous medium. Clearly it is not just a property of the medium but of the percolating fluid also. However, as our concern is with water only, it may be considered a property of the medium.

I.W.E.S., Groundwater: occurrence, development and protection, 1986, Chapter 4

Darcy's law is often expressed in terms of the specific discharge, defined as the flow rate per unit area:

$$v = \frac{Q}{A} \qquad \qquad \qquad \qquad \qquad \qquad \qquad \qquad \qquad (2)$$

so that:

$$v = K.\frac{h_1 - h_2}{l} \qquad \qquad \qquad \qquad \qquad \qquad \qquad \qquad (3)$$

or in differential form:

$$v = -K.\frac{dh}{dl} \qquad \qquad \qquad \qquad \qquad \qquad \qquad \qquad (4)$$

The negative sign indicates that the flow is in the direction of decreasing hydraulic head, h. The rate of change of hydraulic head with distance, $\frac{dh}{dl}$, is generally referred to as the hydraulic gradient.

The specific discharge, v, has the dimensions of velocity, and indeed is flow rate per unit area. However, the area over which the flow is measured is the total cross-sectional area of the porous medium and so includes areas of both the liquid and solid phases. The actual water velocity will be greater than the specific discharge and will be discussed in a later section.

3. HYDRAULIC HEAD

Before proceeding further it is necessary to consider what is meant by hydraulic head. In the apparatus of Fig. 4.1 reversal of the flow, Q, would result in reversal of the hydraulic gradient $\frac{dh}{dl}$. In this case water would flow "up hill". It is therefore not necessarily true that water flows from a higher elevation to a lower elevation. Nor is it necessarily true that water flows from a higher pressure to a lower pressure. If the flow in the apparatus of Fig. 4.1 is small, the water pressure at the measuring point nearest the outflow end will, in fact, exceed that at the measuring point nearest the inflow end. The hydraulic head measured by the piezometers in the apparatus of Fig. 4.1 may be expressed in terms of the elevation of, and the water pressure at, the measuring point as:

$$h = z + \frac{p}{\varrho g} \qquad \qquad \qquad \qquad \qquad \qquad \qquad \qquad (5)$$

where z is the elevation relative to datum,

   p is the water pressure relative to atmospheric pressure,

   ϱ is the water density and g the acceleration due to gravity.

This does not by itself justify Eqn. (5) as the definition of hydraulic head to be used in calculating flows by Darcy's law. However, Hubbert[2] showed from a consideration of potential energy that the hydraulic head defined in Eqn. (5) is identical to that embodied in Darcy's law. Following Hubbert, the hydraulic head is commonly referred to as the fluid potential. The two components of the hydraulic head, the elevation head and pressure head are shown in Fig. 4.1. The pressure head, like the elevation head, has dimensions of length and is commonly expressed in metres. A few examples will illustrate the relationship between hydraulic head, elevation head and pressure head.

(1) WATER LEVEL IN A PIEZOMETER

The two piezometers in the apparatus of Fig. 4.1 record water levels h_1 and h_2. Since there is no flow along the piezometers the hydraulic head in each is constant along its length. The hydraulic head at the measuring point in the sand column therefore equals the hydraulic head at the water surface. The pressure here is atmospheric so $p = 0$, and hence $h = z$, the elevation of the water surface. The water level in a piezometer therefore indicates the hydraulic head at the measuring point.

(2) VERTICAL FLOWS IN THE SATURATED ZONE

At the water surface the pressure head is zero (relative to atmospheric) so that the hydraulic head here is equal to the water level. If there are no vertical flows through the aquifer, the hydraulic head will be constant over the full saturated depth and equal to the water table elevation. The pressure will increase with depth in a hydrostatic manner. It will be more common, however, to find vertical flows, indicating that the hydraulic head changes with depth. In this case the water pressure will deviate from the hydrostatic distribution.

(3) VERTICAL FLOWS IN THE UNSATURATED ZONE

In the zone above the water table the pores are occupied by water and air. The surface tension forces acting at the air-water interfaces are balanced by a pressure differential between the air and water phases. The water pressure will be less than atmospheric pressure so that the pressure head will be negative, but Eqns. (1) to (5) are still applicable. Clearly a piezometer of the type shown in Fig. 4.1 cannot be used to measure hydraulic head in the unsaturated zone as this instrument requires a positive pressure head. A manometer of the type shown in Fig. 4.2 may be used under some conditions.

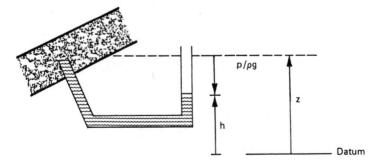

Fig. 4.2. Measurement of head in the unsaturated zone

(4) SALINE INTRUSION—TWO-FLUID HYDROSTATICS

Fig. 4.3 shows a cross-section through an aquifer in which a body of saline water in continuity with the sea underlies a body of fresh water. It is convenient to take sea level as datum for measurement of the elevation head, though selection of any other datum would yield the same results as those which follow.

It is assumed that there are no vertical components of flow in the fresh water zone and that the saline water is static. The hydraulic heads in the two fluids at the position shown may be written:

in the fresh water

$$h_f = z_f = -z_s + p/\varrho_f g \quad \dots \qquad \dots \qquad \dots \qquad \dots \qquad \dots \qquad \dots \qquad \dots \qquad (6)$$

in the saline water

$$h_s = 0 = -z_s + p/\varrho_s g \quad \dots \qquad \dots \qquad \dots \qquad \dots \qquad \dots \qquad \dots \qquad \dots \qquad (7)$$

Eqn. (6) expresses the fact that the hydraulic head in the fresh water zone is uniform over the full depth of fresh water, and hence equal to both the elevation above datum of the water table and to the sum of the elevation head and pressure head at the interface.

Eqn. (7) expresses the fact that the hydraulic head in the saline water zone is uniform over the entire zone, and hence equal to both the elevation of the saline water body at the coast and to the sum of the elevation head and pressure head at the interface. The pressure at the interface must be the same in both fluids and may be eliminated from the equations to give:

$$z_s = \frac{\varrho_f}{\varrho_s - \varrho_f} \cdot z_f \quad \dots \qquad \dots \qquad \dots \qquad \dots \qquad \dots \qquad \dots \qquad \dots \qquad (8)$$

We thus achieve the Ghyben-Herzberg relationship that the depth to the interface below sea level is about 40 times the fresh water head above sea level.

(5) APPLICATION OF DARCY'S LAW

Consider the piezometer installations shown in Fig. 4.4.

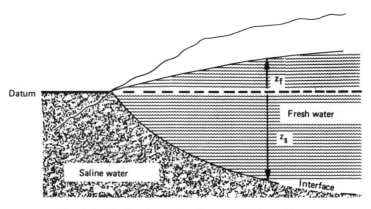

Fig. 4.3.   Saline intrusion in a coastal aquifer

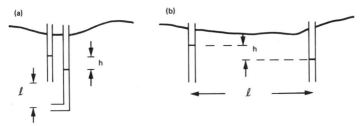

Fig. 4.4. Piezometer installations in the saturated zone

In the case shown in Fig. 4.4(a), the hydraulic gradient over the vertical interval between the two open ends of the piezometers is:

$$\text{hydraulic gradient} = \frac{h}{l} \quad \dots \quad \dots \quad \dots \quad \dots \quad \dots \quad \dots \quad (9)$$

Applying Darcy's law, the downward rate of flow of groundwater may be equated to:

$$\text{flow rate} = K.\frac{h}{l} \quad \dots \quad \dots \quad \dots \quad \dots \quad \dots \quad \dots \quad \dots \quad (10)$$

where K is the hydraulic conductivity. If K is in units of m/d, then the flow rate will also be in units of m/d. The downward flow rate through a cross-sectional area of 1 m² will be:

$$\text{volumetric flow rate} = K.\frac{h}{l} \, \text{m}^3/\text{d} \quad \dots \quad \dots \quad \dots \quad \dots \quad \dots \quad (11)$$

In the case shown in Fig. 4.4(b), the horizontal component of flow may be determined as:

$$\text{flow rate} = K.\frac{h}{l} \quad \dots \quad \dots \quad \dots \quad \dots \quad \dots \quad \dots \quad \dots \quad (12)$$

or:

$$\text{volumetric flow rate} = K.\frac{h}{l} \, \text{m}^3/\text{d}$$

This type of analysis is commonly applied to groundwater level contour maps (Fig. 4.5). The contour map would be constructed from water levels measured in piezometers and wells, and is generally assumed to indicate the average hydraulic head over the full saturated depth.

If the contour interval is h, the rate of flow between points A and B may be expressed:

$$\text{flow rate} = K.\frac{h}{l} \quad \dots \quad \dots \quad \dots \quad \dots \quad \dots \quad \dots \quad \dots \quad (13)$$

where K is the hydraulic conductivity.

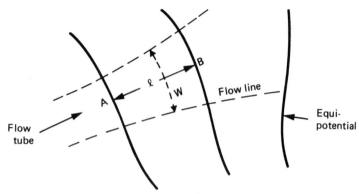

Fig. 4.5.   Contour map flow analysis

If the saturated depth is b, the rate of flow along the stream tube shown in Fig. 4.5 is:

$$\text{volumetric flow rate} = K.bW. \frac{h}{l} \quad \dots \quad \dots \quad \dots \quad \dots \quad \dots \quad (14)$$

where the flow rate is now a volumetric flow rate measured over the full saturated depth.

The product bK is commonly called the transmissivity and expresses the ability of an aquifer to transmit water over its full depth of saturation. Eqn. (14) may then be expressed:

$$\text{volumetric flow rate} = T.W. \frac{h}{l} (or \ T.W.i) \quad \dots \quad \dots \quad \dots \quad (15)$$

where i is the hydraulic gradient in the direction of flow. Eqn. (15) is a widely used derivative of Darcy's law.

In the cases of Fig. 4.4(b) and Fig. 4.5 analysis permits the horizontal flow rate only to be determined. There may be vertical flows but these cannot be calculated. Similarly, the arrangement of Fig. 4.4(a) allows only vertical flows to be measured.

4. STORAGE

The porosity of an aquifer formation is the fraction of volume occupied by void space. In the saturated zone this void space will be filled with water. A simple method of measuring porosity is effected by weighing a sample when saturated and again after heating to complete dryness. The loss of weight may be equated to the volume of water which fills the void space when the sample is saturated and the porosity may be determined by dividing this volume by the total volume of the sample. If all the grains of the porous matrix were equally sized spheres, the porosity would range between 26 and 48 per cent depending on the packing arrangement. This range is, in fact, typical of sands and gravels. In most porous media however, there will be a wide range of particle sizes so that interstices between larger grains will be partially filled with smaller grains resulting in a reduction in porosity. The porosities of some typical porous media are given in Table 4.I.

TABLE **4.I.**   **Typical Porosity Ranges**

Medium	Porosity (per cent)
Clay	45-55
Sand	35-40
Gravel	20-40
Chalk	20-50
Sandstone	15-30
Limestone	1-10

Not all of the water stored in the interstices of a rock is available for exploitation. If the water table is lowered by natural recession or by groundwater pumping, water will drain from the pore space, but some water will be retained. The specific retention is defined as the volume of water which a unit volume of rock will retain against the force of gravity when drained from a saturated state. The volume of water which drains is termed the specific yield. The forces which retain water in the pore space are primarily those of surface tension and adsorption. Because of surface tension water will be more strongly held in small pores than in large pores, so that a dominant factor in the relationship between specific yield and specific retention is the distribution of pore sizes in the rock. On the other hand, adsorption is a surface area dependent phenomenon and will be important in those media having a high specific surface area such as clays. The gravity drainage of a porous medium from full saturation is not an instantaneous process. As water drains from the pores and is replaced by air, so the hydraulic conductivity will be progressively reduced, delaying further drainage.

The specific yield is the volume of water released from storage in an unconfined aquifer per unit surface area of aquifer per unit decline in water table elevation. It has already been shown that unit decline in water table elevation is equivalent to unit decline in hydraulic head, so that specific yield may be defined in terms of hydraulic head. In a confined aquifer specific storage is defined as the volume of water released from storage in a unit volume of aquifer for a unit decline in hydraulic head. Water is not released, however, by draining of the pore space as occurs in a water table aquifer. Instead, the reduction in hydraulic head results in a reduction in fluid pressure (Eqn. (5)) which causes (Jacob[3]):

(a) a compaction of the aquifer structure and
(b) an expansion of the water.

Both result in a release of water from storage. It may be shown[3] that the specific storage S_s is given by:

$$S_s = \varrho g \left(\alpha + n\beta \right) \qquad \ldots \qquad \ldots \qquad \ldots \qquad \ldots \qquad \ldots \qquad \ldots \qquad \ldots \qquad (16)$$

where

ϱ = water density (kg/m^3)
α = aquifer compressibility (m^2/N)
β = water compressibility (m^2/N)
n = porosity

In general, the dominant contribution to specific storage comes from the aquifer compressibility.

In an unconfined aquifer, a decline in hydraulic head will result in release of water from storage by drainage of the pore space through which the water table falls and release of water from aquifer compaction and water expansion. However, the specific storage will usually be much smaller than the specific yield and may be ignored in unconfined aquifer studies.

The coefficient of storage, S, may be applied to both confined and unconfined aquifers and is defined as the volume of water released from storage per unit surface area of aquifer, per unit decline in hydraulic head. For unconfined conditions the coefficient of storage is equal to the specific yield. For confined conditions, the coefficient of storage is given by:

$$S = bS_s \qquad \ldots \qquad \ldots \qquad \ldots \qquad \ldots \qquad \ldots \qquad \ldots \qquad \ldots \qquad \ldots \qquad \ldots \qquad (17)$$

where b is the saturated thickness. It is, therefore, implicitly assumed that the hydraulic head declines by one unit over the full depth.

Typically the storage coefficient in an unconfined aquifer will be in the range 0.01 to 0.4, whilst in a confined aquifer values will generally range between 0.00001 and 0.001. It will be evident that for a given fall in hydraulic head the storage change in an unconfined aquifer will be much greater than that in a confined aquifer.

Changes in storage in an aquifer are usually reversible so that the relationship between storage and hydraulic head is the same for both falling and rising head. The only condition under which this is not valid is where an aquifer, or more probably an aquitard, has consolidated following intensive groundwater pumping. The consolidation, which may be manifested in land subsidence, can result in an irreversible change in hydraulic properties of the water-bearing stratum (Freeze and Cherry[4]).

5. SECONDARY CHARACTERISTICS

The concepts of hydraulic conductivity, porosity and storage have so far been described in terms of water movement through a porous medium. In many aquifers, however, water moves predominantly through fractures or solution channels. In these cases the hydraulic conductivity and porosity are said to be of secondary origin. Water movement through fractures or solution channels may be extremely rapid and turbulent. Under these conditions Darcy's law would not be valid and a number of workers have proposed modifications to Eqn. (4) (Halek and Svec[5]). Where the network of openings is relatively dense, however, it appears that over a large enough sample of the aquifer Darcy's law may be applied without modification. This has been common practice in the UK both in the analyses of pumping tests and in the development of groundwater models. One important feature which has received attention is the variation of aquifer properties with depth resulting from the non-uniform distribution in depth of fissures. Fissures may also play an important role in solute transport processes as discussed in a later section.

Secondary openings resulting from tectonic movements and solution enlargement are particularly important in the major aquifers of the UK, the Chalk, the Sandstones and Limestones. Laboratory measurements of specific yield and hydraulic conductivity will, in these aquifers, be of very limited use in field investigations. Indeed, the concept of hydraulic conductivity in a fractured or fissured aquifer is not very meaningful and it is common practice to describe the ability of an aquifer to transmit water by its transmissivity. Transmissivity has already been defined as the product of the hydraulic conductivity and the saturated depth. In an aquifer having a hydraulic conductivity which varies with depth, as it will do for example in a fissured aquifer, the transmissivity will be given by:

$$T = \int K\,dz \qquad \ldots \qquad \ldots \qquad \ldots \qquad \ldots \qquad \ldots \qquad \ldots \qquad \ldots \qquad \ldots \qquad (18)$$

where z is the depth and the integral is over the full saturated depth. In field determinations of aquifer properties, by test pumping for example, it is the transmissivity which is determined. Only in exceptional circumstances will the distribution of hydraulic conductivity with depth be measured.

Typical ranges of specific yield and transmissivity for some UK aquifers are given in Table 4.II.

Table 4.II. Specific Yield and Transmissivity of Some UK Aquifers

Aquifer	Specific yield (per cent)	Transmissivity (m^2/d)	Flow type*
Sand	10-20	50- 200	I
Gravel	15-25	250-2000	I
Chalk	1- 4	20-2000	F
Sandstone	5-20	15-1500	I + F
Limestone	0.5- 5	100-4000	F

*I = Intergranular F = Fracture or Fissure

6. EQUATIONS OF GROUNDWATER FLOW

Darcy's law allows flow rates to be related to hydraulic head from knowledge of hydraulic conductivity or transmissivity, and changes in hydraulic head may be related to changes in storage through the concept of storage coefficient. By combining these relationships an equation describing the flow of water through a porous medium may be derived. The equation can take various forms depending on whether the flow is assumed to be one-, two- or three-dimensional and on whether steady state or transient conditions apply. Transient conditions apply when the hydraulic head changes with time. This is, of course, the usual case. However, it is often advantageous to consider steady state conditions in which the hydraulic head does not change with time but is in balance with the aquifer inputs and outputs.

The equation of flow will first be developed for one-dimensional steady state conditions before introducing time dependence into the formulation. The most commonly used equation for two-dimensional transient flow will then be developed.

One-Dimensional Steady State Flow

Consider flow in the X-direction only as, for example, along the sand-filled tube of Fig. 4.1. The flow equation is derived by evaluating the flows into and out of a thin slice of the tube (Fig. 4.6).

Under steady state conditions there will be no change in storage within the sand, so that:

$$Q_{in} = Q_{out} \qquad \ldots \qquad \ldots \qquad \ldots \qquad \ldots \qquad \ldots \qquad \ldots \qquad \ldots \qquad \ldots \qquad (19)$$

and, applying Darcy's law, Eqn. (4) gives:

$$-KA\frac{dh}{dx}\bigg|_x = -KA\frac{dh}{dx}\bigg|_{x+\Delta x} \qquad \ldots \qquad \ldots \qquad \ldots \qquad \ldots \qquad \ldots \qquad (20)$$

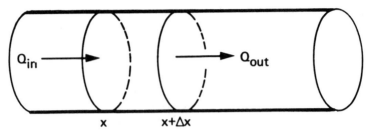

Fig. 4.6.   One-dimensional flow formulation

The suffices indicate that one derivative is evaluated at position x, and the other at position $x + \Delta x$, where Δx is a small increment in x. By the rules of differential calculus, Eqn. (20) reduces to:

$$K \frac{d^2h}{dx^2} = 0 \qquad \ldots \qquad \ldots \qquad \ldots \qquad \ldots \qquad \ldots \qquad \ldots \qquad \ldots \qquad \ldots \qquad (21)$$

if K is uniform along the tube, or:

$$\frac{d}{dx}\left(K \frac{dh}{dx} \right) = 0 \qquad \ldots \qquad \ldots \qquad \ldots \qquad \ldots \qquad \ldots \qquad \ldots \qquad \ldots \qquad (22)$$

if K is variable along the tube.

Either equation describes the variation in hydraulic head in one-dimensional flow. For any particular case the equation may be solved when boundary conditions are specified. In the apparatus of Fig. 4.1, for example, the boundary conditions may be written:

$$\begin{aligned} h &= h_1 \text{ at } x = 0 \\ h &= h_2 \text{ at } x = l \end{aligned} \qquad \ldots \qquad \ldots \qquad \ldots \qquad \ldots \qquad \ldots \qquad \ldots \qquad (23)$$

where x is distance along the tube measured from the piezometer recording the level h_1. The solution of Eqn. (21), subject to these boundary conditions, is:

$$h = h_1 + \frac{x}{l}(h_2 - h_1) \qquad \ldots \qquad \ldots \qquad \ldots \qquad \ldots \qquad \ldots \qquad \ldots \qquad (24)$$

so that the hydraulic head, h, falls linearly between the two piezometers. The boundary conditions could have been specified differently, as in Eqn. (25):

$$h = h_1 \text{ at } x = 0$$
$$\qquad \ldots \qquad \ldots \qquad \ldots \qquad \ldots \qquad \ldots \qquad \ldots \qquad (25)$$
$$Q = -KA \frac{dh}{dx} \text{ at } x = l$$

The solution of Eqn. (21) subject to these boundary conditions is:

$$h = h_1 - \frac{Q}{KA} x \qquad \ldots \qquad \ldots \qquad \ldots \qquad \ldots \qquad \ldots \qquad \ldots \qquad (26)$$

The reader may verify that solutions (24) and (26) are exactly equivalent. It is a general feature of the groundwater flow equations that boundary conditions may be specified in terms of prescribed hydraulic heads or prescribed flows.

For one-dimensional flow in an aquifer with transmissivity T, Eqn. (22) becomes:

$$\frac{d}{dx}\left(T\frac{dh}{dx}\right) = 0 \qquad \dots \quad \dots \quad \dots \quad \dots \quad \dots \quad \dots \quad \dots \quad (27)$$

The hydraulic head is equal to the water table elevation in an unconfined aquifer when there are no vertical flows.

ONE-DIMENSIONAL TRANSIENT FLOW

Considering again the flows in the apparatus of Fig. 4.6, the net rate of flow into the slice may be equated to the rate of increase of storage within the slice. That is:

$$Q_{in} - Q_{out} = S_s.A.\Delta x.\ \frac{dh}{dt} \qquad \dots \quad \dots \quad \dots \quad \dots \quad \dots \quad \dots \quad (28)$$

where S_s is the specific storage as previously defined. Applying differential calculus, as before, yields the equation:

$$\frac{\partial}{\partial x}\left(K\frac{\partial h}{\partial x}\right) = S_s\frac{\partial h}{\partial t} \qquad \dots \quad \dots \quad \dots \quad \dots \quad \dots \quad \dots \quad (29)$$

For transient, one-dimensional aquifer flow Eqn. (29) becomes:

$$\frac{\partial}{\partial x}\left(T\frac{\partial h}{\partial x}\right) = S\frac{\partial h}{\partial t} \qquad \dots \quad \dots \quad \dots \quad \dots \quad \dots \quad \dots \quad (30)$$

where S is the storage coefficient. The derivatives in Eqns. (29) and (30) are equivalent to those in Eqns. (22) and (27) but in the transient case the hydraulic head is a function of two independent variables, distance and time, and so partial derivatives must be used.

To solve the transient flow equation it is necessary to specify boundary conditions and, in addition, an initial condition. This is the hydraulic head, or water level, at the initial time. For example, consider the decay of a groundwater mound (Fig. 4.7).

The boundary conditions may be written:

$$h = H \text{ at } x = 0 \text{ and at } x = l \qquad \dots \quad \dots \quad \dots \quad \dots \quad \dots \quad \dots \quad (31)$$

The solution depends on the aquifer properties T and S, and on the shape of the water table at time $t = o$. For one case, that of a sinusoidal initial water table, Eqn. (30) may be readily solved. Thus with initial condition:

$$h = H + A.\sin\left(\frac{\pi x}{l}\right) \dots \quad \dots \quad \dots \quad \dots \quad \dots \quad \dots \quad \dots \quad (32)$$

the solution is:

$$h = H + A.\sin\left(\frac{\pi x}{l}\right).\exp\left(-\frac{T}{S}.\frac{\pi^2}{l^2}.t\right)\dots \quad \dots \quad \dots \quad \dots \quad (33)$$

Water levels decay exponentially at a rate depending on the ratio T/Sl^2 as water flows out of the aquifer at the two constant head boundaries. For a high value of the ratio the mound decays rapidly, and for a low value the decay is slow. The solution

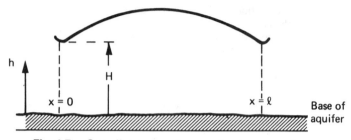

Fig. 4.7.   One-dimensional groundwater mound

would be different for any other initial condition, though the rate of decay would again be controlled by the ratio T/Sl^2.

TRANSIENT TWO-DIMENSIONAL FLOW

The most widely applied form of the groundwater flow equation is that developed for two-dimensional, transient flow. This equation is commonly used for catchment studies of both confined and unconfined flow. The equation is formulated in terms of the average hydraulic head at each point in the catchment. The average, in this case, is taken over the full saturated depth, and may be equated to the water level in a borehole which is open to the aquifer over the full saturated depth. In an unconfined aquifer, the average hydraulic head may be equated to the water table elevation if vertical flows are small.

The equation of flow, equivalent to the one-dimensional Eqn. (30), may be written:

$$\frac{\partial}{\partial x}\left(T_x \frac{\partial h}{\partial x} \right) + \frac{\partial}{\partial y}\left(T_y \frac{\partial h}{\partial y} \right) = S \frac{\partial h}{\partial t} \qquad \ldots \qquad \ldots \qquad \ldots \qquad \ldots \qquad (34)$$

where x and y are orthogonal space co-ordinates.

The hydraulic head is now a function of three independent variables—x, y and t, The transmissivity is a function of position and direction.

In a fractured aquifer, for example, tectonic movements could result in better developed openings in one direction than in another. If T_x and T_y differ the aquifer is said to be anisotropic; if they are the same the aquifer is said to be isotropic. The transmissivities can also vary with position. When this is the case the aquifer is said to be heterogeneous. When the transmissivities are spatially uniform the aquifer is homogeneous.

TABLE 4.III.   Specification of Boundary Conditions

Boundary Condition	Specification
Surface water in intimate contact with groundwater	Prescribed head
Partially penetrating river	Flow proportional to head difference between river water and groundwater
Groundwater catchment boundary	Prescribed zero flow
Termination of aquifer	Prescribed zero flow

The solution of Eqn. (34) yields the variation of hydraulic head, or water level, over the catchment at all times from the initial time. Boundary conditions must be specified at all points around the perimeter of the catchment and an initial distribution of h is required. As has already been demonstrated, the boundary conditions can take the form of prescribed heads or prescribed flows or, in some cases, a combination of the two. Some of the more commonly used boundary conditions are given in Table 4.III.

7. RECHARGE AND DISCHARGE

The effects of recharge to, and discharge from, an aquifer may be included in the flow equation. If the recharge rate is p (L/T) and the discharge rate q (L/T) then, with the two-dimensional formulation, the equation of flow becomes:

$$\frac{\partial}{\partial x}\left(T_x \frac{\partial h}{\partial x}\right) + \frac{\partial}{\partial y}\left(T_y \frac{\partial h}{\partial y}\right) = S\frac{\partial h}{\partial t} - p + q \quad \dots \quad \dots \quad \dots \quad (35)$$

In an unconfined aquifer the recharge rate p may represent percolation from the unsaturated zone, due to rainfall, in which case p will vary with time. In a semi-confined aquifer the recharge rate p may represent leakage from overlying or underlying strata. Hantush[6] proposed that such recharge be evaluated as:

$$p = \frac{K'}{m}(H-h) \quad \dots \quad \dots \quad \dots \quad \dots \quad \dots \quad \dots \quad \dots \quad \dots \quad (36)$$

where H is the water level in the overlying or underlying aquifer,
K' is the hydraulic conductivity of the intervening aquitard,
and m is the thickness of the aquitard.

It will be seen that this is a direct application of Darcy's law with the assumption that the external hydraulic head, H, is constant. The equations of flow, (35) and (36), have been successfully applied to regional groundwater studies (Prickett[7] and Oakes and Skinner[8]) and to pumping tests.

If steady conditions prevail the hyrdaulic heads, or water levels, will not change with time and the time derivative in Eqn. (35) may be set to zero. The resulting equation is the two-dimensional, steady state equation:

$$\frac{\partial}{\partial x}\left(T_x \frac{\partial h}{\partial x}\right) + \frac{\partial}{\partial y}\left(T_y \frac{\partial h}{\partial y}\right) + p - q = 0 \quad \dots \quad \dots \quad \dots \quad (37)$$

Since water cannot be released from or taken into storage, the recharge must exactly balance the discharge. Flows into or out of the aquifer at the boundaries will contribute to this mass balance, as well as the recharge and discharge rates which appear explicitly in Eqn. (37). This equation is, generally, much easier to solve than the transient flow equation but is, of course, less widely applicable.

8. SOLVING GROUNDWATER FLOW EQUATIONS

In studies of groundwater resource assessment, development or management it is often required to predict the hydraulic heads which will prevail under postulated demand patterns. This prediction is achieved by solving the appropriate equations of groundwater flow subject to specified boundary and initial conditions. The

TABLE 4.IV.   Common Forms of the Groundwater Flow Equation

Geometry	Formulation	Equation of flow	Application
Cartesian	2-dimensional, plan, transient	$\dfrac{\partial}{\partial x}\left(T_x\,\dfrac{\partial h}{\partial x}\right) + \dfrac{\partial}{\partial y}\left(T_y\,\dfrac{\partial h}{\partial y}\right) = S\,\dfrac{\partial h}{\partial t} - p + q$	Confined aquifers with zero (or small) vertical flows, often applied to unconfined aquifers; boundary and initial conditions required.
Cartesian	2-dimensional, plan, steady state	$\dfrac{\partial}{\partial x}\left(T_x\,\dfrac{\partial h}{\partial x}\right) + \dfrac{\partial}{\partial y}\left(T_y\,\dfrac{\partial h}{\partial y}\right) + p - q = 0$	Confined aquifers with zero (or small) vertical flows; often applied to unconfined aquifers; useful for simulation of average annual water levels; boundary conditions required.
Cartesian	3-dimensional, transient	$\dfrac{\partial}{\partial x}\left(K_x\,\dfrac{\partial h}{\partial x}\right) + \dfrac{\partial}{\partial y}\left(K_y\,\dfrac{\partial h}{\partial y}\right) + \dfrac{\partial}{\partial z}\left(K_z\,\dfrac{\partial h}{\partial z}\right) = S_s\,\dfrac{\partial h}{\partial t}$	Saturated zone; if unconfined a water table boundary condition is needed; other boundary and initial conditions required; little used.
Cylindrical	2-dimensional, transient	$\dfrac{\partial}{\partial r}\left(K_r\,\dfrac{\partial h}{\partial r}\right) + \dfrac{K_r}{r}\,\dfrac{\partial h}{\partial r} + \dfrac{\partial}{\partial z}\left(K_z\,\dfrac{\partial h}{\partial z}\right) = S_s\,\dfrac{\partial h}{\partial t}$	Saturated zone problems having a radially symmetric flow field, e.g. close to a pumped well; initial and boundary conditions required, including at water table in unconfined aquifer.
Cylindrical	1-dimensional, transient	$\dfrac{\partial}{\partial r}\left(T_r\,\dfrac{\partial h}{\partial r}\right) + \dfrac{T_r}{r}\,\dfrac{\partial h}{\partial r} = S\,\dfrac{\partial h}{\partial t} - p$	Radially symmetric flow in confined aquifers with zero (or small) vertical flows; often applied to unconfined flows; commonly used in numerical simulation of pumping tests; boundary and initial conditions required.

aquifer, or the boundary and initial conditions, will invariably be too complex to allow an exact solution of the governing flow equation by analytical methods. Nevertheless, these direct solutions of the type developed in Eqn. (33) can be of great use in the early stages of a groundwater study. Analytical solutions also form the basis of pumping test analyses. In these cases, the aquifer is usually approximated as an isotropic, homogeneous medium and the boundary and initial conditions are also simplified. Solutions to the steady state flow equation are often employed to provide predictions of average water levels. A number of solutions to simple flow problems will be developed in the next section. In those cases where analytical methods cannot handle the complexity of the aquifer or its boundary and initial conditions, approximate solutions may be obtained by mathematical modelling or simulation techniques. These are fully described in Chapter 6.

The equations of flow have, so far, been developed in cartesian co-ordinates for one and two-dimensional flow. Other co-ordinate systems may be used and may make solution of the equations simpler in some cases. The most commonly used forms of the groundwater flow equation are given in Table 4.IV.

9. GROUNDWATER MOVEMENT

In cases where boundary conditions are simple the groundwater flow equation may often be solved analytically. A number of such solutions have been developed for the analysis of pumping tests under a variety of conditions and these are fully described in Chapter 5. Analytical solutions have the advantage over numerical solutions that the manner in which the various parameters affect the solution is immediately obvious. In this section solutions to a variety of regional flow problems will be described. In many cases these solutions can be put to practical use even though the aquifer may be idealised and the boundary conditions simple. An important principle used to develop some analytical solutions must be considered first.

SUPERPOSITION

In most of its forms, the equation of groundwater flow is linear so that if two independent solutions can be found, say h_1 and h_2, then any linear combination, $ah_1 + bh_2$ is also a solution subject to boundary conditions being satisfied. This is easily verified in the case of Eqn. (34), for example. The principle of superposition is a very powerful analytical tool and has been used extensively in the development of solutions to the groundwater flow equations (Bear[9]).

FLOW TO A RIVER

The flow of groundwater through an unconfined aquifer towards a river is described approximately by Eqn. (38):

$$\frac{\partial}{\partial x}\left(T_x \frac{\partial h}{\partial x}\right) + \frac{\partial}{\partial y}\left(T_y \frac{\partial h}{\partial y}\right) = S \frac{\partial h}{\partial t} - p \qquad \dots \qquad \dots \qquad \dots \qquad (38)$$

For simplicity it will be assumed that the aquifer is homogeneous and that transmissivity is constant, independent of water level h. If the recharge rate, p, is constant in space and time then the steady flow of water towards a long, straight river at $x = 0$ is given by:

$$T\frac{d^2h}{dx^2} + p = 0 \dots \qquad \dots \qquad \dots \qquad \dots \qquad \dots \qquad \dots \qquad \dots \qquad \dots \qquad (39)$$

Several assumptions have been made to realise Eqn. (39) and as with any solution of the groundwater flow equations, those assumptions will need to be carefully assessed in any particular case. If we select as datum the level of water in the river then we may write as a boundary condition:

$$h = 0 \text{ at } x = 0 \quad \dots \quad \dots \quad \dots \quad \dots \quad \dots \quad \dots \quad \dots \quad \dots \quad (40)$$

Because the hydraulic head is constant with depth it is implicitly assumed that the river fully penetrates the aquifer. A second boundary condition may be specified at the groundwater divide:

$$\frac{dh}{dx} = 0 \text{ at } x = L = l \quad \dots \quad \dots \quad \dots \quad \dots \quad \dots \quad \dots \quad (41)$$

The conceptual model for this problem is shown in Fig. 4.8.
Eqns. (39), (40) and (41) may be readily solved to give:

$$h = \frac{p}{T}\left(lx - \frac{x^2}{2} \right) \quad \dots \quad \dots \quad \dots \quad \dots \quad \dots \quad \dots \quad \dots \quad (42)$$

The assumption that the recharge rate, p, is constant with time is, of course, completely unrealistic. However, if p is equal to the average annual recharge rate, then Eqn. (42) will give the mean water table elevation during an average year. The elevation of the water table at the groundwater divide is given by:

$$h_L = \frac{pl^2}{2T} \quad \dots \quad \dots \quad \dots \quad \dots \quad \dots \quad \dots \quad \dots \quad \dots \quad (43)$$

which may be used to obtain an estimate of the average catchment transmissivity in an unconfined aquifer draining to a river.

The validity of this formula may be demonstrated by its application to a chalk catchment in East Anglia (Oakes[10]). The river draining the catchment is not straight, nor is the groundwater divide. Nevertheless, it is possible to select a typical flowline and to estimate the parameters of Eqn. (43) as:

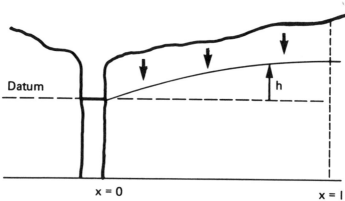

Fig. 4.8. Section through idealised river-aquifer system

$$p = 0.18 \text{ m/a}$$
$$= 5.0 \; 10^{-4} \text{ m/d}$$
$$h_L = 70 \text{ m}$$
$$l = 11 \text{ km}$$

Applying Eqn. (43) gives a mean catchment transmissivity of:

$$T = 430 \text{ m}^2/\text{d}$$

The catchment was the subject of a detailed groundwater model study in which the transmissivity was estimated to range from 50 to 1000 m^2/d, with an average value of about 450 m^2/d.

The assumption that the river fully penetrates the aquifer is not as restrictive as it would first appear. A boundary condition which more realistically represents the convergence of flow lines towards a river can be specified in place of Eqn. (40). The solution obtained will, in most cases, be very similar to Eqn. (42).

Change in River Stage

If an aquifer discharges to a river, groundwater levels will fluctuate in response to changes in river stage. In the absence of stage changes, groundwater levels will vary with infiltration or pumping. We may, however, apply the principle of superposition to show that the fluctuation in groundwater levels due to changes in river stage only is given by:

$$T \frac{\partial^2 h}{\partial x^2} = S \frac{\partial h}{\partial t} \qquad \dots \qquad \dots \qquad \dots \qquad \dots \qquad \dots \qquad \dots \qquad \dots \qquad (44)$$

where h is the increase or decrease in groundwater level due to stage change.

In formulating Eqn. (44) we have made the usual assumptions of:
(i) horizontal flow and hence, full penetration of the river;
(ii) transmissivity independent of saturated depth.

The conceptual model is shown in Fig. 4.9.

If we assume a sinusoidal fluctuation in river stage and that there is no response to stage changes at large distances from the river, then the boundary conditions may be written:

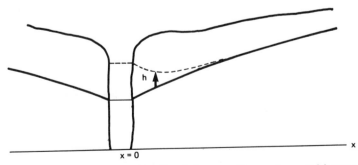

Fig. 4.9. Section through idealised river-aquifer system, subject to river stage changes

$h = h_o \sin wt$ at $x = 0$

$h = 0 \qquad$ at $x = \infty$ $\quad \cdots \quad \cdots \quad \cdots \quad \cdots \quad \cdots \quad \cdots \quad$ (45)

After some time has elapsed, the groundwater levels will fluctuate in cyclic equilibrium and under these conditions the solution of Eqn. (44) is (Walton[11]):

$$h = h_o \exp(-x \sqrt{wS/2T}) \sin(wt - x \sqrt{wS/2T}) \quad \cdots \quad \cdots \quad \cdots \quad (46)$$

The range of water level fluctuations in an observation well at a distance x from the river is given by:

$$2h_{max} = 2 h_o \exp(-x \sqrt{wS/2T}) \quad \cdots \quad \cdots \quad \cdots \quad \cdots \quad \cdots \quad (47)$$

and clearly decreases rapidly as x increases. The sinusoidal fluctuations in river stage cause waves to be transmitted through the aquifer. The velocity with which these waves propagate through the aquifer may be calculated to be:

$$\text{velocity of propagation} = \sqrt{2wT/S} \quad \cdots \quad \cdots \quad \cdots \quad \cdots \quad (48)$$

The controlling parameter is the aquifer diffusivity, T/S, which occurs in many analytical solutions to the transient groundwater flow equation. It may be possible to use Eqn. (46), (47) or (48) to calculate the aquifer diffusivity when the river stage is fluctuating. Solutions may also be obtained for other boundary conditions—for example, an abrupt change in river stage[9].

An important result which follows from the principle of superposition should be noted. It has already been stated that Eqn. (44) gives the change in groundwater level due to change in river stage alone. In particular, this equation will apply if there is a strong regional flow to the river as indicated in Fig. 4.9 by the steep groundwater gradient. In this instance groundwater flow may always be towards the river, even when the river stage is oscillating. Waves will be transmitted through the aquifer, according to Eqn. (46), but these waves need not cause groundwater flow to be reversed. This principle is found in many other cases, that head changes may be transmitted through an aquifer just as readily when the regional flow is in a contrary direction, as when it is in the same direction.

WELL IN A CIRCULAR ISLAND

Steady flow to a well completely penetrating a homogeneous aquifer may be described by the equation:

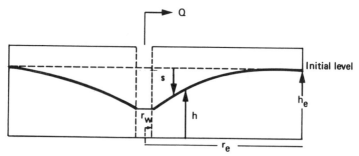

Fig. 4.10.   Steady radial flow to a pumping well

$$T \left(\frac{d^2h}{dr^2} + \frac{1}{r} \frac{dh}{dr} \right) = 0 \qquad \ldots \quad \ldots \quad \ldots \quad \ldots \quad \ldots \quad \ldots \quad (49)$$

For a well pumping at a steady rate, Q, the boundary condition at the well face may be written:

$$2\pi r_w T \frac{dh}{dr} = Q \text{ at } r = r_w \qquad \ldots \quad \ldots \quad \ldots \quad \ldots \quad \ldots \quad (50)$$

where r_w is the well radius. If the water level is maintained constant at the outer boundary (Fig. 4.10) then:

$$h = h_e \text{ at } r = r_e \quad \ldots \quad \ldots \quad \ldots \quad \ldots \quad \ldots \quad \ldots \quad \ldots \quad (51)$$

The solution of Eqn. (49), subject to boundary conditions (50) and (51), is[3]:

$$h = h_e + \frac{Q}{2\pi T} \ln \left(\frac{r}{r_e} \right) \qquad \ldots \quad \ldots \quad \ldots \quad \ldots \quad \ldots \quad (52)$$

which may be written in terms of drawdown from the rest water level as:

$$s = \frac{Q}{2\pi T} \ln \left(\frac{r_e}{r} \right) \qquad \ldots \quad \ldots \quad \ldots \quad \ldots \quad \ldots \quad \ldots \quad (53)$$

The simplicity of the solution results from the prescribed head condition at the outer boundary, a fixed distance r_e from the pumping well. The solution is strictly applicable only to a circular island with a well at the centre. However, Eqn. (53) has been widely applied to problems in which the outer boundary condition cannot be clearly defined. The reason for this is that the logarithmic term is relatively insensitive to the value of r_e used. For example,

if $r_e = 1000$ m and $r = 10$ m

then $\ln \left(\frac{r_e}{r} \right) = 4.61$

whereas if $r_e = 2000$ m and $r = 10$ m

then $\ln \left(\frac{r_e}{r} \right) = 5.30$

and the difference between estimates of drawdown using the two different values of outer radius is only 15 per cent.

The drawdown, s, of Eqn. (53) is seen to vary inversely with transmissivity, a fact which may be used to provide an estimate of transmissivity from water level data close to a well pumping at a steady rate. The method requires the measurement of water levels at two different radii and application of Eqn. (52) in the modified form:

$$T = \frac{Q}{2\pi(h_2 - h_1)} \cdot \ln \left(\frac{r_2}{r_1} \right) \qquad \ldots \quad \ldots \quad \ldots \quad \ldots \quad \ldots \quad (54)$$

WELL NEAR TO A RECHARGE BOUNDARY

By the principle of superposition, the steady state drawdown distribution resulting from an abstraction well and a recharge well operating at the same rate is:

$$s = \frac{Q}{2\pi T} \ln \left(\frac{r_e}{r} \right) - \frac{Q}{2\pi T} \ln \left(\frac{r_e}{r'} \right) = \frac{Q}{2\pi T} \ln \left(\frac{r'}{r} \right) \quad \ldots \quad \ldots \quad (55)$$

where r is the distance from the point of observation, P, to the abstraction well and r' the corresponding distance to the recharge well. Adopting the co-ordinate system of Fig. 4.11 the drawdown along the y-axis, where $r' = r$, is zero.

The solution to the right of the y-axis therefore corresponds with that of a well pumping near to a fully penetrating river, along the length of which the drawdown is zero. The outer boundary now represents the circumference of two circles, one centred on each well and so must be located at infinity. This does not matter, however, as the outer radius does not feature in the final solution, Eqn. (55). In cartesian co-ordinates the drawdown is given by:

$$s = \frac{Q}{4\pi T} \ln \left[\frac{(x + a)^2 + y^2}{(x + a)^2 + y^2} \right] \quad \ldots \quad \ldots \quad \ldots \quad \ldots \quad \ldots \quad (56)$$

where (x, y) are the co-ordinates of the observation point (Fig. 4.11).

For observation points close to the abstraction well Eqn. (56) may be approximated by Eqn. (53) with r_e equal to $2a$, that is twice the distance between the abstraction well and the river. The approximation will be correct to within 5 per cent when $\frac{r}{a} < 0.25$. Correspondingly, Eqn. (54) may be applied to determine T provided the observation points are close to the abstraction well. For more distant measurements, Eqn. (55) may be applied directly to calculate transmissivity.

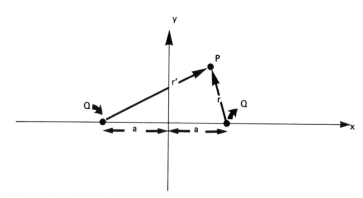

Fig. 4.11.   Abstraction well-recharge well configuration for steady state flow

10. UNSATURATED FLOW

In an unconfined aquifer the zone above the water table is commonly referred to as the unsaturated zone, or more aptly, the partially saturated zone. Drainage of a porous material from full saturation, following a lowering of the water table, results in:

(1) a decrease in the cross-sectional area available for flow, and hence, a decrease in hydraulic conductivity;
(2) severance of some flow paths as pores empty, further reducing the hydraulic conductivity.

The pressure head will also decline during drainage as water is retained in smaller and smaller pores. The pressure in the water phase will be less than atmospheric pressure, so that the pressure head will be negative. The relationships between the three variables, moisture content, hydraulic conductivity and pressure head are difficult to measure. Fig. 4.12 shows, schematically, the relationships for chalk, after the work of Ballif[12] and Wellings and Bell[13]. The general features of the curves are typical of a wide range of porous media, though the absolute values may vary considerably.

It should be noted that a certain negative pressure head or suction must be reached before the water content falls appreciably. A consequence of this is that in the zone immediately above the water table, where the pressure is slightly negative, the pore space may be almost fully saturated. This zone is commonly called the capillary zone and its extent above the water table, the capillary rise. The capillary rise can range between a few centimetres for coarse sands to several hundred centimetres in fine-grained deposits such as chalk and clay.

Water fluxes through the unsaturated zone may be calculated from Darcy's law, but solution of the appropriate flow equations is generally extremely complex because of the dependence of hydraulic conductivity and pressure head on water content. Solution is further complicated by the fact that the curves of Fig. 4.12 are not unique but dependent on antecedent conditions and, in particular, on whether the profile is wetting or drying. For vertical movement of water, Darcy's law may be written:

$$v = -K(\theta)\,\frac{dh}{dz} \quad \ldots \qquad \ldots \qquad \ldots \qquad \ldots \qquad \ldots \qquad \ldots \qquad \ldots \qquad \ldots \qquad (57)$$

where v is the specific discharge;
             h is the total hydraulic head;
             z is the vertical ordinate, usually measured upwards from some datum;
and $K(\theta)$ is the hydraulic conductivity, dependent on moisture content, θ.

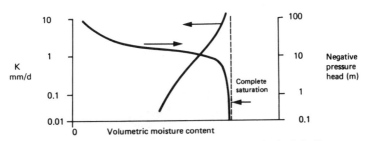

Fig. 4.12. Unsaturated characteristics typical of chalk

Expressing hydraulic head as the sum of the elevation head and pressure head, (Eqn. (5)), Eqn. (57) becomes:

$$v = - K(\theta) \left(1 + \frac{1}{\varrho g} \frac{dp\,(\theta)}{dz} \right) \qquad \cdots \qquad \cdots \qquad \cdots \qquad \cdots \qquad \cdots \qquad (58)$$

where p is the pressure, which will be negative and a function of moisture content.

The associated equation of mass conservation is:

$$\frac{\partial \theta}{\partial t} = - \frac{\partial v}{\partial z} \qquad \cdots \qquad \cdots \qquad \cdots \qquad \cdots \qquad \cdots \qquad \cdots \qquad \cdots \qquad (59)$$

The coupled Eqns. (58) and (59) have been solved by analytical and numerical techniques for a variety of boundary conditions (Phillip[14], Watson and You[15]). The principal problem is the determination of the characteristic curves $K\,(\theta)$ and $p\,(\theta)$. These can vary markedly for different media, so that no solution technique can be said to be universally superior. The main interest in solving the equations is to obtain a better understanding of the infiltration processes, and hence of the movement of pollutants from the land surface to the water table.

11. SOLUTE MOVEMENT

Substances dissolved in water, solutes, will generally move through porous media at the prevailing groundwater flow rate. There is a tendency, however, for the solute to spread both in the direction of flow and in the transverse direction. This spreading will cause an increase in the size of the solute plume and a commensurate decrease in solute concentrations in groundwater. The spreading is commonly referred to as hydrodynamic dispersion, and results from the variability about the mean of water velocities within the porous matrix (Fig. 4.13) and, on a larger scale, from aquifer heterogeneities (Fig. 4.14).

The mean velocity at which the water molecules move is given by

$$u = \frac{v}{\theta} = - \frac{K}{\theta} \frac{dh}{dx} \qquad \cdots \qquad \cdots \qquad \cdots \qquad \cdots \qquad \cdots \qquad \cdots \qquad (60)$$

where θ is the volumetric water content and may usually be equated to the total porosity.

The rate of mass transfer of solute by hydrodynamic dispersion is assumed to be proportional to the concentration gradient, drawing an analogy with other diffusive processes such as heat transfer and molecular diffusion. The constant of proportionality in this case is called the dispersion coefficient. The general

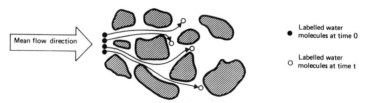

Fig. 4.13.   Dispersion on microscopic scale

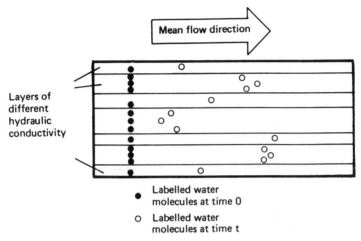

Fig. 4.14.   Dispersion on macroscopic scale

three-dimensional mass transport equation is very complex and the nature of the formulation is more easily understood by considering the equation for one-dimensional flow in the x-direction. From a mass balance consideration, similar to that used to derive the groundwater flow equation, it may be shown that[4]:

$$\frac{\partial C}{\partial t} = -\frac{\partial}{\partial x}(uC) + D_L\frac{\partial^2 C}{\partial x^2} + D_T\frac{\partial^2 C}{\partial y^2} + D_T\frac{\partial^2 C}{\partial z^2} + C_V \qquad \ldots \quad (61)$$

where C is solute concentration in groundwater (gm/m^3)
    u is the mean pore velocity (m/d)
    D_L is the longitudinal dispersion coefficient (m^2/d)
    D_T is the transverse dispersion coefficient (m^2/d)
    C_V is the solute source term ($gm/m^3/d$)
    t is the time (d)
and y and z are co-ordinates orthogonal to the flow direction, x.

The first term on the right hand side of Eqn. (61) is the rate of mass transfer due to water movement, or convection. The second term describes dispersion in the direction of flow, and the third and fourth terms describe dispersion transverse to this direction. In general D_L will be much larger than D_T, but there may be significant spreading of solute in a direction transverse to the flow.

To solve Eqn. (61) boundary and initial conditions must be specified. For all but the simplest cases, the equation can be solved only by the numerical methods described in Chapter 6. The three main problems in obtaining a solution are:

(a) specification of the velocity field, u. In Eqn. (61) the velocity is assumed to be uni-directional but, in general, the two-dimensional velocity components in the horizontal plane will be required. These are obtained by solving the complementary groundwater flow equation. In some instances there may be significant variations of solute concentration with depth so that the problem is three-dimensional.

(b) specification of the dispersion coefficients, D_L and D_T. It has been demonstrated experimentally[4] that the dispersion coefficients may be expressed:

$$D_L = \alpha_L u + D^*$$
$$D_T = \alpha_T u + D^* \quad \cdots \quad \cdots \quad \cdots \quad \cdots \quad \cdots \quad \cdots \quad \cdots \quad \cdots \quad (62)$$

where D^* is the coefficient of molecular diffusion for the solute in a porous medium, and α_L and α_T are characteristic lengths known as the longitudinal and transverse dispersivities. At most groundwater flow velocities, the mechanical mixing terms are orders of magnitude larger than the molecular diffusion coefficient which can therefore be ignored. Much has been written about the mechanism of dispersion (Fried[16], Schwartz[17]). Dispersivity is certainly dependent on the scale of measurement. Values measured on laboratory samples are commonly less than 1 cm, whereas longitudinal dispersivities up to 120 m have been inferred from large scale aquifer pollution studies. These differences reflect the scale of heterogeneities found in large samples typical of field scale pollution incidents, compared with laboratory samples. A number of experiments to measure dispersivity in the field have been reported (Fried[16], Oakes and Edworthy[18] and Sauty[19]). These experiments generally take the form of a pumping test with tracer added to groundwater through an observation well or a recharge test with tracer added to the recharge water. Dispersivities of the order of a few metres have been calculated from such tests and must be considered as representative of a local scale, perhaps up to 50 m. These values would not, in general, be appropriate to large scale pollution incidents. In these cases the best measure of dispersivity comes from matching a numerical groundwater quality model to field observations.

(c) specification of the source term, C_v. For simple mass balance purposes, it is clearly necessary to estimate reliably the total mass of solute input to an aquifer. For a detailed analysis, the distribution in space and time of inputs is required. Furthermore, because solutes move relatively slowly in aquifers, a long history of inputs, perhaps over tens of years, may be required to understand present problems. The source term must also account for concentration changes due to chemical reactions, decay, and exchange between the moving water and the aquifer material or static water. The latter is especially important in the Chalk in which water movement in the saturated zone occurs through fissures, whereas at least 95 per cent of the total water content is the relatively static water stored in the matrix.

To illustrate the relationship between convection and dispersion of solute, a simple one-dimensional experiment, for which there is an analytical solution, will be described.

LONGITUDINAL DISPERSION OF SOLUTE

Water flows through the porous medium in the apparatus of Fig. 4.15 at a steady velocity. A non-reactive tracer is introduced into the inflow continuously from time zero. Initially the concentration of solute in the column is zero.

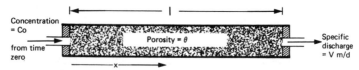

Fig. 4.15.   Apparatus for l-d dispersion experiment

The concentration of tracer in the outflow relative to that in the inflow is usually plotted against time, and comprises the breakthrough curve. In the absence of dispersion, the tracer will pass through the column as a plug, and the breakthrough curve will be a step function as shown in Fig. 4.16. The time to breakthrough will be given by:

$$t_1 = l\theta/v \qquad \dots \quad \dots \quad \dots \quad \dots \quad \dots \quad \dots \quad \dots \quad \dots \quad (63)$$

When longitudinal dispersion is included Eqn. (61) may be solved analytically, for the appropriate boundary conditions, to give[16]:

$$\frac{C}{C_o} = \frac{1}{2}\, erfc \left[\frac{x - vt/\theta}{2\,\sqrt{D_L t}} \right] \quad \dots \quad \dots \quad \dots \quad \dots \quad \dots \quad (64)$$

The full solution contains an additional term which may be neglected in general. The complementary error function, $erfc$, ranges between 0 and 2, and takes a value of 1 for zero argument. This indicates that the 50 per cent concentration breakthrough occurs at time t_1 (Eqn. (63)), corresponding to transit through the column at the average pore velocity. Dispersion results in some tracer moving more rapidly and some less rapidly than this, as shown in Fig. 4.17.

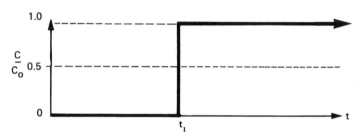

Fig. 4.16.   Tracer breakthrough with no dispersion

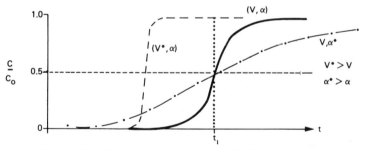

Fig. 4.17.   Tracer breakthrough with dispersion

The dispersion coefficient in Eqn. (64) may be equated to the product of the pore velocity and the aquifer dispersivity. The effect on the breakthrough curve of increasing the dispersion coefficient may therefore be viewed from two different perspectives:

(i) increase velocity, dispersivity the same;
(ii) velocity the same, increase dispersivity by replacing porous medium.

Typical breakthrough curves for these options are shown in Fig. 4.17. When the velocity alone is increased the breakthrough curve becomes sharper and will approach that for plug flow at sufficiently high velocities. In this latter case, solute transport is dominated by the convection term. If the medium is replaced by one with a higher dispersivity, whilst the mean pore velocity is unaltered, the spread of tracer is more pronounced and dispersion will play a major role in the transport process.

12. PROBLEM SOLVING

Techniques of simulating groundwater quality changes have developed rapidly in the last few years. Few of the simulations of field problems are based on analytical solutions of the mass transport equation such as Eqn. (64). Even if flow is uni-directional and the one-dimension form of the transport equation may be used, the complexity of boundary and initial conditions and of solute source terms will generally preclude an analytical solution. Simulation may be achieved by mathematical modelling as described in Chapter 6. Such methods are being increasingly used to aid groundwater development, management and protection policies. Some of the problems which have been the subject of model studies are listed below:

(1) saline intrusion into aquifers;
(2) pollution by landfill leachates;
(3) pollution by agricultural activities;
(4) surface disposal of mine drainage waters;
(5) artificial recharge;
(6) deep well disposal;
(7) upconing of mineralised water from depth;
(8) irrigation.

13. REFERENCES

1. Darcy, H. 1856 "Les fontaines publiques de la ville de Dijon", Dalmont, Paris.
2. Hubbert, M. K. 1940 *J. Geol.*, 48, 785, The theory of groundwater motion.
3. Jacob, C. E. 1950 'Flow of Groundwater' in "Engineering Hydraulics", Wiley, New York.
4. Freeze, R. A. and Cherry, J. A. 1979 "Groundwater", Prentice-Hall, New Jersey.
5. Halek, V. and Svec, J. 1979 "Groundwater Hydraulics", Elsevier, Amsterdam.
6. Hantush, M. S. 1956 *Trans. Am. Geophys. Union,* 37, 702, Analysis of data from pumping tests in leaky aquifers.
7. Prickett, T. A. 1975 'Modelling techniques for groundwater evaluation' in "Advances in Hydroscience, Volume 10", Academic Press, New York.
8. Oakes, D. B. and Skinner, A. C. 1975 "The Lancashire conjunctive use scheme groundwater model", Technical Report TR12, Water Research Centre, Medmenham.
9. Bear, J. 1972 "Dynamics of fluids in porous media", Elsevier, New York.
10. Oakes, D. B. 1981 *Trans. Geol. Soc. S. Afr.,* 84, 135, A numerical model of a stream-aquifer system subject to delayed rainfall recharge.
11. Walton, W. C. 1970 "Groundwater resource evaluation" McGraw-Hill, New York.
12. Ballif, J. L. 1978 *Ann Agron.*, 29, 123, Porosité de la Craie. Appréciation de la taille et de la répartition des pores.
13. Wellings, S. R. and Bell, J. P. 1980 *J. Hydrol.*, 48, 119, Movement of water and nitrate in the unsaturated zone of Upper Chalk near Winchester, Hants., England.
14. Phillip, J. R. 1969 'Theory of Infiltration' in "Advances in hydroscience, Volume 5", Academic Press, New York.
15. Watson, K. K. and You, S. K. 1980 "Comparison of analytical and numerical solutions of water movement in unsaturated soils", Agricultural Engineering Conference, Geelong, Australia.
16. Fried, J. J. 1975 "Groundwater Pollution", Elsevier, Amsterdam.
17. Schwartz, F. W. 1977 *Wat. Res. Res.,* 13, 743, Macrodispersion in porous media; the controlling factors.
18. Oakes, D. B. and Edworthy, K. J. 1977 "Field measurements of dispersion coefficients in the United Kingdom", Conference on Groundwater Quality, Water Research Centre, Reading.
19. Sauty, J. P. 1980 *Wat. Res. Res.,* 16, 145, An analysis of hydrodispersive transfer in aquifers.

Chapter 5

WELL TESTS

1. PURPOSE OF WELL TESTS

HYDRAULIC tests may be performed on wells or boreholes specifically sunk and fitted with pumps for that purpose, on boreholes at various stages during their drilling or on existing boreholes and operating wells.

The principal aims of such tests are to determine the characteristics of:

(1) the well;
(2) the local aquifer;
(3) the regional aquifer.

The design and conduct of a particular test will depend upon the priorities assigned to these aims. In general, data collected from a test designed to reveal well characteristics will be of little value in the determination of regional aquifer characteristics and *vice versa*. It is important when deciding on the aim of a specific test, to bear in mind the cost. A budget adequate to fulfil all three aims will be much higher than that required for a more restricted purpose. Aiming to do too much with inadequate funds may generate test data which partially fulfil all three purposes but fail to be satisfactory for any one. In other words, if the budget for testing is limited, the expectation of fulfilling all three aims is similarly limited and careful thought must be applied to deciding the priorities for the test.

DETERMINATION OF WELL CHARACTERISTICS

Well characteristics are properties of the well and the material properties of the surrounding aquifer. The interacting factors (Fig. 5.1) which contribute towards, and influence well characteristics include:

(a) geometry—well depth, diameter, well wall surface roughness;
(b) aquifer material—grain size, degree of cementation, discontinuity structure (joints and fissures);
(c) construction—degree of fracturing, extent of smearing, constancy of diameter, type of casing and/or screen;
(d) development—pack emplacement and design, efficiency of removal of smearing, success of acidization.

All these factors will contribute towards the hydraulic behaviour of the well and are to some extent independent of the local and regional aquifer characteristics. Well behaviour is a function of the flow of water within the well to the pump and the very local flow of water through the well walls which may comprise:

(i) 'normal' aquifer material;
(ii) aquifer material modified by development e.g. acidization or fines removal to create 'natural' pack;
(iii) 'artificial' pack material.

The flow regime involved close to the pump is not the laminar regime which applies over most of the aquifer during pumping. The transition from laminar to turbulent flow will take place close to the pump and the velocity profile and flow regime within the well and well walls will depend on the pumping rate and pump position.

Well characteristics are required to decide on:

(1) pump selection;
(2) pump position;
(3) long-term pumping costs;
(4) need for further well development.

Tests for well characteristics involve the preparation of yield/drawdown curves for one (or more) pump positions. The water pumped may also be analysed for suspended solids in conjunction with the yield/drawdown tests.

DETERMINATION OF LOCAL AQUIFER CHARACTERISTICS

Short-term pumping tests lasting a few days on single wells will be very largely influenced by local rather than regional aquifer characteristics. Aquifer characteristics include not only water transmission and storage properties but also the interactions with local boundary conditions and local point sources and sinks.

Aquifer transmission and storage properties will vary on the local scale (Fig. 5.2) due to:

(a) sedimentological variability (grain-size and mineralogical changes);
(b) discontinuity-pattern variability (faults, joints, fractures and fissures);
(c) saturated-thickness variations (folding, water table fluctuations and confined-unconfined changes).

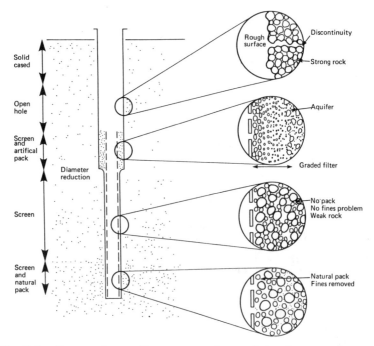

Fig. 5.1. Geometric, aquifer, construction and development factors

Local horizontal and vertical inhomogeneity and anisotropy of transmission and storage properties will arise from all three factors. The variation of saturated thickness may mean that aquifer properties show significant seasonal variations.

Boundary conditions include a number of hydrological and geological situations (Fig. 5.3):

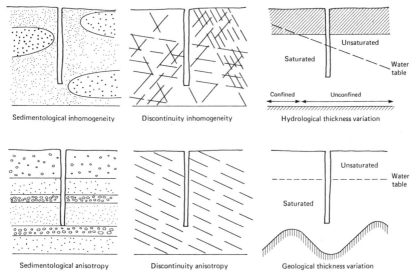

Fig. 5.2. Aquifer properties causing hydrogeological variability

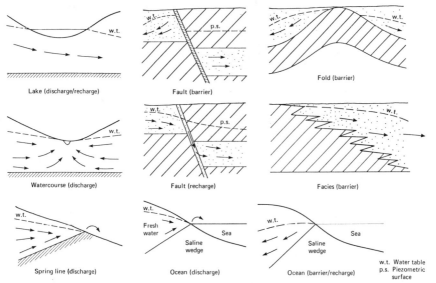

Fig. 5.3. Hydrogeological and geological boundary conditions

   (i) hydrological boundaries such as oceans, lakes, surface watercourses (streams and rivers) or spring lines (perennial and intermittent). Normally these represent recharge/discharge boundaries although high density saline water may act as a barrier to flow;

  (ii) geological boundaries such as faults (recharge or barrier), facies changes (barriers due to abrupt changes of rock type and permeability) or folds (barriers due to abrupt changes in saturated thickness).

Boundaries close to well sites will affect local aquifer behaviour and well yields but may not be of regional significance. For example, a fault which locally restricts flow to a well may cause only a very minor deflection of regional groundwater level contours. Local sources and sinks (Fig. 5.4) may be significant both in terms of their contribution to the flow pattern and their effect on water quality. Sources may include, for example:

  (1) agricultural slurry lagoons;
  (2) mine waste tailings lagoons;
  (3) local spray irrigation areas;
  (4) septic tank discharges;
  (5) ponds and other stagnant standing water.

Sinks are less common but may include:

  (a) other abstraction wells;
  (b) isolated local springs.

All the sources listed, in particular, represent potential water quality hazards and the rate of flow from such sources can increase dramatically when pumping gradients are imposed. Well tests will determine the influence and extent of such sources and sinks on the local well behaviour.

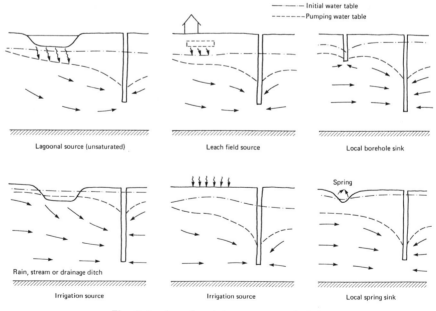

Fig. 5.4. Local point sources and sinks

DETERMINATION OF REGIONAL AQUIFER CHARACTERISTICS

Long-term tests lasting several weeks or months on multiple wells are necessary to determine the regional characteristics of an aquifer. Individual pumping sites will remain dependent on local factors but the regional response of groundwater levels and the overall effect on surface watercourses and spring lines will reflect the aquifer as a regional entity. Regional aquifer tests are very costly and take the form of a pilot or preliminary groundwater development scheme.

The foregoing discussion of aquifer variability on a local scale also applies on the regional scale, although some local sources of variation are likely to be 'averaged out' when the aquifer is considered on a regional scale. Boundary conditions remain an important factor to be defined by the test but consideration of local sources and sinks is replaced by the delineation of regional recharge and discharge areas and their implications for water quality. A regional test scheme will attempt to assess:

- (i) the boundary conditions for the aquifer as a whole;
- (ii) regional variations in aquifer properties both for 'average' and 'drought' water level conditions;
- (iii) the extent of recharge and discharge areas;
- (iv) the effect on river or spring flows and other surface water bodies;
- (v) the quality implications of regional recharge in relation to agricultural, mining, industrial and other pollution hazards.

The test procedure and design will involve pumping at several sites over an extended period of time and perhaps repeated tests for different initial water table levels.

2. TEST METHODS

The testing techniques available for aquifers can be conveniently divided into those which involve little or no discharge from the aquifer and those which involve the abstraction of significant quantities of water. The latter are the main tools of the hydrogeological and groundwater engineer in the assessment of aquifer characteristics. They are also often complex, time consuming and costly to carry out. The small-scale zero or limited discharge tests, on the other hand, are simple, quick and cheap. They are somewhat neglected but may provide valuable hydrogeological information, particularly as part of a groundwater development feasibility study or during the preliminary stages of other investigations. The testing technique and analytical method for the small-scale tests will first be described and will be followed by the better known large-scale test methods.

SMALL-SCALE TESTS

Small-scale tests can be subdivided into the following classes:

- (1) rising and falling head tests;
- (2) slug and bail tests (special case of (1));
- (3) constant head tests;
- (4) packer tests (special case of (3));
- (5) tracer dilution tests.

Rising and Falling Head Tests

Both rising head tests (called slug tests for open holes) and falling head tests (called bail tests for open holes) can be carried out on wells with a variety of test sections

(Fig. 5.5(a)):

(a) tube wells (open only at base);
(b) piezometers (open over restricted section);
(c) open holes (open over whole aquifer thickness).

Open hole tests are a separate class of slug and bail tests to be discussed later but both the principles and practical details of testing are very similar. For tube wells and piezometers, in addition to the well type, the location of the test section with respect to impermeable sub-horizontal boundaries is important. Fig. 5.5(b) shows a test section adjacent to a no-flow boundary and in a uniform aquifer. In the former case the aquifer is assumed to be saturated and therefore confined. In the latter the sections are assumed to be saturated but may or may not be confined. The test is carried out to determine the hydraulic conductivity of the aquifer in the vicinity of the test section.

In the falling head test, a fixed volume of water, which is sufficient to cause a conveniently measurable 'instantaneous' rise in water level, is rapidly introduced to the well and the water level in the hole is recorded as the water flows into the

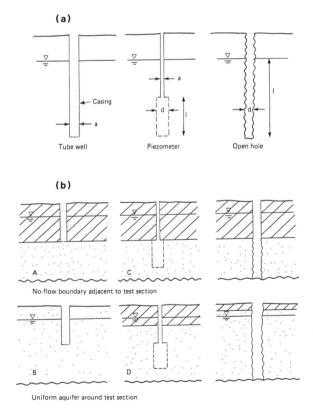

Fig. 5.5.   Rising and falling head test: (a) well types; (b) test conditions

surrounding aquifer from the well. In practice, the fixed volume is poured into the well from a bottle or drum and head readings are taken with a conventional dipmeter until 90 per cent of the applied test head has dissipated. Readings should be taken after 1, 2, 4, 8, 15, 30 and 60 minutes and so on. The time interval between readings should only be increased if the head loss between readings is less than 5 per cent of the applied test head (see Example 1).

In the rising head test, a fixed volume of water, of sufficient quantity to cause a conveniently measurable 'instantaneous' fall in water level, is rapidly removed from the well and the head recorded as water flows from the surrounding aquifer into the well. In practice, the water is removed by a bailer or by siphoning and head readings are taken in the same way as suggested for the falling head test until 90 per cent of the applied test head is restored.

The test data are analysed by plotting the negative of the natural logarithm of the fraction of the remaining head to be recovered against time, that is, $-ln[(H-h)/H-H_o]$ against t (Fig. 5.6(a)–(c)). Hvorslev[1] defines the basic time lag, T_o, when $-ln[(H-h)/H-H_o)] = 1$. This point is easily found from the data plot (Fig. 5.6(c)) where $(H-h)/(H-H_o) = 0.37$. The Hvorslev[1] reference is rather inaccessible but excellent summaries are given by Cedergren[2] and Lee et al[3]. The value of hydraulic conductivity is given by:

$$K_m = \pi a^2 \frac{F}{T_o} \text{ and } K_h = m\,K_m$$

where K_m is the mean hydraulic conductivity   (dimensions)
                                                                          (L/T)
        a is the tube diameter (Fig. 5.6(a))   (L)
        T_o is Hvorslev's basic time lag (Fig. 5.6(c))   (T)
        F is a factor dependent on geometry (L^{-1})

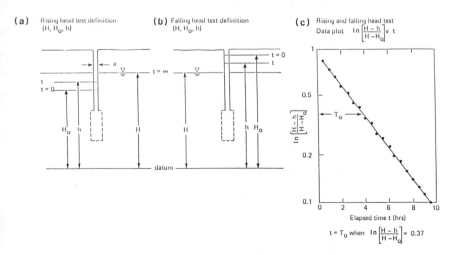

Fig. 5.6.   Rising and falling head tests: definitions and data plot

Let d be the test section diameter (Fig. 5.5(a))   (L)
         l be the test section length (Fig. 5.5(a))   (L)
        K_h be the horizontal hydraulic conductivity   (L/T)
        K_v be the vertical hydraulic conductivity   (L/T)

Now for convenience some further definitions are required:

Define K_m as $\sqrt{K_h \cdot K_v}$ (L/T)
       m as $\sqrt{K_h/K_v}$ (dimensionless)
       α as ml/d (dimensionless)
       L_1 as $ln\left[\alpha + \sqrt{1 + \alpha^2}\right]$ (dimensionless)
       L_2 as $ln\left[2\alpha + \sqrt{1 + (2\alpha)^2}\right]$ (dimensionless)

Now the geometric factors F_A, F_B, F_C and F_D for cases A, B, C, and D (Fig. 5.5(b)) are simply written:

$$F_A = 1/8d \qquad\qquad\qquad F_B = 1/11d$$
$$F_C = L_2/8\pi\alpha d \qquad\qquad F_D = L_1/8\pi\alpha d$$

For $\alpha > 4$ (as it is likely to be for practical cases):

$$L_1 \simeq ln\,[2\alpha] \qquad\qquad \text{and} \quad L_2 \simeq ln\,[4\alpha]$$

Rising head tests are slightly preferred to falling head tests since the inflow of water to the aquifer may also involve fine suspended particles 'clogging' the aquifer.

Example 1. A rising head piezometer test was carried out by siphoning one litre of water from a silty aquifer. The initial aquifer head was 2 m below datum and the access tube diameter was 25 mm. The 'well-point' was 50 mm in diameter and had a length of 150 mm. The results over a 7 hour period of water level recovery were:

Time (mins)	0	1	2	4	8	15	30	60	120	180	240	300	360	420
Head (m)	2.00	4.03	4.02	4.01	3.97	3.92	3.80	3.59	3.24	2.96	2.75	2.58	2.46	2.35

The initial fall in water level $(H-H_o)$ may be deduced from the tube diameter and volume removed:

$$V = H\text{-}H_o \cdot \frac{\pi a^2}{4}$$

$$H-H_o = 4V/\pi a^2 = 4 \times \frac{10^{-3}}{3.14} \times \frac{10^3}{25} \times \frac{10^3}{25} \text{ m}$$

$$= 2.04 \text{ m}$$

The piezometer was installed in the middle of a thick uniform sand horizon. Calculate the hydraulic conductivity of the sand assuming that the ratio of the horizontal to vertical permeability is 100. Thus:

$$m = \sqrt{\frac{100}{1}} = 10$$

1. Plot $ln\left[\dfrac{H\text{-}h}{H\text{-}H_o}\right]$ against t and deduce the basic time lag T_o (when

$$ln\left[\frac{H\text{-}h}{H\text{-}H_o}\right] = 0.37).$$

From Fig. 5.7, T_o = 4.0 hours = 14 400 seconds

2. Calculate $\alpha = ml/d = 10 \times \dfrac{150}{50} = 30$

3. Calculate $L_1 = ln\,[2\alpha] = 4.10$

4. Calculate $F_D = L_1/8\pi\alpha d = \dfrac{4.10}{8} \times \dfrac{1}{3.14} \times \dfrac{1}{30} \times \dfrac{10^3}{50}$

$$= 1.09 \times 10^{-1}\ m^{-1}$$

5. Calculate $K_m = \pi\alpha^2\,\dfrac{F}{T_o} = 3.14 \times \dfrac{25}{10^3} \times \dfrac{25}{10^3} \times \dfrac{1.09}{1.44} \times \dfrac{10^{-1}}{10^4}$

$$= 1.49 \times 10^{-8}\ m/s$$

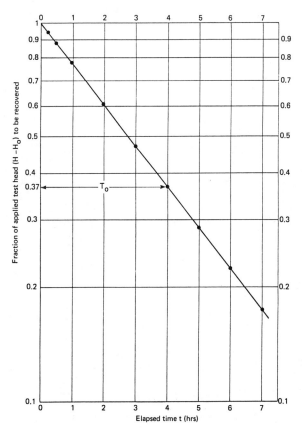

Fig. 5.7. Hvorslev semilog plot (for sandy aquifer) (Example 1)

Slug and Bail Tests

Slug and bail tests differ from falling and rising head tests in that the test section extends, or is assumed to extend, over the entire saturated thickness of the aquifer. A value of horizontal hydraulic conductivity is determined.

In the slug test a fixed volume or 'slug' of water is injected into the test well. The volume required is relatively large (by comparison with falling head piezometer tests) and should be sufficient to 'instantaneously' raise the water level in the well by 2–3 m. In water wells, hydraulic conductivity is relatively high and in slug tests the rate of change of water levels is often very fast. A dipmeter is normally inadequate and automatic recording by a pressure transducer placed 1–2 m below the initial water level is recommended. It is very important that the 'slug' is injected instantaneously and because of the practical difficulties this presents, the use of a 'displacer' to raise the head in the well has been developed. The displacer comprises a hollow, heavily weighted, tube of known volume sufficient to raise the well level by 2–3 m. In the test the displacer is lowered to a level immediately above the water surface and then rapidly immersed to cause an instantaneous water level change (Fig. 5.8(a)).

In the bail test a fixed volume of water is removed using a bailer. Again a 2–3 m change in water level is required and again automatic water level recording equipment is necessary to obtain sufficiently frequent readings. To start the test, the bailer is gently lowered into the well and allowed to fill with water. Time must be allowed for any head rise, caused by displacement on introduction of the bailer, to dissipate. The test begins when the bailer is rapidly withdrawn (Fig. 5.8(b)). Because of the rapid water level response normally found in slug and bail tests, the tests are normally repeated 5 times. Errors may arise if the approximation of an instantaneous change in head is not good. The higher the aquifer hydraulic

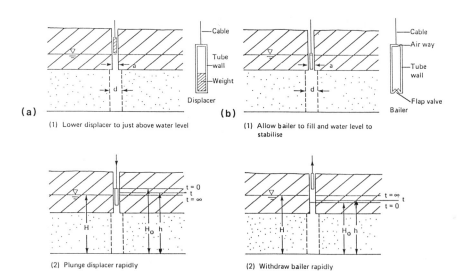

Fig. 5.8.   (a) Use of displacer; (b) Use of bailer

conductivity, the more rapid the water level response, and the more critical the instantaneous head change requirement becomes. The test data are analysed by plotting the fraction of the head restored against the base 10 logarithm of time, that is (Fig. 5.9) $(H-h)/(H-H_o)$ against log (t). This is the reverse of the plotting format for rising and falling head tests. The test interpretation procedure has been developed by Papadopoulos and Cooper[4] and for confined wells can be extended (Papadopoulos *et al*[5]) to the unconfined case. The procedure involves matching the field curve with a series of type curves (Appendix I) as follows:

1. Plot $(H-h)/(H-H_o)$ against log $[t]$ (field curve).
2. Overlay the field curve and type curves (Fig. 5.9) ensuring that $(H-h)/(H-H_o)$ scales are common and both axes are parallel.
3. Find the position for which the best fit to one of the type curves is obtained.
4. Read off the value of $t = t_m$ on the field curve which corresponds to any value of W on the type curves. It is convenient to choose $W = 1$ but not essential.
5. Note the value of the type curve parameter A for the match.
6. The value of hydraulic conductivity is given by:

$$K_h = \frac{W_m a^2}{16 l t_m} \text{ or } \frac{a^2}{16 l t_m} \text{ (for } W_m = 1)$$

where K_h is the horizontal plane hydraulic conductivity   (L/T)
       a is the tube diameter (Fig. 5.8)   (L)
       l is the test section length (Fig. 5.8)   (L)

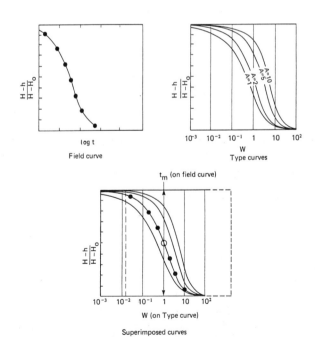

Fig. 5.9.   **Field curve-type curve superposition for slug and bail tests**

W_m is the type curve match point (Fig. 5.9)   (dimensionless)
t_m is the field curve match point (Fig. 5.9)   (T)

In theory the value of A can be used to estimate the storage coefficient, S:

$$A = - \log \left[\frac{d^2 S}{a^2} \right] \text{ hence } S = \frac{a^2}{d^2} \exp(-2.3A)$$

where A is the gradient of the W v $(H-h)/(H-H_o)$ type
       curves (Fig. 5.9)   (dimensionless)
       d is the test section diameter (Fig. 5.8)   (L)
       a is the tube diameter (Fig. 5.8)   (L)
       S is the aquifer storage coefficient   (dimensionless)

The values of S derived from this formula are *extremely unreliable* and their calculation is not recommended.

The main limitations of slug and bail tests are their vulnerability to 'clogging' of the test section and to hydraulic conductivity enhancement induced by washing fines from the aquifer around the well.

Example 2. A slug test was carried out in a confined well cased through 10 m of shale at 300 mm diameter and open-hole for a further 15 m in sandstone at 150 mm diameter (Fig. 5.10). The well terminates at the base of the sandstone in shale. The initial piezometric head was 4 m above the base of the casing and the head was raised 2 m by a displacer to instigate the slug test (to 6 m above the base of the casing). The following data were collected during the test (measured in m above the base of the casing):

Elapsed time (mins)	0	0.1	0.2	0.5	1	2	4	8	15	30
Head (m)	6	5.80	5.63	5.39	5.02	4.52	4.21	4.07	4.04	4.03

Calculate the horizontal-plane hydraulic conductivity of the sandstone and estimate the confined storage coefficient.

1. From the data given $H = 4$ m above datum and $H_o = 6$ m above datum, hence $H-H_o$, the head increment, is 2 m.
2. Plot the field curve $[(H-h)/H-H_o]$ v $\log t$ (Fig. 5.10).
3. Overlay the field curve with the type curves in Appendix I(a). In this case, when $W = 1$, $t_m = 0.625$ mins.
4. From the data given $l = 15$ m; $a = 0.15$ m.
   Hence

$$K_h = \frac{0.15 \times 0.15}{16 \times 15} \times \frac{1}{.625 \times 60} = 2.5 \times 10^{-6} \text{ m/s}$$

The transmissivity $T = Kl = 3.75 \times 10^{-5}$ m²/s
                            $= 3.24$ m²/d

5. Estimate the value of A for the match point $A_m = 3.5$. The storage coefficient may thus be estimated:

$$S = \frac{0.15}{0.3} \times \frac{0.15}{0.3} \exp(-2.3 \times 3.5) = \frac{1}{4} \exp(-8.05)$$

$$= 8 \times 10^{-5}$$

Constant-Head Tests

When field values of hydraulic conductivity are too high to obtain reasonably accurate records of the rate of change of head in rising/falling or slug/bail tests, a constant-head test is indicated. Two variants of the constant-head test are used:

(i) the Hvorslev[1] test—using a single piezometer or well point
(ii) the Thiem[6] test—using two or more observation piezometers or boreholes.

The test requires that steady-state flow conditions are established and that the corresponding head and injection/abstraction rate are recorded. If an extended period of injection/abstraction is required to obtain steady flow conditions or the rates of injection/abstraction are more than a few litres/sec then a transient analysis is recommended, using the test procedures described in a later section.

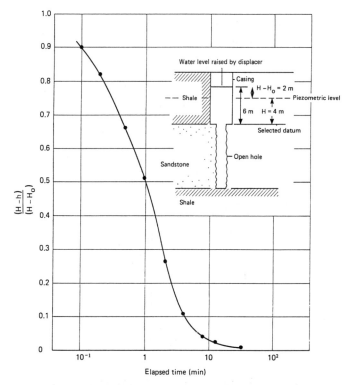

Fig. 5.10. Field curve for slug test (sandstone) (Example 2)

In the Hvorslev test, water is injected into the test well at a constant rate Q, until a constant head $H-H_o$ is established (Fig. 5.11). Hvorslev[1] gives analytical formulae for the well geometries A, B, C and D (Fig. 5.5(b)). The equations are also given by Cedergren[2] and Lee et al[3]. The shape factors F_A, F_B, F_C and F_D are those given earlier. The average and horizontal hydraulic conductivities, K_m and K_h (L/T) are given by:

$$K_m = \frac{4QF}{(H-H_o)} \text{ and } K_h = m\,K_m$$

where Q is the constant injection rate (L^3/T) and
        F is the shape factor F_A, F_B, F_C or F_D (L^{-1}).
Q is positive for abstraction and negative for injection.

In the Thiem test, piezometers are installed to monitor the steady drawdown for at least two radial distances from the test well. Normally at least three observation

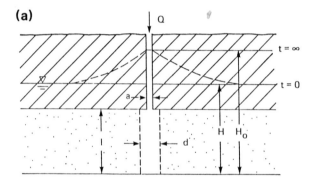

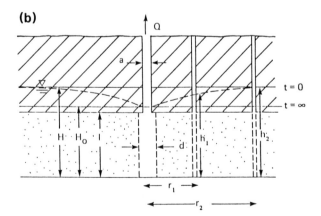

**Fig. 5.11.   (a) Hvorslev constant head test
              (b) Thiem constant head test**

points at radial distances from 3 to 20 m are recommended. Pump abstraction rates in the range of 1 to 100 l/s are used. The test well is pumped at a constant rate (discharge is measured over a triangular or rectangular notch weir) and steady state drawdowns are recorded in the pumped well and at the observations wells. Thiem[6] first analysed the steady-state radial flow to a confined well to give the horizontal hydraulic conductivity K_h as follows:

$$K_h = \frac{Q ln[r_2/r_1]}{2\pi \, l \, (h_2 - h_1)}$$

where l is the length of the test section (Fig. 5.11(b))   (L)
       h_1 is the head at radial distance r_1 (Fig. 5.11(b))   (L)
       h_2 is the head at radial distance r_2 (Fig. 5.11(b)   (L)
       Q is the constant abstraction rate   (L^3/T)

It is recommended that the Thiem test is only used as an estimate of K_h in the vicinity of a well that has been pumped for a sufficiently long period so that water levels are only changing very slowly and are close to equilibrium.

Example 3. An isotropic coarse sand aquifer 9 m thick is underlain and overlain by clays. The drawdown values recorded by three piezometers at different radial distances were:

Radial distance (m)	30	90	215
Drawdown (m)	1.0	0.72	0.35

for a constant pumping rate of 9 l/s. The drawdown in the pumping well (diameter 1.5 m) was 2.05 m. Calculate the aquifer hydraulic conductivity.

1. Use the Hvorslev equation for the pumped well. Referring to Fig. 5.5(b), case C is most appropriate:

   $F_C = L_2/8\pi\alpha d$
   $\alpha = ml/d$ (assume $m = 1$ − isotropic case)
   $\alpha = 1 \times 9/1.5 = 6$
   $\alpha > 4$ hence: $L_2 = ln\,[4\alpha] = ln\,[24] = 3.18$
   $F_C = L_2/8\pi\alpha d$

   $$F_C = \frac{3.18}{8} \times \frac{1}{3.14} \times \frac{1}{6} \times \frac{1}{1.5}$$
   $$= 1.41 \times 10^{-2}\,m^{-1}$$

2. The hydraulic conductivity is thus given by:

   $$K_h = m\,K_m = \frac{4mQF}{(H-H_o)} = \frac{4}{2.05} \times 1 \times 9 \times 10^{-3} \times 1.41 \times 10^{-2}$$
   $$= 2.48 \times 10^{-4}\,m/s$$

3. Use the Thiem equation for the observation wells at 30 and 90 m:

   $ln\,[r_2/r_1] = ln\,[3] = 1.10$

$$K_h = \frac{Q.ln\,[r_2/r_1]}{2\pi l\,(h_1-h_2)} = \frac{9}{2} \times \frac{10^{-3}}{3.14} \times \frac{1.10}{9} \times \frac{1}{(1.0-0.72)}$$

$$= 6.25 \times 10^{-4} \text{ m/s}$$

and similarly for other observation wells as follows:

Observation wells at r_1 and r_2	$K_h = \dfrac{Q.\,ln\,r_2/r_1}{2\pi l(h_2-h_2)}$ m/s
30 and 90	6.25×10^{-4}
90 215	2.48×10^{-4}
30 215	3.75×10^{-4}

The scatter of values $2.48 - 6.25 \times 10^{-4}$ m/s is typical of field tests. A scatter of around half to one order of magnitude is often found in practice.

Packer Tests

Packer tests represent a special category of constant-head tests which are particularly popular in determining the hydraulic conductivity of fractured rocks. The tests take their name from the cylinders with inflatable, flexible jackets used to hydraulically isolate the well test section. Packer tests are sometimes called Lugeon tests after the French engineer who pioneered their use. The principle of packer testing is to carry out constant-head tests on small test sections of the well isolated by a packer or packers. The value of results from packer tests in screened wells or wells with natural or artificial gravel packs may be unreliable since isolation of the test section in such cases is impossible to guarantee.

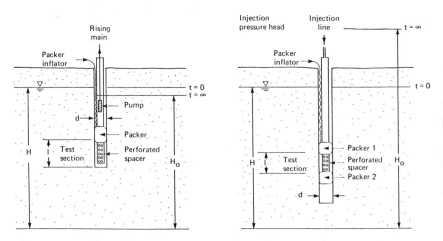

Fig. 5.12. (a) Single abstraction arrangement; (b) Double-injection arrangement

Two types of test can be carried out (Fig. 5.12):

(1) Single packer tests divide the well into two isolated sections (above and below the packer). Injection or abstraction may take place from either section. Single packer tests may be used to progressively test a well as drilling proceeds (although problems of wall smearing and clogging may be apparent);
(2) Double packer tests are more common where two packers isolate a specific test section. Profiling packer tests may be carried out using a set of 50 per cent overlapping successive sections. The distance between packers is fixed by the length of the perforated spacer section (normally 1 to 6 m).

The procedure for a packer test is to measure the volume of water injected per unit time for a series of injection pressures. Common practice is to use a standard drill pump to supply water to the test section. This is not recommended since both piston pumps and, to a lesser extent, rotary pumps, generate pressure pulsations which make both practical measurements of injection pressure and subsequent test analysis difficult. Aeration of the injected water can also create problems where direct pumping is used.

Two injection systems are suggested:

(a) Use of multiple constant-head tanks at different levels has been suggested by Pearson and Money[7]. In practice a pressure head range from ground surface to +5 m is about all that can be conveniently obtained on a typical site (without extensive pipework or major construction of towers);
(b) Use of a pressure tank system using a gas bottle to provide the pressure (compressor will generate pulsations). This system will provide a large pressure range but the flow-rate that can be maintained is limited by the tank size.

Whatever system is used, if injection pressure is not measured by a transducer in the downhole test section, then all pressure readings must be corrected for the head loss in the pipework. Flow rate may be measured in a variety of ways:

(i) as volume change per unit time by monitoring the volume injected;
(ii) directly, using an impeller flow meter (not recommended since such meters tend to 'stick' at low flows);
(iii) directly, using a differential-pressure flow-meter.

Ideally, a continuous record of flow rate is required but if this is not possible, a record of incremental flow rate at every 2 minutes is recommended.

Analysis of packer tests has not been extensively investigated but a review of recent practice is given by Houlsby[8]. The formulae used are generally based on the Thiem[6] equilibrium solution of the equations of radial flow although Jacob and Lohman[9] have analysed the transient case and a curve fitting technique for flow v time curves is available.

The normal formulae used for packer test analysis take the form:

$$K_h = \frac{Q.ln(2l/d)}{2\pi l \ (H\text{-}H_o)} \quad \text{for } l > 5d$$

$$K_h = \frac{Q.sinh^{-1} \ (l/d)}{2\pi l \ (H-H_o)} \quad for \ 10d > 2l > d$$

where K_h is the horizontal plane hydraulic conductivity   (L/T)
       Q is the injection (or abstraction) rate   (L^3/T)
       l is the length of the test section   (L)
       d is the diameter of the test section   (L)

H is the applied injection (or abstraction) pressure
head   (L)
H_o is the initial piezometric head (or pore pressure)   (L)

The equations are written in such a way that the sign convention Q positive for abstraction, negative for injection, is implied.

The errors and assumptions inherent in the test procedure and analysis of packer test results are such that the final values of hydraulic conductivity should be regarded as half order or order of magnitude estimates.

Example 4. A packer test was carried out in fractured rock using two packers 2 m apart in a 150 mm diameter well. The mid-point of the test section was 25 m below ground surface and the initial water level was 2 m below ground surface. The tests were conducted using gas pressures acting on a water reservoir. From the test flow-rate v time plots (Fig. 5.13) the following data are deduced:

	Injection head, $H-H_o$ (m)	Injection flow, Q (l/min)	$\dfrac{Q}{(H-H_o)}$ (m³/s/m)
Stage 1	9.6	12.3	2.14×10^{-5}
Stage 2	20.6	25.2	2.03×10^{-5}
Stage 3	39.6	49.1	2.07×10^{-5}
Stage 4	19.6	22.4	1.90×10^{-5}
Stage 5	10.4	12.2	1.96×10^{-5}

From the information given $l = 2$ m and $d = 0.15$ m. Hence $l > 5d$. The hydraulic

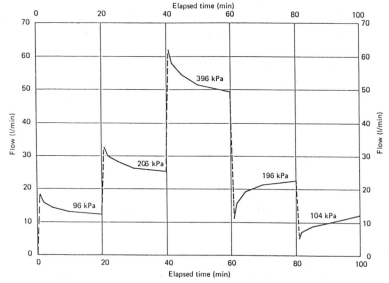

Fig. 5.13.   Packer test flow v time curves (sandstone) (Example 4)

conductivity is thus given by:

$$K_h = \frac{Q}{H-H_o} \cdot \frac{ln(2l/d)}{2\pi l} = 0.261 \frac{Q}{(H-H_o)} \text{ m/s}$$

Entering $\dfrac{Q}{H-H_o}$ in m^3/s/m gives the following values of K_h for the various stages:

Stage	K_h (m/s)
1	5.6×10^{-6}
2	5.3×10^{-6}
3	5.4×10^{-6}
4	5.0×10^{-6}
5	5.1×10^{-6}

The value of K_h obtained from the test is consistent over the estimates from each stage but subsequent constant-rate tests gave a value of 1.0×10^{-6} m/s. Packer tests tend to over-estimate hydraulic conductivity by as much as an order of magnitude because the 'equilibrium' injection flow is not a true steady-state value.

Tracer Tests

The point-dilution method is a tracer test developed in the USSR in the late 1940s to yield an estimate of the average linear velocity of groundwater in a

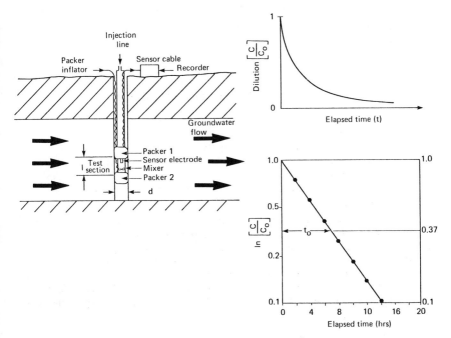

Fig. 5.14.   Point-dilution tracer test

formation. The method is described in detail by several authors, the paper by Drost *et al*[10] being the most accessible.

A section of well is isolated by packers (Fig. 5.14). A tracer is quickly introduced by injection and continuously mixed with the well water in the test section by a mechanical mixer. It is then diluted gradually by the natural throughflow of groundwater. The concentration of the tracer is continuously monitored by a downhole detector and a plot of tracer dilution with time is obtained. Early experiments used isotope tracers but such expense is unnecessary. Electrodes are commercially available to monitor chloride or fluoride ion concentration or simply electrical conductivity.

The analysis of the test data involves plotting the natural logarithm of the dilution (ratio of trace concentration at time t (C) to initial concentration of tracer (C_o)) $ln \left[\dfrac{C}{C_o} \right]$ against time t. The average bulk flow velocity is given by:

$$\bar{v} = - \frac{\pi d}{4lt} ln \left[\frac{C}{C_o} \right]$$

where d is the test section diameter   (L)
       l is the test section length   (L)
       C_o is the initial tracer concentration (M/L^3)
       C is the tracer concentration at time t (M/L^3)
       t is the elapsed mixing time   (T)

$\bar{v}$ is estimated from the gradient of the semi-log dilution v time curve. The value t_o (analogous to the time lag T_o in Hvorslev's equations' (section 2.1)) can be read off when $\dfrac{C}{C_o}$ = 0.37. The average velocity is given by:

$$\bar{v} = \frac{\pi d}{4t_o}$$

and the hydraulic conductivity can now be estimated using the equation:

$$K_h = \frac{\bar{v}\theta_f}{W_f i_w}$$

where K_h is horizontal hydraulic conductivity   (L/T)
       $\bar{v}$ is average flow velocity   (L/T)
       θ_f is aquifer flow porosity   (dimensionless)
       W_f is a constant dependent on well construction (dimensionless)
       i_w is the hydraulic gradient   (dimensionless)

W_f depends on the geometry of any well screen and the radius and hydraulic conductivity of any pack material. θ_f is approximated by the aquifer specific yield and i_w may be estimated from a groundwater level contour map.

Point-dilution tracer tests provide a relatively cheap order of magnitude estimate of hydraulic conductivity. No source of water for injection is required neither are there any problems in disposing of pump discharge. The mechanical mixer and tracer concentration sensor may be 'built-in' to a special packer assembly which can be used repeatedly.

Example 5. A 150 mm diameter gravel well, in an area where the regional groundwater gradient is 1.5 m/km (0.0015) was the subject of a point-dilution tracer test using a special 1.5 m spacing packer fitted with a mixer and fluoride specific-ion electrode. The aquifer specific yield was estimated to be 9 per cent. The test was started by injecting 100 ml of sodium fluoride solution (containing 10 000 mg/l F^-) into the test section. The following data were extracted from a chart record of the specific-ion electrode response:

Elapsed time (hrs)	0	0.2	0.5	1	2	4	6	8	10
F^- concentration (mg/l)	30	23.7	27.0	24.2	19.6	12.8	8.3	5.4	3.5

The well factor W_f may be taken to be unity. Estimate the aquifer horizontal-plane hydraulic conductivity:

1. Plot $ln\left[\dfrac{C}{C_o}\right]$ against t and read off the value of t_o when $\left[\dfrac{C}{C_o}\right] = 0.37$ (Fig. 5.15). The value of t_o is 4.67 hrs.

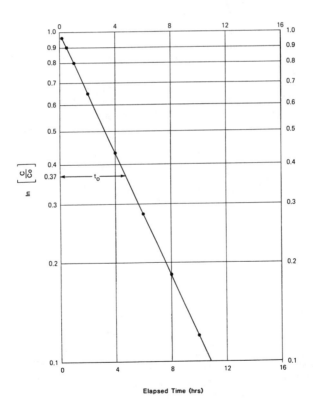

Elapsed Time (hrs)

Fig. 5.15. Point-dilution semilog plot (gravel) (Example 5)

2. Now calculate the average mass flow velocity under the natural groundwater gradient:

$$\bar{v} = \frac{\pi d}{4t_o}$$
$$= \frac{3.14}{4} \times \frac{0.15}{4.67 \times 60 \times 60}$$
$$= 7.0 \times 10^{-6} \text{ m/s}$$

3. Finally estimate K_h using the gradient and flow porosity (taking $W_f = 1$)

$$K_h = \frac{\bar{v}\, \theta_f}{W_f i_w}$$
$$= \frac{7.0 \times 10^{-6}}{1} \quad \frac{9 \times 10^{-2}}{1.5 \times 10^{-3}}$$
$$= 4.2 \times 10^{-4} \text{ m/s.}$$

LARGE-SCALE TESTS—WELL TESTS

The tests reviewed have involved the injection and abstraction of relatively small quantities of water or none at all. As a consequence, analysis of such tests tends to yield values of aquifer properties characteristic in the immediate vicinity of the well. The tests also determine properties which relate to the water levels prevailing at the time of the test.

For many hydrogeological assessments such limited test procedures may (and often do) yield inappropriate parameters for the prediction of the more widespread, longer-term behaviour of the aquifer. Larger scale, more extensive tests are required to gain such data. These tests are often referred to as 'pumping tests' and can be both costly and complex. Large-scale tests require pumping capacity comparable to 'production' rates and are designed to evaluate 'aquifer response' to major perturbations of water levels in adjacent observation wells in addition to the test well.

They are conveniently reviewed under five headings:

(1) step-drawdown tests;
(2) constant-discharge tests;
(3) variable-discharge tests;
(4) recovery tests;
(5) multiple-well tests.

Step-Drawdown Tests

The purpose of a step-drawdown test is to determine the characteristics of the well (as opposed to the aquifer) and to prepare a yield/drawdown curve which may be used both for the selection of permanent pumping equipment and the assessment of potential production pumping costs. The test and analysis procedure is described in detail by Rorabaugh[11] and Clark[12]

At least four increasing abstraction 'steps' are recommended with the final abstraction rate as close as possible to the maximum well yield (or at least the maximum capacity of the test pump). Two alternative test procedures may be adopted (Fig. 5.16):

   (*a*) consecutive steps;
   (*b*) intermittent steps.

In the **consecutive step test**, for each constant abstraction rate step, the water levels in the pumped well (and any observation wells) are noted for elapsed times of 1, 2, 4, 8, 15, 30, 60 and 120 minutes. A 2 hour step is normally adequate to approach a 'pseudo equilibrium' drawdown in the test well but the length of step may be extended to 4 or 8 hours if necessary. At the end of the step, in the consecutive test, the abstraction rate is immediately increased and a further set of drawdown measurements made. The procedure is repeated until the final abstraction step. Recovery levels after the cessation of pumping should be recorded (using the same time intervals for reading as for an abstraction step). A normal consecutive step test will involve increasing abstraction rate steps but the order of steps may in some cases be random and the elapsed time for steps can be varied. Reverse consecutive tests are sometimes performed when the first step involves the maximum abstraction rate.

In **intermittent step tests**, readings are made in the same way as for consecutive tests but a full recovery is recorded after each step. These tests take longer (and are therefore more expensive) than consecutive tests but in addition to providing a yield/drawdown curve to characterise the well, they also provide a series of independent constant-rate tests from which aquifer properties can be deduced if observation well readings have been made.

Analysis of step-test data can be divided into two distinct parts:

   (i) analysis for yield/drawdown well characteristics;
   (ii) analysis for storage and transmission aquifer properties.

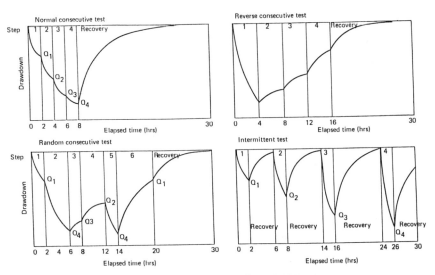

Fig. 5.16 Step-drawdown tests

For the purposes of aquifer property determination, a consecutive step test may be treated as a variable-discharge test (see later section) and an intermittent step test as a series of constant-discharge tests (see later section).

The primary aim of step-drawdown tests is to determine the yield/drawdown characteristics of the well and to determine the well efficiency.

The yield/drawdown curves may take a number of forms (Fig. 5.17). The 'normal' form of curves, A on Fig. 5.17, show a decelerating gradient with increased yield and enable a maximum 'safe-yield' for a reasonable drawdown to be assigned to each well. The 'breakaway' curves, B on Fig. 5.17, show an undulating gradient with increasing yield. Sections of high gradient imply drawdown through more productive horizons in the well, where increased yield can be obtained for small increments of drawdown. Such curves are often found in fissured or layered aquifers where effective hydraulic conductivity varies with depth. Curves C and D on Fig. 5.17 indicate inadequate step-tests. In C, the gradient of the curve remains virtually constant and it is uncertain what a maximum safe yield may be. In D, the gradient increases with increasing yield. If tested at higher rates of abstraction the well may adopt either pattern A or B, and a 'safe yield' can then be estimated.

Estimates of well loss, aquifer loss and well efficiency can be made if observation well responses can be analysed to predict the aquifer transmissivity and storage coefficient. The *productivity* of a production well is generally expressed as the specific capacity which is the ratio of the yield to drawdown. The total drawdown (s_t) at a production well involves a head component due to turbulent losses as water passes through the screen casing and pump intake, called the well loss (s_w). The

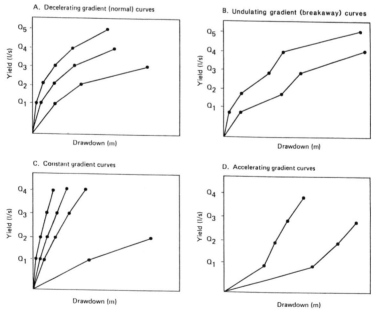

Fig. 5.17.   Yield-drawdown curves

remainder of the drawdown is attributable to laminar head losses in the aquifer—the aquifer loss (s_a). The ratio of the aquifer loss to the total drawdown (s_a/s_t) is known as the well efficiency. The aquifer loss can be estimated from values of transmissivity and storage coefficient by estimating the drawdown at the well, alternatively Jacob[13] gives the following equation for the estimation of well loss:

$$s_w = CQ^2$$

where s_w is the well head loss   (L)
       Q is the abstraction rate   (L^3/T)
       C is the well-loss constant   (T^2/L^5)

The value of C can be estimated from step test data, where all steps are of equal length, according to Jacob[13]:

$$C = \frac{\Delta s_i/\Delta Q_i - \Delta s_{i-1}/\Delta Q_{i-1}}{\Delta Q_{i-1} + \Delta Q_i}$$

where Δs_i is the ith incremental drawdown step   (L)
      ΔQ_i is the ith incremental abstraction step   (L^3/T)

Walton[14] suggests that for a homogeneous aquifer, a fall in the value of C with increasing abstraction indicates well development. If C increases, clogging of the well screen or well wall may have occurred. These conclusions, of course, assume that the yield/drawdown curves are of the normal type (Fig. 5.17A).

The Theis[15] solution for radial flow to a confined well in an infinite aquifer has the solution for head loss through the aquifer as:

$$s_a = \frac{Q}{4\pi T}W(u)$$

where Q is the abstraction rate   (L^3/T)
      T is the aquifer transmissivity   (L/T^2)
      $W(u)$ is a constant for a fixed time   (dimensionless)

This equation will be extensively discussed later in the chapter and may be simply written:

$$s_a = BQ.$$

Thus the total drawdown at the pumped well may be written:

$$s_t = s_a + s_w = BQ + CQ^2 = [B + CQ]Q$$

The well efficiency s_a/s_t may be written:

$$E = \frac{s_a}{s_t} = \frac{B}{B + CQ}$$

It is clear from this formula, since B and C must be positive and finite, that the efficiency of a production well declines with increasing abstraction rate and that well design should attempt to minimise turbulent losses in the well (the well-loss coefficient C). Pumping costs are related to the total head loss at the production well and increased yield may be offset by increased costs at high values of Q. The maximum safe yield of a well is therefore not necessarily the optimum economic yield.

Intermittent step tests can be analysed as a series of constant-rate tests to give good estimates of T (transmissivity) from the pumped well response (see following section). For consecutive step tests the problem is more difficult.

In the consecutive step-drawdown test a series of variable abstraction rates follow one another with no time for recovery. The analysis of data for the pumped well to give values of aquifer properties is described by Logan[16] and Eden and Hazel[17].

The simplest analysis, due to Logan[16], assumes that the drawdown at the end of each step is an equilibrium value and adopts the Thiem[6] solution as a model:

$$s_t = \frac{Q}{2\pi T} \ln \left[\frac{r_i}{r_w} \right] \text{ or } T = \frac{Q}{2\pi s_t} \ln \left[\frac{r_i}{r_w} \right]$$

where r_i is the radius of influence of the well   (L)
            r_w is the effective (actual) well radius   (L)
            s_t is the total drawdown at the well   (L)

Experience suggests that r_i/r_w is about 1 000 and Logan[16] recommends that the equation be reduced to:

$$T = C_o \frac{Q}{s_t}$$

where C_o is constant, found by experience to be in the range 1.2–2.1, and 1.5 is a reasonable value in order to obtain a crude value of transmissivity.

Eden and Hazel[17] base their pumped well analysis on the Jacob equation including aquifer loss and well loss:

$$s_t = s_a + s_w = BQ + CQ^2$$

$$s_t = \frac{Q}{4\pi T} \ln \left[\frac{2.25\ Tt}{r^2 S} \right] + CQ^2$$

The equation may be extended to multiple steps:

$$s_t = \sum_{i=1}^{i=n} \frac{\Delta Q_i}{4\pi T} \ln \left[\frac{2.25T\ t_i}{r^2 S} \right] + CQ_i^2$$

where ΔQ_i is the ith abstraction increment   (L³/T)

$$Q_i = \sum_{i=1}^{i=n} \Delta Q_i \text{ is the total abstraction rate}$$ (L³/T)

t_i is the elapsed time since the ith increment of abstraction began.
The equation may be further simplified:

$$s_t = \frac{1}{4\pi T} \ln \left[\frac{2.25\ T}{r^2 S} \right] \sum_{i=1}^{i=n} \Delta Q_i + \sum_{i=1}^{i=n} \Delta Q_i \ln [t_i] + CQ_i^2$$

Writing:

$$A = \frac{1}{4\pi T} \ln \left[\frac{2.25\ T}{r^2 S} \right]$$

gives:

$$s_t = AQ_i + \frac{1}{4\pi T} \sum_{i=1}^{i=n} \Delta Q_i \ln [t_i] + CQ_i^2$$

A plot of s_t against $ln[t]$ gives a series of linear sections with gradients of $AQ_i/4\pi T$ from which estimates of T can be made.

The second term in the equation involves the summed transient aquifer response to each pumping increment. In theory, the gradient of the semilog plot will increasingly underestimate T in successive steps due to residual response for previous increments. In practice, these changes in gradient should prove relatively small.

For data from pumped wells, the intercepts of the semilog plot depend upon the residual aquifer response and the well loss in addition to the aquifer properties and therefore estimation of storage coefficient from such tests is practically impossible. An estimate may be obtained however from observation well data and the method will be subsequently described.

Example 6. A step-drawdown test on a 450 mm diameter well gave the following results for 4×2 hr steps

Yield (Q) (l/s)	10	20	40	60
Drawdown (s) in well (m)	1.24	2.59	5.61	8.95

Calculate the well loss constant for each increase in abstraction rate and deduce the well stability and efficiency.

1. Calculate ΔQ and Δs for successive increments:

$\Delta Q (m^3/s)$	10^{-2}	10^{-2}	2×10^{-2}	2×10^{-2}
Δs (m)	1.24	1.35	3.02	3.34

2. Calculate $\Delta s_i/\Delta Q_i$; $- \Delta s_{i-1}/\Delta Q_{i-1}$ and $\Delta Q_i + \Delta Q_{i-1}$ for successive increments and from the ratio determine C:

$\dfrac{\Delta s_i}{\Delta Q_i} - \dfrac{\Delta s_{i-1}}{\Delta Q_{i-1}}$	11	16	16
$\Delta Q_i + \Delta Q_{i-1}$	2×10^{-2}	3×10^{-2}	4×10^{-2}
C m/$(m^3/s)^2$	550	533	400

The value of C changes quite abruptly during the last step of the test indicating development, probably by removal of fines around the well giving reduced entry velocities.

3. The well efficiency is given by:

$$E = \frac{s_a}{s_t} = \frac{s_t - s_w}{s_t} = \frac{s_t - CQ^2}{s_t}$$

C (prior to the instability) has an average value of about 540 m^{-5}s^2 or m/$(m^3/s)^2$. Hence E can be estimated for abstraction rates up to 40 l/s:

	10	20	40
Yield (l/s)	10	20	40
Drawdown (m)	1.24	2.59	5.61
Well loss (m)	0.05	0.22	0.86
Aquifer loss (m)	1.19	2.37	4.75
Efficiency (per cent)	96	92	85

Example 7. In the previous example, the detailed time/drawdown (m) data were as follows:

Rate (l/s) \ Elapsed time (mins)	1	2	4	8	15	30	60	120
10	0.85	0.92	1.00	1.05	1.08	1.12	1.17	1.24
20	2.15	2.21	2.26	2.31	2.36	2.41	2.55	2.59
40	4.95	5.06	5.16	5.25	5.34	5.43	5.52	5.61
60	8.25	8.36	8.46	8.56	8.66	8.76	8.86	8.95

Estimate the aquifer transmissivity.

1. A preliminary estimate of T can be made using the approximate equation $T = 1.5 \, Q/s_t$ of Logan[16] taking the constant C_o to be 1.5.

Q (l/s)	10	20	40	60
s_t (m)	1.24	2.59	5.61	8.95
T (m²/d)	1045	1001	924	867

2. The estimate may be improved by using the well loss coefficient (C) from Example 6.

$$T = \frac{1.5}{E} \frac{Q}{s_t} = 1.5 \frac{Q}{s_a}$$

Q (l/s)	10	20	40	60
S_a (m)	1.19	2.37	4.75	7.01
T (m²/d)	1089	1094	1091	1109

This gives a more consistent average value of 1096 m²/d.

3. Finally T may be estimated by plotting the drawdown against $\log [t]$ (Fig. 5.18). Values of Δs_m for a log time cycle are used to deduce T from the

gradient of the semilog plot, using the Jacob[13] approximation formula:

$$T = \frac{2.3}{4\pi} \frac{\Delta Q}{\Delta s_m} = 0.183 \frac{\Delta Q}{\Delta s}$$

where ΔQ is the pumping increment

ΔQ (l/s)	10	10	20	20
Δs_m (m)	0.15	0.155	0.31	0.30
T (m²/d)	1054	1020	1020	1054

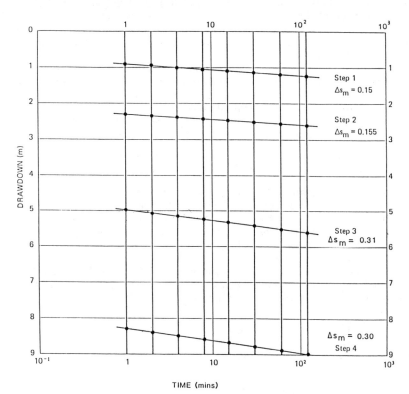

Fig. 5.18. Consecutive step-test—semilog time drawdown plot
(Example 7)

Constant-Discharge Tests

Constant-discharge tests are the most important tool of the hydrogeologist in finding aquifer properties. Their analysis has received extensive attention in the literature. Kruseman and de Ridder[18] provided an excellent compilation of the 'state of the art'.

The best constant-discharge tests are preceded by an equipment test of a few hours' duration a day or so before the full test. This gives an opportunity to determine appropriate control valve settings for the test and enables logistics of data collection to be tried out in addition to the equipment.

If there is the possibility that the surface water system may be interconnected with the aquifer and the former is likely to be affected during the test then provision must be made to measure spring and stream flows. It is also important that the pumped water is discharged at a point where it will not recirculate to the well thus influencing the test results.

A constant-rate test should *never* involve a significant change in the abstraction rate. Any major change must result in abandonment and restart of the test. The object of the test is to determine aquifer properties as precisely as possible and any rate fluctuations will complicate or invalidate subsequent analysis. If a test is restarted a period of not less than 3 times the total elapsed pumping period should be allowed for recovery. Recovery of water levels does not imply full aquifer recovery since in an unconfined or leaky aquifer system the unsaturated water content profile must also recover.

Pump discharge should be continuously recorded using a triangular or rectangular notch weir tank. If continuous recording is not possible, readings should be taken at least every hour to check that a constant rate is maintained. All minor control valve adjustments must be noted.

The necessary duration of constant discharge tests depends on a large number of factors. A preliminary estimate can be based on the discharge rate:

Discharge rate (l/s)	< 5	5–10	10–30	30–50	>50
Duration of test (days)	1	2	4	7	10

These recommendations may be reduced if a nearby barrier boundary condition is found or increased if a recharge boundary or delayed yield effect occurs. The duration of a test should *always* be at the discretion of the analyst who is to use the data since premature curtailment can render a long period of expensive pumping inconclusive in terms of the identification of aquifer characteristics—the primary aim of a constant discharge test.

Water levels should be recorded in the pumped well and all observation wells for a period before the start of the test so as to establish any natural trend in groundwater level at the site and during the test according to the following schedule:

immediately prior to pumping then
every   30 secs up to 10 mins from start of test
   „   5 mins for 10–60 mins
   „   15 mins for 1–4 hrs
   „   30 mins for 4–8 hrs
   „   1 hr for 8–24 hrs
   „   2 hr for 1-2 days
   „   4 hr for 2–4 days
   „   8 hr for 4–7 days
   „   12 hr for 7 days to completion.

This schedule allows for some redundancy of data but if any significant changes take place in the hydrological environment during the test period then the reading schedule should be restarted from the time of the change; for example, if the abstraction rate is changed, a nearby well begins to abstract, or a major spring ceases to flow. It is always better to have too much data than too little.

Analysis of constant-rate tests is a major topic in its own right. A huge number of analytical solutions have been obtained to take account of a large variety of hydrogeological circumstances such as:

(1) confined conditions;
(2) unconfined conditions;
(3) confined-unconfined transitions;
(4) delayed-yield from storage;
(5) leakage from overlying/underlying formations;
(6) recharge/barrier boundaries;
(7) partial penetrating wells;
(8) wells of finite diameter

and many more. Additionally, numerical models have become increasingly used for deducing aquifer properties from test data.

A simple (perhaps simplistic) approach to analysis is to consider all data initially in terms of the Theis[15] solution for radial, non-leaky, confined flow to a fully penetrating well in a uniform aquifer of infinite areal extent. The most appropriate analytical method is then determined by examination of the way in which the field curve deviates from the 'ideal' Theis solution.

To this end, Appendix I (a)–(h) has been prepared to provide a series of type-curve models (based on the references quoted):

Appendix I (a) Slug test curves (Papadopoulos et al[5])
       I (b) Confined aquifer with lateral boundaries (Ferris et al[19] and Hantush[20])
       I (c) Confined aquifer with leakage from above (Hantush and Jacob[21] and Hantush[22])
       I (d) Partially penetrating wells (Hantush[23])
       I (e) Confined-unconfined transition (Moench and Prickett[24])
       I (f) Unconfined aquifer with delayed yield (Neuman[25])
       I (g) Finite diameter wells (Papadopoulos and Cooper[4])
       I (h) Constant-head discharge curves (Jacob and Lohman[9]).

Analysis of test data involves matching the log-log type curves with the field curve plot of ln $(H\text{-}h)$ (drawdown) against ln (t) (time). The definition of parameters for generalised, transient radial flow is given in Fig. 5.19. The curve fitting procedure is most simply explained for the 'ideal' Theis curve (Fig. 5.20). The solution has the form:

$$H - h = \frac{Q}{4\pi T} W(u)$$

where H is the initial head   (L)
       h head at elapsed time t (L)
       Q abstraction rate   (L^3/T)
       T aquifer transmissivity   (L^2/T)
       $W(u)$ a well function   (dimensionless)
       $u = r^2 S/4Tt$ (dimensionless)
       r radial distance from pumped well   (L)
       S storage coefficient   (dimensionless)
       s drawdown $(H\text{-}h)$ at r (L)

The match point on the field curve gives a value of drawdown s_m and time t_m. This is conveniently (but not essentially) chosen to be coincident with $1/u_m = 1$ and $W(u_m) = 1$.

Thus:

$$s_m = \frac{Q}{4\pi T} W(u_m) = \frac{Q}{4\pi T} = 1$$

Hence:

$$T = \frac{Q}{4\pi s_m}$$

and

$$u_m = \frac{r^2 S}{4 T t_m} = 1$$

Hence:

$$S = \frac{4 T t_m}{r^2} = \frac{Q t_m}{\pi r^2 s_m}$$

The curve matching should be carried out ensuring that the appropriate axes of the

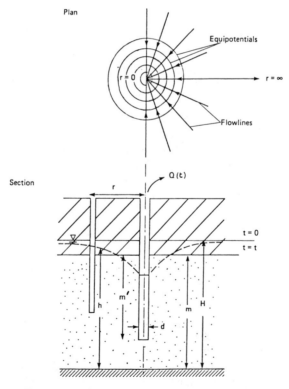

Fig. 5.19. Generalised transient radial flow

type and field curves remain parallel. If $W(u_m) = 1$, $1/u_m = 1$ cannot be used as a match-point. Any other point may be used.

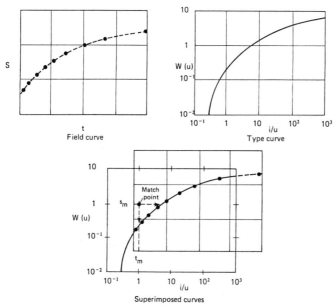

Fig. 5.20. Theis curve fitting procedure

The function $W(u)$ is the exponential integral:

$$W(u) = \int_u^o \frac{e^{-u}}{u} \, du \simeq - \gamma - \ln u$$

where $\gamma = 0.5772$ is Euler's constant.

This approximation, suggested by Cooper and Jacob[26], is valid when $u \le 0.01$. The Theis equation for drawdown may be manipulated and written as:

$$H - h = \frac{Q}{4\pi T} \ln \left[\frac{2.25 r^2 S}{T} \right] - \frac{Q}{4\pi T} \ln (t)$$

Writing $A = \dfrac{Q}{4\pi T} \ln \left[\dfrac{2.25 r^2 S}{T} \right]$ and $B = \dfrac{Q}{4\pi T}$ reveals a simple linear relationship between $(H - h)$ drawdown and $\ln (t)$ time:

$$H\text{-}h = A - B \ln (t).$$

Estimation of the slope $-B$ and intercept A of a plot of drawdown against log of time (Fig. 5.21) will yield aquifer properties. If the drawdown increment (Δs_m) is read from the line in Fig. 5.21 for a whole log (base 10) cycle of t (such that log $(t) = 1 = 2.3 \ln (t)$) then:

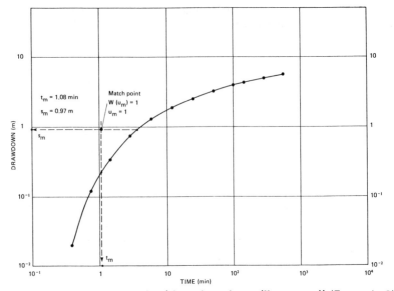

Fig. 5.21. Theis log-log plot (time-drawdown (limestone)) (Example 8)

$$s_{m1} = A - 2.3 \, B \log (t_1)$$
$$s_{m2} = A - 2.3 \, B \log (t_2)$$
$$s_{m1} - s_{m2} = \Delta s_m = 2.3 \, B \, (\log (t_2) - \log (t_1))$$
$$= 2.3 \, B \log (t_2/t_1)$$

For a whole log cycle $\log (t_2/t_1) = 1$ thus:

$$\Delta s_m = 2.3 \, B = \frac{2.3 \, Q}{4\pi T}$$

and

$$T = \frac{2.3Q}{4\pi \Delta s_m} = 0.183 \, \frac{Q}{\Delta s_m}$$

If the linear section of the curve is extrapolated backwards and the time (t_m) is read off for zero drawdown then:

$$A = B \, ln \, (t_m)$$

$$\frac{A}{B} = ln \, \frac{2.25r^2S}{T} = ln \, t_m$$

$$t_m = \frac{2.25r^2S}{T}$$

$$S = \frac{Tt_m}{2.25r^2} = \frac{2.3Q}{9\pi r^2} \, \frac{t_m}{\Delta s_m} = 0.0814 \, \frac{Q}{r^2} \, \frac{t_m}{\Delta S_m}$$

If the result of a Theis curve-fit exercise reveals significant deviation from 'ideal' behaviour then considerations must be given to the many other analytical solutions. The form of the log-log curves for a number of these are given in Appendix I, (b)–(g). It is recommended that expert guidance be sought in performing more complex analyses.

For the case of bounded aquifers (Appendix Ib):

$$H - h = \frac{Q}{4\pi T}(W(u) \pm W(u'))$$

where $W(u')$ represents the 'image' well resulting from the boundary condition (Ferris *et al*[19] and Hantush[20]).

For confined leaky aquifers (Appendix Ic):

$$H - h = \frac{Q}{4\pi T} W(u, \frac{r}{B})$$

where the parameter $\frac{r}{B}$ reflects the 'leakiness' and $B = \sqrt{T/K'}$ and K' is the hydraulic conductivity to thickness ratio for the leaking bed (Hantush and Jacob[21]).

For partial penetration (Appendix Id):

$$H - h = \frac{Q}{4\pi T} W(u, \frac{r}{m}, \gamma)$$

where m is the aquifer thickness (L) and
γ is the proportion of the aquifer penetrated (dimensionless).

For confined-unconfined transitions (Appendix Ie):

$$H - h = \frac{Q}{4\pi t}W(u_A, u_B, v)$$

where u_A is the "confined" value of $u = \frac{r^2 S_u}{4Tt}$;

u_B is the "unconfined" value of $u = \frac{r^2 S_c}{4Tt}$;

v is the value of $u = \frac{R^2 Su}{4Tt}$ when R is at the boundary of the confined-
-unconfined transition.

v is a constant and can be estimated from $\frac{Q}{4\pi Th'}$ where h' is the initial excess pressure head for the aquifer. Moench and Prickett[24] tabulate $\frac{Q}{4\pi Th'}$ and v.

For delayed yield from storage (Appendix If):

$$H - h = \frac{Q}{4\pi T} W(u_A, u_B, \eta)$$

where u_A is the "confined" value of $u = \dfrac{r^2 S_c}{4Tt}$

u_B is the "unconfined" value of $u = \dfrac{r^2 S_u}{4Tt}$

η is r^2/m_2 where m is the initial unsaturated thickness (Neuman[25]).

For finite diameter wells (other solutions assume a line source) (Appendix Ig):

$$H - h = \frac{Q}{4\pi t} W(u_w, \alpha)$$

where $u_w = \dfrac{r_w^2 S}{4Tt}$ for a well of effective radius r_w,

and $\alpha = \dfrac{S r_w^2}{r_c}$ where r_c is the radius at which the drawdown is measured $(r_c > r_w)$.

This solution is valuable when the well-bore itself contributes significantly to the volume of water produced (Papadopoulos and Cooper[4]).

For details of these and other more complex analyses the reader is referred to the excellent compilations of Kruseman and de Ridder[18] and Stallman[27].

Example 8. A well of diameter 450 mm in a confined limestone aquifer was tested at a constant rate of discharge of 25 l/s for a period of 4 days. The time/drawdown data collected from an observation well 30 m distant were as follows:

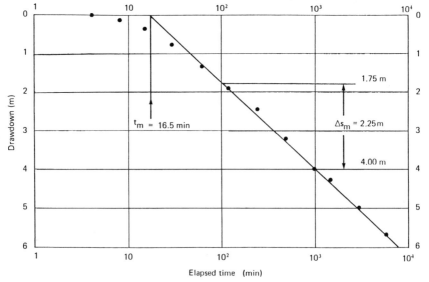

Fig. 5.22.   Jacob semilog time-drawdown plot (limestone) (Example 8)

Elapsed time	minutes						hours				days			
	1	2	4	8	15	30	1	2	4	8	16	1	2	4
Drawdown (m)	0.00	0.00	0.02	0.12	0.34	0.75	1.30	1.88	2.41	3.17	3.98	4.26	4.95	5.66

Estimate the aquifer properties T and S using the Theis log-log-plot and the Jacob semilog plot analyses:

(a) Theis Curve Fitting
    The log-log plot (Fig. 5.21) gives values of $s_m = 0.97$ m and $t_m = 1.08$ mins corresponding to the type-curve point $W(u_m) = 1$, $u_m = 1$. Thus:

$$T = \frac{Q}{4\pi} \cdot \frac{1}{s_m} = \frac{25 \times 10^{-3}}{4 \times 3.14} \times \frac{1}{0.97} = 2.05 \times 10^{-3} \text{ m}^2/\text{s} = 177 \text{ m}^2/\text{d}.$$

and

$$S = \frac{Q}{\pi r^2} \cdot \frac{t_m}{s_m} = \frac{25 \times 10^{-3}}{3.14 \times 30 \times 30} \times \frac{1.08 \times 60}{0.97} = 5.9 \times 10^{-4}$$

(b) Jacob's Approximate Method
    The semilog plot (Fig. 5.22) gives values of $\Delta s_m = 2.25$ m corresponding to the drawdown for one log time cycle and the time intercept for zero drawdown of $t_m = 16.5$ mins. Thus:

$$T = \frac{Q}{4\pi} \cdot \frac{2.3}{\Delta s_m} = \frac{25 \times 10^{-3}}{4 \times 3.14} \times \frac{2.3}{2.25} = 2.03 \times 10^{-3} \text{ m}^2/\text{s} = 175 \text{ m}^2/\text{d}$$

and

$$S = \frac{Q}{\pi r^2} \cdot \frac{2.3}{9} \cdot \frac{t_m}{\Delta s_m} = \frac{25 \times 10^{-3}}{3.14 \times 30 \times 30} \times \frac{2.3}{9} \times \frac{16.5 \times 60}{2.25}$$

$$= 8.84 \times 10^{-6} \times 2.56 \times 10^{-1} \times 4.40 \times 10^2 = 1.0 \times 10^{-3}$$

The discrepancy between Theis[15] and Jacob[13] methods is very small for T but for S the Jacob method is in error due to the extreme sensitivity of the intercept on the log (t) scale. In general, the Theis curve fitting technique gives more reliable results, particularly for S.

Variable-Rate Tests

    Variable-rate tests are much less widely employed than constant-rate tests for two major reasons:

    (i) practical difficulties of monitoring and accurately controlling discharge rates,
    (ii) difficulty and complexity of analysis to give estimates of aquifer properties.

    There are however two major types of test which are used widely in practice and fall into the category of variable-rate tests:

    (1) consecutive step-drawdown tests and
    (2) artesian well overflow tests.

In the former case, the conduct and philosophy of testing has been discussed earlier but the analysis of observation well response collected in such tests constitutes a problem better treated as a variable-rate test.

Consecutive Step Drawdown Test Analysis

The consecutive step test, when observation well data are collected, can be analysed to give reliable values of transmissivity and storage coefficient. The analysis uses the principle of superposition used in the Eden and Hazel[7] analysis for pumped wells. The Jacob[13] approximation may be used but a solution based on the 'ideal' Theis curve[15] will be described.

At an observation point the drawdown after time t is given by:

$$s_i = \sum_{i=1}^{i=n} \Delta Q_i \, W(u_i)$$

with

$$u_i = \frac{r^2 S}{4 T t_i}$$

where ΔQ_i is the ith incremental pumping step   (L³/T)
t_i is the elapsed time since the onset of the ith pumping
step   (T).

The analysis proceeds as follows (Fig. 5.23):

1. Plot all data on a log-log time/drawdown basis.
2. Fit a Theis curve to the step 1 data and extrapolate for all other steps (Curve A). Calculate T and S for step 1 as in Example 8.
3. Plot the differences (Δs_1) between step 2 Curve B and the extended step 1 Curve A on a further log-log plot.
4. Fit a Theis curve to the corrected curve B over step 2 and extrapolate curve B for other steps. Calculate T and S for step 2.
5. Repeat the procedure until an estimate of T and S has been made for every step.

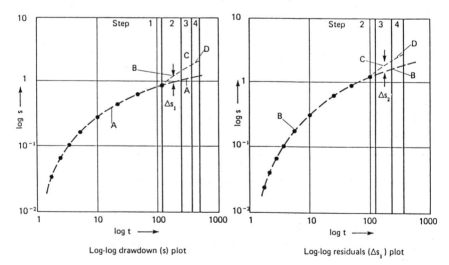

Fig. 5.23. Analysis of consecutive-step variable-rate test (Example 9)

Since all the curves should coincide if T and S are independent of Q then the first step drawdowns and subsequent differences may be averaged or the plots combined by scaling to ΔQ to give a better estimate of T and S. The differencing techniques result in magnification of errors, and after 2 or 3 steps, if drawdowns are small the resultant plots may be unsatisfactory. The quality of data using observation wells is normally much better than for pumped wells since complications of well-loss are avoided.

Example 9. The following drawdown data (m) were collected for an observation borehole 20 m distant from a pumped well which was tested consecutively at rates of 4, 8, 16 and 32 l/s, each step being of 2 hours' duration.

Rate l/s \ Elapsed time (mins)	1	2	4	8	15	30	60	120
4	0.06	0.08	0.10	0.12	0.13	0.15	0.17	0.19
8	0.25	0.27	0.29	0.30	0.32	0.34	0.36	0.39
16	0.52	0.55	0.60	0.63	0.66	0.70	0.74	0.79
32	1.04	1.11	1.20	1.26	1.33	1.41	1.49	1.59

Estimate the aquifer properties T and S.

The data for each stage of the calculation procedure are given in Table 5.I. The values of T and S are 1015 m^2/d and 5×10^{-4}, respectively.

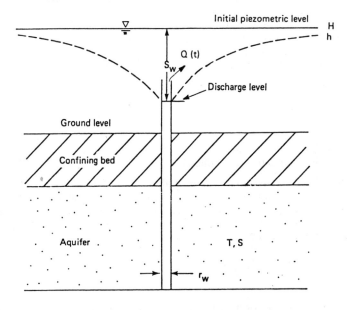

Fig. 5.24. Overflowing well

TABLE 5.I   Consecutive-step, Variable-rate Test Data for Analysis (*Example 9*)

Step				1								2				
Flow rate (l/s)				4								8				
Time from start of step (mins)	1	2	4	8	15	30	60	120	1	2	4	8	15	30	60	120
s_1 (data)	0.06	0.08	0.10	0.12	0.13	0.15	0.17	0.19	0.25	0.27	0.29	0.30	0.32	0.34	0.36	0.39
s'_1 (Theis fit)	0.06	0.08	0.10	0.12	0.13	0.15	0.17	0.19	0.19	0.19	0.19	0.19	0.19	0.19	0.19	0.20
s_2 (residual)	—	—	—	—	—	—	—	—	0.06	0.08	0.10	0.11	0.13	0.15	0.17	0.19
s'_2 (Theis fit)	—	—	—	—	—	—	—	—	0.06	0.08	0.10	0.12	0.13	0.15	0.17	0.19
s_3 (residual)	—	—	—	—	—	—	—	—	—	—	—	—	—	—	—	—
s'_3 (Theis fit)	—	—	—	—	—	—	—	—	—	—	—	—	—	—	—	—
s_4 (residual)	—	—	—	—	—	—	—	—	—	—	—	—	—	—	—	—
s'_4 (Theis fit)	—	—	—	—	—	—	—	—	—	—	—	—	—	—	—	—

Variable-Rate Overflow Tests

The most commonly employed test where the discharge rate varies continuously (rather than in discontinuous steps) is the overflow test. The test is performed by monitoring the water levels and rate of discharge from an overflowing well using a measurement frequency similar to that suggested for constant-rate tests. The initial piezometric head (before overflow is allowed) must be determined using either a manometer or transducer. The overflow discharge should be continuously recorded by a float recorder on a triangular or rectangular notch weir or a device of comparable precision and reliablity.

Outflow tests are actually constant-head tests and their analysis was first described by Jacob and Lohman[9] who gave type curves for non-leaking, confined discharge from an unbounded aquifer.

The discharge (Q) after any time (t) (Fig. 5.24) is given by:

$$Q = 2\pi T s_w \, W(\lambda)$$

with

$$\lambda = \frac{Tt}{r^2_w s}$$

where s_w is the head loss at the well(L)
r_w is the effective well radius(L)

The function $W(\lambda)$ is tabulated by Walton[14]. To determine T and S, the field discharge against time is prepared as a log-log plot and matched against the Jacob-Lohman type curve using the match-point technique described for the Theis curve. A leaky-aquifer solution by Hantush[22] is also available, analogous to the Jacob-Hantush constant discharge solution:

$$Q = 2\pi T s_w \, W(\lambda, \frac{r_w}{B})$$

where B is defined as for the constant-discharge equation and $\lambda \, \sqrt{T/K'}$ where K' is the hydraulic conductivity to thickness ratio for the source bed.

Type curves for the analysis of overflowing wells are given in Appendix I(h).

TABLE 5.1 (continued)

		3								4						Step
		16								32						Flow rate (l/s)
1	2	4	8	15	30	60	120	1	2	4	8	15	30	60	120	Time from start of step (mins)
0.52	0.55	0.60	0.63	0.66	0.70	0.74	0.79	1.04	1.11	1.20	1.26	1.33	1.41	1.49	1.59	s_1 (data)
0.20	0.20	0.20	0.20	0.21	0.21	0.21	0.22	0.22	0.22	0.22	0.22	0.22	0.22	0.22	0.22	s'_1 (Theis fit)
0.32	0.35	0.40	0.43	0.45	0.49	0.53	0.57	0.82	0.89	0.98	1.04	1.11	1.19	1.27	1.37	s_2 (residual)
0.19	0.19	0.19	0.19	0.19	0.19	0.19	0.20	0.20	0.20	0.20	0.20	0.21	0.21	0.21	0.22	s'_2 (Theis fit)
0.13	0.16	0.21	0.24	0.26	0.30	0.34	0.37	0.62	0.69	0.78	0.84	0.90	0.98	1.06	1.15	s_3 (residual)
0.12	0.16	0.20	0.23	0.26	0.30	0.34	0.37	0.37	0.37	0.37	0.37	0.37	0.38	0.39	0.41	s'_3 (Theis fit)
—	—	—	—	—	—	—	—	0.25	0.32	0.41	0.47	0.53	0.60	0.67	0.74	s_4 (residual)
—	—	—	—	—	—	—	—	0.25	0.32	0.41	0.46	0.53	0.60	0.67	0.74	s'_4 (Theis fit)

Example 10. A 450 mm diameter artesian confined well with an initial piezometric head of 18 m above ground surface in a thin gravel aquifer was allowed to overflow through an elbow junction 0.5 m above the ground. The discharge rates for various elapsed times were as follows:

Elapsed time			minutes						hours					days	
	1	2	4	8	15	30	1	2	4	8	16	1	2	4	
Discharge (l/s)	4.35	3.63	3.23	2.88	2.63	2.34	2.14	1.99	1.82	1.74	1.58	1.51	1.41	1.32	

1. Plot log (Q) against log (t) (Fig. 5.25).

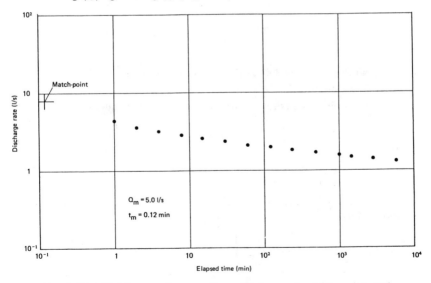

Fig. 5.25. **Field curve for overflow discharge test** (Example 10)

2. Overlay Jacob-Lohman-Hantush type curve and find the match-point $(W(\lambda) = \lambda = 1)$ $Q_m = 5.0$ l/s, $t_m = 0.12$ mins.
Use match-point values to estimate T and S. Thus:

$$T = \frac{1}{2\pi s_w} \cdot Q_m = \frac{5 \times 10^{-3}}{2 \times 3.14 \times 17.5} = 4.55 \times 10^{-5} \text{ m}^2/\text{s} = 3.93 \text{ m}^2/\text{d}.$$

and

$$S = \frac{1}{2\pi r^2_{\ w} s_w} \cdot Q_m t_m = \frac{5 \times 10^{-3} \times .12 \times 60}{2 \times 3.14 \times .225 \times .225 \times 17.5} = 6.5 \times 10^{-3}.$$

Recovery Tests

Recovery tests are very commonly carried out on completion of step-drawdown, constant-rate and variable-rate tests. The water levels are monitored using the same frequency of reading as for a pumping phase (see earlier). The data are relatively easy to obtain but in the case of pumped wells it is essential that the pump be fitted with a non-return foot-valve to prevent the discharge of water from the rising main when pumping ceases.

Recovery tests should be regarded as a check on the data from pumping phases. Storage coefficient values cannot be satisfactorily derived from recovery tests since only the immediate recovery response is dependent on S. Unconfined recovery may be influenced by incomplete resaturation of pores. For analysis it is essential that the pre-recovery pumping history is fully documented.

Analysis of well recovery involves the principle of superposition of drawdowns and is similar to analyses involving boundaries or consecutive pumping tests. The analysis is described by Ferris et al[19] with a more recent and accessible account in the excellent text by Freeze and Cherry[28]. The recovery equation is:

$$H - h = s_r = \frac{Q}{4\pi T} [W(u_p) - W(u_r)]$$

with

$$u_p = \frac{r^2 S}{4 T t_p} \text{ and } u_r = \frac{r^2 S}{4 T t_r}$$

where t_p is the elapsed time since the start of abstraction   (T)
       t_r is the elapsed time since recovery began   (T)

Using the Jacob[13] approximation for $W(u)$ for confined aquifers gives:

$$H - h = s_p = \frac{Q}{4\pi T} \left\{ \ln [u_r] - \ln [u_p] \right\} = \frac{Q}{4\pi T} \ln \left[\frac{u_r}{u_p} \right] =$$

$$\frac{Q}{4\pi T} \ln \left[\frac{t_p}{t_r} \right]$$

It is convenient to plot the amount of recovery rather than the residual pumping drawdown thus:

$$s_r = h - H_o = \frac{-Q}{4\pi T} \ln \left[\frac{t_r}{t_p} \right]$$

and T can be deduced from a semilog plot of $h - H_o$ against $\log \left[\frac{t_r}{t_p} \right]$.

For unconfined wells, the analysis is complicated by the time delay imposed by gravity drainage and resaturation of pores. The storage coefficients are time-dependent functions which may be different for drainage and resaturation. The indeterminate nature of these functions makes unconfined well recovery difficult to analyse unless delayed storage release-resaturation effects can be neglected.

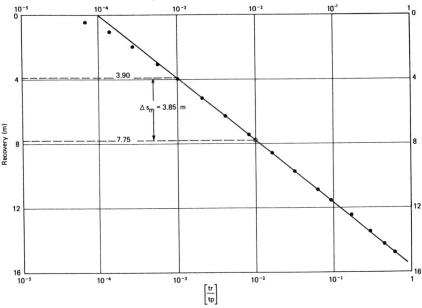

Fig. 5. 26. Recovery test analysis field plot (Example 11)

Example 11. Observations of recovery water levels in an observation borehole 50 m from a pumping well which had been pumped for 10 days at a constant rate of 25 l/s were as follows:

Recovery time	minutes						
	0	1	2	4	8	15	30
Drawdown (m)	15.64	15.19	14.56	13.70	12.63	11.69	10.55

Recovery time	hours						days			
	1	2	4	8	16	11	2	4	8	16
Drawdown (m)	9.38	8.23	7.06	5.93	4.76	4.11	3.23	2.18	1.38	0.88

1. Plot recovery against $\log\left[\dfrac{t_r}{t_p}\right]$ (Fig. 5.26).

2. Read off the recovery for a log time cycle (Δs_m)
$$\Delta s_m = 3.85 \text{ m.}$$

3. Calculate aquifer transmissivity:

$$T = \frac{Q}{4\pi\Delta s_m} = \frac{2.5 \times 10^{-3}}{4 \times 3.14 \times 3.85} = 5.17 \times 10^{-5} \text{ m}^2/\text{s} = 4.5 \text{ m}^2/\text{d}.$$

Multiple-Well Tests

Where regional aquifer response is to be measured it is necessary to conduct tests at multiple-well sites such that the drawdown cones interact. Such tests may be carried out by simultaneously starting several wells but because of the difficulty of collecting 'early time' drawdown data, it is often more convenient for wells to be started on consecutive days. The length of such tests is normally 30 to 100 days and a large number of observation wells, springs and streamflows may be monitored.

Analysis of such data using the analytical solutions for individual wells and the principle of superposition is complex. Normally such tests are analysed by matching the aquifer response with a distributed parameter finite difference or finite element as described in a later chapter.

An analytical approach uses the method of superposition of solutions for multiple wells as follows:

$$(H-h)_i = s_i = \frac{1}{4\pi T} \sum_{i=1}^{i=n} Q_i \, W(u_i)$$

with

$$u_i = \frac{r_i^2 S}{4T t_i}$$

where r_i is the radial distance of the observation point from the ith
        pumping well   (L)
        t_i is the elapsed pumping time for the ith well   (T)

The method is inflexible if unconfined-confined transitions occur and if aquifer characteristics vary spatially. Numerical methods are clearly superior for both the identification of aquifer properties and the prediction of response.

3.   TESTING PHILOSOPHY AND DESIGN

In Section 1 the purpose of well tests has been reviewed and in Section 2 the major test techniques and their analysis have been discussed. It now remains only to consider *why* aquifer properties are determined and *where* such tests should be carried out.

APPROPRIATE TEST SELECTION

The determination of aquifer properties using large-scale (mainly constant-rate) pumping tests has become almost an automatic step in the evaluation of groundwater resources. The advantages of large-scale tests are clear. They provide an estimate of *in situ* properties of a relatively large volume of the aquifer. Both transmission and storage properties are estimated from a single test and information about hydrogeological boundaries and adjacent formations can also be deduced in some cases. The disadvantages of large-scale tests are:

(a) their high cost both in manpower and physical resources;

(*b*) the ambiguity of the interpretation of aquifer characteristics from the observed response.

The high costs of large-scale tests arise from:

(i)   drilling large diameter, high capacity wells;
(ii) installing and running high capacity pumps for extended test periods;
(iii) the drilling of observation wells essential for the analysis of test results;
(iv) the provision of manpower for the numerous observations which must be made over the extended test period.

From these cost factors only (i) can be offset against subsequent resource development if the test wells become production sites.

The ambiguity of analysis arises from the fact that there are an infinity of combinations of aquifer properties and associated boundary conditions which may produce any observed response. The particular solution found by the application of conventional analysis is one possible 'model' but there is no guarantee that it represents the 'real' situation.

Small-scale well tests have been relatively little used by the UK water industry. They provide very local estimates of aquifer properties in the immediate vicinity of the test well and no information on the aquifer as a whole. Small-scale tests are inexpensive, require relatively cheap equipment and can be carried out rapidly with small manpower requirements.

Large-scale tests, including multiple-well tests, are an essential prerequisite to major groundwater resource development schemes where large capital investment in productive wells is under consideration. In many other cases, where funds for well tests are limited, the relative merits of very few large-scale tests compared with numerous cheap small-scale measurements must be carefully weighed. Automatic insistence on large-scale tests for problems of groundwater contamination and assessment of regional flow patterns may be a misuse of limited financial resources.

Large-scale tests are only justified when the aquifer response to a major perturbation of the flow regime must be determined. For problems involving flow under natural gradients a programme of small-scale testing is often adequate.

Test Equipment and Manpower Requirements

The comparative requirements for various types of tests are summarised in Table 5.II. In general, observation wells are only essential for large-scale, constant-rate tests. High capacity pumps similarly are only required for constant-rate tests and step tests. All large discharge tests require weir tanks or similar flow measuring devices. Some small-scale tests (packer and point dilution tests) require special equipment. The manpower requirements for tests involving observation wells can be reduced if automatic recorders are installed but for many large-scale tests the early time data are vital to the analysis and manual back-up is advisable even if recorders are installed, at least for the first few hours of the test.

Test Design and Site Selection

The design, site layout and site selection for well tests depend entirely on the aims of the test.

Small-scale tests to determine aquifer properties affect only the immediate area about the well and so almost any site may be selected. If the aim is to obtain 'typical' aquifer properties certain areas should be avoided:

(1) fault and fracture zones;
(2) the immediate vicinity of springs and major surface watercourses;

TABLE 5.II   Comparative Test Requirements

Maximum test duration (days)	Maximum area affected by test (m²)	Test requirements	Observation wells		Automatic water-level recorders		High capacity pumps	Precise (weir tank) discharge measurement	Minimum manpower to monitor test*	Special equipment
			Essential	Useful	Essential	Useful				
<1	<10	Rising and falling head tests	—	—	—	✓	—	—	1	—
<1	<10	Slug and bail tests	—	—	✓	—	—	—	1	—
<1	<10²	Packer tests	—	—	—	—	—	—	2	✓ See text
<1	<10	Point-dilution tracer tests	—	✓	—	—	—	—	—	✓ See text
<3	<10³	Intermittent step tests	—	✓	—	✓	✓	✓	2	—
<3	<10³	Consecutive step tests	—	✓	—	✓	✓	✓	2	—
<30	<10⁵	Constant-rate tests	✓	—	—	✓	✓	✓	n+2	—
<30	<10⁵	Variable-rate overflow tests	—	✓	—	✓	—	✓	1	—
<30	<10⁵	Recovery tests	—	✓	—	✓	—	—	n+1	—
>30	>10⁵	Multiple well tests	✓	—	—	✓	✓	✓	m(n+2)	—

Note: *n = number of observation wells; m = number of simultaneously operated sites

(3) the immediate vicinity of an aquifer's physical boundaries;
(4) areas of abnormally high or low groundwater head gradient.

If values of aquifer properties typical of these 'special' areas are required then the test sites should be selected accordingly. Most small-scale sites need only to have access for a small portable rig to install the well; the actual test equipment is usually much easier to bring to the site than the rig.

For large-scale tests involving observation wells, the site selection and test layout must be given more thought. Observation well radius with respect to the test well should be chosen with regard to the expected aquifer properties at the site as indicated by Table 5.III. The number and position of observation wells depend on the site geometry with respect to expected hydrogeological and hydraulic boundaries and any expected aquifer property, anisotropy or inhomogeneity. Theoretically for a test in a homogeneous isotropic aquifer, only one observation well is necessary but a minimum of two observation wells is recommended to check the assumption of isotropy (Fig. 5.27(a)). The more the site is suspected to deviate from this simple ideal the more wells are required. If anisotropy is suspected four observation wells are recommended in two orthogonal radial lines (Fig. 5.27(b)). Where boundaries are suspected pairs of wells should be placed on radii parallel

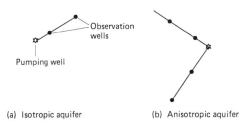

(a) Isotropic aquifer   (b) Anisotropic aquifer

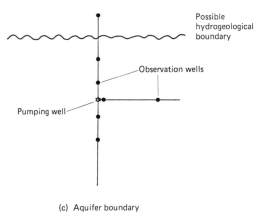

(c) Aquifer boundary

Fig. 5.27. Observation well layouts

and normal to the boundary. Two pairs of wells on normal radii should be positioned on either side of the pumped well and an additional observation well over the boundary should be installed as a check making a total of seven (Fig. 5.27(c)). The well pairs normal to the boundary may be placed symmetrically with respect to the pumped well to facilitate the easy detection of asymmetric response during testing. Test layout and design are discussed at length by Kruseman and de Ridder[18] and Stallman[27].

Large-scale tests may be carried out with a number of different aims and therefore have different site requirements as indicated in Table 5.IV. The common requirements are access for plant and vehicles and facilities for discharge disposal. This latter requirement should not override the test aim and if proximity to a major watercourse is a problem in terms of the test aim an alternative means of disposal should be found. Care must be taken to ensure that the discharged water does not recirculate to the aquifer during the course of the test.

TABLE 5.III   Observation Well Location

Aquifer type	Expected transmissivity (m^2/d)	Expected rate of response	Recommended distance for observation wells (m)
Unconfined	50-500	Very slow	25-35
Unconfined	> 500	Slow	45-60
Confined	50-500	Fast	60-100
Confined	> 500	Very fast	100-2000

TABLE 5.IV   Site Selection

Test aims \ Site requirements	Thick confining layer	High confined head	No confining layer	Remote from faults and fracture zones	Close to faults and fracture zones	Remote from surface watercourse	Close to surface watercourses	Remote from aquifer edge	Close to aquifer edge
'Typical' confined aquifer response	√	√	—	√	—	√	—	√	—
'Typical' unconfined aquifer response	—	—	√	√	—	√	—	√	—
Extent of surface-groundwater interconnection	—	—	√	√	—	—	√	√	—
Location of barrier boundaries	—	—	—	—	√	√	—	—	√
Location of recharge boundaries	—	—	√	—	√	—	√	√	—
Assessment of delayed-yield effect	—	—	√	√	—	√	—	√	—
Location of high yielding pumping sites	—	—	—	—	√	—	√	√	—

Test Control

Large-scale test data should *always* be plotted during the test so that the decision to halt or continue pumping may be continously reviewed in the light of the aquifer response. 'In-test' data analysis may also reveal unexpected features which call for new observations (for example, of spring discharge or streamflow) to be made. Pump breakdown or extreme precipitation may lead to the premature abandonment of tests. Long-term tests should be accompanied by the collection of rainfall, evaporation and barometric pressure data, the latter being especially important where confined response is being measured. Tests should be concluded as soon as possible (because of the expense of pumping) and this means as soon as the aims of the test have been met. The continuation of tests for 7 days when analysis requires only 4 days' data is wasteful and 'in test' analysis should prevent such waste.

4. REFERENCES

1. Hvorslev, M. J. 1951 "Time lag *v* soil permeability in groundwater observations" US Army Corps Engrs Waterways Exp. Sta. Bull 36, Vicksburg, Miss.
2. Cedergren, H. R. 1967 "Seepage, drainage and flow nets", John Wiley & Sons, New York.
3. Lee, I. K., White, W. and Ingles, O. W. 1983. "Geotechnical engineering", Pitman, Marshfield, Mass.
4. Papadopoulos, I. S. and Cooper, H. H. 1967 *Wat. Res. Res.*, 3, 263, Response of a finite-diameter well to an instantaneous charge of water.
5. Papadopoulos, I. S., Bredehoeft, J. D. and Cooper, H. H. 1973 *Wat. Res. Res.*, 9, 1087, On the analysis of slug test data.
6. Thiem, G. 1906 "Hydrologische methoden", Gebhardt, Leipzig.
7. Pearson, R. and Money, M. S. 1977 *Q. J. eng. Geol.*, 10, 221, Improvements in the Lugeon or Packer permeability test.
8. Houslby, A. C. 1976 *Q. J. eng. Geol.*, 9, 303, Routine interpretation of the Lugeon water test.
9. Jacob, C. E. and Lohman, S. W. 1952 *Trans. Am. Geophys. Union*, 33, 559, Nonsteady flow to a well of constant drawdown in an extensive aquifer.
10. Drost, W. *et al* 1968 *Wat. Res. Res.*, 4, 125, Point dilution methods of investigating groundwater flow by means of radioisotopes.
11. Rorabaugh, M. I. 1953 *Proc. ASCE*, 79, 1, Graphical and theoretical analysis of step-drawdown tests in artesian wells.
12. Clark, L. 1977 *Q. J. eng. Geol.*, 10, 125, The analysis and planning of step-drawdown tests.
13. Jacob, C. E. 1946 *Proc. ASCE* 72, 629, Drawdown tests to determine effective radius of artesian wells.
14. Walton, W. C. 1970 "Groundwater resource evaluation", McGraw-Hill, New York.
15. Theis, C. V. 1935 *Trans. Am. Geophys. Union*, 2, 519, The relation between the lowering of the piezometric surface and the rate and duration of discharge of a well using groundwater storage.
16. Logan, J. 1964 *Groundwater*, 2, 35, Estimating transmissibility from routine production tests of water wells.
17. Eden, R. N. and Hazel, C. P. 1973 *Civil Eng. Trans. Inst. Engrs Austr.*, 15, 5, Computer and geographical analysis of variable discharge pumping tests of wells.
18. Kruseman, G. P. and de Ridder, N. A. 1970 "Analysis and evaluation of pumping test data", Intern. Instn. Land Reclamation and Improvement, Bull. 11, Wageningen, Netherlands.
19. Ferris, J. G. *et al* 1962 "Theory of aquifer tests" US Geol. Surv., Water Supply Paper 1536-E.
20. Hantush, M. S. 1959 *J. Geophys. Res.*, 64, 1921, Analysis of data from pumping wells near a river.
21. Hantush, M. S. and Jacob, C. E. 1955 *Trans. Am. Geophys. Union,* 36, 95, Nonsteady radial flow in an infinite leaky aquifer.
22. Hantush, M. S. 1956 *Trans. Am. Geophys. Union*, 37, 702, Analysis of data from pumping tests in leaky aquifers.
23. Hantush, M. S. 1962 *Proc. ASCE*, 127, 268, Drawdown around partially penetrating wells.
24. Moench, A. F. and Prickett, T. A. 1972 *Wat. Res. Res.*, 8, 494, Radial flow in an infinite aquifer undergoing conversion from artesian to water table conditions.
25. Neuman, S. P. 1975 *Wat. Res. Res.*, 11, 329, Analysis of pumping test data from an isotropic unconfined aquifer considering delayed gravity response.
26. Cooper, H. H. and Jacob, C. E. 1946. *Trans. Am. Geophys. Union*, 27, 526, A generalised graphical method for evaluating formation constants and summarising well field history.
27. Stallman, R. W. 1971 "Aquifer test design, observations and data analysis" US Geological Survey, Techniques of Water Resources Investigations, B1, Govt. Printing Office, Washington, DC.
28. Freeze, R. A. and Cherry, J. A. 1979 "Groundwater", Prentice-Hall, New Jersey.

APPENDIX I.   TYPE-CURVE MODELS

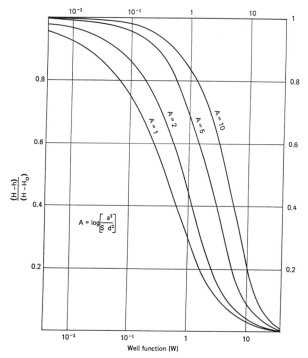

Appendix I(a). Slug test curves (after Papadopoulos *et al*[5])

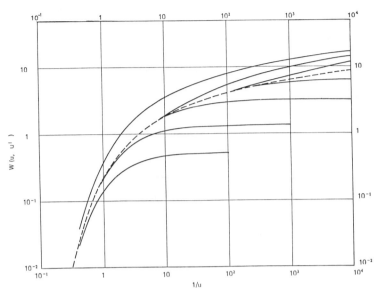

Appendix I(b). Confined aquifer with lateral boundaries (after Ferris *et al*[19] and Hantush[20])

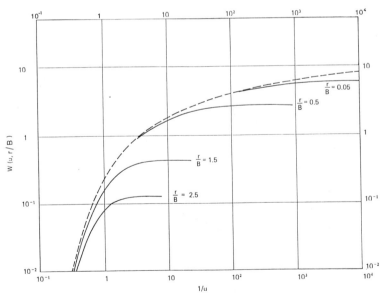

Appendix I(c). Confined aquifer with leakage from above (after Hantush and Jacob[21] and Hantush[22])

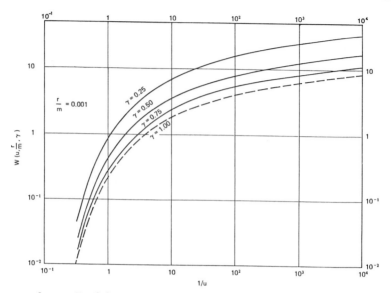

Appendix I(d). Partially penetrating wells (after Hantush[23])

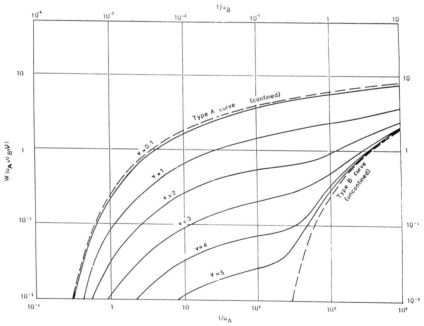

Appendix I(e). Confined-unconfined transition (after Moench and Prickett[24])

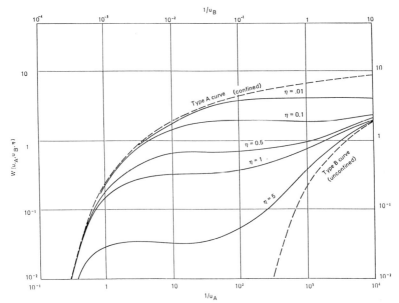

Appendix I(f). Unconfined aquifer with delayed yield (after Neuman[25])

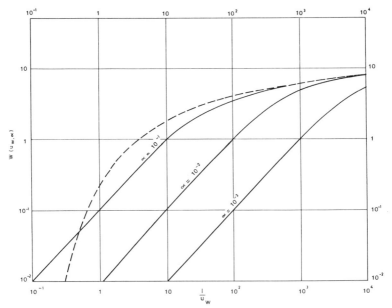

Appendix I(g). Finite diameter wells (after Papadopoulos and Cooper[4])

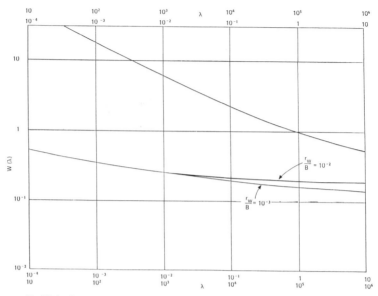

Appendix I(h). Constant-head discharge curves (after Jacob and Lohman[9])

Chapter 6

GROUNDWATER MODELS

1. PURPOSE OF MODELS

GROUNDWATER has always provided a valuable source of water in Britain. In the early stages of its development as a resource, wells or boreholes were located close to the area where water was required and, provided the yield of the borehole was satisfactory, there was no real need to consider the effect of the borehole on the aquifer resources. Boreholes were, therefore, sited in villages, towns and industrial areas. As the demand grew it often proved possible to site new boreholes in the vicinity of existing boreholes but, because of the limited yield of the pumps, most boreholes proved satisfactory.

With certain notable exceptions, borehole yields continued satisfactory up to the 1940s, either because annual recharge was sufficient to replenish the aquifer or because a large volume of water was stored in the aquifer. In certain instances deterioration in water quality occurred. However in London and other large cities the resources were over exploited and failure of wells and boreholes occurred.

During the industrial expansion of the 1950s and 1960s, the total abstraction from many aquifers showed a sudden rise with the result that the abstraction became larger than the recharge or the aquifer reserves diminished rapidly. Due to the slow response of some aquifers the consequences of this over-exploitation were not always immediately obvious and only became apparent after ten or twenty years.

Due to the complex nature of the response of many aquifers, a large number of features need to be considered before the reasons for any change in aquifer behaviour can be understood. For example, it is necessary to consider the aquifer inflows and outflows such as recharge, interaction with rivers, spring behaviour and abstraction. Properties of the aquifer, such as the hydraulic conductivity and storage coefficients, must be determined with particular reference to the influence of fissures and solution channels. Local variations in aquifer properties close to abstraction wells are important as are well losses due to the passage of water through the gravel pack, well screen and pump. The boundaries of the aquifer also need to be identified. In most aquifers there are changes in groundwater head with time; these time-variant effects are usually a combination of seasonal variations due to most recharge occurring in the winter and long-term effects due to abstraction.

The interaction between all these features is usually so complex that it can only be examined by the use of mathematical models of the aquifer behaviour. Models may be used to examine a small region close to an abstraction borehole or alternatively the whole of a region. Interaction with rivers can be investigated and the groundwater model can be combined with a surface water model to allow a study of the conjunctive use of surface water and groundwater.

Therefore the primary reason for using a groundwater model is to assist in understanding the flow through an aquifer. The model will not avoid the need for adequate field work and careful interpretation of the resultant data, but it will provide a check on the consistency of all the assumed parameters. Furthermore, by investigating the sensitivity of the model response to different values of the parameters, a measure of the relative importance of the various parameters can be obtained; this indicates which parameters need to be investigated further. For instance, it may be found that the aquifer response is relatively insensitive to the transmissivity distribution, but is critically dependent on the magnitude of the recharge; this would indicate that further study of the recharge is advisable. Model studies of the quality of groundwater are also important.

Often it is suggested that the mathematical model study should take place towards the end of an investigation. This overlooks the fact that a model can be very useful in the earlier stages of an investigation by indicating the type of information that needs to be obtained. For example, it is important to identify the number of years of aquifer behaviour that need to be considered in an investigation. For some aquifers, the response to recharge is rapid and it is only necessary to consider a period of about two years. For other aquifers the changes in conditions are gradual and it is necessary to consider periods of around one hundred years.

The primary aim of a groundwater model is to represent adequately all the different features of groundwater flow through an aquifer. The study proceeds by modifying the model parameters as further field evidence becomes available, until the model adequately represents the observed field behaviour. The development of a model may take several years, but during the course of model development engineers and hydrogeologists should gain a far greater physical understanding of the aquifer response. Once the mathematical model has been tested satisfactorily, it can be used to explore a variety of methods for exploiting the aquifer resources and predicting the consequences.

The first groundwater models in Britain were devised in the early 1970s and since 1975 certain water authorities have carried out modelling studies of their own aquifers. Other modelling studies have been undertaken by the Water Research Centre, the British Geological Survey, the Institute of Hydrology, and certain universities and consulting engineers. Experience has shown that many engineers and hydrogeologists have grasped the basis of mathematical modelling and applied the techniques to their own problems. Others have gained sufficient understanding to make valuable contributions to modelling studies carried out by others.

In this chapter, the main objective is to indicate how groundwater models are devised. The approach followed considers the various physical features and shows how they can be expressed as functions of groundwater head. The technique of using the finite difference method to represent aquifer problems is presented and sufficient numerical examples given to enable the reader to gain experience in the techniques. Though the main emphasis is given to regional groundwater flow problems, reference is also made to radial flow and quality models. The chapter concludes with information about many of the practical studies carried out in Great Britain.

2. HISTORICAL PERSPECTIVE

The development of methods of analysing groundwater flow has depended on the available techniques. Analytical solutions, often adapted from other branches of applied physics such as heat conduction, formed the basis of many of the earlier solutions. Later, complex variable methods (Polubarinova-Kochina[1], Harr[2]) were utilised for groundwater problems. Numerical solutions were first carried out by hand. Later, electrical analogues were used for steady-state and time-variant problems and in the past fifteen years there have been significant advances in digital computer techniques. Each of the above methods still has a place in the analysis of groundwater flow problems although the assumptions and idealisations inherent in certain analytical techniques limit their reliability when applied to certain field problems.

General textbooks which consider various aspects of the methods for analysing groundwater flow include Todd[3], Walton[4], Bouwer[5], Freeze and Cherry[6], Bear[7], Rushton and Redshaw[8] and Pinder and Gray[9]. A valuable review of computer methods for the analysis of groundwater flow has been prepared by Prickett[10].

ONE-DIMENSIONAL FLOW

A number of useful solutions can be obtained for one-dimensional problems by combining Darcy's Law with the conditions of continuity. Modifications for unconfined aquifers can be made using the Dupuit assumption. Though these are steady-state solutions the effects of different distributions of recharge or variations in transmissivity can be examined. Solutions can be obtained by direct integration or numerical methods.

Time-variant one-dimensional solutions can be obtained by incorporating the effect of the storage coefficient in the formulation. Again, analytical or numerical techniques can be used to solve the equations. One-dimensional solutions have been used by Oakes and Wilkinson[11] to examine the delay in transmitting water through an aquifer from recharge until it reaches a stream. Nutbrown and Downing[12] used a one-dimensional solution to demonstrate that the baseflow recession of a stream does not follow a simple exponential relationship and Rushton and Tomlinson[13] have examined the leakage from streams.

RADIAL FLOW

Many steady-state and time-variant solutions exist for the radial flow to abstraction wells (Chapter 5). The Theim and Theis equations are the most commonly used and development of this initial work was carried out by many workers notably Hantush[14] and Boulton[15].

One drawback of the analytical solutions to time-variant problems is that they lead to expressions which are difficult to evaluate. Digital computer programmes are now used to calculate specific values from these analytical expressions. A large number of new solutions have been presented recently but they suffer from the disadvantage that many of the features that occur in the field, such as transmissivity varying in the aquifer, cannot be included in the analytical solution.

A numerical solution is available for the same differential equations that are used in the analytical curve fitting techniques and the differences between the analytical and numerical results are negligible. However, due to the greater flexibility of the numerical technique, it is possible to include many more of the features that occur in practical situations.

TWO-DIMENSIONAL PROBLEMS

Both regional groundwater flow and problems such as the flow of water through dams and embankments can be idealised as being two-dimensional. Very few of the situations which occur in the field can be solved by analytical methods. Instead, numerical models almost invariably have to be used. Most of the remainder of this chapter is concerned with mathematical model solutions of these two-dimensional problems.

THREE-DIMENSIONAL PROBLEMS

All practical problems are, in fact, three-dimensional. For instance in a regional groundwater flow situation, though the overall flow may be in a horizontal plane, important features such as recharge, river/aquifer interaction or abstraction from a partially penetrating borehole all involve significant vertical components of flow. Attempts have been made to devise three-dimensional numerical models but recent work, described later, indicates that the normal two-dimensional approximation does include the effect of vertical components of flow.

3. AQUIFER MECHANISMS

Frequently aquifers are classified in terms of the rock types; chalk, limestone, sandstone, gravel, etc. Yet a far more important division in terms of aquifer

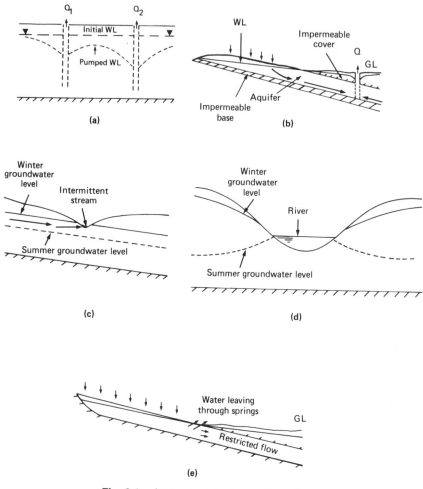

Fig. 6.1.   Important features of aquifers
(vertical scale is greatly exaggerated)

behaviour is the nature of the predominant flow mechanism within the aquifer. Many aquifers have a combination of the features listed below, yet the classification is a guide to the resources of the aquifer and the type of model required. These features are illustrated by simplified sketches in Fig. 6.1.

However before discussing certain practical situations it is important to note that the response of an aquifer is often critically dependent on time. The groundwater heads within an aquifer may vary by only a few centimetres in a year but this can correspond to a significant volume of water. Though valuable information can sometimes be gained from a steady-state approximation, it must be noted that, in most practical examples, the time-variant behaviour of an aquifer must be studied. The length of time that needs to be studied depends on the aquifer characteristics; this is discussed in a later section.

DEWATERING OF AQUIFER

In many aquifers, there is a significant saturated depth which can gradually be exploited by abstraction (Fig. 6.1(a)). Water is taken from storage; this storage may be partially replenished from recharge or by flow from another part of the aquifer. Provided that the aquifer has a significant intergranular permeability and porosity, large volumes of water can be obtained with a lowering of the water table by more than 1 m per annum. When modelling such aquifers, a study of the behaviour over tens of even hundreds of years may be necessary if the aquifer has been exploited for such a long period.

CONFINED–UNCONFINED AQUIFERS

Due to their geological structure aquifers may crop out in the upland areas and be confined beneath permeable strata down-dip. As indicated in Fig. 6.1(b), the water that enters the unconfined region flows down-dip and is abstracted from boreholes in the confined region. Consequently, the outcrop or unconfined region acts as a form of storage reservoir. The time taken for the water to flow through the aquifer between recharge and abstraction from a borehole in the confined part of the aquifer may be of the order of tens or even hundreds of years.

INTERMITTENT STREAMS

In many outcrop regions, intermittent streams have a dominant effect on aquifer response. During the winter, when most of the recharge occurs, these streams act as overflows for the aquifer and carry excess water away (Fig. 6.1(c)). However, during the summer a recession occurs and the water table falls below the stream bed level over the upper reaches of the stream. Consequently the correct assessment of the quantity of water stored in the aquifer is critically dependent on a correct understanding of the stream mechanism.

MAJOR RIVER INTERACTION

The groundwater heads within an aquifer may be dominated by a major river flowing over an aquifer outcrop. The river may be influent over certain reaches and effluent over others. Also the conditions may change during the year as illustrated by Fig. 6.1(d). The quantity of water flowing between the river and the aquifer may be influenced signficantly by the effective permeability of the river bed.

RESTRICTED RECHARGE

Recharge is usually estimated from a water balance, but it is possible that the aquifer will not be able to accept and retain all of this water. Restricted recharge can occur in the circumstances shown in Figs. 6.1(c) and 6.1(d) and also as shown in Fig. 6.1(e). The unconfined region of the aquifer has a sufficiently high transmissivity to accept the recharge, but there is no outlet from the confined region. Consequently little water flows down-dip; most of it leaves the aquifer at springs on the confined-unconfined interface.

The five aquifer mechanisms described are only simplified examples of the complex situations which occur in many aquifer problems. Nevertheless they do indicate that the identification of the flow mechanism is the first step in devising a reliable mathematical model of an aquifer.

4. FORMULATION

A careful formulation or statement of the aquifer problem must be made before modelling work can commence. Other chapters indicate how the field information required for the definition of the aquifer properties and boundary conditions is obtained and interpreted. There are a number of different steps in the formulation.

GOVERNING EQUATIONS

As derived in Chapter 4, the governing equation describing flow in an aquifer is:

$$\frac{\partial}{\partial x}\left(T_x \frac{\partial h}{\partial x}\right) + \frac{\partial}{\partial y}\left(T_y \frac{\partial h}{\partial y}\right) = S\frac{\partial h}{\partial t} - q \quad \cdots \quad \cdots \quad \cdots \quad \cdots \quad (1)$$

(dimensions)

where h is the groundwater head   (L)
T_x and T_y are the transmissivities (L^2/T)
x and y are the space coordinates   (L)
t is the time coordinate   (T)
S is the appropriate storage coefficient (confined or unconfined)
and q is the recharge intensity   (L/T)

Two important features about this equation should be noted. The first is that the equation does not directly contain information about the position of the base or the top of the aquifer and consequently the calculated value of the groundwater head, h, may lie above the top of an unconfined aquifer or below the base of the aquifer. This can be overcome if the aquifer transmissivity is calculated as a function of the vertical distance from the base of an aquifer to the water table. This adds to the computation effort and may lead to numerical instabilities. Secondly, even though Eqn. (1) does not include the vertical coordinate, z, it does include the vertical components of flow. This is demonstrated later in this chapter.

The steady-state form of Eqn. (1) can be obtained directly by removing the time dependent term $S\ \partial h/\partial t$, thus:

$$\frac{\partial}{\partial x}\left(T_x \frac{\partial h}{\partial x}\right) + \frac{\partial}{\partial y}\left(T_y \frac{\partial h}{\partial y}\right) = -q$$

As noted above, the transmissivities, T_x and T_y, and storage coefficient, S, may be functions of the groundwater head, h. Often, if the variation in head is small, it is sufficient to treat T_x and T_y and S as being independent of saturated depth, but for certain aquifers it is essential to represent their variation with the groundwater head. Rarely is it acceptable to say that:

$$T_x = k_x (h - b)$$

where b is the elevation of the base of the aquifer and k_x is a constant horizontal permeability. Usually the local permeability shows significant variations, as indicated by Fig. 6.2. The transmissivity can be calculated as the integral (or sum) of the local permeabilities below the water table.

Since the governing equation (1) can only be solved for most practical situations using numerical techniques, the area of the aquifer is sub-divided by a grid. Values of the transmissivity, storage coefficient and recharge intensity must be defined at all mesh points on the grid. Due to lack of field information, this may be difficult, but estimates must be made and the possible errors arising from uncertainty about the data can be investigated by a sensitivity analysis. Examples of a sensitivity analysis are given in a later section.

EXTERNAL BOUNDARIES

The second stage in the formulation is the identification of the position and nature of the external boundaries of the aquifer. The determination of the position of an aquifer boundary is often reasonably straightforward, but the identification of the hydraulic condition on the boundary may be more difficult. For instance a geological fault may indicate the limit of the aquifer, yet the fault may totally prevent the flow of water or it may be a possible source of water.

Boundary conditions are usually defined in terms of flows. These flows may be zero, or they may take a known value. An external boundary may be at a known head. If it is a specified head this infers that the boundary can provide an infinite source or sink of water. Such a condition frequently occurs at the sea coast or at a major river which fully penetrates the aquifer.

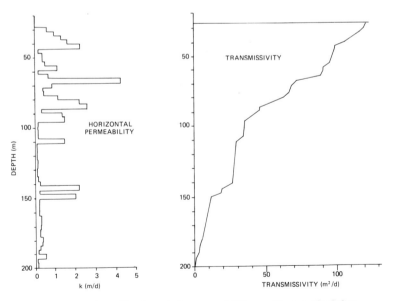

Fig. 6.2. Local horizontal permeability and transmissivity deduced from packer tests

Great care must be taken in the selection of boundaries. It is possible that an aquifer may extend under a sea coast with leakage occurring between the sea and the aquifer through a semi-pervious layer on the sea bed. To model such an aquifer as extending only to the coastline may lead to serious errors. In other instances a fault brings an aquifer into contact with another stratum of lower permeability. It may be necessary to include this lower permeability stratum in the groundwater model.

INFLOWS AND OUTFLOWS

Inflows and outflows to the aquifer occur for a variety of reasons. This sub-section is concerned only with inflows and outflows of known magnitude. The major source of inflow is *recharge* following precipitation. The recharge can often be estimated from a soil moisture balance, though sometimes a small proportion of the precipitation enters directly into the aquifer bypassing the soil moisture store (Rushton and Ward[16]). In other instances there can be a considerable delay between precipitation and subsequent recharge to an aquifer (Oakes[17]). The presence of drift can also limit the recharge (Senarath and Rushton[18]).

Inflow to or outflow from an aquifer may also occur due to *leakage* through overlying semi-permeable strata. The recharge, q, then depends on the difference between the groundwater head, h, and the head above the semi-permeable stratum, H. The effective recharge can be expressed as:

$$q = \frac{k'}{m'} (H - h) \quad \ldots \quad \ldots \quad \ldots \quad \ldots \quad \ldots \quad \ldots \quad \ldots \quad \ldots \quad (2)$$

where k' and m' are the permeability and thickness of the semi-pervious strata (Fig. 6.3).

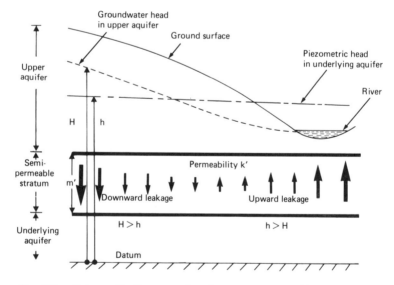

Fig. 6.3.   Schematic diagram showing occurrence of leakage to or from an underlying aquifer

In those aquifers which have been exploited over many years, *abstraction* from wells and boreholes may have influenced the groundwater heads significantly. For a number of years, accurate returns of the quantity abstracted should be available. However, for earlier periods of 20 years or more ago, reliable returns are not normally available yet it is often possible to make reasonable estimates of the abstraction rates from the pump capacity and the date when it proved to be necessary to provide additional boreholes at the site.

RIVERS, STREAMS AND SPRINGS

Rivers, streams and springs are further sources of flows into and out of aquifers. Though they often have a dominant effect on the flow in an aquifer, it can be difficult to include them accurately in an aquifer model. The reason for this is illustrated by Fig. 6.4(a) which indicates the complex flow patterns in the vicinity of a partially penetrating stream. Such a complex situation cannot be represented by a simple formula. Certain tests suggest that the flow to the stream is a function of the difference between the stream elevation and groundwater head, but when the complex pattern beneath the stream is examined, the question arises as to which groundwater head is to be used in such a calculation.

In certain situations, the river/aquifer interaction can be described by a relationship such as that of Fig. 6.4(b). The groundwater head is taken as an average in the vicinity of the river (Connorton and Hanson[19]). The left-hand portion of the curve, in which the river feeds the aquifer, will only apply when there is sufficient water in the river.

Springs function in a similar manner, with the outflow depending on the excess of groundwater head over the elevation of the spring. However, in a number of recent studies a relationship of the form:

$$Q_s = C\,(h - z_s)\,\text{if}\,h > z_s \quad \dots \qquad \dots \qquad \dots \qquad \dots \qquad \dots \qquad \dots \qquad \dots \qquad (3)$$

where Q_s is the spring flow
C is a spring coefficient (L^2/T)
h is the effective groundwater head at the spring node
z_s is the elevation of the spring

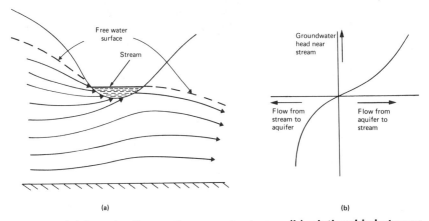

(a)   (b)

Fig. 6.4.   (a) Complex flow pattern near to stream; (b) relationship between groundwater head and flow

did not allow sufficient water to issue from the springs at times of high flow (Rushton et al[20]). This occurs because an increase in the spring flow leads to a decrease in the groundwater head at the spring node which from Eqn. (3) tends to reduce the spring flow. However, a successful representation of the spring flow has sometimes been possible by assuming that the flow is dependent on the groundwater head up-dip and down-dip of the spring as well as at the spring node. The inclusion of transmissivities and storage coefficients which are functions of saturated depth also improved the simulation of springs and streams.

Additional work needs to be carried out to obtain a more complete understanding of the interaction between aquifers and streams, since this interaction often has a dominant effect on the aquifer response. A valuable study by Nutbrown and Downing[12] highlights the complexity of this interaction.

INITIAL CONDITIONS

Since the groundwater head in an aquifer changes with time, it is necessary to specify initial conditions at the start of the simulation. A number of approaches are possible and that chosen will depend on the quality of the field data and also the type of the aquifer. Methods of starting the simulation include the following:

(1) **Field Heads.** For some aquifers there are sufficient observation boreholes to allow reliable groundwater head values to be estimated on the grid to be used in the analysis. In typical aquifers the density of observation wells needs to approach one per square kilometre. Even if a reliable estimate can be obtained of the initial field heads, incorrect values of the transmissivity or storage coefficient may be used for early attempts at modelling the aquifer. This inconsistency may lead to a false pattern in the groundwater head variations even though the initial heads are acceptable.

(2) **Average Heads for Equilibrium State.** Another possibility is that the aquifer was once in an equilibrium state with inflows balancing outflows and the groundwater heads showing a repetitive cycle. Such an equilibrium state did hold in most aquifers before significant abstraction started. If these conditions occurred tens of years ago it is usually acceptable to start the model simulation with average inflows and outflows, thereby simulating the equilibrium state.

(3) **Dynamic Balance.** For many aquifers, the data concerning field heads are limited and the equilibrium state occurred a long time ago. However, a dynamic balance may be achieved by using a typical set of inflows and outflows and running the model until a repetitive pattern is achieved. Though such a dynamic balance does not represent the historical aquifer behaviour in detail, it does provide adequate starting conditions for a detailed simulation.

LENGTH OF SIMULATION

The length of the simulation will depend on a variety of factors, and therefore it is only possible to give overall guidelines. If the aquifer is unconfined and the water levels have been falling for a long period, it is essential to consider the whole period during which the resources have been exploited. This may mean the simulation covers a time period of up to 100 years. Such a procedure is necessary since the model must be able to reproduce the balance between inflow, outflows and water released from storage over this long time period.

For confined aquifers which are in contact with major rivers, a simulation as short as one year may be adequate. Aquifers which are partly confined and partly unconfined are likely to require simulations covering ten or twenty years. The main criterion for deciding the length of the simulation is that sufficient time must elapse to test the validity of the assumed aquifer flow mechanism that has been represented on the model.

An idea of the length of time for a study can be gained by calculating the characteristic time, L^2S/T, where L is a typical length of a flow path in the aquifer from inflow to outflow. A confined aquifer with low storage coefficient and high transmissivity may have a characteristic time of around 100 days whereas for an unconfined aquifer with lower transmissivity the characteristic time could be several hundred years.

The details in which information about the inflows and outflows are required will depend on the nature of the problem. For an unconfined aquifer simulation in which a period of 100 years is modelled, annual values of recharge and abstraction are usually adequate. On the other hand, weekly or even daily abstraction data may be necessary for a confined aquifer study. In general, the aim should be to provide accurate information on a monthly basis.

5. NUMERICAL APPROXIMATIONS

The partial differential equation (1) which describes groundwater flow is based on the condition of continuity and Darcy's Law. Because analytical solutions to this equation cannot be obtained for the type of problem encountered in the field, approximate numerical techniques are used. They require that the space and time coordinates are divided into some form of discrete mesh. Three basic approaches are available: finite difference (Rushton and Redshaw[8]), finite element (Pinder and Gray[9]) and boundary element (Liggett[21]). Though each of these methods uses a different approach in representing the space coordinates, they all use the same form of discrete time approximation. Of the three methods, the finite difference method is the simplest mathematically and therefore it will form the basis of the discussion in this chapter. Comparisons have shown little difference between calculated groundwater heads when using the finite difference and finite element approaches (Davis[22]).

FINITE DIFFERENCE APPROXIMATION—STEADY-STATE

The differential equation for steady-state flow does not include the storage term S; thus Eqn. (1) becomes:

$$\frac{\partial}{\partial x}\left(T_x \frac{\partial h}{\partial x}\right) + \frac{\partial}{\partial y}\left(T_y \frac{\partial h}{\partial y}\right) = -q \quad \ldots \qquad \ldots \qquad \ldots \qquad \ldots \qquad \ldots \quad (4)$$

This equation will be written in finite difference form using a physical argument. A more rigorous method is available based on Taylor's series (Smith[23]). Consider a region of the aquifer covered by an orthogonal grid. The groundwater head is defined at the grid points and the heads at node (i,j) and four surrounding grid points are as indicated in Fig. 6.5. Transmissivities are defined midway between the grid points; the subscripts for the transmissivities should be noted.

In the lumping derivation, the four flows Q_1, Q_2, Q_3 and Q_4 associated with node (i,j) are calculated separately. Thus from Darcy's Law:

$$Q_1 = - \text{ transmissivity} \times \text{width} \times \text{head gradient}$$
$$= - T_{x,i,j} \cdot 0.5\,(\Delta y_j + \Delta y_{j-1}) \cdot (h_{i+1,j} - h_{i,j})/\Delta x_i$$

Similarly,

$$Q_2 = - T_{y,i,j-1} \cdot 0.5\,(\Delta x_i + \Delta x_{i-1}) \cdot (h_{i,j} - h_{i,j-1})/\Delta y_{j-1} \quad \ldots \qquad \ldots \qquad (5)$$
$$Q_3 = - T_{x,i-1,j} \cdot 0.5\,(\Delta y_j + \Delta y_{j-1}) \cdot (h_{i,j} - h_{i-1,j})/\Delta x_{i-1}$$
$$Q_4 = T_{y,i,j} \cdot 0.5\,(\Delta d_i + \Delta x_{i-1}) \cdot (h_{i,j+1} - h_{i,j})/\Delta y_j$$

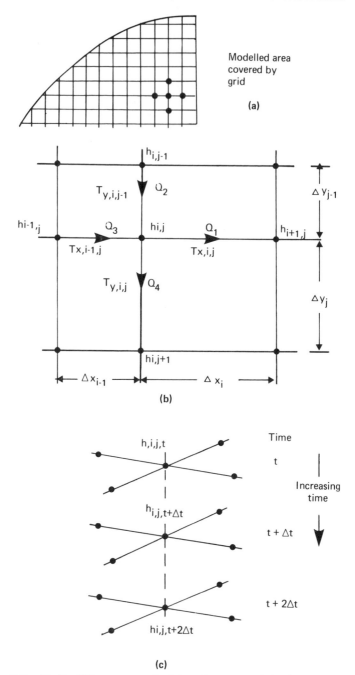

Fig. 6.5.   Finite difference mesh: (a) typical mesh, (b) grid numbering, (c) time approximation

Now the total flow towards node (i,j) plus the water entering the area representing the node due to recharge must sum to zero, hence:

$$-Q_1 + Q_2 + Q_3 - Q_4 + 0.25\, q_{i,j}\,(\Delta x_{i-1} + \Delta x_i)\,(\Delta y_{j-1} + \Delta y_j) = 0 \qquad \ldots \quad (6)$$

On substituting the above equations,

$$0.5\,(\Delta y_{j-1} + \Delta y_j)\,[T_{x,i,j}\,(h_{i+1,j} - h_{i,j})/\Delta x_i + T_{x,i-1,j}\,(h_{i-1,j} - h_{i,j})/\Delta x_{i-1}]$$

$$+ 0.5\,(\Delta x_{i-1} + \Delta x_i)\,[T_{y,i,j}\,(h_{i,j+1} - h_{i,j})/\Delta y_j + T_{y,i,j-1}(h_{i,j-1} - h_{i,j})/\Delta y_{j-1}]$$

$$= -0.25\, q_{i,j}\,(\Delta x_{i-1} + \Delta x_i)\,(\Delta y_{j-1} + \Delta y_j) \quad \ldots \quad \ldots \quad \ldots \quad \ldots \quad (7)$$

For each node a similar equation can be written; this leads to a set of simultaneous equations.

6. TIME-VARIANT BEHAVIOUR

For time-variant behaviour the full form of Eqn. (1) has to be considered. The finite difference form of the storage coefficient multiplied by the rate of change of head can be written as:

$$S\,\frac{\partial h}{\partial t} = \frac{S}{\Delta t}\,(h_{i,j,t+\Delta t} - h_{i,j,t}) \quad \ldots \quad \ldots \quad \ldots \quad \ldots \quad \ldots \quad \ldots \quad (8)$$

The discrete time mesh is illustrated in Fig. 6.5(c). Note that an extra suffix has been added to the groundwater head terms, indicating that the heads are calculated at discrete time steps separated by an interval Δt.

All the terms in Eqn. (1) must be defined at these discrete steps and it is the fact that the terms on the left hand side of Eqn. (1) can be specified at different times that leads to a variety of methods. There are three possibilities; these will be discussed for the case of uniform transmissivity T and regular mesh intervals Δx and Δy.

SPECIFYING THE HEADS AT TIME t

If the heads on the left-hand side of Eqns. (1) and (7) are specified at time t, with constant transmissivity and mesh interval then:

$$T\,(h_{i+1,j} + h_{i,j-1} + h_{i-1,j} + h_{i,j+1} - 4h_{i,j})_t$$

$$= \frac{S\,\Delta x \Delta y}{\Delta t} \cdot (h_{i,j,t+\Delta t} - h_{i,j,t}) - q_{i,j,t+\frac{1}{2}\Delta t} \cdot \Delta x \Delta y \quad \ldots \quad \ldots \quad \ldots \quad (9)$$

Assuming that the heads at time t have already been calculated, there is just one unknown head at time $t+\Delta t$, namely $h_{i,j,t+\Delta t}$. Consequently an equation can be written for the head at time $t+\Delta t$ in terms of known heads and flows. Therefore this gives an *explicit* expression for the heads. The method is classified as a *forward difference* method.

The forward difference method is attractive in that it avoids the need to solve sets of simultaneous equations for each time step. However, if the time step is too large, numerical instabilities can occur. For the case of uniform transmissivity and mesh spacing, the stability criterion is that the time step,

$$\Delta t \leqslant 0.25 \Delta x^2 S/T \quad \ldots \quad \ldots \quad \ldots \quad \ldots \quad \ldots \quad \ldots \quad \ldots \quad (10)$$

A variant of the explicit method called the *alternating direction explicit method* has proved useful in a number of studies (Tomlinson and Rushton[24]) but even that method can lead to inaccurate solutions

Specifying the Heads at Time $t + \Delta t$

A second alternative is to specify the heads corresponding to the flow through the aquifer at time $t+\Delta t$. With constant transmissivity and uniform mesh spacing, Eqns. (1) and (7) become:

$$T\left(h_{i+1,j} + h_{i,j-1} + h_{i-1,j} + h_{i,j+1} - 4h_{i,j}\right)_{t+\Delta t}$$

$$= \frac{S\,\Delta x\Delta y}{\Delta t} \cdot \left(h_{i,j,t+\Delta t} - h_{i,j,t}\right) - q_{i,j,t+\frac{1}{2}\Delta t} \cdot \Delta x\Delta y \qquad \ldots \qquad \ldots \qquad \ldots \qquad (11)$$

There are now five unknown heads and this is therefore an *implicit* formulation. This approximation, which is usually called the *backward difference* formulation, has proved to be the most reliable approximation in groundwater flow analysis. Large time steps can be used and there is no risk of numerical instability. The great advantage of this method is that it automatically satisfies the condition of continuity of flow.

Since it is the approximation that will be used in later discussion, it is written below for varying transmissivity and mesh intervals. The expression $h_{i,j}$ refers to the heads at time $t+\Delta t$ and $\bar{h}_{i,j}$ indicates head at time t:

$$\frac{\Delta y}{\Delta x}\left[T_{x,i,j}\left(h_{i+1,j} - h_{i,j}\right) + T_{x,i-1,j}\left(h_{i-1,j} - h_{i,j}\right)\right] + \frac{\Delta x}{\Delta y}\left[T_{y,i,j} \cdot \left(h_{i,j+1} - h_{i,j}\right)\right.$$

$$\left. + T_{y,i,j-1}\left(h_{i,j-1} - h_{i,j}\right)\right] = S_{i,j} \cdot \Delta x\Delta y\,\frac{h_{i,j} - \bar{h}_{i,j}}{\Delta t} - q_{i,j,t+\frac{1}{2}\Delta t} \cdot \Delta x\Delta y \quad (12)$$

Specifying the Heads at Time t and Time $t + \Delta t$

This is a *central difference* approximation. It is attractive because it is the finite difference approximation with the smallest error. However, it does lead to unstable results in many practical situations[8]. Therefore the two central difference approximations of the Crank-Nicholson approach and the (non-iterative) alternating direction implicit method should be used with great caution.

7. EXAMPLE OF NUMERICAL SOLUTION

In the following section, a relatively simple example will be considered in detail. Full calculations are presented to indicate how finite difference solutions to practical problems can be obtained. The resultant groundwater head values are used to ascertain whether saline intrusion is likely to occur. The form of flow patterns within the aquifer are also considered in detail.

Details of Example

The example concerns an aquifer which has both unconfined and confined regions (Fig. 6.6). Recharge occurs over the outcrop region with a distribution with time as shown in Fig. 6.6(c). Water is lost to a stream in the unconfined region and abstraction in the confined region occurs from two major boreholes with discharge from borehole R equalling one third of the total abstraction. To the north, west and south the boundaries of the aquifer are impermeable, but to the east the aquifer is in contact with the sea.

For ease of calculation a uniform transmissivity of 900 m^2/d applies with a confined storage coefficient of 0.0002 and a specific yield in the unconfined region of 0.05. One important feature of this problem is whether saline water will be drawn from the sea towards abstraction wells.

This problem can be studied using a finite difference numerical solution. The area is divided into a grid of sides 1 km, though in practice for this problem it would be advisable to use a mesh spacing of 500 m. The intersections of the grid lines are called nodes and it is at these nodes that the groundwater heads are calculated.

AVERAGE HEAD SOLUTION

Initially a numerical solution will be presented for a steady-state problem in which average values of the inflows and outflows of the quantities of Fig. 6.6(c) are applied. Fig. 6.6(d) gives numerical values for the groundwater heads for the problem of Fig. 6.6(c); these values are deduced from solutions based on Eqn. (7) but certain of the numerical values are omitted. These missing numerical values can be calculated using the appropriate finite difference equations. It must be stressed, however, that this device of omitting certain values and calculating by direct substitution is for *illustrative* purposes; in practice all the heads are unknown and are calculated simultaneously.

Internal Node with no Inflow or Outflow (node 7,3) (Fig. 6.6(d))

Since the mesh spacings and the transmissivities are uniform, and $q_{i,j}$ is zero, Eqn. (7) can be rewritten with the head at node (i,j) on the left hand side as:

$$h_{i,j} = 0.25 \, (h_{i+1,j} + h_{i,j-1} + h_{i-1,j} + h_{i,j+1})$$

$$= 0.25 \, (1.45 + 4.16 + 9.93 + 6.07) = 5.40 \text{ m}$$

This value of 5.40 m clearly fits in with the surrounding heads.

Internal Node with Certain Heads Negative (node 9,2)

The same finite difference equation holds thus:

$$h_{i,j} = 0.25 \, (0.00 + 0.20 - 2.68 + 0.47) = -0.50 \text{ m}$$

Node on Upper Boundary (node 8,0)

The aquifer does not extend to the north of this node and therefore the boundary can be represented by setting $T_{y,i,j-1}$ and Δy_{j-1} to zero: Eqn. (7) can be simplified to:

$$h_{i,j} = 0.5 \, (0.5 \, h_{i+1,j} + 0.5 \, h_{i-1,j} + h_{i,j+1})$$

Substituting the appropriate numerical values:

$$h_{i,j} = 0.5 \, (0.5 \times 0.44 + 0.5 \times 3.43 + 0.84) = 1.39 \text{ m}.$$

Node at which Abstraction Occurs (node 5,4)

An abstraction from a well of Q (units L^3/T) is represented as an equivalent recharge distributed over the area represented by the nodal point. Thus:

$$q_{i,j} = -\, Q/[0.25 \, (\Delta x_{i-1} + \Delta x_i) \, (\Delta y_{j-1} + \Delta y_j)]$$

Consequently Eqn. (7) can be rewritten to calculate the head at node (i,j) as:

$$h_{i,j} = 0.25 \, (h_{i+1,j} + h_{i,j-1} + h_{i-1,j} + h_{i,j+1} - Q/T)$$

Since $Q = 5000$ m³/d and $T = 900$ m²/d,

$$h_{i,j} = 0.25 \, (10.20 + 14.66 + 20.55 + 18.51 - 5000/900) - 14.59$$

Node at which Recharge Occurs (node 3,4)

At node (3,4) there is recharge of 1.089 mm/day. For this node the head can be calculated as:

$$h_{i,j} = 0.25 \, (h_{i+1,j} + h_{i,j-1} + h_{i-1,j} + h_{i,j+1} + q\Delta x\Delta y/T)$$

$$= 0.25 \, (20.55 + 23.54 + 26.48 + 25.07 + 1.089 \times 10^3/900) = 24.21 \text{ m}$$

Flow to the Sea

The flow between nodes (9,4) and (10,4) can be calculated using the equation for Q_1, thus:

$$Q_1 = - \, T_{x,i,j} \times 0.5 \, (\Delta y_j + \Delta y_{j-1}) \times (h_{i+1,j} - h_{i,j})/\Delta x_i$$

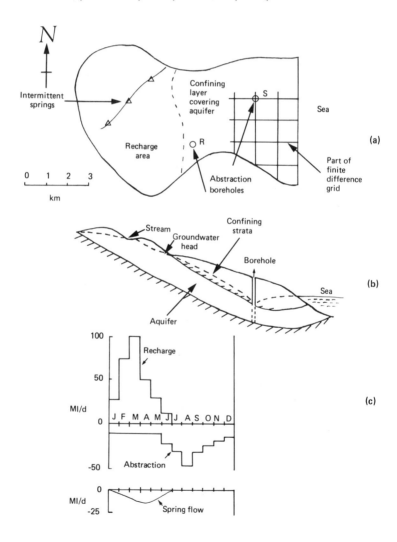

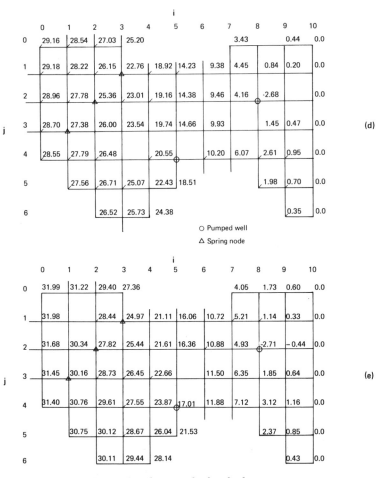

Fig. 6.6. Example of numerical solution
(a) outline of problem
(b) typical section through the aquifer
(c) inflows and outflows for a typical year
(d) groundwater heads for average conditions
(e) groundwater heads for June of a typical year

Substituting the values from Fig. 6.6(d):

$$Q_1 = - 900 \times 0.5 \times 2000 \times (0.0 - 0.95)/1\,000 = 855 \text{ m}^3/\text{d}$$

Flows can be calculated to all the nodes on the coastline. However between nodes (9.0) and (10.0), Δy_{j-1} is zero, hence the multiplying factors are half those for node 4. A similar condition holds for the lowest node. Hence:

$$\Sigma Q = 900[0.5 \times 0.44 + 0.20 - 0.50 + 0.48 + 0.95 + 0.70 + 0.5 \times 0.35]$$
$$= 2002 \text{ m}^3/\text{d}$$

TIME-VARIANT SOLUTION

The simplified problem of Fig. 6.6 can easily be modified to become a time-variant problem. Over the unconfined or recharge area the specific yield is 0.05 and the confined storage coefficient is 1.5×10^{-4}. Results are quoted in Fig. 6.6(e) for a month in which the total recharge is 12.0 Ml/d. A ten day time step is used.

Node in Confined Region (node 5,3)

Since there is no recharge, Eqn. (12) can be rearranged to express the unknown head as:

$$h_{i,j} = \frac{1}{4.0 + S\Delta x \Delta y / T \Delta t}\left[h_{i+1,j} + h_{i,j-1} + h_{i-1,j} + h_{i,j+1} + S\Delta x \Delta y \, \bar{h}_{i,j}/T\Delta t\right]$$

where $\bar{h}_{i,j}$ the head at the previous time step equals 17.10. Thus:

$$h_{i,j} = \frac{1}{4.0 + 1.5 \times 10^{-4} \times 10^6/900 \times 10}\left[11.50 + 16.36 + 22.66 + 17.01 + \right.$$
$$\left.1.5 \times 10^{-4} \times 10^6 \times 17.10/900 \times 10\right] = 16.88 \text{ m}$$

Node in Unconfined Region (node 1,1)

The calculation is similar to that for a confined region but with an additional term for the recharge within the square bracket, $q\Delta x \Delta y / T$. The numerical value of q is $0.0419 \times 12000 \times 10^{-6}$ since the percentage of recharge at this node is 4.19 per cent of the total; the head value at the previous time step is 30.93 and the storage coefficient is 0.05. Therefore:

$$h_{i,j} = \frac{1}{4.0 + 5.55556}\left[28.44 + 31.22 + 31.98 + 30.34 + 30.93 \times 5.55556 \right.$$
$$\left.+ 0.0419 \times 12000/900\right] = 30.81 \text{ m}$$

8. PRESENTATION OF RESULTS

Because the groundwater head is one function that can be measured in the field, the results of a model study are often presented simply in terms of the groundwater heads. However, the model is primarily representing the flow mechanism within an aquifer and therefore diagrams representing the flows within an aquifer are equally important.

GROUNDWATER HEADS

Groundwater Heads on a Section

Since many groundwater models do not contain information about the base or top of the aquifer, a plot of the groundwater heads superimposed on a geological cross-section can be valuable. These heads will refer to a particular time. A typical diagram for an aquifer which is partly unconfined and partly confined is shown in Fig. 6.6(b).

Groundwater Heads in Plan

An alternative form of diagram presents the groundwater heads at a particular instant of time as contours superimposed on a plan of the aquifer. A typical contour plot is shown in Fig. 6.7(a). Unless the aquifer is isotropic, which means that it has the same transmissivity throughout the aquifer, the flow lines will not be at right angles to the lines of equal groundwater head. Therefore contour plots of groundwater head may be misleading when used as a means of visualising the flow pattern.

Groundwater Head Variation with Time

A third method of presenting the groundwater heads is to plot the variation of head at a particular point with time as illustrated in Fig. 6.7(b). These plots are valuable as a means of visualising the response of the aquifer to recharge and abstraction. Node (1,2) is in the unconfined region and shows small annual fluctuations whilst at node (4,2) on the interface between the confined and unconfined regions the head variation is greater. At node (6,2) in the confined region, head variations are about 8 m, whilst in the vicinity of abstraction sites, node (8,2), large variations occur.

GROUNDWATER FLOW

Saline Inflow

One important feature of this aquifer problem is the risk of saline inflow. As demonstrated earlier it is possible to calculate the net flow across the eastern boundary which is in contact with the sea. The manner in which this flow varies with time is indicated by the broken line of Fig. 6.7(c). For the latter part of the year there is a net inflow from the sea but the overall balance is a net outflow.

It is necessary to investigate this saline inflow further and the full line of Fig. 6.7(c) shows the actual saline inflow which is zero for all but five months. A careful study of the flow between nodes (9,2) and (10,2) demonstrates that there is a net inflow averaging 277 m^3/d each year. This would take many years to reach the nearest abstraction well. Even when the water reaches the well it would only be 277/15000 or 1.8 per cent of the total inflow; the remainder of the water comes from the recharge area. Assuming a salinity of 20000 mg/l for the sea water, the salinity of the abstracted water would be 300 mg/l higher than the natural salinity of the fresh water. This approximate approach ignores dispersion.

Flow Distribution

From the groundwater heads it is a straightforward procedure to calculate the magnitude and direction of the flows within the aquifer. These flows can then be presented in a diagram of the form shown in Fig. 6.7(d). This diagram represents the flows within part of an aquifer at a particular time; different diagrams are required at different times of the year.

These flows are presented as the total flow for a mesh area. Consider for example the heads at four adjacent nodes shown in Fig. 6.8; the values are taken from Fig. 6.6(e). Since a square mesh is used of sides 1 km, the flow Q_A can be calculated as:

$$Q_A = -T_x \cdot \text{width} \cdot \frac{\partial h}{\partial x} = T_x \, \Delta h = 900 \, (6.35 - 1.85) = 4050 \text{ m}^3/\text{d}$$

Similarly $Q_B = 3600$, $Q_C = -693$ and $Q_D = -1143$ m^3/d

Thus the flow Q_x at the centre of the mesh is the average of Q_A and Q_B. Hence $Q_x = 3825$ and $Q_y = -918$ m^3/d. The magnitude of the flow is therefore:

$$Q_{max} = (Q_x^2 + Q_y^2)^{1/2} = 3934 \text{ m}^3/\text{d}$$

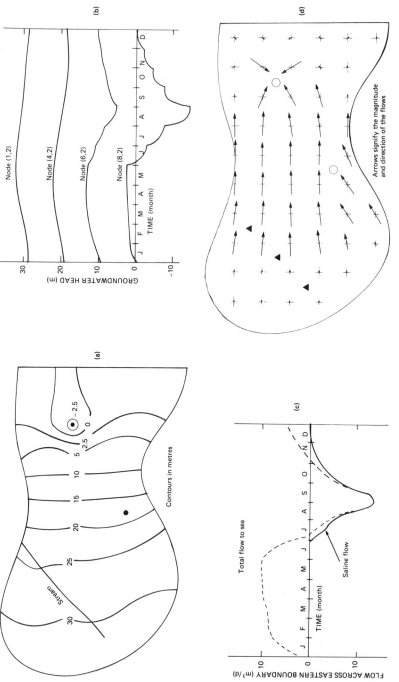

Fig. 6.7.   Presentation of results

(a)   contour plot of groundwater heads for June
(b)   variation of groundwater heads with time
(c)   saline inflows
(d)   flow distribution showing magnitude and direction of flows

inclined at an angle $\tan^{-1}(Q_y/Q_x) = -13.1°$ below the horizontal. This gives the magnitude and direction of the flow through a mesh square of sides 1 km. An example of the usefulness of the flow distribution in a study of the South Humberside Chalk is described in Ref. 25.

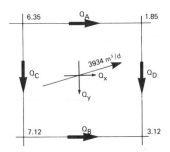

Fig. 6.8.   Calculation of flows from head distribution

9. HORIZONTAL AND VERTICAL COMPONENTS OF FLOW

More detailed information about the flows within the aquifer can be obtained by considering the flows within the aquifer at different depths. The flow patterns in unconfined aquifers are generally far more complex than in confined aquifers. Since water usually enters an unconfined aquifer on the upper surface, there will be a component of vertical flow causing the water to move down into the aquifer. In the vicinity of pumped boreholes the vertical components of flow usually increase since the borehole collects water by lowering the groundwater head. On the other hand a partially penetrating river often induces water to flow from deep in an aquifer by causing upwards vertical components of flow.

The standard groundwater analysis in terms of horizontal transmissivities automatically infers vertical components of flow. There is no need to follow the approach of the standard texts and assume that the vertical components of flow are negligible (Connorton[26]).

Within any aquifer there will be both horizontal and vertical components of flow. Consider, for example, the section of Fig. 6.9(a) which represents a vertical plane of an unconfined aquifer with a partially penetrating river. From a numerical solution, heads have been determined on a one-dimensional mesh.

Two permeability variations will be considered. Consider first the case when the permeability is constant at 50 m/d. Using Darcy's Law and noting the varying saturated depths, the flows per metre width of aquifer can be calculated as:

$$Q_1 = 1.348 \text{ m}^3/\text{d/m}, Q_2 = 1.940 \text{ m}^3/\text{d/m} \text{ and } Q_3 = 0.897 \text{ m}^3/\text{d/m}.$$

The difference between Q_1 and Q_2 represents the inflow into the aquifer over the area associated with node B. This inflow, which equals 0.592 m³/d/m, represents either the recharge if it is a steady-state example or a combination of storage change and recharge for a time-variant situation. At node C the net inflow of -1.043 m³/d/m is equivalent to the storage change, recharge and outflow to a river.

If only the lower 15 m of the aquifer are considered, the flows as shown in Fig. 6.9(b) are respectively 0.675, 0.975 and 0.45 m³/d/m. The increase from 0.675 to

0.975 m³/d/m infers that there is a vertical downwards flow of 0.3 m³/d/m at an elevation of 15 m above the base of the aquifer over the area associated with node B. At node C there is an upward flow of 0.525 m³/d/m; this upward flow is mainly caused by the presence of the river.

Fig. 6.10 shows how the same groundwater head distribution leads to significantly different flows if there is a lower zone of higher permeability overlain by a zone of lower permeability. Vertical flows at 10 m from the base of the aquifer become 0.48 and −0.84 m³/d/m respectively; a significant increase over the results for constant permeability. For further details see Rushton and Rathod[27].

The recognition of the fact that horizontal transmissivities, as used in Eqn. (1), do infer the existence of vertical components of flow is of critical importance in the understanding of regional groundwater flow mechanisms. This simple approach is valid unless the vertical coefficients of permeability are more than two orders of magnitude smaller than the average horizontal permeabilities.

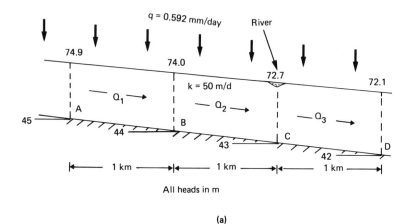

(a)

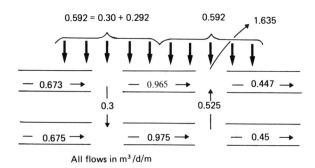

(b)

Fig. 6.9. Horizontal and vertical components of flow; uniform permeability

WATER BALANCE

Another valuable method of presenting the results is by means of an overall water balance. Great care is needed in the presentation of the balance. For instance, if a balance is performed over a period with different water levels at the beginning and end of the period, then the change in groundwater storage may be of significance.

A monthly balance for the simplified problem discussed earlier is presented in Table 6.I with most of the results plotted in Fig. 6.11. The quantity released from confined storage is small but the unconfined storage is of crucial importance. During the winter when the abstraction rate is low, much of the excess water is stored in the unconfined region. However, during the summer much of this water flows to the confined region to meet the abstraction demands. The flow from the eastern boundary with the sea shows a similar response.

For a chalk aquifer in Essex (Fig. 6.12), a more reliable form of balance is indicated in Fig. 6.13, which shows the annual balance for the confined region (Rushton and Senarath[28]). The balance starts from the period when there was little exploitation of the aquifer. Gradually the abstraction increased, but most of this water was provided by flow from the unconfined region. Then from 1920 onwards

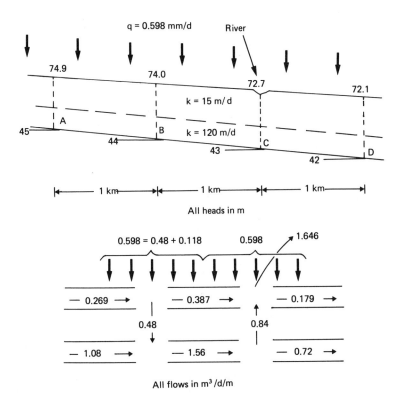

Fig. 6.10.   Horizontal and vertical components of flow; layered aquifer

the abstraction exceeded the water available from the unconfined region, and, though the inflow from the unconfined region increased due to the steeper groundwater gradient, a proportion of the abstracted water was obtained by dewatering overlying strata. The detailed results from 1970 to 1977 show that the

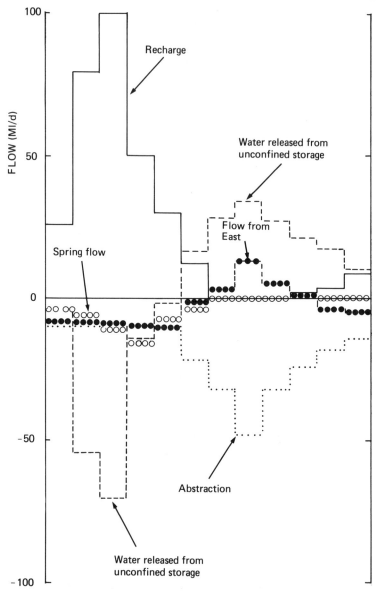

Fig. 6.11.   Water balance for problem of Fig. 6.6

TABLE 6.I.   **Monthly Flow Balance for Simple Example (Ml/d)**

Month	Recharge	Water released from storage		Abstraction	Spring flow	Flow to east
		Unconfined	Confined			
Jan	26.00	−3.82	−0.30	−10.0	−4.0	−7.88
Feb	79.20	−54.28	−0.12	−10.0	−6.0	−8.80
Mar	100.80	−70.82	−0.13	−10.0	−10.0	−9.85
Apr	50.40	−14.36	0.0	−10.0	−16.0	−10.04
May	29.60	−1.60	0.0	−10.0	−8.0	−10.0
June	12.00	+16.70	+0.38	−22.0	−4.0	−3.08
July	0	+28.32	+0.36	−32.0	0	+3.32
Aug	0	+34.25	+0.55	−48.0	0	+13.20
Sept	0	+27.30	−0.38	−32.0	0	+5.08
Oct	2.0	+21.56	−0.20	−24.0	0	+0.64
Nov	3.20	+17.44	−0.16	−18.0	0	−2.48
Dec	8.80	+10.47	−0.12	−14.0	0	−5.15

variations in abstraction rate are met primarily from storage, with the inflow from the unconfined region showing only minor fluctuations.

10. SOLUTION OF EQUATIONS

In the example discussed above, the reality of solving a whole series of simultaneous equations was avoided by quoting most of the results and demonstrating how the remaining groundwater heads can be calculated by direct substitution. In actual groundwater studies, the computational effort may be significant. Various approaches are available in the solution of the equations; the methods that require less computational effort are more likely to lead to instability or other convergence errors. As an alternative to solutions using a digital computer, in which time is divided into discrete time steps, analogue computers can be used in which time remains as a continuous function.

DIGITAL COMPUTER METHODS

The most reliable time approximation is the backward difference approach. There are two approaches to the solution of the backward difference equations (Eqn. (12)). Because there are a large number of unknowns, an efficient method of solving the equations is advantageous. Matrix methods can speed the solution of the equations and the Modified Iterative Alternating Direction Method (Prickett and Lonnquist[29]), the Line Successive Over-Relaxation Method and the Strongly Implicit Method (Pinder and Gray[9]) include matrix methods.

The one feature that these techniques cannot incorporate easily is an internal boundary for which the condition on the boundary depends on the current value of the groundwater head. For instance, the outflow from an intermittent stream or spring may change from a fixed head condition to a no flow condition. The actual condition cannot be determined prior to the start of the time step and therefore trial and error routines need to be incorporated in the calculation. This is most easily achieved if an iterative technique is adopted. The point successive iteration technique is particularly convenient for this type of calculation[8].

Further details of these backward difference methods of solutions can be found in Refs. 8, 29 and 30. In each case a programme listing is given. Solutions can be obtained using many different kinds of computers. If large computers with many significant figures are available, matrix methods can be used. Smaller computers with fewer significant figures are suitable if iterative methods such as successive over-relaxation are selected.

ELECTRICAL ANALOGUE SOLUTION

An alternative method of solving Eqn. (1) is by means of an electrical analogue. A discrete space finite difference approximation is used similar to Eqn. (7), but electrical time remains a continuous function. The analogous quantities are as follows[8]:

(a) voltage is proportional to groundwater head;
(b) electrical resistance is inversely proportional to transmissivity;
(c) electrical current is proportional to quantity of groundwater;
(d) capacitance is proportional to storage coefficient;
(e) electrical time is proportional to physical time.

Though five relationships have been quoted above, only three are independent relationships which can be described by three scaling coefficients[8]. The network consists of a square array of resistors with capacitors representing the storage coefficient connected at each node.

There are two approaches to the resistance capacitance network. In the fast time approach one year of physical time is represented in microseconds of electrical time. This means that relatively cheap electrical capacitors can be used but the function generators representing inflows and outflows and the measuring equipment are expensive. On the other hand, in the slow time approach a year of physical time is represented by about 20 seconds of electrical time. This requires high quality low-leakage capacitors, but the remainder of the equipment is relatively inexpensive. The slow time approach can more easily be used by the non-expert and a further advantage is that it can be linked to digital computer systems.

Resistance-capacitor electrical analogues are particularly useful when there are uncertainties about the nature of the boundaries or initial conditions. This is because the effect of changes in these conditions can be observed on the analogue. Steady-state analogues, which only involve the use of resistors, are often useful in the initial stages of a study to help to visualise the flow situation.

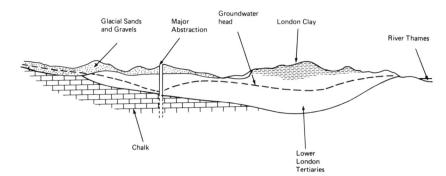

Fig.6.12. Essex Chalk Model; diagrammatic cross-section of aquifer

11. MODIFICATIONS FOR PARTICULAR FEATURES

Certain special techniques need to be introduced in the numerical solutions, to allow the representation of features such as wells, rivers, leakage, change from confined to unconfined conditions, and variation of transmissivity or storage coefficient with depth. These features are summarised in Table 6.II.

12. VERIFICATION OF THE GROUNDWATER MODEL

In devising a groundwater model, there is always considerable uncertainty about the magnitude of many of the parameters. It is therefore very important to ensure that a mathematical model does adequately represent the conditions in an aquifer. Usually limited direct evidence is available and it is necessary to make use of

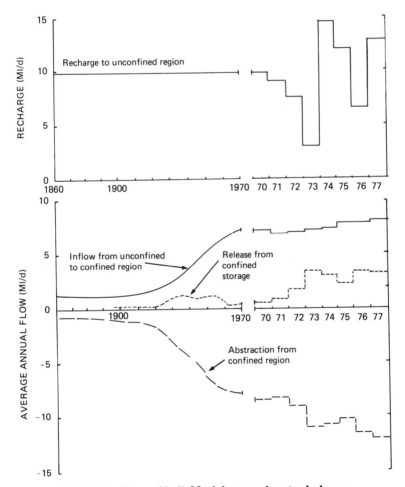

Fig. 6.13. Essex Chalk Model; annual water balance

TABLE 6.II.   Summary Of Techniques for Representing Special Features

Feature	Method	Comments	References
Wells	Represent radial flow towards the well; additional drawdown $= \frac{Q}{2\pi T} \ln\left(\frac{0.208\Delta x}{r_w}\right)$	Field data can be used to derive a more realistic expression for additional drawdown.	Prickett[31] Rushton and Herbert[32]
Partially penetrating rivers	Simulated by introducing additional hydraulic resistances or calculating flows from head differences	Risk of instability. May be very sensitive to river bed coefficients.	Herbert[33] Streltsova[34]
Intermittent rivers	Compare aquifer and stream bed levels	Accretion diagram to check whether water is available	Connorton and Hanson[19] Oakes and Pontin[35]
Leakage	Equivalent to an additional recharge $q_L = k'(H-h)/m$; k' and m are hydraulic conductivity and thickness of semi-pervious strata.	H is the head at the upper face of the semi-pervious strata. Ensure that there is sufficient water available for leakage	Birtles and Reeves[36]
Confined-unconfined change	Storage coefficient changes between confined and unconfined values as water level falls below confining layer.	Essential to represent slow increase of unconfined storage around the borehole.	Oakes and Skinner[37] Rushton and Senarath[28]
Permeability and storage coefficient a function of depth	Transmissivity calculated as the integral of the permeability for full standard depth. Storage coefficient depends on elevation	Adequate to calculate transmissivity and storage coefficient from heads at previous time step. Changes in T and S are frequently significant.	Rushton and Rathod[27] Connorton and Reed[38] Adams and Kitching[39]

additional evidence from different sources. A sensitivity analysis can be very useful as a means of determining whether further field data are necessary before the model can be considered to be reliable. Reference should be made to the case studies listed in Section 17 (Table 6.IV) for examples of model verification.

DIRECT FIELD EVIDENCE

Groundwater Head Variations with Time

Observation wells provide information about the variation of groundwater heads with time as illustrated by Fig. 6.7(b). Direct comparisons can be made between these data and the mathematical model results. However, it must be recognised that the response of an individual borehole may be influenced by the permeability and storage coefficient close to the borehole. Other boreholes at 100 to 1000 m distant may show significantly different responses. The regional groundwater model using a mesh spacing of 1 km or more cannot represent these detailed variations and therefore differences between the field and model values are to be expected. Variations in the groundwater head and the time at which these variations occur are often a clearer indication of the aquifer response than the absolute magnitude of the groundwater heads.

Groundwater Head Contours

A second form of comparison uses the distribution of groundwater heads throughout an aquifer at a particular time. There is often some difficulty in constructing contours of equal groundwater heads when there are insufficient data points. Nevertheless comparisons with field data can be valuable. When examining groundwater contours it must always be remembered that the flows occurring in the aquifer are a function of both the heads and the transmissivities. Unless the transmissivity is everywhere constant, the flow lines may not be at right angles to the groundwater contours.

Spring or River Outflows

Independent checks on the aquifer model can sometimes be made by comparing the field and calculated outflows from springs and rivers. If the extreme values both at times of intensive recharge and during drought periods can be modelled accurately, there can be confidence in the validity of the model.

INDIRECT FIELD EVIDENCE

Since the main purpose of a model study is to understand the flow of groundwater it is important to examine the distribution of the flows. As was shown in Fig. 6.7(d), diagrams can be constructed of the magnitude and direction of flows in an aquifer; unfortunately it is not possible to measure the actual flows within an aquifer. Nevertheless there is a great deal of indirect evidence that allows a check to be made on the order of the flows.

Evidence that can be used to estimate the order of magnitude of the flows includes hydrochemistry (Edmunds[40]), environmental isotopes (Lloyd[41]) and geophysical methods (Robinson and Oliver[42]). Often the most useful check is in regions where very little flow occurs. A model which represents regions of low flow adequately is one in which the flow balance is reproduced accurately.

This is demonstrated in the South Humberside Chalk. To the north and to the south of Grimsby there are areas where old saline water has been stationary for a long period. The transmissivities in these regions are only slightly below the typical values, and therefore the low flow condition must occur because water is flowing elsewhere. The manner in which this occurs is illustrated by the flow diagram of Fig. 6.14.

LENGTH OF MODEL SIMULATION

A simulation must always continue for a sufficiently long time for the inadequacies in the model to become apparent. For a confined aquifer a period of two or three years is often adequate but for unconfined aquifers much longer periods must be modelled.

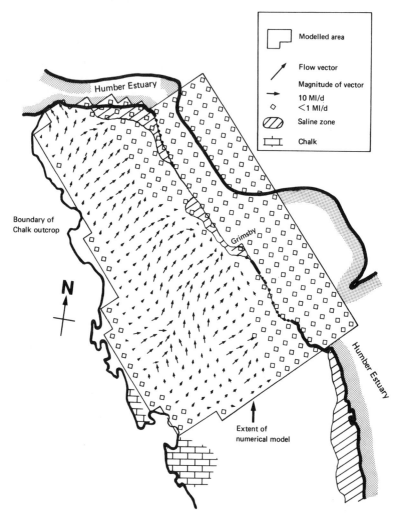

Fig. 6.14.   Flow diagram, South Humberside Chalk Model, showing regions of high salinity

If, for instance, an unconfined aquifer is being dewatered, the average fall in groundwater heads may be of the order of half a metre a year. By using an incorrect estimate of recharge and compensating for this by an incorrect value of the storage coefficient, a simulation may appear to be adequate. However, if the simulation includes a period when the total abstraction was significantly smaller (or greater) then the inadequacies in the simulation would become apparent.

SENSITIVITY ANALYSIS AND THE INVERSE METHOD

There will always be considerable uncertainty about many of the aquifer parameters. For example, it is difficult to obtain information about the magnitude of the transmissivity and storage coefficient throughout the aquifer. Reliable estimates of the magnitude and distribution of recharge are also difficult to obtain. Uncertainties also arise about the position and nature of boundaries.

The effect of these uncertainties can be investigated by varying each of the parameters in turn and determining the effect on the heads and flows. If, for example, it seems probable that the transmissivities could be in error by 30 per cent, two additional solutions are obtained with the transmissivity increased by 30 per cent or decreased by 30 per cent. If the major flow mechanism is controlled by the transmissivity, then the modelled heads and flows may be significantly different, but if the principal feature is the gradual dewatering of the aquifer, changes in transmissivity may have a negligible effect.

This form of sensitivity analysis can also be carried out by changing the storage coefficient or changing the recharge. In many aquifer studies, changes in the magnitude of the recharge have proved to be the most important effect. Other parameters which can be investigated by a sensitivity analysis include the position and nature of the boundaries, initial conditions and different aquifer/river interactions. Each of these can be investigated by means of a sensitivity analysis.

In certain instances sufficient data are available to permit values of the transmissivity and storage coefficient to be estimated. If there are adequate values of the groundwater heads and their variation with time and knowledge of the recharge and other flows, it is possible to rearrange Eqn. (1) to deduce the aquifer transmissivities and perhaps storage coefficients (Morel[43]). This technique, called the inverse method, can only be used for aquifers in which the flow mechanism is relatively straightforward; for other aquifers it can give misleading results (Neuman[44]).

13. PREDICTION AND FORECASTING

The real purpose of carrying out an aquifer study is to be able to predict the probable behaviour of an aquifer in the future. This prediction can either be concerned with the long-term trends or with the detailed short-term behaviour. The long-term response will be termed *prediction*, and the short-term behaviour *forecasting*.

Before any reliable prediction or forecasting can be carried out, the aquifer model must be thoroughly tested to ensure that it does adequately represent the aquifer response. For instance, it is dangerous to predict for the next twenty years when the aquifer model has been tested for only two years. Again, it is unwise to use an aquifer model to predict the response during a drought period when the model has only been tested against average conditions. Another questionable practice is to use a model to predict the aquifer behaviour due to a large number of abstraction wells when the aquifer response has been tested for only a few wells.

It is not possible to give rules as to the conditions which must be satisfied before an aquifer model can be used for prediction, since the response of each aquifer is so different. Nevertheless, certain guidelines can be given. The first is that the prediction should not be continued for a period longer than that for which the model has been tested. Another guideline is that predictions which cause the groundwater heads to go outside the bounds of those observed in practice should be treated with caution. Then, when predictions have been made, it is essential to continually update the model as the historical response can be compared with these predictions.

One of the major uncertainties in making predictions is that the future recharge patterns are unknown. Attempts at overcoming this can be made by relatively short-term forecasting. An example of forecasting in a limestone aquifer is described by Rushton and Tomlinson[45]. The greatest difficulty was to obtain a reasonable estimate of the recharge. Since the recharge depends on precipitation and evaporation, forecasts have to be made of the magnitude of each of these quantities. Evaporation can be forecasted with some certainty, but the forecasting of precipitation is much more difficult. Three approaches were followed, to use annual average values of rainfall, monthly average values or values derived from a generation technique. Both the annual average and the monthly average values proved to seriously underestimate the recharge. This underestimate arises because recharge usually occurs following above average precipitation; taking averages therefore tends to lead to recharge values that are very small.

When a generation technique such as a Box-Jenkins type expression is used, in which the predicted rainfall depends on the values during the preceding months and the value for the same month one year previously, the forecasted recharge is consistent with the typical recharge values. The suitability of the forecasts was tested by attempting to predict the aquifer responses for three months ahead and then comparing them with the actual response. Certain of the results are shown in Fig. 6.15. Thus, for example, the aquifer model is run using historical data until the

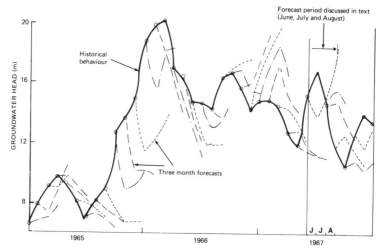

Fig. 6.15.   Forecasts of aquifer response
(broken lines for forecasted values; full line for actual response)

end of June 1967. Forecasts for precipitation and potential evaporation are made and, using the actual soil moisture deficit at the end of June 1967, forecasted estimates of the recharge can be calculated. These recharge forecasts are used in the model with historical values of spring flow and abstraction to predict how groundwater heads will vary over the ensuing three months. Forecasted values for the end of June, July and August 1967 are 13.6, 15.5 and 17.2 m, respectively, compared with the historical values of 16.3, 14.9 and 11.8 m. Fig. 6.15 indicates that although there are considerable variations in the quality of the forecasts, they do in general indicate the correct trends. It should be noted that this discussion refers to an aquifer with a rapid response; the behaviour in unconfined aquifers with a slower response is easier to predict.

14. RADIAL FLOW MODELS

Most of this chapter is concerned with regional groundwater flow modelling, yet much information can be gained about an aquifer from the radial flow due to pumping tests. Usually pumping tests are analysed using type curve methods (Chapter 5) but there are frequently portions of the drawdown response which do not match the idealised type curves. Therefore it is valuable to have a method whereby the various features assumed to cause the deviations from the type curves can be tested. This can often be achieved by means of a numerical model of radial flow.

Assuming radial symmetry for the permeability, storage coefficient and boundary conditions, the flow can be described in terms of radial coordinates.

Three approximations can be used in which different simplifying assumptions are made.

(i) In the first, vertical components of flow are neglected and the differential equation then becomes:

$$T_r \left(\frac{1}{r} \frac{\partial s}{\partial r} + \frac{\partial^2 s}{\partial r^2} \right) = S \frac{\partial s}{\partial t} + q \qquad \dots \qquad \dots \qquad \dots \qquad \dots \qquad \dots \qquad (13)$$

where T_r = the radial transmissivity
$\quad\quad r$ = radial co-ordinate
and s = drawdown below initial rest level which equals $(H-h)$ where H is the rest level for the aquifer.

Introducing an alternative co-ordinate in the radial direction:
$$a = \log_e (r) \qquad \dots \qquad \dots \qquad \dots \qquad \dots \qquad \dots \qquad \dots \qquad \dots \qquad \dots \qquad (14)$$

Eqn. (13) may be rewritten as:

$$T_r \frac{\partial^2 s}{\partial a^2} = r^2 \left(S \frac{\partial s}{\partial t} + q \right) \qquad \dots \qquad \dots \qquad \dots \qquad \dots \qquad \dots \qquad \dots \qquad \dots \qquad (15)$$

This equation is similar to the one-dimensional form of Eqn. (1) For convenience the co-ordinate, a, is divided into equal mesh intervals Δa. This is equivalent to a logarithmic increase in radius as illustrated in Fig. 6.16. A backward difference time approximation is used and since there is only one space co-ordinate, the resultant simultaneous equations can be solved efficiently.

Using this numerical approach, it is possible to reproduce all the standard type-curves derived from analytical solutions including the Theis solution, recovery behaviour, leakage, delayed yield, well storage etc. In addition it is possible to represent variable abstraction rates, variable saturated depth, permeability and storage coefficients that vary with depth and radius, recharge occurring during the test, influence of outer boundaries, well losses, changes between confined and unconfined conditions and a number of other features. The technique has been used to study a number of complex aquifer problems[8].

(ii) A simple development of this approach allows the inclusion of vertical components of flow. Two groundwater heads are defined at each radial mesh point; the free surface head and the average head in the lower part of the aquifer. Equivalent vertical hydraulic resistances are included which are proportional to the vertical permeability. The inclusion of the vertical permeabilities has proved important in the analysis of a shallow gravel aquifer (Rushton and Booth[46]).

(iii) If the aquifer is multi-layered and the abstraction well is partially penetrating, then it may be necessary to have a detailed mesh in both radial and vertical directions. The governing equation then becomes:

$$\frac{\partial}{\partial r}\left(k_r \frac{\partial h}{\partial r}\right) + \frac{k_r}{r}\frac{\partial h}{\partial r} + \frac{\partial}{\partial z}\left(k_z \frac{\partial h}{\partial z}\right) = S_s \frac{\partial h}{\partial t} \quad \dots \quad \dots \quad \dots \quad \dots \quad (16)$$

where k_z is the vertical permeability and S_s is the specific storage coefficient. Recharge or water released from storage at the water table can be included as part of the water table boundary condition. As the water table falls, modifications need to be made to the mesh to represent the changes in geometry at the free surface. Since both horizontal and vertical

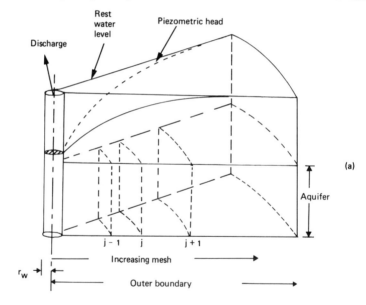

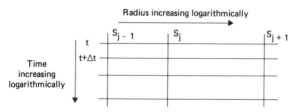

Fig. 6.16.   Grid spacing for radial flow approximation

mesh subdivisions are used there are many unknown heads at each time step requiring the solution of a large number of simultaneous equations. When solving the numerical form of Eqn. (16) instability problems can occur at large values of r.

This detailed model can give valuable information about the flow pattern within multi-layered aquifers. The manner in which water can be drawn from depth towards a partially penetrating well can also be investigated (Yar[47]).

15. FLOW IN VERTICAL SECTIONS

Useful information can also be gained about the flow in complex situations by considering a vertical cross-section of an aquifer. The governing equation is:

$$\frac{\partial}{\partial x}\left(k_x \frac{\partial h}{\partial x}\right) + \frac{\partial}{\partial z}\left(k_z \frac{\partial h}{\partial z}\right) = S_s \frac{\partial h}{\partial t} \qquad \cdots \qquad \cdots \qquad \cdots \qquad \cdots \qquad (17)$$

where k_x and k_z are the permeabilities in the horizontal and vertical directions. Recharge and the effects of specific yield are included in terms of the free surface condition on the upper boundary.

Solutions in three dimensions are also possible. However lack of sufficiently detailed data usually means that such detailed solutions cannot be justified. Further information about these techniques and their application can be found in Ref. 8.

16. MODELLING QUALITY CHANGES

In the previous sections attention has been confined to the quantity of water flowing; the issue of the changing quality of the water is a further important feature. The inclusion of the effects of quality adds an additional degree of complexity and difficulties involved in estimating the appropriate parameters. This means that it is often difficult to devise adequate models.

Only a brief review of some of the more important aspects will be given here; for more information the reader should consult Gelhar and Wilson[48] and Fried[49].

At least three approaches are available. The first approach is to obtain numerical solutions to the governing differential equations. Two mechanisms apply; one, convection, is similar to the quantity analysis which has been considered in the previous sections. The second equation concerns dispersion which for one-dimensional flow and constant dispersion coefficients can be written as:

$$\frac{\partial c}{\partial t} = -\frac{\partial}{\partial x}(u.c.) + D_L \frac{\partial^2 c}{\partial x^2} + D_T \frac{\partial^2 c}{\partial y^2} + D_T \frac{\partial^2 c}{\partial z^2} + C_v$$

where
$\quad u$ = mean pore velocity $\qquad\qquad\qquad\qquad\qquad\qquad$ (L/T)
$\quad c$ = mass concentration of the solute $\qquad\qquad\qquad\qquad$ (M/L^3)
$\quad t$ = time $\qquad\qquad\qquad\qquad\qquad\qquad\qquad\qquad\qquad$ (T)
$\quad D_L, D_T$ = hydrodynamic dispersion coefficients of the solute in
$\qquad\qquad$ the longitudinal and transverse directions $\qquad\qquad$ (L^2/T)
and $\quad C_v$ = source term $\qquad\qquad\qquad\qquad\qquad\qquad\qquad$ (M/TL^3)

For further discussion see Chapter 4, Section 11.

This one-dimensional formulation is adequate for the analysis of certain field problems; in other situations it is necessary to consider two-dimensional formulations in plan or in section. Methods of obtaining numerical solutions to the dispersion problems are discussed by Fried[49]. Serious errors can arise due to the occurrence of numerical dispersion during the calculations. The effect of this numerical dispersion can sometimes be minimised by adjusting the size of the discrete space and time intervals. Both finite difference and finite element approximations can be used.

In a second approach the velocities throughout the field are determined, using the techniques described in the previous sections. Then attention is concentrated on the regions where difficulties are likely to be encountered due to quality effects. Analytical solutions for the dispersion are used with the predetermined velocities. Two examples of the use of analytical solutions are described by Al-Niami and Ruston[50,51]. One concerns the prevention of dispersion by a flow in the opposite direction and the second concerns the movement of a contaminant towards an abstraction well. Table 6.III illustrates the manner in which dispersion causes contamination to occur in a shorter time than if dispersion was insignificant. With the occurrence of dispersion, the well is contaminated within 1 000 days, but if the dispersion is ignored the model suggests that contamination of the well would only occur after 6 000 days.

A third more approximate approach assumes that the contaminant flows at the actual velocity of the water. A solution in terms of the quantity is obtained by dividing the resultant Darcy velocity by the effective porosity. Due to dispersion effects, the actual movement of the contaminant is likely to be more rapid than this approach suggests, yet these calculations can give the right order of the travel times. The example of Table 6.III is an instance where the inclusion of the dispersion is essential.

This brief section cannot do justice to the complex problems of quality modelling. Quality effects are of great significance in waste tips, nitrate movement in soils, saline intrusion, upconing and a number of other important practical problems. A conference in 1981[52] illustrated the practical importance of this topic. Far more work on this aspect of groundwater flow is likely to be carried out in the coming years.

17. CASE STUDIES

Table 6.IV summarises a number of recent case studies in Britain. The list is certainly not exhaustive, but it is prepared to demonstrate the wide variety of different conditions in the aquifers. The case studies are divided into three groups, Regional Models, Radial Flow Models and Quality Models; some would have been more reliable had the simulation continued over a longer period.

Table 6.IV illustrates a number of important features in the use of models to investigate groundwater flow in aquifers. Each aquifer has unique features which may have a significant influence on the yield of the aquifer. Unless these features are identified, the model is unlikely to be reliable. Thus for the Southern Lincolnshire Limestone, rapid recharge is an important feature, for the Lambourn Valley and the Candover Catchment the decrease in permeability with depth critically affects the yield of the aquifers and in the Vale of York the vertical leakage is significant.

Equally important is the length of the simulation. For the Lower Mersey Basin and the Braintree aquifers, the simulations extend over more than 100 years since the gradual dewatering has been occurring during that period. With the South Humberside aquifer the simulation extends over the period for which significant abstraction has occurred, otherwise it is not possible to obtain satisfactory starting conditions. In each of these studies there have been only limited data with which comparisons can be made in the early stages of the simulation.

TABLE 6.III. Concentration C/C_0 Due to an Instantaneous Change in Concentration C_0 on a Circular Section 300 m from an Abstraction Well (Discharge rate of well 627 m^3/d; aquifer thickness 70 m; porosity 0.19; dispersion coefficients (D) 1.5 m^2/d)

Time	Radius from well (m)					
(days)	300	200	100	30	10	1
(a) Including Dispersion Effect						
300	1.0	0.005	0.0	0.0	0.0	0.0
600	1.0	0.068	0.0	0.0	0.0	0.0
1800	1.0	0.487	0.108	0.038	0.035	0.033
3600	1.0	0.812	0.557	0.454	0.447	0.444
6000	1.0	0.951	0.874	0.839	0.837	0.835
(b) Ignoring Dispersion Effect						
300	1.0	0.0	0.0	0.0	0.0	0.0
3600	1.0	1.0	0.0	0.0	0.0	0.0
5500	1.0	1.0	1.0	0.0	0.0	0.0
5950	1.0	1.0	1.0	1.0	0.0	0.0
5995	1.0	1.0	1.0	1.0	1.0	0.0
6000	1.0	1.0	1.0	1.0	1.0	1.0

Two examples of the radial flow model are quoted. In each study, valuable information about the properties of the aquifer and the boundaries was gained. The models represented the behaviour both in the abstraction and the observation boreholes. Since the effects of recharge and recession can be included, the numerical radial flow models can be used to estimate the long term resources of these boreholes.

Of the three quality models, one is concerned with the contamination of a chalk aquifer due to mine discharge. This requires the study of the transport and dispersion over an area of around 150 km^2 for a period of 50 years. The second study concerns radial flow towards an abstraction well; this study was carried out in an attempt to estimate the dispersion coefficients. In the third example, the effect of nitrates from sewage spreading is considered. The model utilises flows calculated from a groundwater flow model to route nitrate through the saturated zone.

18. CONCLUSIONS

This chapter has reviewed the use of groundwater models in understanding, interpreting and predicting the flow in aquifers. A successful model suggests that a good understanding has been obtained of the flow mechanism and all the inter-related parameters. In the course of developing a successful model it is usually necessary to review certain of the parameters, which may involve the reinterpretation of field data or it may be necessary to obtain further field data. Even when an apparently successful model has been devised, it is essential to check its response in succeeding years as more data become available.

The models for regional groundwater flow have been developed over a number of years and can be used with confidence by water engineers. The radial-flow model is also straightforward to use and can assist in understanding the flow in the vicinity of abstraction wells. Quality models require further refinement, but with care, idealisations can be introduced which allow the use of numerical or analytical approximations.

TABLE 6.IV.   Details of Selected Case Studies

	Rock Type	Aquifer type C = confined U = unconfined	Boundaries	Approx area (km^2)	Length of simulation (years)	Special features	References
REGIONAL MODELS							
Southern Lincolnshire Limestone	Limestone	C/U	Groundwater divide, faults reducing transmissivity	600	20	Rapid recharge, varying transmissivity and storage coefficient, high spring flows	Rushton and Redshaw[8]
Lambourn Valley	Chalk	U/C	Groundwater divide, spring line, rivers	800	10	Intermittent streams, transmissivity decreasing with depth, pilot scheme	Rushton and Rathod[33] Connorton and Hanson[19]
Vale of York	Sandstone	U/C	Rivers, groundwater divide, reducing transmissivity	1200	5	Vertical leakage downwards in recharge area, upwards near river	Reeves et al[55] Morel[54]
Candover Valley	Chalk	U	Groundwater divides and rivers	100	6	Storage coefficient and transmissivity significantly higher in the zone of water table fluctuation	Birtles and Reeves[36] Headworth et al[56] Rushton and Rathod[27]
Fylde	Sandstone	C/U	Groundwater divide, rivers, recharge from adjacent carboniferous strata	250	10	Extensive pumping to cause dewatering. Possible saline intrusion	Oakes and Skinner[37]
Shropshire Sandstone	Sandstone	U/C	Rivers and streams, ground water divides	400	5	Interaction with partially penetrating rivers. Well field design for river regulation	Liddament et al[57]
South Downs Chalk	Chalk	U	Groundwater divides, rivers, sea	250	5	Control of saline intrusion by careful abstraction policy	Nutbrown et al[58]
Worfe	Sandstone	U/C	Adjacent impermeable strata, rivers, groundwater divides	250	20	Interaction with rivers, overall water balance of surface water and groundwater	Miles and Rushton[59]
South Humberside Chalk	Chalk	U/C	Groundwater divides, flow under Humber Estuary	700	40	Influence of gravels. Represent history from before abstraction commenced	Spink and Rushton[60]
Braintree	Chalk	C/U	Groundwater divides, coastline. Include chalk and Lower London Tertiaries	100	100	Limit recharge with delays through boulder clay. Dewatering around abstraction sites	Rushton and Senarath[28]
Lower Mersey Basin	Sandstone	U/C	Mersey Estuary, adjacent less permeable strata	300	130	Representation of long history, limited recharge through drift and boulder clay	Ireland and Brassington[61]
RADIAL FLOW MODELS							
Lambourn	Chalk	U	Permeability and storage coefficients vary with depth	30	0.1	Tests from differing rest levels. Local and average permeabilities identified	Connorton and Reed[38] Rushton and Chan[62]
Ashton Keynes	Limestone	C/U	Interference due to neighbouring boreholes. Distant unconfined boundary	100	0.3	Effect of a step test. 3 day test with recovery and 72 day test each provide information	Gonzalez and Rushton[63]
QUALITY MODELS							
Tilmanstone	Chalk	U	Groundwater divide, springs, inflow resulting from mine discharge	150	50	Quantity and quality in dual porosity medium	Headworth et al[64] Bibby[65]
Clipstone	Sandstone	U	Artificial recharge by borehole, radial flow	10^{-2}	0.04	Dispersivity in radial flow. Examination of flow mechanism in field	Oakes and Edworthy[66]
Stour Valley (Staffs)	Sandstone	U	Recharge from sewage spreading and leaching of agricultural soils	70	80	Simulation of nitrate concentrations in groundwater. Influence of unsaturated zone	Oakes et al[67]

19. REFERENCES

1. Polubarinova-Kochina, P. Y. 1962 "Theory of Ground Water Movement" Princeton University Press.
2. Harr, M. E. 1962 "Groundwater and Seepage", McGraw-Hill, New York.
3. Todd, D. K. 1980 "Groundwater Hydrology", 2nd Ed., Wiley, New York.
4. Walton, W. C. 1970 "Groundwater Resources Evaluation", McGraw-Hill, New York.
5. Bouwer, H. 1978 "Groundwater Hydrology", McGraw-Hill.
6. Freeze, R. A. and Cherry, J. A. 1979 "Groundwater", Prentice-Hall, New Jersey.
7. Bear, J. 1979 "Hydraulics of Groundwater", McGraw-Hill.
8. Rushton, K. R. and Redshaw, S. C. 1979 "Seepage and Groundwater Flow", Wiley, Chichester.
9. Pinder, G. F. and Gray, W. G. 1977 "Finite element simulation in surface and subsurface hydrology", Academic Press, New York.
10. Prickett, T. A. 1975 *Advances in Hydroscience*, 10, 1, Modelling techniques for groundwater evaluation, Academic Press, New York.
11. Oakes, D. B. and Wilkinson, W. B. 1972 "Modelling of groundwater and surface water systems, 1. Theoretical relationships between groundwater abstraction and base flow", Water Resources Board, Reading.
12. Nutbrown, D. A. and Downing, R. A. 1976 *J. Hydrol.*, 30, 327, Normal-mode analysis of the structure of baseflow-recession curves.
13. Rushton, K. R. and Tomlinson, L. M. 1979 *J. Hydrol.*, 40, 49, Possible mechanisms for leakage between aquifers and rivers.
14. Hantush, M. S. 1964 *Advances in Hydroscience*, 11, 282, Hydraulics of wells, Academic Press, New York.
15. Boulton, N. S. 1963 *Proc. ICE*, 26, 469, Analysis of data from non-equilibrium pumping tests allowing for delayed yield from storage.
16. Rushton, K. R. and Ward, C. 1979 *J. Hydrol.*, 41, 345, The estimation of groundwater recharge.
17. Oakes, D. B. 1982 *Trans. Geol. Soc. S. Afr.*, 84, 135, A numerical model of a stream aquifer system subject to delayed rainfall recharge.
18. Senarath, D. C. H. and Rushton, K. R. 1983 *Ground Water*, 22, 142, A routing technique for estimating aquifer recharge.
19. Connorton, B. J. and Hanson, C. A. 1978, 61, "Regional modelling-analogue and digital approaches", Thames Groundwater Scheme Conference, Institution of Civil Engineers, London.
20. Rushton, K. R., Smith, E. J. and Tomlinson, L. M. 1982 *J. IWES*, 36, 369, An improved understanding of flow in a limestone aquifer using field evidence and mathematical models.
21. Liggett, J. A. 1977 *J. Hyd. Div., ASCE*, 103, HY4, 353, Location of free surface in porous media.
22. Davis, J. M. 1975 "Two-dimensional groundwater flow", Technical Report No. 5, Water Research Centre, Medmenham.
23. Smith, G. D. 1965 "Numerical solution of partial differential equations", Oxford University Press.
24. Tomlinson, L. M. and Rushton, K. R. 1975 *J. Hydrol.*, 27, 26, The alternating direction explicit method for analysing groundwater flow.
25. Anon, 1978 "South Humberbank Salinity Research Project, Final Report to the Anglian Water Authority", Depts. of Geol. Sci. and Civ. Eng., University of Birmingham.
26. Connorton, B. J. 1980 "Numerical solution of quasi-linear regional groundwater flow equations with reference to the chalk aquifer of the Berkshire Downs", MSc dissertation, Mathematics Dept., University of Reading.
27. Rushton, K. R. and Rathod, K. S. 1981 *J. Hydrol.*, 50, 229, Aquifer response due to zones of higher permeability and storage coefficient.
28. Rushton, K. R. and Senarath, D. C. H. 1983 *J. Hydrol.*, 62, 143, A mathematical model study of an aquifer with significant dewatering.
29. Prickett, T. A. and Lonnquist, C. G. 1971 "Selected digital computer techniques for groundwater resources evaluation", Illinois State Water Survey, Bulletin 55.
30. Trescott, P. C., Pinder, G. F. and Larson, S. P. 1976 "Techniques of water-resource investigation of the United States Geological Survey", US Geological Survey, Book 7, Chapter CI.
31. Prickett, T. A. 1967 *Ground Water*, 5, 38, Designing pumped well characteristics into electrical analogue models.
32. Rushton, K. R. and Herbert, R. 1966 *Geotechnique*, XVI, 264, Groundwater flow studies by resistance network.
33. Herbert, R. 1970 *Ground Water*, 8, 29, Modelling partially penetrating rivers on aquifer models.
34. Streltsova, T. D. 1974 *J. Hyd. Div., ASCE*, 100, HY8, 1119, Method of additional seepage resistances—theory and application.
35. Oakes, D. B. and Pontin, J. M. A. 1976 "Mathematical modelling of a chalk aquifer", Technical Report TR 24, Water Research Centre, Medmenham.
36. Birtles, A. B. and Reeves, M. J. 1977 *J. Hydrol.*, 34, 97, Computer modelling of regional groundwater systems in the confined-unconfined flow regime.

37. Oakes, D. B. and Skinner, A. C. 1975 "The Lancashire conjunctive use scheme groundwater model", Technical Report TR 12, Water Research Centre, Medmenham.
38. Connorton, B. J. and Reed, R. N. 1978 *Q. J. eng. Geol.*, 11, 127, A numerical model for the prediction of long term well yield in an unconfined chalk aquifer.
39. Adams, B. and Kitching, R. 1979 *Hydrol. Sci. Bull.*, 24, 487, The simulation of transmissivity, storativity and evapotranspiration in a digital model of a fissured dolomite aquifer near Ndola, Zambia.
40. Edmunds, W. M. 1981 'Hydrogeochemical investigations' in "Case studies in groundwater resources evaluation", Clarendon Press, Oxford.
41. Lloyd, J. W. 1981 'Environmental isotopes in groundwater' in "Case studies in groundwater resources evaluation", Clarendon Press, Oxford.
42. Robinson, V. K. and Oliver, D. 1981 'Geophysical logging of water wells' in "Case studies in groundwater resources evaluation", Clarendon Press, Oxford.
43. Morel, E. H. 1976 "Determination of the transmissivity and storage coefficient of the chalk in the Lambourn catchment", Resources Division Report 19, Central Water Planning Unit, Reading.
44. Neuman, S. P. 1975 "Role of subjective value judgement in parameter identification, modelling and simulation of water resources systems", North Holland Publishing Co., Amsterdam.
45. Rushton, K. R. and Tomlinson, L. M. 1980 *Wat. Resources Bull.*, 17, 406, Operating policies for a surface-groundwater system.
46. Rushton, K. R. and Booth, S. J. 1976 *J. Hydrol.*, 28, 13, Pumping test analysis using a discrete time-discrete space numerical method.
47. Yar, M. 1982 "Mathematical modelling of salinity in groundwater flow", MSc Thesis, Dept. of Civil Eng., University of Birmingham.
48. Gelhar, L. W. and Wilson, J. L. 1974 *Ground Water*, 12, 399, Groundwater quality modelling.
49. Fried, J. J. 1975 "Groundwater Pollution", Elsevier, Amsterdam.
50. Al-Niami, A. N. S. and Rushton, K. R. 1977 *J. Hydrol.*, 33, 87, Analysis of flow against dispersion in porous media.
51. Al-Niami, A. N. S. and Rushton, K. R. 1978 *J. Hydrol.*, 39, 287, Radial dispersion to an abstraction well.
52. Anon, 1981 "Quality of groundwater", Proceedings of an International Symposium, Elsevier, Amsterdam.
53. Rushton, K. R. and Rathod, K. S. 1980 *Hydrol. Sci. Bull.*, 25, 325, Flow in aquifers when the permeability varies with depth.
54. Morel, E. H. 1980 *Q. J. eng. Geol.*, 13, 153, The use of a numerical model in the management of the chalk aquifer in the Upper Thames Basin.
55. Reeves, M. J. *et al* 1974 "Groundwater resources in the Vale of York", Water Resources Board, Reading.
56. Headworth, H. G. *et al* 1982 *J. Hydrol.*, 55, 93, Evidence for a shallow highly permeable zone in the Chalk of Hampshire UK.
57. Liddament, M. W. *et al* 1978 "The use of a groundwater model in the design, performance, assessment and operation of a river regulation scheme", IIASA International Symposium on Logistics and Benefits of Using Mathematical Models of Hydrologic and Water Resources Systems, Pisa.
58. Nutbrown, D. A. *et al* 1975. *J. Hydrol.*, 27, 127, The use of a digital model in the management of the chalk aquifer in the South Downs, England.
59. Miles, J. C. and Rushton, K. R. 1983 *J. Hydrol.*, 62, 159, A coupled surface water and groundwater catchment model.
60. Spink, A. E. F. and Rushton, K. R. 1979 *Proc. International Assoc. for Hydraulic Research Congress, Cagliari, Italy*, 5, 169. The use of aquifer models in the assessment of groundwater recharge.
61. Ireland, R. J. and Brassington, F. C. 1981 *The Science of the Total Environment*, 21, 261. An investigation of complex saline groundwater problems in the permotriassic sandstones of North West England.
62. Rushton, K. R. and Chan, Y. K. 1976 *Ground Water*, 14, 82, Pumping test analysis when parameters vary with depth.
63. Gonzalez, M. and Rushton, K. R. 1981 *Ground Water*, 19, 510, Deviations from classical behaviour in pumping test analysis.
64. Headworth, H. G. *et al* 1980 *Q. J. eng. Geol.*, 13, 105, Contamination of a chalk aquifer by mine drainage at Tilmanstone, East Kent, UK.
65. Bibby, R. 1981 *Wat. Res. Res.*, 17, 1075, Mass transport of solutes in dual-porosity media.
66. Oakes, D. B. and Edworthy, K. J. 1977 "Field measurements of dispersion coefficients in the United Kingdom" Conference on Groundwater Quality—Measurement, Prediction and Protection, Water Research Centre, Reading.
67. Oakes, D. B. *et al* 1981 *The Science of the Total Environment*, 21, 17, The effect of farming practices on groundwater quality in the United Kingdom.

Chapter 7

HYDROGEOLOGICAL INVESTIGATIONS

1. INTRODUCTION

HYDROGEOLOGICAL investigations vary widely in scope from a response to a single inquiry calling for no more than a desk study using published data and a site inspection, to substantial projects spanning many years and involving large project teams with capital budgets measured in millions of pounds. The technical objectives may also vary widely, some concentrating on water supply and water resources and others oriented towards groundwater quality problems. The scale and scope of the study may differ, depending on the country in question and its level of social and technological development. For instance, the major groundwater resource-oriented hydrogeological studies carried out in the UK in the 1960s and 1970s are now less common, but work of this nature, on a wider and broader scale, is now frequently undertaken overseas. In the more developed countries, where groundwater abstraction, mineral extraction and waste disposal may compete for the use of one aquifer, the emphasis is towards detailed information for groundwater management and protection.

Despite this diversity hydrogeological investigations have much in common. They will require the integration of the many specialist skills which are featured in the various chapters of this volume. They may well encompass the many other fields of science and engineering with which hydrogeology is often allied. Groundwater problems, although they are generally not understood by the general public, and by non-technical clients, often give rise to strong public interest or concern. It is therefore often a feature of groundwater investigations that there will be extensive liaison and consultations with a wide variety of interests. None of these features exclusively characterises hydrogeological investigations, but they do require that special attention is given to project planning, to a definition of the objectives and scope of the study, and to the method of reporting and review. In the case of commissioned studies these aspects will feature prominently in the contract between client and specialist. A similar approach is desirable in less formally commissioned investigations.

Whatever their size, the main objectives of such investigations remain the same. They are to obtain knowledge of all the factors influencing the problem and an understanding of the relationships and processes involved. A systematic approach is needed whereby studies, measurements and investigations are carried out to evaluate all the various factors and components, and one can do no better in undertaking hydrogeological studies than to start by evaluating sequentially the components of the water balance equation. Not all hydrogeological studies are specifically concerned with water resources, some are concerned with water quality studies, but all will involve consideration of the flow of groundwater through aquifers. In fact, three such relationships exist, which between them cover all hydrogeological studies. They are the water balance equation, the water quality equation and Darcy's Law. A systematic study of each of their parameters will ensure that important elements are not overlooked, that an understanding of the processes is at least attempted, if not obtained and, not to be overlooked, that a measure of the errors and uncertainties in the calculations is obtained.

A simplified hydrological cycle is shown in Fig. 7.1 and from this the water balance equation may be written as:

$$\underbrace{(P\text{-}E_t) + R_e + U_e}_{\text{gain}} = \underbrace{R_o + R_i + R_g + U_o}_{\text{loss}} \pm \underbrace{(\Delta S_g + \Delta S_m)}_{\text{change of storage}}$$

where $(P\text{-}E_t)$ = effective rainfall
R_e = surface inflow from adjacent catchments
U_e = groundwater inflow from adjacent basins
R_o = surface outflow
R_i = interflow
R_g = base flow
U_o = groundwater outflow to an adjacent basin or to the sea
E_t = evapotranspiration
ΔS_g = change in groundwater storage
ΔS_m = change in soil moisture

The quality of groundwater at specific locations in an aquifer is a complex function of the physicochemical and biological processes occurring in an aquifer, the external inputs, and the quality of the groundwater flowing into an area. The inputs and processes will vary with time and so therefore will groundwater quality. An expression (see also Chapters 3 and 15) for the water quality may be written as:

$$K = G_w \cdot \underbrace{f(I_p.I_r.S.L_p.L_d)}_{\text{inputs}} \cdot \underbrace{f(c.m.b.)}_{\text{processes}} \cdot \underbrace{f(t)}_{\text{time}}$$

K = resulting water quality
G_w = chemistry of groundwater flowing into the area
I_p = chemical inputs from rainfall
I_r = chemical inputs from surface waters
S_o = chemical inputs from soil
L_p = leachate from point pollution (for example, landfill sites, sewage effluents, surface spills)
L_d = leachate from dispersed pollution (for example, fertilisers)
c = physicochemical processes
m = mechanical processes
b = biological processes
t = time

The quantity of water flowing through an aquifer is governed by its hydraulic conductivity which may be expressed by the Darcy equation as follows:

$$k = b.i.w/Q$$

(dimensions)

where k = hydraulic conductivity   (L/T)
Q = groundwater flow (L^3/T)
b = aquifer thickness   (L)
i = hydraulic gradient   (dimensionless)
w = width of flow zone   (L)

A hydrogeological investigation may require the systematic study of each of the parameters in the three equations (expressions) given above or a more restricted

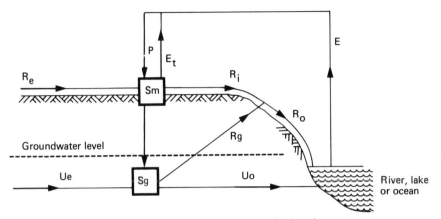

Fig. 7.1. Simplified hydrological cycle

approach may be satisfactory and lead to a solution or analysis of the problem. The determination of the parameters will need to lie within the framework of information concerning the topography, geology, drainage pattern and the past and proposed water resource or waste disposal activities in the area. The purpose of this chapter (bearing in mind that many matters are dealt with in detail in other chapters) is to review the methods of evaluating the components in the above equations (expressions) and to show their relative importance for different types of investigation.

The activities which make up a hydrogeological investigation can be more fittingly grouped into the six sections which comprise the next part of this chapter. However, it is worth listing the studies needed to determine the parameters in the above equations (expressions) and this is done in Table 7.I.

2. TECHNICAL COMPONENTS

GEOLOGICAL FRAMEWORK

Reports and Maps

Before drawing up proposals for a hydrogeological investigation a thorough review of available information should be made. This will reduce costs by avoiding duplication of work already done, and by preventing drilling and field tests being made in the wrong locality or to the wrong depth.

Technical information relating to the study or adjacent areas should be reviewed. Sources of such information are:

(1) national topographic maps;
(2) national geological maps and reports;
(3) soil survey maps;
(4) case studies in text books;
(5) papers in international journals;
(6) proceedings of conferences, symposia, etc;
(7) university theses;
(8) consultants' reports (to governments and other organizations);
(9) reports by local, regional or national agencies, bureaux or authorities responsible for the control, regulation or use of water resources.

The National Reference Library has the biggest collection of books, international journals and periodicals in Britain and is the most likely place to track down the less common references. All libraries in the UK have reference volumes of the Association of Special Libraries and Information Bureaux (ASLIB), which list libraries, information centres and units attached to universities etc., which are of a specialist nature. Computer-based bibliographic information systems have been developed extensively over the last decade. These may be accessed worldwide through the international telephone services. AQUALINE and GEOARCHIVE are data bases of particular value in that they contain many references to groundwater papers and reports.

In most countries geological information will be held by the country's Geological

TABLE 7.I.   Principal Hydrogeological Parameters and Studies Required in Their Assessment

Symbol	Equation Parameter	Studies Required
Water Balance Equation		
$P\text{-}E_t$	Effective rainfall	Catchment definition, areal distribution, daily and seasonal variations, long-term changes in rainfall and evapotranspiration
R_c	Surface inflow	Stream gauging, bed seepages, tracer tests
U_e	Groundwater inflows	Geology, hydraulic gradients, aquifer definition, aquifer properties, borehole logging
R_o	Surface outflow	Stream gauging, aerial thermal surveys
R_i	Interflow ⎫	Separation of flow components from stream flow
R_g	Base flow ⎭	records
U_o	Groundwater outflows	As for U_e
ΔS_g	Change in groundwater storage	Well records, water table maps, water level fluctuations, historic trends, pumping tests, barometric changes
ΔS_m	Changes in soil moisture	Soil moisture measurements, soil types, land use studies, soil moisture deficits
Water Quality Expressions		
G_w	Chemistry of inflowing groundwater ⎫	Borehole drilling, sampling, *in situ* instrumentation, monitoring, chemical analysis, changes in time,
I_p	Chemical input from rainfall ⎪	records of waste disposal, agricultural and other
I_r	Chemical input from surface water ⎬	activities
S	Chemical input from soil ⎪	
L_p	Point pollution ⎪	
L_D	Dispersed pollution ⎭	
s	Sorption, precipitation ⎫	Aquifer mineralogy, chemical analysis, laboratory
i	Chemical interaction ⎭	experiments
m_s	Mechanical dispersion	Coefficient of dispersivity, aquifer properties
m_f	Molecular diffusion	Coefficients of molecular diffusion, porosity, fissure geometry
b	Biological processes	Biochemical analysis
Darcy's Equation		
Q	Groundwater flow	Borehole logging, flow net analysis, base flow, numerical models, records of water resource developments
k	Aquifer permeability	Field tests, laboratory experiments, grain size, mathematical models
b	Aquifer thickness	Geology, borehole records, drilling geophysical surveys
i	Hydraulic gradient	Water table maps
w	Width of flow zone	Geology, catchment definitions, drainage network

Survey or by the government department responsible for mining and natural resources. In the UK the British Geological Survey (BGS) library is a useful starting point for geological maps and information in Britain and overseas, as is the Water Research Centre (WRC) at Medmenham, near Reading, for reference on water.

The BGS has the responsibility for the systematic geological mapping of Great Britain on the scale of 1:10000 and the publication of new and revised maps, reports, memoirs and bulletins. Published maps are available for Great Britain on a scale of 1:50000, although maps for many areas are still available only on the old scale of 1:63360 (1 inch to a mile). There is a move towards the production of maps on the 1:25000 scale covering smaller areas and accompanied by short reports. Field maps on a scale of 1:10000 are available for inspection at the BGS library in Wallingford.

In addition to the technical information on groundwater a picture should be built up of the climate, relief, drainage and vegetation of the area, the political, social, economic and administrative structure of the region and its economic and historic development. Reports on these topics may be available from:

(*a*) Governments
(*b*) United Nations Education, Scientific and Cultural Organization (UNESCO)
(*c*) United Nations Food and Agricultural Organization (FAO)
(*d*) World Health Organization (WHO)
(*e*) The Council of Europe

Aerial and Satellite Photography and Remote Sensing

Aerial and satellite photography provides an increasingly diverse source of valuable information, particularly in under-developed countries and poorly-surveyed regions. Existing information may be available from:

(i) single and stereoscopic black and white and colour aerial photographs;
(ii) infrared photographs and infrared linescan surveys;
(iii) gamma ray, ultraviolet, infrared and microwave multi-spectral satellite imagery;
(iv) colour and false-colour photography.

Basic aerial photographic cover varies widely from one country to another in the amount of cover, the scale, resolution and, not least, the accessibility of photographs. Frequently the lack of topographic maps, their inappropriate scale, uncertain reliability or age, make aerial photographs an essential component of hydrogeological and other investigations. The need for up-to-date land-use information or photographs to assist in geological interpretation makes aerial photographs invaluable, while paired aerial photographs, capable of stereoscopic analysis, permit elevation and changes in elevation to be measured accurately. Infrared photographs and linescan surveys can be useful for identifying spring outflows or seepages, warm effluent discharges to rivers and tidal waters, and shallow water table areas.

Aerial black and white stereoscopic photographs can be obtained for the whole of the UK on scales from 1:60000 down to 1:10000. Photographs are available from 1940 onwards and the last total aerial survey was made in 1969 by the RAF with 60 per cent overlap for stereoscopic projection. Special infrared aerial coastal surveys have been made by the Ordnance Survey. Details of all aerial black and white and infrared photographs are held by the Department of the Environment Air Photographic Unit, Prince Consort House, Albert Embankment, London (and for Wales and Scotland by the Welsh Office, Cardiff, and the Scottish Development Office, Edinburgh, respectively). The Air Photographic Unit also holds records of aerial photographic surveys made by commercial organizations, which can then be approached directly for photographic prints.

The advent of orbiting earth resources and weather satellites since 1972 has transformed our knowledge and understanding of the Earth and its processes. The US National and Aeronautical Space Agency series of LANDSAT satellites carry multi-spectral scanners, and scan the whole of the Earth's surface every 18 days. Conventional colour and false-colour photographs are reconstructed from the images produced with a resolution of 80 m. Other satellites placed in drifting or geo-stationary orbit by various space agencies (US, USSR, Japan and the European Space Agency) provide additional information. The speed of technical information and the capability of the US Space Shuttle to put very large instruments into orbit will mean that advances in the range and resolution of remote sensing will continue to accelerate. Photographs in real or false colours can be obtained from the Earth Resources Observation Systems Data Centre in the US, or from the other space agencies on request.

Borehole Records and Groundwater Data

Details of wells and boreholes, their construction, the strata encountered, yields, drawdowns, and some information on groundwater quality, are contained in the BGS well catalogues and inventories which are available for south-east England and parts of East Anglia, Hampshire and Wiltshire. BGS propose to follow these well inventories for the other major aquifers in England. Some additional information on boreholes may be held by the water authorities. It is worth noting that water well drillers in England and Wales are statutorily required to provide details of construction and water levels in boreholes exceeding 15 m in depth.

Hydrogeological maps of many areas in England have been produced by BGS in collaboration with water authorities, the chalk aquifers of southern and eastern England being particularly well covered. These maps are on the scale of 1:100 000 and show the outcrop areas of the aquifers, structural contours, water table and piezometric contours, springs, public water supply abstraction sources, hydro-chemical data and areas of coastal salinity. Maps for most other parts of England and Wales are planned on scales of 1:100 000 and 1:250 000.

Hydrogeological maps for Europe have been prepared and published by the International Association of Hydrogeologists (IAH). Twenty-five sheets have been prepared on a common scale of 1:500 000. They can be obtained from the IAH office in Hanover.

More recently the Council of Europe has co-ordinated the preparation of maps for European countries showing groundwater resources and usage as a series of overlays.

Information on groundwater levels in England and Wales is published by the DoE. The 'Groundwater Year Books' compile groundwater level records from nearly 100 measuring authorities and are available in four volumes from 1964-80. Computer-archived data on groundwater levels are held by the water authorities and the BGS, and the DoE holds a selected and representative collection of national data.

Geological and Geophysical Field Surveys

Once the geological information from published geological maps, reports, memoirs, drilling records, etc. has been collected, collated and assimilated, it may be necessary to undertake geological field surveys of selected areas. This may be needed to check the accuracy of the published information in the light of changes in geological interpretation or through base maps being out of date. The detail and time required for field mapping will depend on the information being sought, because it may be necessary to accompany the exercise by augering shallow boreholes, soil and rock sampling, examination and analysis. In most hydrogeo-logical studies, however, detailed field studies are likely to be of a hydrogeological nature and feature as proposals for drilling as part of a proper investigation.

Geophysical surveys are becoming increasingly more used in hydrogeological studies with the advent of more advanced techniques for interpreting field data. Electrical resistivity is by far the most commonly used technique and applicable in identifying strata of different electrical conductivity, or where waters of different salinities are present. They are also useful for locating bedrock below underlying overburden, but as with all geophysical techniques, good field data on lithology and groundwater salinity are needed to interpret the field data with confidence. The recently developed electro-magnetic method is useful for speedy surveys where large changes of electrical conductivity in shallow groundwaters occur in relatively homogeneous strata.

Seismic refraction, by means of an explosive charge, weight drop or hammer blow, is a useful technique for locating the bedrock surface beneath overlying superficial deposits. Gravity prospecting is useful as a reconnaissance tool for locating faulted or other structural boundaries and for the mapping of alluvium-filled valleys. More detailed information on both surface and downhole geophysical methods is given in Chapters 8 and 9.

HYDROGEOLOGICAL PROPERTIES

The introduction to this chapter listed the more important of the quantitative measurements of the properties of an aquifer and the groundwater it contains. These are the essential numerical raw materials of any hydrogeological study and a quantitative approach to any groundwater quality or quantity problem cannot be undertaken without them. For many of the variables a number of methods of measurement or estimation are available, which often vary both in the complexity and cost of execution and in the accuracy of the result. It is a matter of judgement which method should be used for any particular study, taking account of the needs of the study and the technical and financial resources available. This section makes reference to the more important of the parameters in turn, with special attention to the relevance of the various methods of determination and the limits upon their use. A detailed description of some of the methods and their application is given in Chapters 4, 5 and 6.

Hydraulic Conductivity

Hydraulic conductivity is defined by Darcy's Law and is a measure of the flow of water through unit cross-sectional area of an aquifer under unit gradient. The dimensions are L/T and in British practice most commonly quoted in metres per day. European practice is to use metres per second but this has the disadvantage of inconvenient numerical values and lack of consistency with the commonly used units for transmissivity (m^2/d) and flow (m^3/d).

The possible natural variation in hydraulic conductivity of materials is large, covering at least 13 orders of magnitude. There is a broad general correlation with lithological type as shown in Fig. 7.2 but it should be noted that any one lithological type may itself vary over two or three orders of magnitude. In many situations the extent of the variation may be more important than the precise values. Because of this wide variation estimates of hydraulic conductivity within an order of magnitude can be of value in many applications and variations of the order of 25 per cent may be of negligible significance.

Determinations of hydraulic conductivity can be made by both laboratory and field methods. Field methods vary in scale between those directed towards measurements of individual horizons or small sections of aquifer and those intended to measure aquifer properties in bulk so as to determine regional flows. The values obtained by testing at differing scales may vary and it is important that the method of test is appropriate to the particular application. These aspects are considered further later.

Estimation of Hydraulic Conductivity from Physical Properties

For granular porous media several methods are available for estimating hydraulic conductivity from data on grain size distribution. These are not always reliable but they provide a useful guide and have the benefit, particularly in reconnaissance studies, that the basic field data are easily obtained. The best known method, due to Hazen, is based on the D_{10} value obtained from a standard particle size grading curve and takes the form:

$$K = AD_{10}^{2}$$

where A equals 864 when K is in metres/day and D is in millimetres. Other more elaborate methods are available from the literature, using estimates of the grain size distribution and incorporating estimates of porosity (Bear[1] and Todd[2]). A general relationship between porosity and hydraulic conductivity exists for many sands and unfissured sandstones and once this relationship has been established it provides a ready method of extending information on hydraulic conductivity.

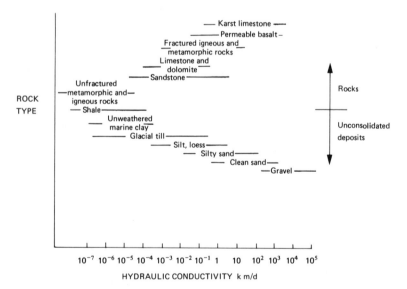

Fig. 7.2.   Range of values of hydraulic conductivity and permeability

(after Freeze and Cherry, Ref. 4, Chapter 4)

Laboratory Determinations

Direct measurements of saturated hydraulic conductivity may be made in a laboratory permeameter. Since hydraulic conductivity depends to a large degree on the packing density of the individual rock particles, samples should be undisturbed. This presents particular problems for unconsolidated aquifers. For rock samples, plugs cut from cores can be inserted directly into a permeameter providing care is taken to ensure a good seal along the sides of the plug. Hydraulic conductivity will often vary in different directions and plugs can be cut at different orientations to examine differences between, say, horizontal and vertical hydraulic conductivity. A falling head or constant head permeameter test may be used, but the former is better suited to samples with low conductivity. Materials with a very low hydraulic conductivity cannot be easily measured in a permeameter system and hydraulic conductivity for these materials is usually determined indirectly from the results of a consolidation test (Terzaghi and Peck[3]). Laboratory permeameter tests suffer from the drawback that samples are usually small and they may be disturbed from their field condition when installed in a permeameter. If laboratory tests are to be used to establish a picture of the hydraulic conductivity of the aquifer in bulk then a large number of samples must be taken to accurately represent the range of variation of permeabilities likely to be present. In addition many consolidated aquifers exhibit a primary permeability due to the fabric of the aquifer material itself, and a second, and often greater permeability, due to fractures or fissuring. It is rare for the contribution due to secondary permeability of this type to be measured during laboratory experiments. For this reason hydraulic conductivities of many consolidated aquifers determined from laboratory tests will be less than those determined from field tests.

Field Determination of Hydraulic Conductivity

Two different sorts of test come into this category which may be called single well tests and pumping tests, respectively. The theoretical basis for these tests is given in Chapter 4 and the method of analysis in Chapter 5.

Single Well Tests. These include the limited single well pumping test and the various types of slug and displacement tests all of which involve tests on a single, usually small diameter, well or piezometer and involve the injection or removal of relatively small quantities of water over a short time. These tests obtain values of hydraulic conductivity for only a small proportion of the aquifer adjacent to the well or piezometer. They all have advantages over laboratory determinations in that they can be carried out on both existing and newly constructed monitoring points and they do not require the careful collection of field samples. However, because of the limited volume of aquifer investigated, and because of the common inherent local variation in permeability the results can be difficult to interpret without good lithological control. A more powerful technique is the use of the Lugeon type test, either by water injection or pumping, with a double packer assembly to determine permeability over a defined interval at various depths. By this means a profile of field permeability changes with depth can be determined.

Pumping Tests. Pumping tests are carried out over a longer period and are usually at much higher rates of abstraction than the single well tests. This enables hydraulic conductivity measurements to be made of the aquifer at some distance from the well itself. The results reflect the hydraulic conditions of a volume of aquifer and thus lead to an understanding of regional characteristics.

Pumping test data give a value of transmissivity (T) which relates hydraulic conductivity (K) and saturated aquifer thickness (b) in the form:

$$T = Kb$$

For homogeneous isotropic media the appropriate value of b to use is the full saturated thickness of the aquifer at the site. Corrections can be made in the analysis to determine transmissivity if the borehole does not fully penetrate the aquifer. Where the aquifer is strongly anisotropic, with a horizontal hydraulic conductivity significantly greater than vertical hydraulic conductivity, it is appropriate to take the saturated thickness to be equivalent to the saturated thickness of aquifer penetrated by the borehole under test.

It is rare to achieve close repeatability of transmissivity values from analysis of test results using different methods or from the use of the same method during different stages of the same test.

It is thus normal to take an average value for transmissivity which it is usually inappropriate to quote to more than two significant figures.

Other methods of estimating transmissivity, which are commonly used, are from specific capacity (yield/drawdown ratio) data from sources operating under steady state conditions, from the application of Darcy's Law to the analysis of flow nets (see Chapter 4) derived from water level maps and by use of numerical modelling techniques to solve the 'inverse problem' from a known distribution of groundwater levels and recharge values (see Chapter 6).

Groundwater Storage

Storage is an important component of the flow-balance equation. The concept of water released from aquifer storage is somewhat different depending on whether the aquifer is confined or unconfined (see Chapter 4). The use of the term storage coefficient or storativity as a measure of aquifer storage is best restricted to the confined condition. The appropriate storage term for unconfined aquifers is the specific yield which may be regarded as the storage coefficient when full gravity drainage is complete.

Storage Coefficient (Storativity) of a Confined Aquifer

This may be defined as the volume of water which an aquifer releases per unit surface area per unit decline in head due to expansion of the rock matrix. In confined aquifers it generally has values in the range 0.005 to 0.00005. It cannot be easily or satisfactorily determined by laboratory methods.

The storage coefficient can be calculated from the water level hydrograph of a borehole in a confined aquifer and a barograph record for the same period. This depends upon calculating the barometric efficiency of the borehole, which is the ratio of the change in piezometric head in the confined aquifer to the change in atmospheric pressure (expressed in metres of water) which caused it. However, the most common and best method of measuring storage coefficient is by the analysis of pumping test data. Normal analytical methods require that at least one observation borehole is available in order that a storage coefficient can be calculated.

Where more than one observation well is available it is not uncommon for the values of storage coefficient from the individual wells to vary noticeably, perhaps by an order of magnitude or more. While this may be an indication of systematic changes in the storage properties of the aquifer with distance or direction, it may equally be due to the inherent difficulties of curve matching methods (see Chapter 5). To reduce these problems it is desirable to calculate storage coefficients on data unaffected by either removal of water from storage in the well itself (early time data particularly on low abstraction rates) or by boundary effects (late time data).

Specific Yield

Specific yield is the volume of water which drains from an aquifer under the influence of gravity, expressed as a percentage by volume of the drained formation.

The specific yield of an unconfined aquifer is always significantly higher than the confined storage coefficient because of the drainage process which takes place when the head is reduced. Typical values lies in the range of 1 to 30 per cent, the former being typical of fissured strata with only a limited amount of intergranular storage, and the latter from coarse gravel deposits. It can be determined from core samples in the laboratory if the aquifer is relatively homogeneous and unfissured. A good relationship exists between specific yield and porosity in homogeneous aquifers and may be reliably determined by this means once a relationship has been established but it is most usually and reliably determined from the analysis of pumping test data. Due allowance must be made for the phenomenon of delayed yield which complicates the analysis, especially in high storage and locally anisotropic aquifers. Delayed yield results from the slow drainage of water from the formerly saturated zone and its effects may disappear only during the later stages of a test.

Regional Values of Transmissivity and Storage Coefficient

Few aquifer systems are homogeneous and isotropic. This is particularly true in the UK where the two principal aquifers, the Chalk and the Permo-Triassic sandstones, both rely, in varying degrees, for their high transmissivities on water transmission through fissures. In the case of the Chalk a large proportion of the active storage is also contained within fissures. The inhomogeneities in the hydraulic system caused by the variable development of fissures are superimposed on the anisotrophy caused by hydraulic conductivity and storage properties of the matrix itself through, for example, variation in grain size or degree of cementation. In these situations the values obtained for hydraulic conductivity or transmissivity and storage coefficient may be scale dependent, depending on the volume of aquifer measured.

Despite these problems it has been established by long experience that both analytical and numerical methods of study, all derived from theory of flow in porous media, can be successfully applied to these types of aquifer (see Chapters 4 and 6). It is necessary, however, to ensure that the values of aquifer parameters used in flow analysis are selected with regard to the scale at which they are to be used, and that, for example, transmissivity values for an aquifer model with a 1000 m mesh spacing are not based, uncritically, on hydraulic conductivity data obtained from laboratory analysis of cores. Long et al[4] illustrate this concept by reference to a "representative elementary volume" of aquifer, below which widely varying values of hydraulic conductivity might be determined, depending on scale of sample, whereas above this volume it remains sensibly constant and a practical working value can be determined.

Leakage

In many hydrogeological systems leakage of water from adjacent formations or surface water bodies is a significant input to the flow balance equation. In arid areas, where recharge derived from precipitation is low, it may be the dominant input. In many cases the leakage may be induced from a river or adjacent low permeability formation by pumping from the aquifer and the leakage then becomes a significant feature in the groundwater development, by both reducing drawdown and increasing the exploitable yield of the resource. Analysis of leaking aquifer systems, whereby the volumes contributed by leakage may be quantified from pumping test data, is described in Chapter 5. The techniques may require monitoring not only in the principal aquifer but also in the leaky formation or adjacent to the leakage source. Most analytical methods assume that flow through the leaking horizon is vertical in direction and that flow through the main aquifer is horizontal. With this assumption the vertical hydraulic conductivity of the leakage layer can be calculated, giving a measure of the potential support to abstraction from the adjacent aquifer.

Porosity of a Rock Sample

The porosity is the ratio of the volume of voids to the total sample volume. It is a fundamental physical property of the aquifer material. A distinction can be drawn between primary porosity which is a property of the material itself and which is influenced by such factors as particle size, texture and degree of sorting, and secondary porosity which results from such modifying features as post-depositional fracturing or secondary solution. For these reasons the range of porosity, even in one lithological type, can vary widely. Values of the order of 40 per cent are found in uniformly graded gravels whereas many rock types can exhibit very low porosities, sometimes effectively zero. Clay deposits can have very high porosities, up to 70 per cent, although this is coupled with very low hydraulic conductivities. A positive correlation between porosity and hydraulic conductivity is only likely to be valid for a limited range of lithological type.

Laboratory tests may only determine primary porosity if the secondary porosity feature is not represented in the laboratory sample. This will lead to an underestimate of field porosity and is another example of the scale factor described earlier. In a fully draining rock the porosity would equal the specific yield. However, due to surface tension and other effects full drainage is seldom achieved and the specific yield value is almost always less—and often appreciably less—than the porosity.

Knowledge of porosity is very important in quality studies as it enables travel times for solutes to be calculated. The velocity of flow calculated from Darcy's Law does not give the average rate of migration of individual water or solute molecules. In order to estimate the average travel time for a solute it is important to recognise that the flow passes only through that proportion of the cross sectional area where there are voids. The average linear velocity ($\bar{v}$) is related to the Darcian velocity (v) as

$$\bar{v} = v/n$$

when n is the porosity of the aquifer.

Flow Regime

Although in some applications, such as two-dimensional aquifer models, it is desirable to know the average flow characteristics of large volumes of an aquifer, there are other types of study where a detailed understanding of local inhomogeneities is very important.

Typical examples of this are the local occurrence of fissuring contributing to borehole yield and the presence of local low permeability layers segmenting the aquifer and impeding solute migration. Permeability profiles with depth can be built up either by laboratory analysis of core samples, or by successive injection or pumping tests between packers. This information can be supplemented by downhole geophysical logging, using the techniques described in Chapter 9.

Of the commonly available methods, formation resistivity and natural gamma logs will most readily indicate changes in formation characteristics, and flow and temperature/conductivity logs identify effects on the flow regime. Natural flow in boreholes is normally too small to be detected by mechanical flow meters unless the borehole is open to two aquifers with abnormal hydraulic potential difference between them or the borehole exhibits flowing artesian conditions. Special methods can be applied, such as the use of the heat pulse technique of measurement or by adapting dilution gauging techniques to use in boreholes. More simply, flow can be artificially induced either by pumping the test borehole or an adjacent pumping source.

At many locations more than one aquifer may be present. This may be immediately apparent from the geological succession in that the feature which separates the aquifers, often a low permeability horizon, may be mapped as a separate lithological unit. However, single rock units may equally form multi-aquifer systems if there is sufficient systematic permeability variation. Certain aquifer types frequently show this phenomenon and if it is anticipated the investigation works should be designed accordingly. Evidence of a layered aquifer will often manifest itself from differences in groundwater potential with depth. These may be suspected if problems arise in producing a groundwater level map in an area where boreholes are of different depths, or if there are changes in groundwater level or rate of overflow during drilling or if there are changes in rate or direction of the vertical flow in a borehole proven during geophysical logging. Chapter 11 describes the special attention that needs to be paid to observation borehole design in multi-aquifer systems.

QUALITY STUDIES

The chemistry of groundwater is covered in Chapter 3 and pollution studies in Chapter 15. There are, however, a number of points which are particularly important at the investigation stage and these are described below.

Sampling and Analysis

A major factor increasing the complexity of groundwater quality studies over those concerned primarily with groundwater quantity is the problem of sampling and analysis. The issues which need to be considered at the planning stage in relation to sampling are:

(1) are there enough points from which samples can be taken?;
(2) is there likely to be variation in quality with depth and how can this be allowed for?;
(3) can disturbance or contamination during sampling be reduced to an acceptable minimum?

Factors to be considered in relation to analysis are:

(a) will a sample as received at the laboratory differ from the sample collected in the field?; if so, what methods of field analysis or sample stabilisation should be adopted?;
(b) what determinands need to be measured to meet the objectives of the project? Is the list realistic with the sample volumes expected?;
(c) will the analytical methods used give results which can be validly compared with historic data from the project area?;
(d) should all samples received be analysed as a matter of course or could a more cost

TABLE 7.II. Comparison of Methods of Sampling Chemical Depth Profiles of the Saturated Zone

Method	Advantages	Disadvantages	Comments
Piezometer points at various depths	Relatively easy to construct. Limited volume and restricted circulation reduces mixing in the column. Head can be simply measured.	Limit to depth if sampled by suction. Must be relatively large diameter to accept samplers	Method likely to become more commonly used with advent of small diameter submersible sampling pumps
Pore water extraction from cores	Also includes the unsaturated zone. Provides a very detailed profile if core recovery good.	Destructive sampling, expensive to repeat. Time series data must be obtained by one of the other methods. Problem of contamination from drilling. Small volume samples.	Expense rules this out for routine sampling but has a role in special projects
Packer sampling	Equipment mobile; can be used in any hole of suitable diameter. Does not commit borehole permanently to quality sampling. Can be combined with yield tests to relate quality to physical aquifer properties. Large volume samples.	Time consuming and labour intensive compared with other methods of open hole sampling. Pumping rate must be kept low to avoid leakage and short circuiting.	Not best used for permanent installation but sufficiently flexible to be used for periodic sampling of important boreholes
Gas ejection samplers at various depths	Good for regular repeat sampling.	Permanently installed; separated transducer must be used to measure head. Liable to silt up and cannot be cleared.	Widely used but has drawbacks and is likely to be replaced by piezometers as pumps become available

effective method be devised involving initial selective analysis with a detailed follow up if justified?

The programmes of sampling and analysis need to be considered at the same time because the decisions on one operation may influence the way the other operation is carried out.

Sample Sites. Water samples may be taken from streams, springs and wells or boreholes. The boreholes used may already exist or they may be purpose constructed for the groundwater study. The majority of the samples are likely to be taken from boreholes but the use of spring and stream samples should not be neglected, especially at the reconnaissance stage. Stream samples may be affected by run-off from other catchments, which will influence both quality and dilution and this must be allowed for. Spring samples taken at low natural discharge are likely to reflect groundwater conditions most closely.

The admixture of groundwater outflow and surface runoff in watercourses can be a good indicator of the local river/aquifer flow regime and in favourable circumstances this will be highlighted by quality changes, especially in temperature, which can be detected by in-river thermometry or from infrared aerial survey.

Borehole Sampling. It is difficult to take meaningful groundwater samples from boreholes. This is a fact not sufficiently widely appreciated, with the result that much groundwater data now exists of only limited scientific value. Water contained as a free water column in a borehole is in a very different environment from that contained within the rock matrix. Physical, chemical and biological processes all take place in the borehole column which can lead to unrepresentative samples being taken. An open borehole is suitable only for samples intended to be representative of the full penetrated depth and should be ideally sampled by pumping. Pumping should be at a rate adequate to clear water in and around the well. "Depth samples" in open boreholes will be subject to the problem of convective mixing in the water column. Repeat samples taken at fixed depth at intervals to provide a more representative average will induce mechanical mixing although this problem is reduced by using "through flow" samplers. None of these methods allows a reliable depth profile of water quality to be built up unless the changes are large, for instance as seen at a saline interface. Even here caution must be used. Cases are known where saline interfaces observed in standing columns in open boreholes are at different levels to interfaces in the aquifer itself because of movement of the interface in the borehole under the influence of vertical head differentials in the aquifer.

Four methods of selective sampling at depth are now in use; each has its own advantages and disadvantages, which are summarised in Table 7.II.

The composition of the materials used in the manufacture of the sampling equipment should be carefully considered, especially if the study involves looking for organic contaminants. Plastic well casing and piezometer tubing will contaminate samples with organic carbon and are best avoided. Careful sterilisation of sampling equipment is essential when collecting samples for microbiological analysis.

Contamination is a particular problem with pore water extraction from cores. Wherever possible drilling should be by air flush methods, although this may pose limitations to depth of drilling. Coring using 'mylar' or similar material as an inner sheath to the core barrel assists the preservation and handling of core material. Where biodegradation is likely to be a problem in studies of organic pollutants or nitrates, freezing of core samples at or near the drilling site may be desirable. This technique has the additional advantage that the frozen core samples are more robust to handle if the rock is naturally weak. Despite use of air and protective sheaths, core samples are at risk of contamination from the drilling process or by migration of fluids from higher or lower layers. For this reason cores should be taken at a reasonably large diameter (100 mm) so that edge effects can be eliminated by removal of outer layers of the core. These precautions are also necessary if it is possible to obtain driven cores of 100 mm diameter.

Range of Determinands

The range of determinands analysed will be influenced by the specific needs of the project and possibly by the volume of available sample. Unless there is good reason to omit them it is recommended that all samples are analysed in the laboratory for:

Sodium	Chloride
Potassium	Sulphate
Calcium	Alkalinity
Magnesium	Total oxidised nitrogen
Total dissolved solids	Ammoniacal nitrogen
Electrical conductivity	pH value

Other determinands which should be considered for inclusion, depending on the nature of the project, or perhaps be included for less frequent analysis are:

Soluble Iron	Fluoride
Soluble Manganese	Orthophosphate
Heavy metals	Total organic carbon
(Zn, Cu, Cd, Pb, Cr, Ni)	Dissolved CO_2
Silica	Dissolved O_2
Phenols	

Where sample volumes are likely to be limited it is useful to agree in advance a sequence of priority for the agreed determinands so that as far as possible maximum effective use is made of the sample.

Relatively inexpensive portable chemical analysis kits for field use are available and while these do not give the precision of laboratory determinations they may be particularly valuable in guiding a sampling programme at an isolated site or where there are problems with sample degradation during storage or transport (Hutton[5]).

Presentation

Water quality data involving measurements of many determinands at varying depths and sites can be voluminous. For the purposes of scientific analysis and for presentation of results it is often necessary to use various forms of graphical or diagrammatic display. Examples of commonly used methods are shown in Table 7.III and in Fig. 7.3, which summarise the applications, advantages and disadvantages of each method. Different applications will favour a different choice of graphical method (Fig. 7.3) and none is ideal in every circumstance.

History of Chemical Inputs

The observed hydrogeochemical regime is a function of both chemical inputs and chemical processes. The chemical processes are likely to remain constant with time but there may well be temporal variation in inputs. For studies of major basins where the timescale of significant hydrological change is measured in thousands of years any changes, perhaps in isotope ratios because of changing climatic conditions, will be slight and only relevant to very advanced sampling programmes. On the more local scale man-made activities may significantly alter the input and these must be documented if the groundwater quality system is to be understood. Examples are changes in the composition of rainfall, applications of fertiliser to soils, changes in agricultural regime and the incidence of point source pollution of all kinds. The data sources from which the chemical inputs can be estimated are varied and often inadequate. Rainfall chemistry data are not widely recorded, although in recent years a number of stations have been established in the UK.

Fertiliser data are available for certain areas from agricultural statistics although the coverage is often poor. Changes in land use can only be determined by reference to infrequent land-use surveys which may not be relevant to the period of interest. Documented records on the history of tipping at landfill sites are often not available or do not give sufficient detail of the materials disposed of and the relevant period of time. Despite all these drawbacks it is important to record as far as possible all these possible quality inputs.

Transport Processes

To understand and quantify the transport processes operating in a groundwater quality problem it will be necessary to consider the three constituent processes:

(i) advection—solute movement due to flowing groundwater;
(ii) dispersion—mechanical mixing and diffusion within the medium;
(iii) reaction—chemical and biological reactions and radioactive decay.

Advection. This may be regarded as the flow of solute within the groundwater body unaffected by dispersive processes. It is a function of the hydraulic conductivity and porosity of the formation and of the hydraulic gradient (see Chapters 4 and 6). The rate of solute movement is given by the average linear velocity calculated with a knowledge of the porosity of the aquifer. This concept may be very useful in situations where dispersive effects are small. It can be used to calculate likely transport times and may therefore be helpful, for example, in the design of an observation well network around a landfill site.

Dispersion. Dispersion arises from mechanical mixing as flow takes place through the aquifer and gives rise to a spread of travel times because of the varied tortuosity of the many possible flow paths through the medium. It is independent of the type of solute. Molecular diffusion also contributes to this effect but except at very low velocities it is very much smaller than hydrodynamic dispersion and for nearly all practical purposes can be discounted. Dispersion not only takes place in the direction of the groundwater gradient but also, to a reduced degree, in a transverse direction. In cases of moving fronts, say in the case of marine saline intrusion, the transverse dispersion is not evident and may be disregarded. However, with point source pollution it is the transverse dispersion which gives rise to the characteristic plume shape of the pollutant. In this type of problem it is desirable to attempt to establish both the longitudinal and transverse dispersion coefficients. Unfortunately, this is very difficult and costly to do satisfactorily.

There is also evidence that both longitudinal and transverse dispersion may be scale dependent. Laboratory measurements of dispersion on core or reconstituted aquifer material are almost invariably much lower than field determinations.

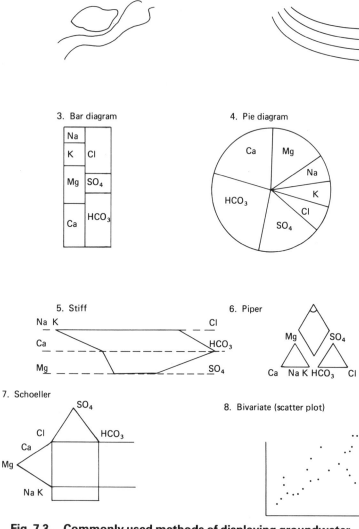

Fig. 7.3.   Commonly used methods of displaying groundwater chemistry data

(to be read with Table 7.III)

TABLE 7.III. Summary of Most Commonly Used Methods of Displaying Groundwater Chemistry Data

Method (see Fig. 7.3)	Description	Comments
1. Isopeth	'Contours' of equal concentration for a single determinand	Commonly used for demonstrating systematic areal variation of one ion. Hard to compare distributions for different ions
2. Trend Surface	Surface fitting by least squares method	Can be used to isolate simple trends from complex or 'noisy' data. Rare that adequate data available for groundwater chemistry applications
3. Bar diagram 4. Pie diagram 5. Stiff diagram	The most commonly used of a number of methods of demonstrating the ionic composition of a single sample	Size of sample indicates total ionic concentration. Proportionate sizes of individual parts of the diagram show proportions of the ionic species. Good for quick visual comparison of complete analyses. Stiff generally preferred for displaying areal differences on a map.

6. Piper	Trilinear plot of cations and anion proportions. Combined to give a single point in a rhombus field	Good for combining a large number of complete analyses on one graph from which grouping, mixing and trends can be seen. Drawbacks are that because concentrations are expressed as percentages:
		  (i) variation in absolute concentration not shown clearly
		  (ii) analyses of similar mix but different total concentrations are not differentiated

7. Durov	Development of Piper	Overcomes drawback (ii) of Piper by providing linear concentration scales for two variables
8. Schoeller	Semilog plot of ionic concentrations	Good for displaying relative concentrations but confusing with large data sets
9. Bivariate (scatter) plots	The simplest of a number of common graphical techniques for comparing two variables	Directly compares the ions in absolute terms and helps overcome drawback (i) of Piper

Recently attempts have been made to determine bulk dispersive properties over many square kilometres of aquifer, using models to interpret the results (Chapter 6) but the number of measurements are few. The current lack of field data on hydrodynamic dispersion, the difficulty and high costs of making field determinations, and the uncertainty of general applicability are major constraints on the use of models based on the advection-dispersion equations to predict the fate of solutes in the groundwater regime. These facts must be recognised in setting objectives for groundwater quality studies.

Reaction. The migrating solute, in addition to being diluted by the effects of advection and dispersal, may also be involved in chemical reactions. A large number of possible processes may take place but the majority may be classified under the three general headings of oxidation-reduction, sorption-desorption, solution-precipitation processes. These will normally be identified by sampling and analysis at experimental or investigative sites and by comparing concentrations at different points along the flow path. Two typical examples are studies of pollution migration through the unsaturated zone where a vertical profile of pore water concentrations is built up and sampling of a pollution plume down groundwater gradient from a point source of pollution. In each case the observed concentrations will be the combined product of advective, dispersive and reactive processes. Only the reactive processes will be unique to the individual chemical species and for a particular contaminant they may be most clearly revealed by the changes in concentration when compared with a conservative (relatively non-reactive) substance such as chloride. It is possible to model the effect of the various reactions on the rate of migration providing that numerical information governing the rate of reaction appropriate to conditions in the aquifer is available. In view of the complexity of the possible reactions and the paucity of field data this is rarely achievable. Because of the limits on field data relating to dispersion and reaction there is a practical limit to the extent to which it is possible to quantify these processes in relation to field problems.

It is for this reason that groundwater quality models, which have been developed to handle a large variety of groundwater flow and quality problems, are more commonly used to help understand processes in idealised and simplified examples rather than field conditions. Attempts have been made to derive dispersion coefficients and reaction using an inverse method by calibrating models against observed field data. This approach is limited by the realisation that a combined flow/quality model has so many variables that no solution in a situation of sparse reliable field data can be considered unique.

Geophysics

Both surface and downhole geophysical logging can enhance the understanding of groundwater quality problems (see Chapters 8 and 9). The most valuable surface geophysical technique is the resistivity survey. Where the resistivity contrast between groundwater bodies is strong, these can be mapped with a high degree of reliability in shallow groundwater systems. Examples of this approach commonly found in the literature are marine saline intrusion, connate water bodies at the margins of exploitable aquifers and leachate plumes from landfill sites. As with many other applications of geophysics the resistivity technique is best used in the preliminary phase of an investigation to help decide whether a problem exists, to assess the scale of the problem and to help plan an investigation programme. The cost of borehole drilling is one of the most substantial items in many investigations and experience in many studies has shown that economies can be achieved by improving borehole siting by the prior use of geophysics.

The fluid downhole geophysics logs can assist in the interpretation of the groundwater quality regime. It must be remembered, however, that the measurements are being made in a borehole which itself may have significantly modified the natural groundwater quality regime and thus the results may not always accord with those obtained from, say, surface geophysics or pore water profiles from borehole cores. If hydraulic disequilibrium exists between two aquifers of different groundwater quality penetrated by a single borehole, then the flow from the aquifer with higher groundwater head will contaminate the other aquifer locally around the borehole. If a situation of this type is allowed to persist for a significant period then data on the natural quality of the groundwater in the receiving aquifer may be permanently lost.

RESOURCES

The most fundamental part of many hydrogeological investigations is the calculation of water resources of the study area. This involves the determination of the factors in the water balance equation, given earlier. Before this can be done the catchment of the study area needs to be determined. This will frequently be the starting point of the investigation.

Catchment Definition

Aquifer catchment areas can be determined from geological maps, topographic maps, or water table contour maps, depending on available information. If sufficient water level data are available, and if the aquifer is sufficiently homogeneous and widespread, then water table contour maps provide the most accurate means of delineating catchment areas. When using such maps the accuracy, reliability, and time-base of the water level data, from which the maps are drawn, should be checked. Possible changes in catchment area may result from rising or falling water levels, which change the position of the watershed boundaries.

Where water table contour maps are not available, or cannot be prepared from assembled data, it will be necessary to estimate the aquifer recharge area by reference to topographic maps, from which the drainage basin can be assessed, and geological maps which will show the extent of the permeable strata within the catchment. Generally it is not possible to deduce from these maps the extent of transfers of groundwater out of and into the catchment, and these may be quite significant.

For confined aquifers it is necessary to define the areas of potential recharge on outcrop strata which provide the resources of the confined aquifer, and the exercise to do this is similar to that described above for unconfined aquifers. The definition of areas of recharge for confined aquifers is equally important to that for unconfined aquifers, for if confined permeable strata lack sources of recharge they can have no potential for a sustained water resource development. In such cases the water is obtained from storage in the aquifer and it is not replenished. This 'mining' of water leads to a progressive fall in groundwater levels and the eventual abandonment of the well field. This approach may be justified on economic grounds, particularly in the more arid countries, but seldom so in the west, unless it is accompanied by artificial recharge.

If it is planned to establish or extend a groundwater monitoring network in the catchment under study, so as to determine the impact of a resource development scheme, then it should be remembered that large groundwater abstractions are no respecters of groundwater divides, where they do not constitute geological boundaries, and the effects of the proposed development may extend into adjacent catchments.

Frequently, lack of historic data on groundwater levels or stream flows means that the changes from normal conditions which will occur, as a result of pumping, cannot be determined. In such cases it will be necessary to estimate the natural conditions, in the catchment under development, by comparison with an adjacent and unaffected catchment. The need for groundwater level or stream flow data, to provide such correlation estimates, needs to be recognised at the outset of the investigation and provision for appropriate hydrometric measurements incorporated in the overall scheme. The area to be used for providing data for correlation must be sufficiently distant from the development area to remain unaffected by the proposed abstractions.

Rainfall, Evaporation and Soil Moisture

Rainfall is the primary resource input in most catchments. If the water resource assessments are to be reliable then several years of daily rainfall data from a number of stations within the catchment area are needed. Generally this requirement can be met in the UK, and correlation between records from one station and another will permit missing records to be estimated. In some countries rainfall data may be sparse, and historic records non-existent and this may limit the scope of the water resource assessment.

In the UK measurement of daily rainfall is co-ordinated by the Meteorological Office, Bracknell, and information on rainfall is contained in their publications 'British Rainfall' and the 'Rainfall Supplement'. The first 'British Rainfall' was produced in 1862 when 500 stations were included, and this had increased to over 6000 stations when the last edition of 'British Rainfall' was published for 1968. Since then this publication has been replaced by the monthly and annual 'Rainfall Supplement' which is currently available up to 1972. Enquiries for information on rainfall should not be made to private rainfall observers but should be directed to the Meteorological Office or the relevant water authority, if it is the measuring body. Charts and tapes from automatic rainfall recording instruments are mainly held by the water authorities, but copies of this information may be held at the Institute of Hydrology, Wallingford.

The measurement of potential evaporation from evaporation pans or tanks and irrigated lysimeters, and the measurement of the meteorological parameters needed in the calculation of potential evaporation (temperature, vapour pressure, wind speed and sunshine) is carried out mainly at Air Ministry stations, agricultural and other research establishments, water authority and water company pumping stations. Automatic climatological stations are now increasingly being used for recording the meteorological parameters, including those needed for the calculation of potential evaporation using the Penman method. As with rainfall, the Meteorological Office and the water authorities are the main bodies holding this information.

In situ soil moisture is measured by some water authorities and research bodies using neutron probes, but it is difficult to apply this information to the overall resource studies. Soil moisture deficits are an intrinsic part of the calculation of actual evaporation, for which rainfall, potential evapotranspiration and the soil and vegetation characteristics (jointly expressed in the term root constant) are needed, using the Penman/Grindley method. As with potential evapotranspiration, computer programs are widely available for making these laborious calculations.

Calculations of soil moisture deficit, actual evaporation and net infiltration can be made to different degrees of accuracy. Estimates can be made using monthly data assuming a single type of vegetation/soil cover over the catchment. More detailed calculations can be made on a daily basis when a large number of soil and land use types can be incorporated in the calculations. For these detailed calculations, land use survey maps, produced by the Agricultural Research Council's Soil Surveys of England and Wales, are a valuable starting point.

The calculation of actual evaporation from a catchment permits the residual rainfall or effective rainfall to be determined ($R\text{-}E_t$). In permeable catchments with very porous soils this quantity equals the net infiltration to the aquifer. For aquifers which are covered by semi-permeable or superficial deposits the net infiltration to the aquifer may be substantially less than the effective or residual rainfall. Detailed catchment studies and measurements may show what proportion of the effective rainfall reaches the aquifer (this proportion is termed the infiltration coefficient) but the paucity of such data provides a severe constraint in resource assessments in many areas. Direct run-off from paved and urban areas and modifications to natural drainage systems by man's activities all make the task of determining natural recharge to aquifers difficult.

River Flows

While rainfall and evapotranspiration data can provide one means of calculating the long-term average resources of the catchment, they may also be equally represented by average outflows from the catchment by rivers, streams and springs. In most areas, particularly those with poor and unreliable meteorological data, it will be a better policy to measure river flows, because together with abstraction and other inputs to and outputs from the catchment, they can provide a useful measure of the available resources. This is particularly so in the case of poorly-defined groundwater catchments. Together with rainfall and evaporation and the other factors in the water balance equation, river flow data will allow the magnitude of errors in the equation to be estimated.

With the availability of daily records of river flow it is possible to construct flow hydrographs and separate the groundwater component of stream flow from that of direct runoff and interflow. For many spring-fed rivers in southern England, draining chalk catchments, the groundwater component, known as base flow, can exceed 90 per cent of total river flow, and figures of 50 per cent or more are common in permeable catchments in other parts of England.

In the UK, information on river flows and river flow measurements is contained in the 'Surface Water Year Book' published by the Department of the Environment. These year books started with records of 28 gauging stations in 1935 and have grown, until by 1973 details were provided of 869 stations. Similar and more detailed information may be obtained from reports and publications of the water authorities, and the statutory periodical surveys of resources and water use under s.14, Water Resources Act 1963, and more recently under s.24, Water Act 1973, are the most useful for this purpose.

Groundwater Levels

Groundwater level data are not only input parameters to the water balance equation, but are needed to define catchment areas at the start of the study (already described), and to permit changes in groundwater storage to be assessed.

The effects of groundwater storage can be estimated by using groundwater level data to select a period for the long-term water balance assessment for which the groundwater levels at the end of the period are the same as those at the start. This period should be as long as possible to minimise errors due to storage changes. If a long record is not available then the groundwater level data can be used to estimate the increase or reduction in groundwater held in storage over the short period. This is done by calculating the change in the volume of saturation in the aquifer between the beginning and end of the period and by multiplying this by an estimated value of storativity so as to calculate the gain or loss of water to or from the aquifer. A value for storativity may be known from test pumping analysis, laboratory determinations, the calibration of numerical models, or from the analysis of natural groundwater level responses.

Groundwater Quality Data

The availability of groundwater level data has been referred to earlier in this chapter. Groundwater chemical and quality data are generally sparse and tend to be dispersed. Sources of quality data include the BGS well catalogues, water authority and water company annual reports and water authority (s.24, Water Act 1973) periodic surveys of water use and management. The amount of information held varies greatly but most commonly includes pH, conductivity, hardness, alkalinity, total dissolved solids, biological oxygen demand, ammonia, and the chemical concentrations of the most common cationic elements, calcium, magnesium, sodium and potassium, and the most common anionic elements, chloride, sulphate, sulphide, nitrate, nitrite, together with total dissolved iron and manganese. Concentrations of less common elements are unlikely to be published in generally available reports. Most water authorities have established groundwater quality networks for obtaining a profile of present groundwater quality in their aquifers and for monitoring long-term changes which might take place.

Abstractions

Abstraction of groundwater may account for a substantial proportion of available resources in permeable catchments, and indeed there are many catchments in England which are over-prescribed. Therefore the calculation of authorised and actual abstractions, the return of abstracted water to the aquifer by way of septic tank discharges, or mains leakages and the pattern in abstraction with time, are a vital part of the water balance assessment.

The control of abstractions in different countries and states varies greatly both in terms of individual rights and statutory and administrative controls, and it is beyond the scope of this chapter to describe international practice. In England and Wales abstractions from surface waters and groundwaters are controlled by the water authorities. In Scotland and Northern Ireland no statutory control exists over groundwater abstraction. The licensing provisions of the Water Resources Act 1963 (see also Chapter 16) require each water authority to hold a register of all licence applications and licensed abstractions giving information on the location and purpose of the abstraction and the licensed quantities. These registers are available for inspection by the public at all reasonable hours. Details of actual quantities abstracted by licensed abstractors will vary from one authority to another depending on the requirements they specify in licences for the provision of such information. This information is not normally available to the public without the approval of the abstractor. Groundwater abstractions for domestic purposes are not licensable under the Water Resources Act 1963 and while these generally amount to only small quantities, they should not be disregarded.

Other Gains and Losses to the Catchment

Other water balance components may remain to be measured or estimated before the total picture is complete, but they could well present greater difficulties than the main components already described.

Groundwater inflows into and out of the catchment are not likely to be measurable but it may be possible to estimate them from Darcy's Law, for which estimates of hydraulic gradient, transmissivity and aquifer width are needed. Alternatively, an estimate of their magnitude might possibly be made from the changes in stream base flow at measured river flow sites.

There are other components of the full water balance which are not included in the equation given in the introduction to this chapter. Surface water evaporation is not likely to be significant unless the study catchment possesses large lakes or water bodies but, if necessary, this can be readily determined from measured or calculated potential evaporation already described.

Evaporation direct from the groundwater table is unlikely to be significant unless large areas of very shallow groundwater occur accompanied by aquaphilic plants.

Water Balance

Having assembled all the data for rainfall, evaporation, stream flow and groundwater storage changes, plus those for minor components, an attempt should be made to obtain a water balance for annual periods, or, more suitably, for as long a period for which records exist. Depending on the accuracy and reliability of the input data, a period of 3-5 years is likely to be the minimum period suitable for such water balances.

3. OTHER CONSIDERATIONS IN PLANNING A HYDROGEOLOGICAL INVESTIGATION

In planning a hydrogeological investigation consideration must be given at the outset to several other matters, including;

  (1) legal and planning requirements;
  (2) access and services;
  (3) public relations;
  (4) effects on water users;
  (5) environmental effects and ancillary studies.

LEGAL AND PLANNING REQUIREMENTS

These may comprise:
  (a) consent or other authorisation from bodies responsible for planning or controlling new developments;
  (b) purchase, leasing, acquisition of interests rights in land for sites for boreholes, pipelines or other works;
  (c) statutory orders, licences, consents, permits or other legal authorisations for the proposed works;
  (d) compliance with statutory or other requirements for the provision or submission of information relating to the proposed works (e.g. drilling records, abstraction and discharge returns).

In England and Wales the abstraction of water from boreholes is controlled by provisions contained in the Water Resources Act 1963 (see Chapter 16). In Scotland and Northern Ireland no statutory control exists over groundwater abstraction, and no authorisation is required to sink or abstract water from a borehole. The licensing provisions of the Water Resources Act 1963 require that virtually all abstractions from underground strata must be licensed by one of the ten water authorities in England and Wales. Several exemptions are provided, such as where the water is to be used for domestic purposes of the licence holder. Where a test borehole is sought to ascertain the presence of groundwater or the effects of abstraction on other wells, streams, etc., then the borehole may be sunk and tested under a consent issued by a water authority under s.24(9) of the Act. Following the test pumping of a borehole a licence must be obtained if the abstraction is to be made permanent. Persons planning to sink a borehole are advised to discuss in advance their proposals with the water authority concerned.

Under s.7 Water Act 1945 (s.4 (Scotland) Act 1946) a person sinking a borehole greater than 15 m in depth is required to give notice to the BGS of his intention to do so and to submit a record of strata and water encountered.

The discharge of test-pumped water to a watercourse is not generally considered to require a consent from the water authority but it is an offence to permit polluting matter to enter a stream, and if it is considered that the groundwater to be abstracted and discharged into a stream is likely to be contaminated or polluted it is advisable to consult the relevant water authority.

ACCESS AND SERVICES

The acquisition of sites for boreholes and routes for pipelines and other works, are matters, strictly, which lie outside the ambit of this manual, because the means by which sites are acquired will depend on the rights of landownership of the country in which the investigation is being carried out, as well as the preferences of those administering the investigation.

In the UK sites for boreholes and other works can be bought, leased or licensed, and rights of access for construction and maintenance of pipelines obtained as wayleaves. None of these means of acquisition obviates the likelihood of obtaining planning permissions from the relevant authority. Statutory powers to compulsory acquire sites and rights of access do exist for statutory bodies but they should be avoided whenever possible.

Once borehole sites have been selected, checks will need to be carried out with electricity, gas, water and telephone services that the proposed works will not interfere with underground pipes and cables, or overhead power and transmission lines.

Power for pump-testing boreholes may be provided by petrol or diesel pumps, air compressor, or spindle or submersible pumps powered by mains electricity or generator. The merit of providing mains electricity for lengthy test pumping will need to be considered at an early stage, while the noise from petrol or diesel motors or generators may create a nuisance or contravene local byelaws. Lastly, additional constraints may exist if sites are within National Parks, Areas of Outstanding Natural Beauty and Sites of Special Scientific Interest.

PUBLIC RELATIONS

If the investigation is to run smoothly and have a successful outcome it will be prudent not to neglect consultations with, and provision of information to, other interested organizations and persons. For investigations in foreign countries it will be sensible at the outset to obtain the advice of the embassy or legation in the country concerned as to what procedures, authorisation, consultations or courtesies need to be observed.

In the UK the nature of consultations required will depend on the size and nature of the investigation, but these may include: the regional water authorities, the metropolitan, county, district and parish councils of England and Wales, the regional, island and district councils of Scotland, the Nature Conservancy Council, the Ministry of Agriculture, Fisheries and Food, the National Farmers' Union, the Country Landowners' Association, the Council for the Preservation of Rural England, the Countryside Commission, members of parliament, land owners, farmers and other interested environmental and conservation groups. While consultation with statutory bodies and interest groups can be time-consuming and frustrating, the process may well pay dividends in removing or reducing objections to proposals for permanent works if the investigation is found to be successful.

EFFECTS ON OTHER WATER USERS

The development of groundwater schemes frequently conflicts with the interests of other water users. The lowering of groundwater levels through large-scale pumping may cause wells to dry up and affect pumping levels in private boreholes. These often require boreholes to be drilled to replace shallow hand-dug wells, and existing boreholes to be deepened and pumps lowered. Sometimes it may be cheaper and more convenient to provide a mains supply as an alternative.

The effects on springs and spring-fed supplies are generally less easy to overcome. Springs are particularly vulnerable to groundwater abstraction and in many cases can only be maintained by the provision of a local borehole to provide a compensation discharge, or by making a discharge from a more distant water supply. Watercress beds in southern England, which derive their water from overflowing artesian boreholes and springs, are particularly vulnerable to such developments. Protection can be afforded against the effects of groundwater augmentation schemes, which only operate for short periods in dry years, by the provision of temporary pumping plant for the artesian boreholes with suitable financial compensation provided for their operation.

It is characteristic of streams draining permeable catchments that their ephemeral upstream lengths flow only in winter. These are known in parts of the country as 'bornes' or 'winterbornes', and they can rise for a distance of 10 km above the perennial heads of the streams. Winterbornes, again, are vulnerable to the effects of groundwater abstractions, and may only be maintained as a visual amenity by providing an artifical impermeable bed to the stream and the discharge of compensation water.

ENVIRONMENTAL EFFECTS AND ANCILLARY STUDIES

The undertaking of a field programme of drilling and testing often arouses public anxiety over emotive issues which may or may not have substance. These may be, for instance, the lowering of the water table below the root zones of plants and trees, the drying out of soil through groundwater abstraction, the effect of abstraction on springs and surface ponds, the settlement of the land surface through consolidation of clays, and the effect of lowered groundwater levels on rare ecological habitats. While the mounting of a hydrogeological investigation may provide for an extensive monitoring programme of groundwater levels, water quality and stream flows, it may be wise, if not essential, to instigate regular surveys and monitoring so as to assuage public concern, and to obtain technical data to refute unfounded allegations.

Land Use Surveys

It is sometimes claimed that lower groundwater levels following abstraction dry out soil profiles and affect the growth of plants and trees. If it is considered at the outset of the investigation that this question is likely to become an issue, it will be wise to undertake regular soil moisture monitoring using downhole soil moisture neutron probes, and undertake a survey of land use and trees before abstraction takes place. It may be advantageous to employ a specialist consultant at the outset to independently assess the effects of groundwater abstraction on plants, trees and land use.

Land Subsidence

Settlement of the land surface following extensive abstraction from confined aquifers has occurred in many parts of the world. London has subsided 6-18 cm in the last 100 years, Venice some 15 cm since 1930, but the most dramatic situation is in Mexico City where 50 m thickness of soft lake clays have consolidated up to 8 m.

Settlement arises through the reduction in piezometric pressure in confined aquifers through abstraction and the consolidation of clays which overlie them. The drainage of pore water out of clays is, by its nature, slow and consequently consolidation can take place over a very long period of time. Recently-deposited clays and peats will be more susceptible to consolidation than older clays which, through their own weight and that of overlying strata (which may have subsequently been eroded), will be naturally well-consolidated and less prone to subsequent compression.

Nevertheless, the consolidation of clayey strata, through abstraction from underlying aquifers, and groundheave following recharge, may pose a problem which should not be overlooked at the outset of the investigation, and as in the case of agricultural surveys, it may be prudent to institute field measurements. Fortunately, technology can assist in this more than in the case of agricultural surveys, and the following studies may be included:

(i) Land surveys—these will involve the regular levelling of observation points in the area of risk and relating these to remote datum points outside the area. Steel level pins, 1 to 2 m long, cemented into the subsoil, beyond the range of seasonal surface drying, have proved to be good observation points.

(ii) Soil studies—the consolidation properties of clay cores from boreholes can be determined in the laboratory.

(iii) Piezometers may be installed in boreholes in the clay to measure the changes in piezometric pressure which occur as a result of lowering groundwater levels.

(iv) *In situ* settlement devices can be installed in the boreholes. These are fixed to a telescopic tube and anchored at various levels in the clay stratum. Changes in level, relative to the base of the borehole which should be into a stable stratum, are measured using an accurate electrical probe lowered down the borehole.

A combination of these devices, which are readily available from the field of soil mechanics and foundation engineering, together with topographic surveys, will demonstrate conclusively whether settlement has taken place, or is likely to take place, as a result of groundwater abstraction.

ECOLOGICAL EFFECTS

In some instances, it may be claimed that groundwater abstraction will harm unusual and rare ecological environments which succour distinctive flora and fauna. These may, for instance, comprise wetlands or marshy areas, where atypical plants and shrubs harbour rare plants and insects. The question of whether the preservation of such ecosystems is of greater value than the development being proposed must be resolved by the overall economic-political circumstances of the country in question, but there should be an awareness at the outset of the potential difficulties, and scientific data obtained by suitably qualified personnel to assess the scale of the problem.

4. ORGANIZATIONAL ASPECTS OF GROUNDWATER INVESTIGATIONS

Although hydrogeological investigations vary widely in scope (see Section 1) there are certain organizational aspects which should be observed in all investigations, particularly in relation to the setting of objectives, reporting progress, and assessing costs and benefits.

SETTING OF OBJECTIVES

Every investigation, no matter how large or small, has objectives. For an investigation to be effectively managed these objectives should be clearly identified and agreed by all participating parties. The objectives should establish the major subject areas to be investigated and the facts which need to be established. They should also identify the end point of the study and the way the study is to be phased. The establishment of clear objectives will assist the study by:

(1) enabling achievement to be measured throughout the life of the investigation;
(2) assisting in project reporting and review of progress.

Absence of defined objectives may lead to:

(a) unnecessary expenditure;
(b) misuse of specialist skills;
(c) deviation from the essential tasks, especially when delays and difficulties occur;
(d) the setting of unrealistic targets.

REPORTING AND REVIEWING PROGRESS

At the same time as objectives are established the method of reporting progress needs to be agreed. The scope and frequency of these reports will depend upon the scale of the study. Large investigations are likely to be co-ordinated by a steering committee of clients and specialists, or of participating agencies or departments, and this will call for regular progress reports. These can be brief, summarising activities and interim findings. They will be the primary source of information by which progress will be monitored against objectives and they permit the programme to be kept under review. Very large or long-running projects may involve a two-tier steering committee structure, with a lower tier technical committee meeting more frequently and overseeing in detail the progress of the study. This will report to a higher committee charged with overall responsibility for the investigation.

Such a formal system will be inappropriate for many hydrogeological investigations. Nevertheless, unless technical control is through normal line management, some form of co-ordination and review of all projects is necessary.

In addition to regular management reports there is also a need for full technical reporting, possibly at intervals during the study and certainly at its completion. A technical report serves a number of different purposes: to document the findings, to describe the method of study and to record the data collected. Different people at different times will require access to all of these and it is helpful if the report is structured to make reference to each easy. A convenient method of reporting is to split the material into three parts, separately bound if necessary, as follows:

(i) a summary of the major findings and their implications with recommendations for future action, Any data or maps essential for understanding this part of the report should be included;
(ii) a full report of the investigation describing the work done and giving a summary of the data obtained in support of the conclusions;
(iii) compilation of data in tables and graphs.

ASSESSMENT OF COSTS AND BENEFITS

The choice of such factors in investigations as borehole density is normally seen as a matter for professional judgement which cannot be objectively assessed. Providing sufficient time is available the problem can be approached by a method of staged investigation so that a more informed judgement about optimum scheme design can be made by evaluation of results at each stage. This approach also has its cost penalties because of the extended commitment to specialist staff and the additional cost which will be incurred by repeat mobilisation of contractors. It can be helpful to consider ranges of investment levels in relation to the likely costs of any scheme which may follow from the results of the investigation. For most studies it is possible to make an assessment of the level of investment in the study below which no practical return can be achieved. If an estimate can also be made of the level of diminishing returns this gives a rough envelope of costs within which the study might be expected to fall. Depending on the level of technology it is recognised that investment in research may vary between 1 and 10 per cent of the capital value of the project.

Groundwater studies may not be at a high level of technology but they deal with complex natural environments rather than laboratory conditions so it might be reasonable to expect expenditure in the range 5 to 10 per cent. Therefore if the study is leading to a capital scheme which can be costed it is possible to test whether the expenditure on the investigation is a reasonable and typical proportion of the final costs. Unfortunately such a test cannot so easily be applied to all types of study, for example into groundwater pollution or aquifer rehabilitation, where potential capital investment cannot be reliably quantified until the study is complete.

5. CASE STUDIES

Groundwater investigations cover a wide range of scale from the very small which may involve only a desk study or a single observation borehole, to the very large regional development where possibly 100 or more wells are required. There are however some elements common to all investigations but other elements which are specific to the nature and size of the activity. The final part of this chapter uses five groundwater studies to indicate common requirements and highlight specific requirements in each case.

RESOURCE RECONNAISSANCE

A common type of hydrogeological investigation concerns the reconnaissance of groundwater resources in areas which, in terms of water resources, are largely unexplored and undeveloped. The various questions which need to be answered are:

(1) are resources available for development?;
(2) where are they located?;
(3) how much can be abstracted?;
(4) how best should they be exploited?;
(5) is an investigation needed to provide firmer information on which to base proposals?

Most studies of this type are likely to be limited to desk studies, for which the first task is to assemble as much documentation and data as is thought to be needed. Data sources include topographical, geological and hydrogeological maps, aerial photographs, published reports and papers, borehole records, meteorological, hydrological and hydrogeological data. Naturally, in an area with largely unknown and undeveloped water resources there is likely to be relatively scant information available, but the information gathering exercise must be thoroughly pursued so that work is not duplicated or wasted at a later time.

Aquifers

The starting point will be the geology of the area. Geological maps are likely to be available, even if of poor quality or small scale, and these will give the first clue as to the existence of potential aquifers. The presence of igneous or metamorphic rocks is likely to be unfavourable, while sedimentary rocks may well suggest water-bearing strata. Aerial photographs are likely to be of value in identifying rock types and particularly geological structures.

Recharge

The presence of a recharge area is essential for subsequent resource utilisation unless aquifer storage is to be developed or 'mining' is considered acceptable. Where a concealed basin of permeable strata is to be developed it is even more important to identify the distance and size of recharge areas.

Some meteorological data will be needed to make some assessment of annual recharge, its seasonal pattern and annual variations, and armed with this information and the potential area of recharge, some estimate can be made of the resources which might be available. As a general guide, 0.4 m of recharge p.a. on 1 square kilometre of permeable strata will provide an average of 1 000 cubic metres of water per day.

Aquifer Yield

By now a picture will have emerged as to the theoretical resources of the study area, and depending on whether development is seen as being limited to replenishable resources, or as a short-term exploitation, an idea should be forming as to the potential aquifer yield. The drainage system and particularly stream flow data, if available, will give some information on the presence of usable resources and where they can best be exploited. The location of spring discharges, spring seepages, swallow holes, solution caves and disappearing streams, all will provide useful information on where the permeable strata may be gaining or losing water, and such information may prove vitally important.

Means of Development

Some information is likely to be available from diverse sources to suggest possible means of aquifer development. Water well records will be invaluable. Topographic maps, or even archaeological information, might indicate present or past dug wells, water holes, oases, soaks, etc., suggesting a shallow water table. Surface streams which maintain their flow during dry periods in a lowland terrain suggest a shallow water table, as would the presence of valley or outwash deposits. The lack of surface streams, the occurrence of thick or variegated deposits, highly inclined strata, as well as overlying impermeable deposits all may suggest the lack of a shallow water table.

Where the groundwater table is near the surface, development could be by hand-dug wells, shallow large-diameter wells, driven slotted tube wells connected to a central abstraction system, or porous or loosely-jointed horizontal pipes feeding to a centrally-pumped sump.

For deeper aquifers, the means of development are less varied, being limited to cable-tool or rotary-drilled boreholes, with or without slotted screen and artificial packs. The different types of drilling which could be employed are referred to in Chapter 13.

Need for Field Investigations

With the completion of the desk study it may be considered necessary to undertake limited field studies before any reasonable first appraisal can be made of the availability of resources and the nature of the aquifer. The scale of such an investigation will depend on the available funds in relation to the potential worth of the resource once developed and the time available. The study may include geological field mapping, geophysical and aerial surveys, stream gauging, rainfall, evaporation and percolation monitoring, groundwater level and quality surveys, and may even include limited observation and test borehole drilling. However, these investigations are unlikely to be very extensive at this reconnaissance stage and would be directed towards confirming the presence of potable water in the most promising areas, its depth, and reaching a decision and reporting on whether it is worth mounting a major investigation or development programme or whether no further investigations are warranted and the resource should be abandoned.

Assessing the Potential for a New Groundwater Source

In developed countries like the UK true reconnaissance studies are rare. Most areas of aquifer outcrop have been investigated at some time in the past and have some existing groundwater abstraction. It is not unusual, however, for the quality of existing data to be poor and for essential basic data on geology or regional water levels to be lacking. In these situations many of the elements of the basic reconnaissance survey will be necessary.

A typical problem which may be posed is to assess whether groundwater abstraction in an area already subject to development may be increased, and to select the best and most economic location for the new well(s). Frequently there is already existing abstraction with an infrastructure of water mains. This and other similar non-hydrological factors may strongly influence the decision on economic grounds. The various questions which need to be answered by the hydrogeologist or water engineer are:

(*a*) are sufficient exploitable resources available to allow a new abstraction to be sanctioned?;

(*b*) can they be exploited by existing plant or by new plant on an existing site?;

(*c*) is a new site required and where should it be?

(*d*) if a number of new sites are possible, what are the merits and drawbacks of each?

Size of Resource

The assessment of resources must be based on a discrete groundwater unit for which boundaries can be identified, either geological, such as stratigraphic or structural boundaries, or hydrological, such as groundwater divides or rivers. If sufficient geological and hydrogeological information is not available it must be obtained. Recharge from surface infiltration can be estimated from meteorological data and should if possible be checked by comparing it with measured or estimated outflow from the groundwater unit made up of abstraction from wells or base flow to rivers. If resources as assessed from rainfall recharge exceed the authorised groundwater abstraction then, in principle at least, there is a potential for additional abstraction. Whether it is likely to be sanctioned depends on any abstraction control policy which may be applied in that area. This policy will take into account such factors as the requirements upon groundwater outflow to support watercourses and the impact that pumping the newly proposed wells would have on existing authorised groundwater abstractors. In addition to assessing available resources from rainfall the potential for induced recharge must be considered. Even in a situation where most or all of the recharge from rainfall is being exploited it may be possible to consider further abstraction if it is made up by induced flow from adjacent rivers.

Existing Sites

If the water balance for the unit reveals a groundwater surplus available for further development, the next step is to assess whether the abstractions from existing wells can be increased. There are many instances where new pumping stations have been constructed when a thorough appraisal of existing works would have shown unutilised potential which could have been exploited and thereby delayed or even avoided entirely the need for new works. Pumping stations are often rated with "safe yields" which are characteristics of the borehole or the installed pumping plant and not of the aquifer in that location. A typical example would be a rural source which was initially developed and equipped to meet a small demand but has subsequently been incorporated into a larger supply system. This source may not have been reassessed but assumed to have a yield limited to its original design capacity.

An indication of below optimum use can be obtained from an inspection of operational yield/drawdown data, if available, but this is rarely adequate and it is much preferable if a full study of the site can be carried out (see Chapter 9). Typically this involves geophysical logging of all available boreholes on the site under both static and pumping conditions, downhole television inspection and a multi-step drawdown test (see Chapter 5) of one or more of the available boreholes. Samples for chemical analysis should be taken during the test and should be studied along with the fluid logs for any indication of changes in water chemistry at higher pumping rates. This should enable the detailed hydrology of the site to be assessed together with checks on borehole construction details and an assessment of well efficiency. Engineering records of the site should be inspected to check for the existence and location of side and interconnecting adits which, when present, can greatly complicate interpretation. Downhole inspection is very important and if installed pumps prevent this, steps should be taken to log at least one borehole with the pump removed, possibly coupled with inspection and maintenance. The results of this work may reveal that higher yields are likely to be possible if pump size and/or depth is changed. Alternatively it may be shown that well construction or casing deterioration is inhibiting yield and that greater quantities might be obtained from borehole rehabilitation or by drilling a new source with different casing diameter or depth specification. The boreholes may prove to be adequately sized and equipped but the size and character of the site may be such that additional boreholes could be installed without unduly reducing the yield from the existing wells.

New Sites

Even if the study of existing sites does not reveal any potential for additional development, the information obtained will greatly enhance the understanding of the local hydrogeology and thus assist in the selection of new sites. These data should be supplemented by additional water level surveys, groundwater quality surveys and downhole logging at any suitable wells or boreholes. If aquifer geometry is uncertain, or if mineralised water is suspected, surface geophysical methods may be of assistance.

In some aquifers, such as the Chalk, transmissivity may vary widely from place to place; information from pumping tests, from detailed study of water table and piezometric gradients and by analogy with other areas of similar geology and topography, may assist in defining likely high transmissivity zones. In both the Chalk and the Triassic sandstones well yield is greatly influenced by the occurrence of fissures—the location of these is rarely predictable and there are documented cases of substantial variation even between two boreholes on one site. In faulted terrain the chance of intersecting faults and thereby enhancing borehole yields may influence the choice of site. On the other hand, in some situations faults have been shown to be the means by which deep, highly mineralised connate waters may be readily drawn to higher aquifers.

When all the geological and hydrogeological factors have been considered it is likely that zones rather than precise localities will emerge. Within these zones non-geological factors in site selection, such as access, availability of points of discharge for test pumping, proximity to pipelines and availability of power supplies will need to be taken into account. It is rare that only one possible site is available for the new well, so that the judgement of the hydrogeologist on the estimated yield of each site will need to be assessed against the broader engineering requirements and costs before one or more locations is selected for drilling. The uncertainties, coupled with the high cost of large diameter borehole drilling, mean that, unless the hydrogeology of an area is very well understood, initial drilling at favoured sites should be exploratory in nature. A 200 mm diameter borehole keeps drilling costs down but gives an adequate size of hole for the majority of downhole logging and pumping tests. If following a successful pumping test a large diameter well is required, then the hole can be enlarged by reaming.

INVESTIGATION FOR REGIONAL GROUNDWATER SCHEMES

The most complex type of groundwater resources study, which incorporates the elements of the two types of study previously described, is for the major development of groundwater resources on a regional scale. The detail of investigation applied to an individual situation must be expanded to cover a whole area for which there may previously have been only a reconnaissance level survey. The study may have a number of objectives. In the UK such studies have usually been directed towards various forms of conjunctive use of ground and surface water.

In other countries the need may be for direct and continuous industrial or public supply or for periodic irrigation of crops. In the UK these schemes are designed to exploit groundwater resources within the limits set by available recharge, whereas in arid areas the concept of the scheme may allow for 'mining' of water in groundwater storage. Only rarely in the UK have these schemes had any element of artificial augmentation of resources by induced or direct recharge (see Chapter 14), whereas in other areas these techniques have been more widely used either for enhancement of resources or to provide barriers to saline flow. Because the scope of such schemes may be wide it is only possible to indicate the broad areas which such an investigation should encompass.

Geological and Hydrogeological Framework

As with investigations of all sizes it is necessary to build from existing data sources. The results of any initial investigation programme should give as complete as practicable a picture of the geology of the aquifer in question, in particular its geometry, its flow properties, its flow balance and the controls on groundwater chemistry. Because regional investigations usually take years to complete, and have correspondingly larger budgets, they usually encompass field work programmes to obtain basic data that would not normally be considered in smaller studies. For example, one difficulty that is common in small-scale hydrogeological investigations is the inability to check estimates of groundwater resources from meteorology data by comparison with estimates of system outflow, because river flow data are rarely available or records are not long enough. Within the scope of a large regional study it should be possible to provide for purpose-constructed flow-gauging facilities at the point or points of interest. Another limitation in smaller scale studies, particularly of high-storage aquifers, is that pumping tests are rarely long enough to provide an estimate of the unconfined storage coefficient. Again it should be possible in the context of a larger study to carry out long-term aquifer tests, possibly as part of a multiple-well group test, to assess the long-term aquifer storage coefficient reliably.

Full use should be made at the outset of the programme of all possible sources of regional data (water levels, water quality, aquifer tests, geophysical logging and geophysical surface surveys) to build up adequate basic data against which to plan and assess the results of the field experiments. The location and specification of test boreholes and observation boreholes and the design of single or group pumping tests are influenced by the conceptual model of the hydrogeology of the system, which has come from the preliminary resource reconnaissance study. It is important not to hold on too tightly to the early concepts concerning the hydrogeology of the system, but to be prepared to change ideas as new data become available. Groundwater development on a regional scale will involve major changes in the flow regime over a wide area. Unless the characteristics of the complete aquifer system are documented and understood it is not possible to assess the implications on yield, water level, water quality and environmental aspects which will ensue.

Selection of Areas for More Detailed Study

Regional groundwater investigations typically cover areas from 100 km^2 upwards. Many aspects of the study can and should be conducted over the whole area so that any areal variation in the hydrological regime can be identified. Individual and well-field pumping tests will generally be concentrated in one or more localised areas, either for reasons of economy, or more likely so that the effects of localised intensive draft on storage can be observed. The location of the sites for the well-field, or pilot study area, needs to be chosen with care. The works need to be in a position where, should full-scale development proceed, they can be fully used so that some of the investigation expenditure can be offset against the capital costs of the project.

The hydrogeological conditions in the pilot area must be representative of the investigation area as a whole. If conditions are variable thoroughout the investigation area this may indicate the need for more than one pilot study area. The quality of meteorological and hydrometric data for the pilot area needs to be of a high standard so that interreactions between ground and surface water can be adequately assessed. If, as for many schemes in the UK, the object of the study is to assess groundwater storage for river regulation, it is desirable that sufficient well-field capacity be installed for the pilot tests, so that the volume of augmentation is an adequate proportion of natural river run-off under likely test conditions. Coupled with this there should be an adequate control area, with similar hydrogeological conditions and with suitable groundwater level measurement and flow gauging facilities, so that reliable predictions of natural run-off and groundwater levels can be prepared for the well-field area by extrapolation from the control area data (Wright[6]).

Modelling Aspects

Most studies of this type are supported by hydrological modelling. The degree of the modelling may be limited to providing information on scheme efficiency, for instance to compare the effects of pumping with the depression in natural stream flow which is necessary to assess the net gain of a river augmentation scheme (see Chapter 6). In these cases simple correlation or lumped parameter models calibrated against measurements made in the test and control catchments may be adequate and there are examples where they have been successfully used. However, a discretised numerical model of the groundwater system will normally offer far greater benefits (see Chapter 6). The setting up of the model helps to clarify the concepts of the way in which the aquifer system operates. Much can be learned about the system during the calibration process. It also provides a test of the adequacy of the data network and indicates where additional data are needed. A proven model can be used to compare the yields for a range of pumping rates and well-field configurations that are beyond pilot scale studies. It will thus have an essential role in planning regional aquifer development strategies.

Groundwater Quality

A comprehensive groundwater quality sampling exercise should be regarded as standard practice for groundwater investigations of all scales but it assumes a special significance in major well-field tests because of the potential for large-scale abstraction to induce charges in groundwater quality. It is important to assemble a picture of groundwater quality over the area and to ensure that the variations seen are consistent with the conceptual model of the flow regime and likely chemical processes between the aquifer matrix and groundwater in transit through it.

The changes in groundwater chemistry induced by the exploitation of the resource may be a significant operating constraint. The amount of water abstracted during any pilot-scale tests may not be sufficient to cause changes in the quality of the pumped water and thus any monitoring must also cover areas where quality interfaces are known to exist or might develop, such as along coasts, near rivers, near faults or connate water bodies. Groundwater quality variations may exist with depth and understanding of this will be important in assessing likely quality changes necessary to install nested sampling points to ensure that any changes are recorded.

Environmental Aspects

Regional groundwater schemes involving changes in the groundwater regime over a large area may have significant effects on the environment. Even if the effects are small or can be adequately compensated they may still attract public attention. It is important in planning regional investigations that these issues are appreciated and adequate steps taken to obtain the necessary data to document the potential environmental effects. Issues which may be generally grouped under the heading of environmental aspects and which have arisen during proposals to undertake regional groundwater development include:

   (i)   diminution of the water level in private, generally shallow, boreholes and wells;
  (ii)   effects on stream flow as a detriment to water supply, fisheries and general amenity;
 (iii)   effects on flow from springs and water levels in pools and ponds fed by them;
  (iv)   effects on wetland areas of nature conservation value;
   (v)   in the case of river augmentation by groundwater, effects on the river water quality and thereby on the ecology of the receiving watercourse;
  (vi)   effects on the moisture content of the soil and on crops dependent upon it;
 (vii)   subsidence of land due to dewatering of unconsolidated strata.

Monitoring programmes can be designed to deal with all these issues and provide data on the likely scale of the effects. For many of them modelling techniques are available to provide a means of extrapolating effects observed in a test situation to those which will apply in an operating scheme. For the first five examples experience exists in the UK for providing systems for compensating for or ameliorating the effects caused by operating regional groundwater schemes. The latter two situations do not arise widely in the UK hydrogeological environment.

DEVELOPMENT AND MANAGEMENT OF COASTAL AQUIFERS

The development and management of aquifers in contact with the sea presents a rather special case and involves ideas of abstraction and monitoring which may be usefully applied to other situations. Aquifers are in contact with the sea along much of eastern and south-east England, although most of the published information on saline intrusion concerns the western coast of the United States and parts of mainland Europe.

The questions posed are:

(1) what proportion of available resources are abstracted?
(2) what are the salinities and water levels in observation and abstraction boreholes at or near the coast?
(3) what daily and seasonal changes take place, and have there been historic trends in abstraction, salinities and water levels?
(4) how does the aquifer respond to tidal fluctuations and what mechanism of saline intrusion exists?
(5) can the aquifer be managed more effectively to control intrusion and make better use of the resources?

Available Resources

Problems with salinities of coastal aquifers are invariably associated with excessive abstraction from boreholes located very close to the coast. For this reason we are dealing here with aquifers which are already highly developed. Whilst it does not provide an answer to, or even necessarily an understanding of, the problem there is a need at the outset to obtain an appreciation of the resources available. This will require the availability of groundwater level data so as to draw a water table map from which the groundwater catchment can be determined. This allows the overall available resources to be compared with abstractions.

It may be that the calculations show that the abstractions exceed the resources available, in which case a problem clearly exists, but it may show that the overall resources available are sufficient and that the salinity problem is just the result of localised and concentrated over-abstraction.

Coastal Information

The most important items of information in such problem areas are the water levels and salinities of all coastal boreholes, plus abstraction rates of those boreholes which are pumped. It is essential to build up a picture of how these three basic parameters are inter-related, how they respond to ordinary, common, spring and surge tides, as well as their response to seasonal changes in aquifer potential. The use of water level recorders can provide invaluable information on such responses and down-hole geophysical logging (mainly conductivity and temperature) and depth sampling are likely to extend the range of knowledge appreciably.

Since salinities in aquifers along coastal margins can respond quickly to groundwater abstractions, every effort should be made to obtain historic data on

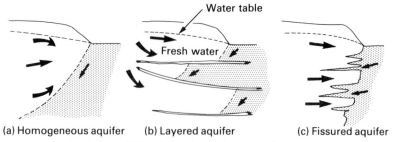

(a) Homogeneous aquifer   (b) Layered aquifer   (c) Fissured aquifer

Fig. 7.4.   Saline intrusion into coastal aquifers

salinities, water levels and abstraction rates, because they may indicate the reason for any sudden historic worsening of the problem, or what might have been a safe and stable aquifer yield in former times.

Aquifer Responses

The invasion of coastal aquifers by modern seawater is only one of several types of saline groundwater which recent geochemical studies have shown to exist. These may be saline or brackish connate water, mineralised groundwaters from saliferous deposits, or bodies of old and largely static saline water inland or at great depth.

Seawater can invade homogeneous aquifers in the classical Ghyben-Herzberg mode in which a curved wedge of saline or brackish water penetrates the fresh water aquifer at depth inland from the coast. Circulation of fresh and saline water is as shown on Fig. 7.4 and dynamic equilibrium is maintained by a positive outflow of freshwater at the sea margin. In layered aquifers (Fig. 7.4(b)) the movement is more complicated, while in fissured aquifers seawater can move speedily in and out of the aquifer in a manner which bears little resemblance to the classical mechanism (Fig. 7.4(c)).

The elucidation of the mechanism of saline intrusion is important in understanding how it can be controlled, but the means of achieving this understanding are likely to be costly and involve a great deal of effort. Observation boreholes will be needed, with the depths of penetration into the aquifer and lengths of lining carefully selected. Cored boreholes may be needed to obtain fresh undisturbed samples of aquifer, and to extract pore-water by high-speed centrifuge for chemical analysis. Down-hole geophysical logging using a wide-ranging suite of electrical, temperature and other logs will be needed, and these may have to be repeated over tide cycles and seasonally to obtain an understanding of what is happening. *In situ* down-hole resistivity and conductivity probes are likely to be marketed in the near future which will allow these parameters to be recorded continually at pre-set depths in the borehole and at short time intervals.

Aquifer Management

Problems with salinities in coastal boreholes generally arise because too much abstraction is permitted too close to the land margin. A reduction in abstraction rates, the use of a greater number of boreholes, or the shifting of abstraction to further inland, can well lead to speedy improvement. Resource calculations will show whether the catchment abstraction is excessive, and if this is the case then a reduction in overall net abstraction will have to be achieved if the problem is to be controlled.

In extensive coastal aquifers it is frequently the case that borehole salinity is only a problem in the summer at times of low groundwater potential, while during the winter surplus resources discharge to waste as beach or sea springs. The adoption of an abstraction regime which taps surplus spring flows from coastal abstraction boreholes in the winter, while permitting the recovery of aquifer storage, can lead to significant increases in aquifer development. With such a regime, abstraction rates from coastal boreholes are gradually reduced in the summer, as inland boreholes become dominant and make use of aquifer storage.

Such a strategic abstraction policy cannot be practised in a vacuum. Coastal and inland observation boreholes are required to monitor responses and provide information to permit the timely switching of abstraction boreholes seasonally. Additional benefit can be obtained by remote telemetered control of abstraction rates, water levels and water quality so that the operational controller can increase or decrease abstraction rates to make the greatest use of the resources at his disposal.

Lastly, mathematical models are a useful tool to provide assistance in aquifer management. Numerical two-dimensional finite element or finite difference models of the aquifer can provide an understanding of different abstraction regimes for different states of aquifer head and natural recharge, outside the range of those previously encountered. They can pinpoint areas where data are lacking or where additional sources can usefully be considered. Numerical operational models can be developed to complement the aquifer models to provide day-to-day advice to the operators on which sources are cheapest to operate, but checked periodically with the aquifer model to ensure that aquifer storage is being maintained at safe levels.

The presence of saline intrusion in coastal aquifers should not necessarily lead to the aquifer and its resources being abandoned. Generally the problem can be reversed and, depending on the nature of the aquifer, residence time, recharge and location, the aquifer frequently can be rehabilitated quite speedily. The adoption of the above ideas for investigation, monitoring, control and modelling can help achieve this goal.

Investigation and Precautions for Emergency Spillages and Discharges

This case study deals with the investigation of an emergency spill or discharge of a contaminant into an aquifer, measures for clearing the pollutant, and precautions which may be taken to prevent, limit, or control such occurrences. The questions posed are as follows:

(a) what is the quantity and nature of the contaminant spilled or discharged?;
(b) over what area is the aquifer contaminated or polluted and how quickly is it spreading?;
(c) how has the contaminant reacted with the aquifer and how does it reside in the unsaturated and saturated zones?;
(d) how can it be removed?;
(e) can such occurrences be controlled or prevented in future?

Nature and Quantity of Contaminant

Whether the spillage or leakage of contaminant is from an overturned road tanker containing oil or chemicals, or from a leaking or fractured fuel or chemical store, it is more than likely that the composition of the contaminant is the one positive piece of information available.

Assessing the amount of the contamination is likely to be more of a problem particularly in the case of leaks from storage tanks or underground pipes, which may have gone undetected for a long period. Nevertheless the fullest inquiries must be pursued in order to assess, as accurately as possible, the volume of contaminant which has escaped or has been spilt.

Area of Contamination

If the pollution of the aquifer is to be prevented and the spread of the contaminant arrested it is essential to know what area of the aquifer is contaminated or polluted. This can be a difficult task. The movement and spread of a contaminant in an aquifer depends on many factors, such as the direction and rate of groundwater flow, its dilution, reaction or mixing with the host water, chemical dispersion within the aquifer, and chemical diffusion between different aquifer porosity states (see Chapter 15).

If insufficient groundwater data exist, boreholes will need to be sunk to determine the direction of groundwater flow, and then sampled to determine the concentration and limits of the plume of pollution. As well as determining this two-dimensional picture, it is also necessary to find out how deep into the aquifer the contamination has reached. This can present serious difficulties because the depth of contaminant occurring in a borehole may bear little resemblance to what exists in the aquifer. There needs to be an awareness at the start that purpose-drilled boreholes may well provide misleading information, and moreover they can, by penetrating different aquifer layers, lead to the movement of contamination into previously unpolluted zones. Care with the location, design, construction and sampling of observation boreholes is therefore paramount.

Dilution and degradation of the pollutant in the aquifer may be sufficiently rapid that no special measures are necessary following the spill. However, an evaluation of the problem may show that the drilling of pumped boreholes to remove or scavenge the contamination will be required. Because of shortage of time, these may need to be included in the observation drilling programme. These boreholes should be large enough to permit a submersible pump of adequate capacity. A surface-powered suction pump may be preferable in the case of shallow pollution, but air flushing, using a surface compressor, is unlikely to be applicable for removing pollution at the surface of the water table, because of the need for proper submergence of the air inlet. Scavenger boreholes need to be sited and constructed with great care, and provision made for the separation and disposal of the pollutant.

Reactions of the Contaminant

Conservative contaminants, such as chloride or nitrate, remain within the system and do not normally react chemically with the country rock. The problems they pose comprise identifying where they reside in the aquifer, whether in the saturated zone or in the unsaturated zone, or in the case of double-porosity aquifers, such as chalk, whether the pollutant has exchanged by diffusion with uncontaminated pore water. Generally a chemical balance between contaminant input and output can be determined and this helps in limiting the extent of the uncertainties.

This is not the case with contamination from oils and volatile compounds. Part of an oil spill might reach the saturated zone and spread thinly over the surface of the water table, some will be absorbed by and adsorbed on the aquifer material in the unsaturated zone, and some might evaporate or volatilise at the surface, during passage through the unsaturated zone, or directly from the water table. It is therefore often difficult within the aquifer to account for all the leakage or spillage which is known to have occurred.

Precautions against Emergencies

It is not the purpose of this case study to give a comprehensive review of measures to deal with emergency spillages and leaks or precautions to prevent aquifer pollution. Some points are worth noting however.

In the case of oil and chemical storage containers, their siting in concrete bunds is now standard practice, and the use of clay bund walls for larger containments is becoming common. Oil interceptors in trunk road and motorway soakaways are now also incorporated at the design stage where highways cross permeable strata, and procedures now exist for involving water authorities in emergency spills, where there is a risk of surface streams and underground strata becoming polluted.

Where groundwater sources are particularly vulnerable, as for instance where they lie close to an embanked major highway, then it may be worthwhile considering special precautionary measures in the event of a major accident involving spillage. Such measures might include the blanketing of the ground below the embankment with impermeable material and possibly a bunded clay wall to retain any spillage within such an area. The drilling of a standby scavenger borehole might also be contemplated as an ultimate safety check in the event of aquifer pollution threatening vital water supplies.

The adage that "prevention is better than cure" is very apt for aquifers at risk from pollution, because valuable water resources can be lost permanently or for a very long period by the careless and unthinking activities of man. Growing awareness of these consequences is leading to the gradual adoption of wide-reaching aquifer protection measures, the introduction of progressive anti-pollution law, and a more enlightened attitude from the community.

6. REFERENCES

1. Bear, J. 1972 "Dynamics of fluids in porous media", Elsevier, New York.
2. Todd, D. K. 1959 "Groundwater hydrology" (1st edn.), Wiley, New York.
3. Terzaghi, K. and Peck, R. B. 1948 "Soil mechanics in engineering practice", Wiley, New York.
4. Long, J. C. S. et al 1982 Wat. Res. Res., 18, 645, Porous media equivalent for networks of discontinuous fractures.
5. Hutton, L. G. 1983 "Field testing of water in developing countries", Water Research Centre, Medmenham.
6. Wright, C. E. (Ed.) 1970 "Surface water and groundwater interaction", UNESCO Studies and Reports in Hydrology No. 29, Paris.

1. Drilling a water well in the Yemen Arab Republic
2. Air circulation drilling for water wells in Guinea Conakry, West Africa
3. Rotary drilling for water wells in the Yemen Arab Republic
(Courtesy of George Stow & Co Ltd)

Chapter 8

SURFACE GEOPHYSICAL TECHNIQUES

1. INTRODUCTION

DURING the past ten years there has been worldwide development in the application of geophysical techniques in hydrogeological investigations. Both downhole and surface geophysical methods are now routinely used by hydro-geologists in water authorities in the United Kingdom and by many consultants overseas. These workers take advantage of a wide range of modern techniques and instrumentation which have resulted largely from recent advances in electronics.

This chapter discusses the various surface geophysical techniques, including recent developments. Downhole (borehole) geophysics, which may often be thought of as surface geophysics turned through an angle of ninety degrees, is discussed in Chapter 9. Although the two types of geophysics can be considered complementary, surface geophysics is generally employed at a very early stage in a groundwater investigation, before boreholes are drilled, while logging techniques are employed later to obtain detailed information on aquifer properties.

In this chapter important terms and concepts are briefly mentioned and the relative advantages and disadvantages of the various techniques discussed. Common errors encountered in geophysical reports are also introduced.

Considerable emphasis has been placed on the various applications of geophysics for it is believed that with this understanding the hydrogeologist will be in a better position to liaise with a qualified geophysicist in the planning stages of a geophysical survey.

Several geophysical techniques can be used in groundwater studies but the resistivity method is generally employed, because of its clear response to variations in groundwater salinity and the quantitative nature of the results obtained. For this reason the resistivity technique is described below in greater detail than other less widely used methods.

2. THE ELECTRICAL RESISTIVITY METHOD

INTRODUCTION

The principle of the electrical resistivity method is the measurement of an earth resistance by passing low frequency current into the ground through two metal stakes or electrodes and measuring the potential difference resulting across another two electrodes. If the distance between the four electrodes is known then this, together with the current and potential measurements, may be used to calculate a "resistivity" of the earth.

The resistivity of rocks displays a wide range and a knowledge of subsurface resistivity will often allow the type of rock to be recognised. Fig. 8.1 summarizes common rock resistivities, including those of some major aquiferous rocks. Measurement of resistivity does not allow a unique determination of rock type as there is considerable overlap between the properties of various types. However, other geological information is often available which enables many of the ambiguities to be eliminated.

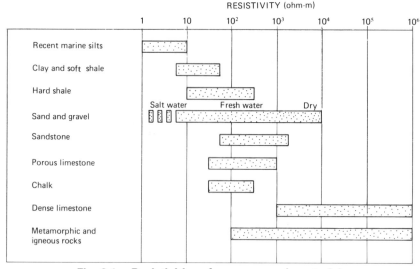

Fig. 8.1.   Resistivities of common rock materials

Conduction of electricity through rocks is of two types. Electronic conduction occurs when the mineral grains are electrically conductive, as with minerals such as chalcocite, pyrite and magnetite. Most common mineral grains such as quartz, feldspar and calcite, however, are non-conductive and in rocks composed only of these, conduction is ionic or through ions in the interstitial fluid. Conduction through clays is both electronic and ionic. Because current flow in subsurface formations is normally ionic, interstitial water salinity and rock porosity both play a great part in determining rock resistivity. For this reason the resistivity technique has proved most useful for tracing variations in groundwater salinity (see Example 4, Section 13).

PRINCIPLES

The electrical potential V at any point P on the surface of a homogeneous half-space due to current I entering the ground at C is given by:

$$V = \frac{\varrho I}{2\pi r} \quad \dots \quad \dots \quad \dots \quad \dots \quad \dots \quad \dots \quad \dots \quad \dots \quad \dots \quad (1)$$

where r is the distance between C and P and ϱ is the resistivity of the earth.

In practice, current must enter the earth at one point, $C1$, and leave at another point, $C2$. The potential difference, ΔV, is measured between two potential electrodes $P1$ and $P2$. Therefore:

$$\Delta V = V_{P1} - V_{P2}$$

$$\Delta V = (V_{P1C1} - V_{P1C2}) - (V_{P2C1} - V_{P2C2}) \dots \quad \dots \quad \dots \quad \dots \quad (2)$$

where V_{P1C1} is the potential at $P1$ due to current entering at $C1$.

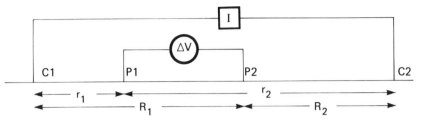

Fig. 8.2. Generalised electrode arrangement

If the distances between different electrodes are defined as in Fig. 8.2, Eqn. (2) can be rewritten as:

$$\Delta V = \frac{\varrho I}{2\pi} \left(\frac{1}{r_1} - \frac{1}{r_2} - \frac{1}{R_1} + \frac{1}{R_2} \right) \qquad \ldots \qquad \ldots \qquad \ldots \qquad \ldots \qquad \ldots \qquad (3)$$

or $\Delta V = \varrho I K$ where K is known as the geometric factor and depends on the spacing between electrodes and their arrangement, and ϱ is the resistivity of a homogeneous earth.

Over a normal heterogeneous subsurface, the measured resistivity is a weighted mean of the resistivities of all the individual bodies of rock which make up the earth and is termed the "apparent" resistivity, ϱa.

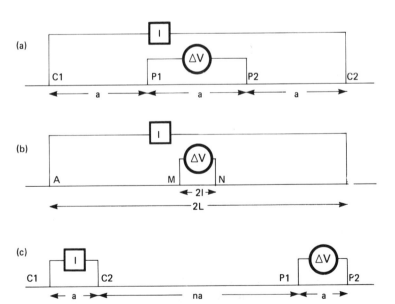

Fig. 8.3. Common electrode arrangements: (a) Wenner, (b) Schlumberger and (c) dipole-dipole

The arrangement of electrodes is referred to as the "array" or "configuration", the Wenner, Schlumberger and dipole-dipole being the most common electrode arrangements employed. Each of these arrays has particular advantages under different conditions.

WENNER ARRAY

In this arrangement the four electrodes are arranged collinearly (Fig. 8.3a) and are equally spaced: $r_1 = R_2 = a$ and $R_1 = r_2 = 2a$. Therefore Eqn. (3) can be rewritten as

$$\varrho_a = 2\pi a \frac{\Delta V}{I} \quad \dots \quad \dots \quad \dots \quad \dots \quad \dots \quad \dots \quad \dots \quad \dots \quad (4)$$

SCHLUMBERGER ARRAY

In this collinear arrangement (Fig. 8.3b) the distance between the potential electrodes is very small compared with the distance between the current electrodes. Traditionally with this arrangement the current electrodes are referred to as A and B and the potential electrodes as M and N. Normally $\overline{AB} \geqslant 5\overline{MN}$ and ϱa defined as:

$$\varrho_a = \pi \cdot \frac{(\overline{AB}/2)^2 - (\overline{MN}/2)^2}{\overline{MN}} \cdot \frac{\Delta V}{I} \quad \dots \quad \dots \quad \dots \quad \dots \quad \dots \quad (5)$$

DIPOLE-DIPOLE ARRAY

This collinear electrode arrangement is illustrated in Fig. 8.3c. Each pair of either current or potential electrodes is called a dipole. The distance between the two dipole centres, $(n+1)a$, is significantly larger than each dipole length (a). In this case the apparent resistivity is defined by:

$$\varrho_a = \pi \frac{\Delta V}{I} n \cdot (n+1)(n+2) \cdot a \quad \dots \quad \dots \quad \dots \quad \dots \quad \dots \quad (6)$$

DEPTH OF INVESTIGATION

The depth of investigation of an electrode arrangement is the depth from which most of the signal originates. Roy and Apparao[1] have calculated the depth of investigation for each of the common electrode arrangements. These are:

Configuration	Depth of Investigation
Wenner	$0.11D$
Schlumberger	$0.12D$
Dipole-Dipole	$0.20D$

where D is the distance between the outer two electrodes. Although these figures are applicable only to a homogeneous earth they provide a useful guide to selecting maximum electrode spacings and also permit a comparison between different electrode arrays.

EFFECT OF NEAR-SURFACE LATERAL RESISTIVITY EFFECTS

Fig. 8.4 presents signal contribution sections[2] for the Wenner, Schlumberger and dipole-dipole arrays over a homogeneous earth. The signal contribution section shows the relative contribution to the total measured resistance of a unit volume of earth at any point. The earth around each electrode gives the greatest contribution but negative areas normally cancel with positive areas and so, in fact, little signal comes from this region unless a strong lateral change in resistivity occurs. If, for example, a large boulder occurs to one side of an electrode, the negative zone will no longer cancel with a positive zone and an erroneous measurement will be made.

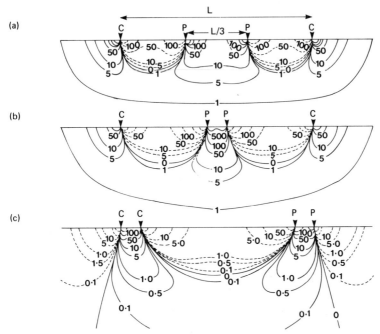

Fig. 8.4. Signal contribution sections for: (a) Wenner, (b) Schlumberger and (c) dipole-dipole configurations (after Barker[2])
(broken lines represent negative contours)

Many of the irregularities observed on sounding curves and horizontal traverses are caused by the presence of boulders, ditches, tracks, fences and other features close to the electrodes. For this reason it is always wise to position the traverse or sounding lines away from tracks or similar features and in the middle of fields.

RECIPROCITY

The Principle of Reciprocity[3] states that the roles of the current and potential electrodes may be reversed without affecting the measured resistance. For example, the resistance measured with the normal Wenner arrangement *CPPC* could also be measured with its reciprocal arrangement *PCCP*. It follows from this that it is not only the depth of current flow that determines the depth of investigation but the relative separation between current and potential electrodes.

HORIZONTAL PROFILING

Horizontal profiling is employed to locate lateral changes in resistivity such as those caused by faults, dykes, ore bodies, narrow buried valleys and steeply dipping geoelectrical boundaries. Any electrical configuration may be employed. The spacing is fixed and the whole electrode arrangement is moved progressively along the traverse line after each resistance measurement. Each result is plotted at the geometric centre of the electrode array to form an apparent resistivity profile.

The interpretation of this type of resistivity data is normally qualitative, because theoretical anomalies can be quite complex. Fig. 8.5 shows the anomaly to be expected across a vertical fault. A break in the slope of the curve is obtained as each electrode crosses the fault. In practice the smaller features of the anomaly will be masked by general background noise caused by near-surface lateral resistivity variations. Fig. 8.6 is an example of a horizontal traverse across a buried cliff in Lincolnshire in which the electrode line is kept perpendicular to the line of the traverse. The position of the cliff is given fairly accurately by the sharp drop in resistivity.

Although most electrode configurations may be employed in horizontal traversing, the dipole-dipole and Schlumberger arrays give anomalies of greatest amplitude. However, the Wenner array has equally-spaced electrodes which is a good, practical advantage in profiling.

When the dipole-dipole configuration is employed in horizontal traversing, the results are often plotted as a pseudosection. To do this, several profiles are measured with the dipole separation parameter varying from 1 to 5 or 6. The measured apparent resistivities are then plotted as a pseudodepth section as shown in Fig. 8.7. Edwards[4] has suggested a modification to the conventional technique in which resistivities are plotted according to their depths of investigation. A closer relationship with true depth is then obtained.

VERTICAL ELECTRICAL SOUNDING

In this method vertical variations in resistivity are examined. The centre of the electrode arrangement remains fixed while the inter-electrode spacing is increased

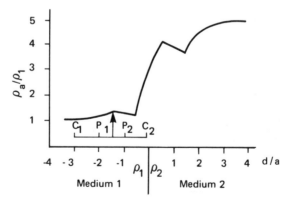

Fig. 8.5.   Variation of apparent resistivity across a vertical boundary using a Wenner configuration laid out in the line of traverse: $\varrho_2 = 5\varrho_1$
(after Griffiths and King[19])

between resistance measurements. Information relating to greater depths is thus obtained as the spacing is increased. These electrical sounding data are plotted on double logarithmic paper with electrode spacing as abscissa and apparent resistivity as ordinate. The resulting sounding curve or apparent resistivity curve may then be interpreted in terms of depths to sub-surface layers and their resistivities.

Each of the electrode arrangements already discussed may be employed in resistivity sounding although the field techniques are often quite different.

Wenner Sounding

The Wenner is the simplest arrangement to employ as all four electrodes are moved between resistance measurements. Calculated resistivities are plotted as a

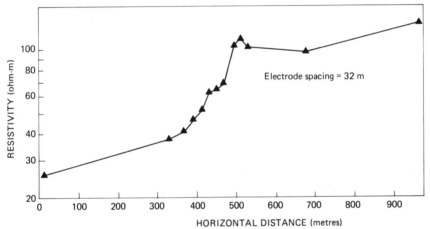

Fig. 8.6. Horizontal resistivity profile across a buried Chalk cliff near Ashby, Lincolnshire (after University of Birmingham[28])

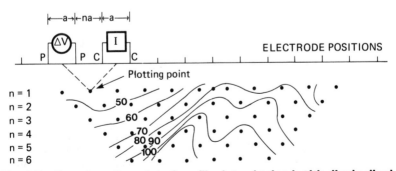

Fig. 8.7. Pseudosection plot of profile data obtained with dipole-dipole configuration

smooth curve against the inter-electrode spacing. Examples of Wenner sounding curves are shown in Fig. 8.8. This is a popular technique, easy to use in practice.

Offset Wenner Sounding

This is a modification of the Wenner technique recently developed[5] to ensure a

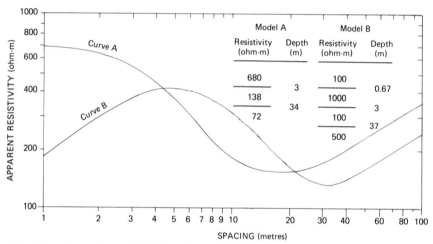

Fig. 8.8.   Examples of (a) three-layer and (b) four-layer apparent resistivity curves

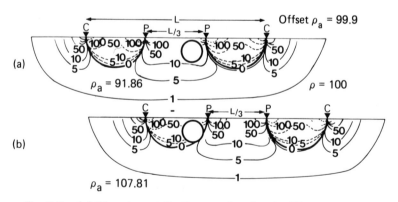

Fig. 8.9.   (a) Signal contribution section for the Wenner array with conducting sphere (negative k) in positive region with background resistivity of 100 ohm-m. (b) Offset position of electrodes. Sphere now falls in a negative region. Distortion of contours due to presence of sphere not shown (after Barker[5])

considerable reduction in the spurious effects due to lateral resistivity variations. The technique is illustrated in Fig. 8.9. Fig. 8.9(a) shows the signal contribution section for the Wenner electrode array. Also shown, drawn to scale, is a buried fully conducting sphere located in an otherwise homogeneous medium of 100 ohm-m. The sphere, which represents a near-surface lateral resistivity variation such as a boulder, is situated in a positively contributing zone and the measured resistivity is calculated as 91.9 ohm-m. If the four electrodes are now "offset" to one side by a distance equal to the electrode spacing (Fig. 8.9(b)) negative regions now fall where positive regions were previously and *vice versa*. This is true except for the region at each end of the electrode line. The resistivity measured in this case is 107.8 ohm-m. The average of these two measurements (99.85 ohm-m) is the "Offset Wenner resistivity". An error due to lateral resistivity effects of around 8 per cent in each case has thus been reduced to less than 0.2 per cent.

Vertical sounding using the Offset Wenner technique is conveniently conducted using a five-electrode array (Fig. 8.10). In practice this is no more difficult than normal sounding, for the additional electrode remains fixed at the centre of the spread. A switching device is used to change from one set of four electrodes to the other.

A multicore cable "Offset Wenner" system, now commercially available, has several advantages over conventional sounding techniques:

1. Increase in quality of sounding data using the "Offset" principle.
2. Decrease in manpower. Used together with a lightweight digital resistance measuring instrument the whole multicore cable system is easily carried and operated by one man.
3. A vertical sounding may be conducted in less than one hour. Consequently, output may be raised to ten soundings per day per man.
4. Spacing errors are eliminated.

As conventional Wenner intepretation techniques can be employed, the Offset Wenner technique is obviously ideally suited to routine hydrogeological investigations under most environmental conditions.

Schlumberger Sounding

The Schlumberger configuration is in widespread use in Europe, Africa and Australia. The current electrodes are moved more frequently than the inner

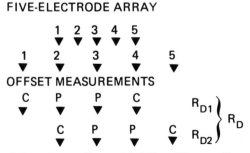

Fig. 8.10.   Principles of sounding with Offset Wenner five-electrode array

potential electrodes. This results in a discontinuous curve (Fig. 8.11). Each segment of the curve represents measurements made with the same spacing between the potential electrodes *M* and *N*.

The measured resistivities are normally plotted against the distance *AB/*2 on double logarithmic paper. For interpretation a smooth curve is drawn through the last points of each segment. This curve represents the approximation of a true potential gradient measurement made with the potential electrodes very close together. When the *MN* distance is increased at the beginning of each segment, the approximation is not as good and there is normally a noticeable difference between the smoothed curve and the initial points of each segment. Generally the distance *MN* should be less than *AB/*5.

The Schlumberger array is commonly employed in arid regions because a much smaller number of electrode positions need be prepared than with the Wenner array.

It is claimed that by using the Schlumberger method the effects of lateral resistivity variations can be eliminated by compensating for the resulting vertical displacement of segments when drawing the smooth curve. In Fig. 8.12, for example, a lateral resistivity effect near one of the potential electrodes has caused the second segment to be displaced upwards. The smooth curve is drawn parallel with the displaced segment, thus removing this spurious effect. In practice, however, it is impossible to say whether the central segment has been displaced upwards or the two outer segments have been displaced downwards.

Dipole-Dipole Sounding

Dipole-dipole soundings are normally conducted only where depths of 150 m or more are to be investigated. A dipole spacing of 50-100 m or more is selected and the two dipoles gradually separated by up to 1000 m or more. The resistivity measurements are plotted against the distance between the centre points of the two dipoles as a sounding curve.

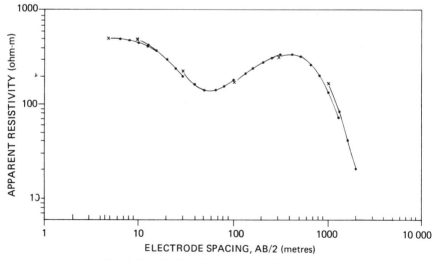

Fig. 8.11. Schlumberger sounding curve

This technique has the advantage that relatively short lengths of cable are necessary. However, this electrode arrangement is sensitive to lateral resistivity variations, so care must be taken in locating electrodes away from surface features such as ditches and metal fences and away from major geological faults and similar features.

SOUNDING CURVE INTERPRETATION

The simplest accurate method for interpreting sounding curves is "total curve matching". The field curve is compared with a family of theoretical curves until one is found which has the same shape as the field curve. Depths and resistivities may then be read from the theoretical curve. The curve fitting method is applicable to two-, three- and four-layer problems. A set of 2 400 theoretical Wenner type three- and four-layer curves has been published by Mooney and Wetzel[6] and a selection of three-layer curves for use with the Schlumberger array by Compagnie Générale de Géophysique[7]. The "total curve matching" method has the disadvantages that it is time-consuming and that a theoretical curve which fits the field data may not be available.

There are also many approximate methods of interpreting electrical sounding curves, such as the Barnes method and the Moore cumulative method, and some of these are still widely used[8]. However, with computers and pocket calculators now widely available it is possible to produce accurate quantitative interpretations, even under adverse field conditions, and there is now no excuse to do otherwise.

Although the interpretation of a sounding curve can be conducted completely automatically using a computer, the programs are large and not easily controlled by the operator to include geological information already available. For this reason the general interpretation technique illustrated diagrammatically in Fig. 8.13 is recommended.

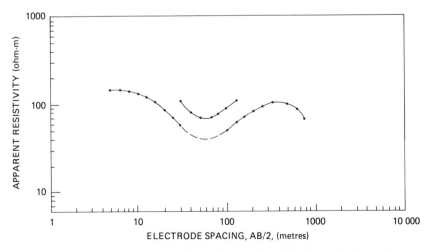

Fig. 8.12. Correction for effect of lateral resistivity variation near potential electrodes on second segment of Schlumberger sounding curve

In this technique an approximate interpretation of the sounding curve is first obtained, using any available technique, but partial curve matching (auxiliary point) techniques[9,10] are recommended for their speed. In this way a model in terms of depths of layers and their resistivities is obtained quickly and efficiently. This model is then used to generate a theoretical sounding curve using the method of linear operators[11]. Recently Koefoed[10] has published programs which enable this curve generation to be carried out on small pocket calculators. The theoretical curve is compared with the field curve and if the initial interpretation is good the two curves will be identical. If the two curves do not agree the model is adjusted and the process repeated until agreement is reached.

Although the process appears straightforward many problems arise which if not recognised will lead to bad interpretation. These problems are summarised below.

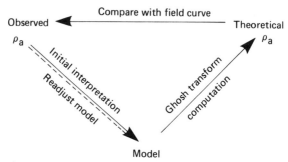

Fig. 8.13. Diagrammatic summary of resistivity sounding curve interpretation

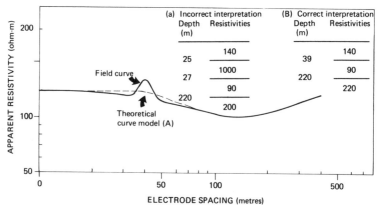

Fig. 8.14. Resistivity sounding curve showing sharp feature due to a local lateral resistivity variation or poor electrode contact

Lateral Resistivity Variations or Thin Gravel Layers

By definition the electrical sounding curve must be smooth. It is the job of the field survey team to ensure that smooth field curves are obtained. Small bumps and troughs on the curve will be caused by near-surface, lateral, resistivity variations and not by thin horizontal layers at depth. Fig. 8.14 shows a resistivity curve with a small feature interpreted as a thin gravel layer at 25 m depth. In fact the theoretical curve shows that the thin gravel layer would not produce such a sharp feature. There is no way that the curve shown in Fig. 8.14 could be reproduced using only horizontally-layered models. This must then have been produced by a lateral resistivity change, probably close to one of the electrodes.

Principle of Equivalence

The interpretation of a sounding curve will sometimes include a layer with a resistivity which is greater than that of the beds above and below it. In this case it is often possible to replace the high resistivity layer in the interpretation with one of different thickness and resistivity while maintaining the accuracy of the interpretation. This can be done as long as the product of the layer resistivity and thickness remains the same. The two interpretations are said to be "equivalent". A similar effect is produced by a layer having a lower resistivity than either the adjacent layers although in this case it is the product of the layer thickness and conductivity which must remain constant.

Principle of Suppression

This relates to a bed with resistivity intermediate between the resistivities of the beds above and below. Such a bed will often not be manifest on the resistivity curve, even when very thick. If, however, the bed is not included in the interpretation, erroneous results will be obtained. Equivalence and suppression are discussed in more detail by Kunetz[3] and Koefoed[10].

Further information on more advanced computer methods of interpretation is given in the excellent monograph by Koefoed[10] on the principles of electrical sounding.

CONSTRUCTION OF GEOELECTRICAL SECTIONS

The next stage in the interpretation of electrical sounding survey data is the construction of geoelectrical sections. The results from the interpretation of several soundings are plotted as a vertical section and if possible some borehole or other geological information is included. A correlation is then made between the formations recorded in the borehole and the layers interpreted from the soundings. It is at this stage that problems of suppression and equivalence are often encountered. However, once these problems have been resolved a correlation is made across the whole survey area with the construction of several geoelectrical sections. An example is shown in Fig. 8.15.

The final stage in the interpretation of a sounding survey is the construction of various isopachyte and contour maps of depth and resistivity. However, this is possible only where sufficient data have been obtained. An interpretation as a geoelectrical section is adequate for many types of investigation.

COMPARISON OF ELECTRODE ARRAYS IN RESISTIVITY SOUNDING

There is considerable debate as to which electrode arrangement is best. In fact, no electrode array is suitable for every condition and an arrangement should be chosen for the particular job envisaged. In Table 8.I the relative advantages and disadvantages of the three most common arrays are summarized.

TABLE 8.I.   **Summary Comparison of Electrode Arrays**

Array	Advantages	Disadvantages	Use
Wenner	Precisely calculated curve. Field checks available. Can be used with multicore cable. Responds well to horizontal layers. Not very sensitive to lateral resistivity variations.	All electrodes moved. Large amount of cable needed.	Normal use in UK or similar conditions.
Schlumberger	Few electrode positions. Shorter cables. Responds well to horizontal layers. Not very sensitive to lateral resistivity variations.	Approximate curve. No field checks available.	In arid conditions or with longer than average cable lengths.
Dipole-dipole	Very short cables. Large depth of investigation.	Sensitive to deep lateral resistivity variations.	With very long spreads where cable lengths cause problems.

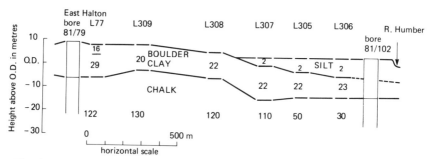

Fig. 8.15.   Use of resistivity sounding interpretations in the construction of a geoelectrical section

3. INDUCED POLARIZATION (IP)

In this method of electrical prospecting a direct current is passed into the ground through two electrodes for a period of several seconds, after which the current is interrupted. During the charging cycle while current is flowing, charge is built up at individual mineral grains. When the current is interrupted the stored charge decays slowly over a period of several seconds and may be observed as a decaying potential difference, ΔV_t, across two potential electrodes (Fig. 8.16). This phenomenon, induced polarization, is described in detail by Sumner[12] and Bertin and Loeb[13].

The magnitude of the IP effect is normally expressed by a parameter termed the chargeability, which is the ratio $\Delta V_t/V$ (millivolts per volt), where V is the charging voltage and ΔV_t is the decaying potential difference measured at one or more points some time after the interruption of the charging pulse. Chargeabilities for some common rock types are shown in Table 8.II.

TABLE 8.II. **Chargeability of Common Rock Materials**

Material	Chargeability mV/V
Peat	0.5–25
Clay/boulder clay	0.5– 5
Shale	5–10
Sandstone	10–65
Limestone	1– 5
Granite	1– 5
Mineralised rock (sulphides, 2-20 per cent)	50–200

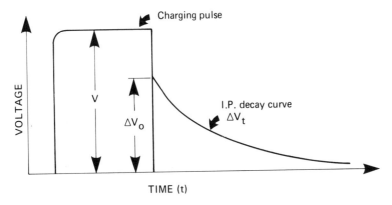

Fig. 8.16. Principle of induced-polarisation measurement

  The induced polarization method is a well developed technique used for prospecting for disseminated metallic ores. However, some sediments, notably clay-bearing sands and sandstones, also show the phenomenon. Clay particles have a natural negative surface charge, and thus attract a layer of cations from the saturating groundwater. Where the clay particles almost close the pore spaces, the cation cloud acts as a barrier to the movement of anions. When a direct current is passed, there is a build-up of anions at these barriers and a depletion elsewhere. When the applied current is interrupted, the anions drift back to their equilibrium positions, resulting in a decaying signal across the potential electrodes.

  Although mainly a recent development, experiments in the use of IP techniques in groundwater investigations were begun almost thirty years ago when Vacquier *et*

al^{14} used this effect to differentiate clean quartz sands saturated with water and showing no IP effect from less permeable sands and gravels with a clay matrix which often exhibit considerable polarization.

The success of many IP surveys conducted in Russia has relied on the much higher polarization shown by saturated alluvial sands, containing a small amount of disseminated clay, over surrounding limestones and sandstones. Fig. 8.17 shows resistivity and IP profiles measured across an alluvium-filled buried valley[15].

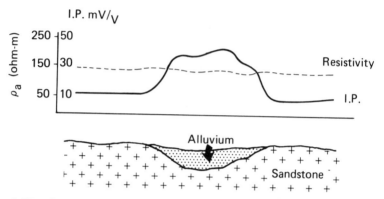

Fig. 8.17. Apparent resistivity and chargeability profiles across a buried valley in the USSR showing no resistivity contrast (after Ogilvy[15])

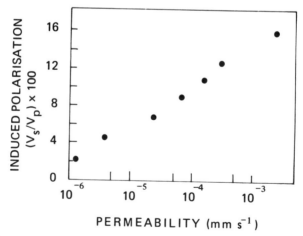

Fig. 8.18. Induced polarisation plotted against permeability for seven samples of Sherwood Sandstone from a single borehole (samples saturated with electrolyte of conductivity 0.025 µS/cm)

Although no change in resistivity is observed, polarization effects up to four times normal are recorded. Groundwater from such buried channels is the principal source of water supply in many parts of Russia.

Recent work by Collar and Griffiths[16] has yielded considerable insight into the relationship between IP and various hydrogeological properties of the Sherwood Sandstone of England. Measurements on small samples of sandstone covering a wide range of permeabilities have indicated that, for a particular groundwater conductivity, chargeability is proportional to the intergranular permeability (Fig. 8.18). Although the exact relationship appears to vary somewhat from place to place and even vertically throughout a stratigraphic succession, relationships such as this are likely to have considerable practical application in the future.

Although only samples exhibiting intergranular flow are generally studied in the laboratory it is possible that IP may also respond to fissure permeability. Certainly IP may be employed to locate very large fissures and Finch[17] describes the use of IP profiling techniques in locating large contaminated fissures in Nottinghamshire. Fig. 8.19 shows an IP pseudosection plotted across such a fissure.

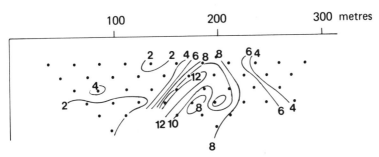

Fig. 8.19. Chargeability (mV/V) pseudosection across a near-vertical fissure in the Sherwood Sandstone, Nottinghamshire (after Griffiths[17])

4. ELECTROMAGNETIC METHODS

The electromagnetic technique is a means of studying subsurface conductivity without the need for making good electrical connections to the ground through metal stakes. In this technique (Fig. 8.20) a transmitter coil, energised with an alternating current at an audio frequency, is placed on the earth and a receiver coil is located a short distance away. The time-varying magnetic field arising from the alternating current in the transmitter coil induces very small currents in the earth. These currents generate a secondary magnetic field which is sensed together with the primary field by the receiver coil.

In two popular modern instruments, the Geonics EM-31 and EM-34, the intercoil spacing and operating frequency are chosen so that the ratio of the secondary to primary magnetic field is linearly proportional to the terrain conductivity. This ratio is measured and a direct reading of conductivity obtained.

The EM-31 has an intercoil spacing of 3.7 m and an effective depth of investigation of about 6 m. The instrument can be carried and operated by one man and is particularly useful for locating near-surface variations of groundwater salinity, gravel deposits, cavities in carbonate rocks, faults and other geological features, quickly and efficiently.

The EM-34 comprises two coils separated by a cable either 10, 20 or 40 m in length. Operated by two men, it is used for investigations down to 30 m. Both methods are unsuitable for examining geological features which might occur below a thin surface layer of good conductivity such as clay.

Electromagnetic techniques have not been employed much in the past in groundwater investigations but are becoming increasingly popular, because qualitative information can be obtained more cheaply and rapidly than by conventional resistivity techniques.

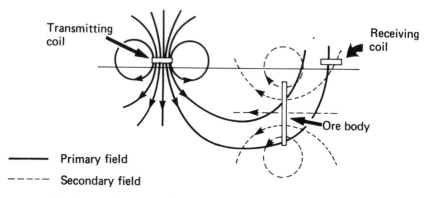

Fig. 8.20. Principle of the two-coil electromagnetic system

5. SEISMIC REFRACTION

Seismic Wave Propagation

In the seismic refraction method an explosive charge, weight-drop or hammer blow is used to generate an elastic pulse (called the "shot") at the earth's surface. Some of the radiating energy, which travels by several paths in the medium, is refracted along subsurface boundaries and returns to the surface to be recorded by a line of detectors (seismometers or geophones). The time-lapse between the shot and the first arrival of the refracted energy at each of the geophones is plotted on a time-distance curve, which provides information on the depths to the refracting horizon and the seismic velocity of the underlying layer.

Seismic energy can travel in two forms through the interior of a solid rock. In the passage of a compressional wave, P, the particle motion is parallel with the direction of the shock wave whilst the passage of a shear wave, S, involves particle vibration perpendicular to the direction of propagation. Shear waves travel slower than P waves and are not propagated in fluids.

The velocities of the wavetypes (Vs and Vp) depend on the density, ϱ, and the elastic moduli of the medium through which the wave is propagating. Only two of the elastic moduli are independent and in terms of Young's Modulus, E, and Poisson's Ratio, σ, the velocities are defined as:

$$Vp = \sqrt{(E/p)(1-\sigma)/(1-2\sigma)(1+\sigma)} \quad \cdots \quad \cdots \quad \cdots \quad \cdots \quad \cdots \quad (7)$$

and

$$Vs = \sqrt{(E/p)(2+2\sigma)} \quad \cdots \quad \cdots \quad \cdots \quad \cdots \quad \cdots \quad \cdots \quad (8)$$

Thus the body wave velocity ratio depends only on σ, so that:

$$Vp/Vs = 1/\sqrt{(1-2\sigma)/(2-2\sigma)} \quad \cdots \quad \cdots \quad \cdots \quad \cdots \quad \cdots \quad (9)$$

As for most consolidated rocks Poisson's ratio is about 0.25, the ratio Vp/Vs is generally around 1.73. P and S wave velocity measurements can therefore be used to compute dynamic estimates of elastic moduli and this is done in engineering geophysics. Although modern signal enhancement seisomographs enable the measurement of accurate shear wave travel times[18], little use has yet been made of this facility in hydrogeology and it is the travel time of compressional waves which is normally measured in seismic refraction surveys.

Other types of seismic wave may sometimes be observed; these are the surface (e.g. Rayleigh) waves whose amplitude decays rapidly with depth and which are therefore limited to the top metre or so of the ground surface. They have velocities lower than shear or compressional waves.

In general the more compact the rock the higher the seismic velocity. Generally the compressional wave velocity of rocks increases with depth, geological age, consolidation, saturation and degree of cementation. Rocks normally exhibit values of Vp between 1.0 and 6.0 m/ms. A broad classification of material in terms of seismic velocity is given in Table 8.III.

TABLE 8.III. **Compressional Wave Velocity in Common Rock Materials**

Material	Seismic velocity m/ms
Air	0.34
Water	1.5
Recent unconsolidated alluvium (dry)	0.5–1.0
Recent unconsolidated alluvium (saturated)	1.0–2.0
Consolidated sandstones	2.0–4.0
Consolidated limestones	3.0–5.0
Igneous and metamorphic rocks	4.0–6.0
Salt and anhydrite	4.0–7.0

PRINCIPLES

Compressional waves travelling downwards from a point at the surface are reflected and refracted at interfaces across which the seismic velocity changes (Fig. 8.21). At any interface the relationship between the angle of incidence, θ_1, and the angle of refraction, θ_2, is given by Snell's Law:

$$\frac{\sin \theta_1}{\sin \theta_2} = \frac{V_1}{V_2} \quad \cdots \quad \cdots \quad \cdots \quad \cdots \quad \cdots \quad \cdots \quad \cdots \quad \cdots \quad (10)$$

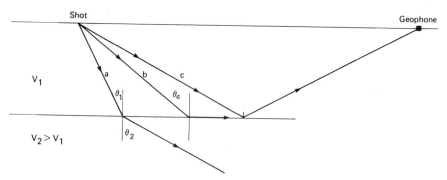

Fig. 8.21.   Wave paths across an interface: (a) refracted ray, (b) critically refracted ray and (c) reflected ray

For the normal case in which $V_2 > V_1$, rays striking the interface at an angle less than the critical angle, θ_c, are partly reflected back to the surface and partly refracted down into the second layer. Rays striking the interface at angles greater than θ_c, are totally reflected to the surface. Rays striking the interface ar precisely the critical angle are in large part refracted along the interface. This energy, which travels at velocity V_2, gradually returns to the surface as head waves where it is recorded by geophones placed on the surface.

At the critical angle of incidence, $\theta_1 = \theta_c$, the angle of refraction, θ_2, is 90° and $\sin \theta_2 = 1$. Therefore the critical angle is defined as:

$$\theta_c = \sin^{-1} \left(\frac{V_1}{V_2} \right) \qquad \ldots \qquad \ldots \qquad \ldots \qquad \ldots \qquad \ldots \qquad \ldots \qquad \ldots \qquad (11)$$

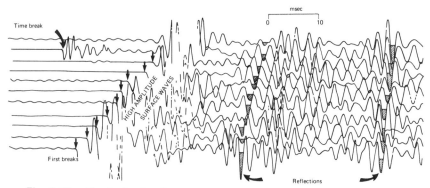

Fig. 8.22.   Typical seismic record; each trace is recorded by a single geophone at increasing distances from the shot

Travel-Time Graphs

For a homogeneous medium the travel time, t, of the first arrival at a geophone, G, a distance, x, from the source, S, is given simply by $t = x/V$, where V is the compressional wave velocity of the medium. Therefore a plot of t against x for a series of geophones along the surface is linear, passing through the origin with a gradient of $1/V$.

With a subsurface which contains several interfaces at depth, the general seismogram (Fig. 8.22) contains many more arrivals than just the "direct" P (and S and surface) waves, since it also includes various reflected and head waves returned to the surface from the interfaces. The first arrivals at any geophone are, however, always P waves and at larger and larger distances from the source the first arrivals return through refraction at deeper and deeper layers.

Single Plane Horizontal Interface

The time taken for energy to travel from S to G (Fig. 8.23), with refraction along a single subsurface interface from C_1 to C_2, is the sum of the travel-times along the three individual segments $\overline{SC_1}$, $\overline{C_1C_2}$ and $\overline{C_2G}$, so that:

$$t = \frac{\overline{SC_1}}{V_1} + \frac{\overline{C_1C_2}}{V_2} + \frac{\overline{C_2G}}{V_1} \quad \ldots \quad \ldots \quad \ldots \quad \ldots \quad \ldots \quad \ldots \quad (12)$$

For a horizontal interface it can then be shown from simple geometry and Eqn. (11) that:

$$t = \frac{x}{V_2} + \frac{2h \cos \theta_c}{V_1} \quad \ldots \quad \ldots \quad \ldots \quad \ldots \quad \ldots \quad \ldots \quad (13)$$

Thus a plot of the time, t, of arrival of this refracted energy against the distance, x, of geophones from the shot will result in a straight line, with a slope equal to $1/V_2$ and intercept equal to $2h.\cos\theta_c/V_1$. Thus if V_1 of the upper medium is calculated from the slope of the direct wave segment the depth, h, to the interface can be determined.

The direct and head wave segments intersect at the crossover point, x_c, given by:

$$x_c = 2h.(V_2 + V_1)^{\frac{1}{2}}/(V_2 - V_1)^{\frac{1}{2}} \quad \ldots \quad \ldots \quad \ldots \quad \ldots \quad \ldots \quad (14)$$

Clearly it is essential to record out to some way beyond the critical distance to obtain both direct and head waves as first arrivals. As a general rule the geophone spread length should be about ten times the depth to the interface.

The interpretation technique described above can be extended to two or more interfaces and equations for this simple type of interpretation are published in standard text books[19,8].

Effect of Dipping Layers

For a horizontal interface it is unimportant at which end of the line of geophones the shot is located. However, if the interface is dipping at an angle ϕ different results will be obtained. This is illustrated in Fig. 8.24. Clearly the time taken for energy to travel from S_1 to G_6 is much less than for energy travelling from S_2 to G_7, although the distance measured at the surface is identical. This fact can be used to calculate the angle of dip of the interface; equations facilitating this computation are also published in standard texts[19].

These calculations can only be realised if sufficient time-distance information is obtained by "reversing" the line of geophones—that is, firing a shot at each end of this line. In fact it is general practice for this and other types of interpretation to fire reversed profiles.

Effect of an Irregular Interface

Seismic refraction lines can be shot across an irregular interface to determine, for example, the form of a buried valley. The time-distance curve obtained in these circumstances is irregular and will not yield to interpretation using the simple methods already discussed. However, methods do exist for the interpretation of this type of data and perhaps one of the simplest and most widely used is the "plus-minus" method described by Hagedoorn[20]. This is the most generally applicable of the seismic refraction interpretation methods.

Generally, seismic refraction surveys are not employed to study problems involving more than three horizontal layers, as any error in the depth interpretation of upper layers is carried through to deeper layers, where it has a much greater

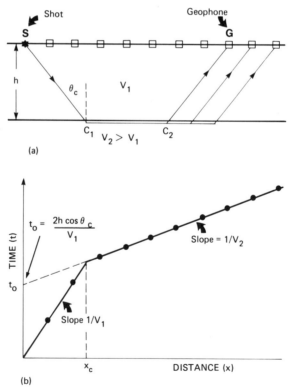

Fig. 8.23. (a) Refraction at a single horizontal interface and (b) associated time-distance graph

effect. Three- or four-layer problems may be interpreted using the Hagedoorn plus-minus approach but recorded data must be good and accurate values obtained for the surface layer velocity.

In addition to the general problem of data accuracy the following technical problems may also be encountered.

Blind-Layer Problem

If the situation arises where velocity decreases with depth and, for example, the second layer velocity is lower than the first layer velocity, critical refraction does not occur and consequently no head waves are generated along the interface. Because no arrivals from the interface are recorded, the second layer is not apparent on the seismogram and is not interpreted. This causes overestimation of depths to deeper interfaces. The problem of blind layers can only be resolved through a study of borehole logs.

Hidden-Layer Problem

A layer becomes seismically hidden if it is too thin to produce head waves which result in first arrivals at the surface. This is shown diagrammatically in Fig. 8.25, where the second layer thickness is small compared with that of the first layer. The head waves produced at the first interface result only in second or later arrivals. Because the second layer is omitted in the interpretation, depths to deeper layers will be underestimated.

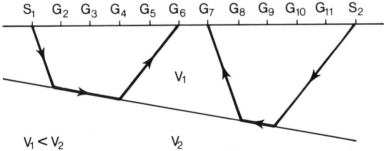

Fig. 8.24. Refraction along an interface dipping at an angle
('shots' at updip and downdip ends of profile)

Air-Wave Problem

In very shallow surveys involving hammer or weight-drop sources, the first layer velocity can be less than the velocity in air (0.34 m/ms). As the air-wave is the first to arrive at near geophones it can be mistaken for the true compressional direct wave, with a consequent overestimation of depth to the first interface. The problem can be overcome with careful adjustment of amplifier gains and by burying the geophones and, if possible, the source.

SEISMIC SURVEYS

For small scale surveys, non-explosive sources such as a hammer blow or weight

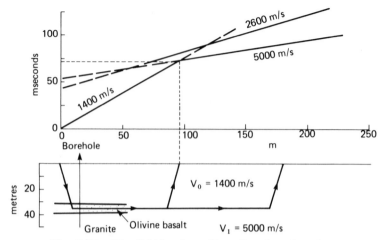

Fig. 8.25. The 'hidden layer' in refraction shooting

drop may be used but their range is very limited, particularly in dry unconsolidated surface conditions. Depths of more than 10 m may be out of range and must then be studied with explosive sources.

Seismic refraction techniques are normally employed in fairly detailed surveys, where considerable information along profiles is required. It is a particularly useful technique for mapping variations in the depth to bedrock, where the latter often provides a good refracting interface. If the bedrock has an upper weathered zone, the depth to compact rock may be all that can be determined, as the weathered zone normally forms a hidden layer.

The explosive source seismic refraction technique requires a team of three and for this reason is more expensive to employ than the resistivity method. However, the seismic refraction technique is the only geophysical method capable of measuring elastic moduli of subsurface rocks and appears to provide a better means for the *in situ* measurement of fracture anisotropy[21].

6. GRAVITY SURVEYING

The gravity method is a useful technique for it is often possible to carry out a gravity survey where seismic refraction and resistivity measurements cannot be made. The object of a gravity survey is to detect horizontal variations in subsurface density by means of the changes they produce in the earth's gravitational field measured at the surface.

THE FIELD SURVEY

In a gravity survey the differences in gravity between a control point or base station and other points in an area are measured. The instrument employed to measure the gravity field, the gravimeter, is a very sensitive spring balance. As it is a natural characteristic of spring materials to creep with age, it is normal to monitor the instrument drift by repeating measurements at a base station at the beginning and end of a day's work and every two or three hours during the survey. Some small differences will be caused by earth tidal effects and these may either be included as part of the drift correction or separately corrected using standard tables.

Gravity surveys conducted as part of a groundwater investigation normally involve the measurement of gravity values along profiles with a spacing between stations of 20-100 m, depending on the size of the feature being studied. More regional surveys, with a station density of 1 or 2 stations per square kilometre, are often employed in oil exploration, for studying large structural geological features, but are unlikely to be of much use in hydrogeological studies.

DATA REDUCTION

The observed gravity values must be corrected to allow for changes with latitude and height and for the attraction of topography. The corrected value is known as the Bouguer anomaly. The various corrections which must be made to the observed data are described below.

Latitude Correction

The earth is not a perfect sphere but has an equatorial radius 20 km greater than the polar radius. As the poles are nearer to the centre of the earth than the equator, gravity increases towards the poles. A small contribution to this variation is made by the acceleration due to the earth's rotation which also varies with latitude. The total gravity increase from equator to pole due to these two effects is around 51 720 g.u. (gravity units).

The variation of gravity with latitude over the surface of the earth is best described by the International Gravity Formula:

$$g = g_o (1 + 5.278895 \times 10^{-3} \sin^2 \phi + 2.346 \times 10^{-5} \sin^4 \phi)\, \text{g.u.} \qquad \dots \quad (15)$$

where g_o is 9780318.5 g.u. (the value of gravity on the equator) and ϕ is the latitude. This equation is used to calculate corrections which must be subtracted from field measured values.

Elevation Correction

The elevation correction takes into account the variation of gravity with height. The corrected value is the gravity value that would be measured at sea level or some other reference level. The correction has two components: the free-air correction and the Bouguer correction.

The free-air correction allows for the decrease in gravity with increase in elevation in free space. This correction is calculated as 3.086 g.u. per metre of elevation.

The Bouguer correction, an approximate correction made to take into account the attraction of the mass of rock between the station and the datum, is calculated from the expression:

$$\text{Bouguer correction} = 0.4187\, \sigma h \text{ g.u./m} \qquad \dots \qquad \dots \qquad \dots \qquad (16)$$

where h is the station height above datum in metres and σ is the density of the near-surface rock in tonnes/m^3 (1 t/m^3 = 1 g/cm^3 = 1 000 kg/m^3).

Terrain Correction

The Bouguer correction is computed on the assumption that the topography is flat and that therefore the sheet of material between the station elevation and datum level can be approximated by a horizontal sheet of material. In situations where there is considerable topographic relief around the station, a further correction for departures from the simple Bouguer approximation must be made. Fig. 8.26 shows a station for which the Bouguer approximation is insufficient to correct for local topographic highs and lows. In both cases, for both high and low topography, gravity values are too small and the terrain correction is always positive.

The terrain correction is calculated by first dividing the area around the station into compartments, normally using a suitable transparent overlay such as the Hammer Chart[22]. The effect of each compartment is determined from tables, the sum of all the effects being the terrain correction. The method is very time consuming and in detailed surveys many of the calculations are computerized.

The effect of topography decreases with increasing distance from the station and therefore it would not be necessary to continue the terrain correction calculations beyond a suitable distance.

The corrected gravity after the application of latitude, free-air, Bouguer and terrain corrections is known as the Bouguer anomaly. It is these values which are contoured and presented as the total Bouguer anomaly map.

Rock Densities

To make accurate Bouguer and terrain corrections it is necessary to have some knowledge of the near-surface rock densities. Some deep density information is also required to produce a reasonable geological interpretation from the Bouguer anomaly map. Generally, rock densities are obtained from laboratory measurements on a representative selection of rock samples obtained from fresh quarry faces or borehole cores. More accurate measurements of near-surface material may be obtained from detailed measurements across small topographic features[23] or from a statistical treatment of the observed gravity values[24].

The range of rock densities encountered is from about 1.5 to 3.0 t/m³. Typical values are shown in Table 8.IV.

TABLE 8.IV.   Densities of Common Rock Materials

Material	Density tonnes/m³
Boulder clay	1.8–2.2
Shale	2.2–2.7
Sandstone	2.0–2.6
Chalk	1.9–2.2
Limestone	2.4–2.7
Granite	2.5–2.7
Basalt	2.9–3.0

INTERPRETATION

The contoured Bouguer anomaly maps may be interpreted qualitatively if little is known about the geology. Steep gradients may represent major faults, long gravity lows may represent sediment-filled channels, and gravity highs may represent basic intrusions. Sometimes anomalies from all these bodies may be present in the same area, in which case the anomalies will interfere with each other and interpretation will be difficult.

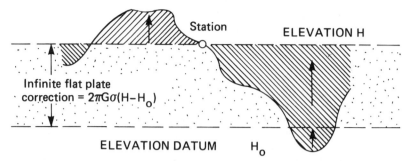

Fig. 8.26.   Schematic diagram of the Bouguer correction, illustrating residual gravitational effects due to undulating terrain

Before a detailed quantitative interpretation is conducted it is normal to separate the anomalies of interest due to near-surface features from anomalies caused by much deeper geological structures. This regional-residual separation is normally obtained by numerical smoothing or digital filtering[25].

The residual anomaly map is then interpreted by comparing profiles across individual anomalies with characteristic curves for standard bodies such as buried spheres, cylinders and slabs. Simple rules governing this type of interpretation are described by Griffiths and King[19].

For more complex interpretations, techniques suitable for computer use can be employed. One popular trial and error method involves the comparison of theoretical curves, generated using the Talwani technique[26], with the field profile and adjustments made in the model until both theoretical and field anomalies are similar. A technique for the iterative interpretation of gravity profiles across sediment-filled valleys is described by Bott[27].

7. APPLICATIONS AND COSTS OF SURFACE GEOPHYSICAL SURVEYS

Surface geophysics can be employed at nearly every stage of a groundwater development scheme to solve a variety of specific problems or merely to provide general information cheaply and rapidly. In the initial reconnaissance stage of aquifer development, geophysics may be used in the delineation of general aquifer structure, for finding faulted and other structural boundaries, and in the location of fracture zones and alluvium-filled valleys. Then it is necessary to site only a small number of boreholes to check the geophysical survey and to provide any detailed geological information which might still be necessary.

In the later stages of the development of an aquifer, geophysical surveys are also an effective means of investigation. Generally at this stage detailed knowledge of aquifer properties and water quality becomes important. Much of this information can be obtained from geophysical surveys which must be carefully planned to make full use of any borehole data available.

Geophysical surveys are most economically employed in the study of large areas where several boreholes are to be sited. The cost of a typical survey covering 10-20 square kilometres would in 1985 be between £3 000 and £8 000 depending on the detail required. This cost is well justified if all boreholes can then be fairly accurately sited.

Sometimes a geophysical survey is conducted to accurately site a single borehole in a geologically complex area. The cost of such a survey would probably be between £500 and £5 000. This is still a worthwhile investment if there is a chance that the borehole could otherwise be drilled into the wrong geological formation.

Table 8.V provides an estimate of the times and costs involved in conducting various types of geophysical survey. A simple routine interpretation would probably be included in this cost, although a careful, detailed interpretation would be an additional expense.

Of course, prices set out in Table 8.V are meant only to be used as a rough guide as they can be misleading if the type of information obtained is not considered. It is possible that in one particular type of investigation only one or two geophysical techniques would be suitable. This choice would again be reduced if quantitative rather than qualitative information is required.

TABLE 8.V.   Comparative Costs of Geophysical Surveys (1985)

Method	Cost/day (£) including allowance for simple routine interpretation	Number in team
Resistivity	500	1–2
Seismic refraction (weight drop source)	600	2–3
Seismic refraction (explosive source)	700	3–4
Electromagnetic	500	1–2
Induced polarization	600	3–4
Gravity	700	2–3

8. GEOPHYSICAL CONTRACTORS AND CONSULTANTS

Although many hydrogeologists have some geophysical training, it is recommended that geophysical surveys be conducted by experienced and qualified geophysicists. A list of geophysical consultants and contractors is given in the Geologist's Directory published by the Institution of Geologists. A few of these geophysical companies specialise in shallow surveys and would be the type of company to be employed in groundwater investigations.

A specialist groundwater geophysicist will also likely be a member of the Institution of Geologists, this indicating a geological interest and competence which is important if reasonably accurate geological interpretation is required as part of the contract.

9. GENERAL STRUCTURAL GEOLOGICAL PROBLEMS

Geological structure is simply a lateral change in the physical properties of rocks (e.g. due to faults, dipping beds or folds). Most geophysical techniques may be employed in studying geological structure but there are limits to the detail which may be studied.

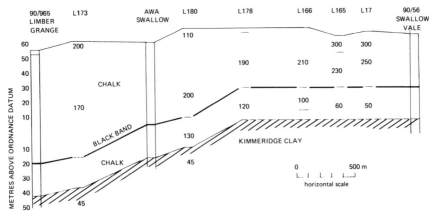

Fig. 8.27. Geoelectrical section across the Caistor Monocline, Lincolnshire
(resistivities in ohm-m)

In the case of a fault in the bedrock the following are the minimum steps which may normally be recorded:

(a) *Resistivity* : 20 per cent change in depth of interface (for example, fault with throw of 20 m at depth of 100 m) if a strong resistivity contrast ($k \geqslant 0.4$) exists.

(b) *Seismic refraction* : 20 per cent change in depth of interface.

(c) *Gravity* : 5 g.u. anomaly minimum i.e. 40 m fault near the surface with 0.30 t/m^3 density contrast.

The more gradual effects of dipping formations may be observed in resistivity surveys by interpreting soundings in terms of horizontal layers and combining the interpretations into a geoelectrical section. Sounding interpretation in terms of horizontal layers is reasonably accurate for dips of up to 30°. An example of a series of resistivity sounding results obtained across the Caistor Monocline[28] in Lincolnshire is shown in Fig. 8.27. Although the structure exhibits dips of 10° or more the interpretation of the soundings in terms of horizontal layers is sufficient to provide good agreement with borehole information.

EXAMPLE 1. RESISTIVITY AND GRAVITY SURVEYS OVER THE SHERWOOD SANDSTONE, NEAR STONE, STAFFORDSHIRE

The area between Stone and Stoke in Staffordshire is for the most part underlain by the Triassic Cannock Chase formation (Bunter Pebble Beds), an aquifer of considerable importance which has recently been further developed here with the opening of the Spot, Blacklake and Moddershall Pumping Stations (Fig. 8.28). At the time these pumping stations were planned, the Cannock Chase formation was thought to outcrop from its faulted western boundary near Moddershall eastwards for 3 km with a further continuation at depth below the overlying Mercia Mudstone. To the north, south and west the aquifer is bounded by marls of the Carboniferous Keele or Mercia Mudstone formations.

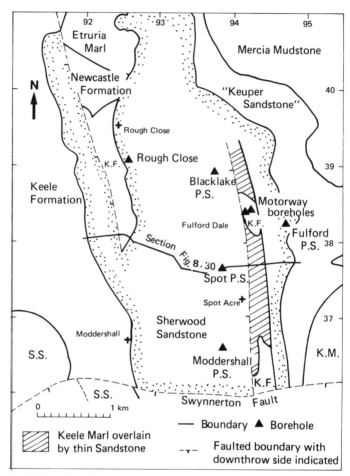

**Fig. 8.28. The Sherwood Sandstone aquifer near Moddershall,
Staffordshire, and location of boreholes**

Recent boreholes, sunk as part of a motorway site-investigation study, indicated that the geology was more complex than had originally been thought. Two boreholes in Fulford Dale revealed an outcrop of Carboniferous marl (Keele formation). This suggested that the Cannock Chase formation, viewed initially as one continuous sandstone aquifer, was perhaps divided into a number of smaller units by upfaulted blocks of Carboniferous marl. This would mean that the real extent of the sandstone aquifer was much less than originally estimated and that the marl could, in the worst situation, prevent water flowing from one sandstone unit to another and could thus reduce the expected yield of the new pumping stations. In fact, falling water levels at these pumping stations suggested that this geological situation did indeed exist.

Obviously there was a need to clarify the geology and to define the areal and vertical extent of the aquifer and, in particular, to map in some detail the locations of upfaulted blocks of marl, especially where these were not at outcrop.

The resistivity sounding technique was suitable for this area as the difference between the resistivity of the Keele Marl (70 ohm-m) and that of the Cannock Chase formation (600 ohm-m) is very large. 113 resistivity soundings were conducted in the area, concentrated near the eastern and western boundaries of the main sandstone block.

The results of the surveys showed without doubt that an uplifted block of marl extends from Fulford Dale in the north to Spot Farm in the south. Although in small areas the marl reaches the surface, it is overlain by up to 20 m of Cannock Chase pebbly sandstones in the area around Spot Acre. To the north of Fulford

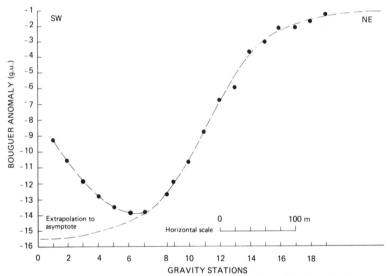

Fig. 8.29. Gravity profile through Spot Acre, Staffordshire

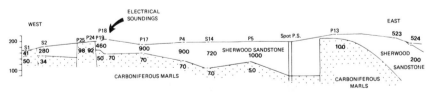

Fig. 8.30. Geoelectrical section through Spot Pumping Station, Staffordshire

(location of section is shown in Fig. 8.28)

Dale the marl dips northwards and becomes progressively deeper.

Near Spot Acre, as it was not possible to set out resistivity cables to confirm the position of the fault, a short gravity profile was conducted along a convenient road. Gravity stations were occupied at 20 m intervals and the measured gravity values corrected for topographical effects using standard procedures. The resulting curve (Fig. 8.29) shows a fault type anomaly between stations 5 and 19, with an additional rise between stations 1 and 5. Use of characteristic curves shows that the fault is steeply dipping and therefore its approximate position is indicated by the mean value of the anomaly which in this case occurs between stations 11 and 12.

Resistivity soundings conducted elsewhere between Fulford Dale and Modder-shall indicate that there are no other uplifted blocks of marl other than those already known. A section showing the geological structure determined by the geophysical survey is shown in Fig. 8.30.

In this example the geophysical surveys indicate that the Cannock Chase formation aquifer exploited by the Spot, Blacklake and Moddershall Pumping Stations is divided into two smaller units by the upfaulted block of marl which also acts as an effective barrier to groundwater flow. The results enabled the water authority to revise its figures of potential yield and consequently the rates of abstraction from the pumped wells were considerably reduced.

10. LOCATION OF BURIED VALLEYS

Narrow, drift-filled valleys may be located using resistivity, electromagnetic, seismic refraction or gravity profiling techniques and many examples have been described[29]. More quantitative information may be obtained over wide, shallow valleys from a series of closely spaced resistivity soundings or from a seismic refraction profile. The following example describes the combined use of gravity profiling and resistivity sounding surveys.

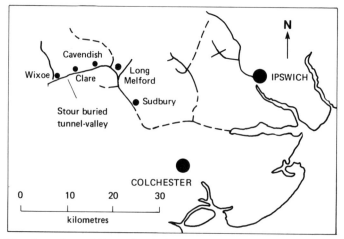

Fig. 8.31.   Location of Stour buried tunnel-valley and associated tunnel-valleys near Colchester, Essex

EXAMPLE 2. GEOPHYSICAL SURVEYS OVER THE STOUR BURIED TUNNEL-VALLEY IN ESSEX

In some parts of the country, very narrow, deep, drift-filled valleys are concealed beneath broader expanses of glacial clays. In East Anglia these buried valleys have been termed "buried tunnel-valleys" after the sub-glacial mode of their formation. A study of buried tunnel-valleys in East Anglia[30] shows that generally they are confined within present river valleys and rarely exceed 800 m in width. More commonly they are 400 m or less in width. Their sidewalls are very steep and may even be vertical and their long-valley profiles are irregular. The channels are filled either wholly with clays or with clays overlying sands and gravels, with some sands and gravels along the valley sides.

Tunnel-valleys in the Chalk areas of East Anglia have a hydrogeological importance in that the transmissivity of the Chalk in the region of the valley is considerably higher than that observed further away. To take advantage of this increased permeability it is necessary to drill close to the buried tunnel-valley and, at least in the case of very deep valleys, it is important not to drill into the valley itself, for large thicknesses of drift can complicate borehole construction and reduce yield. The precise location of a narrow buried-valley by drilling a series of deep boreholes is difficult and expensive. For this reason the use of geophysical techniques in locating buried tunnel-valleys is recommended.

Of particular interest to the Anglian Water Authority is the Stour buried tunnel-valley (Fig. 8.31). The Stour valley between Wixoe and Sudbury is the site of one of the most striking drift-filled channels in the whole of East Anglia, thicknesses of between 130 and 160 m of drift having been recorded between Clare and Cavendish. After preliminary tests a decision was taken to locate this valley, using a detailed gravity survey.

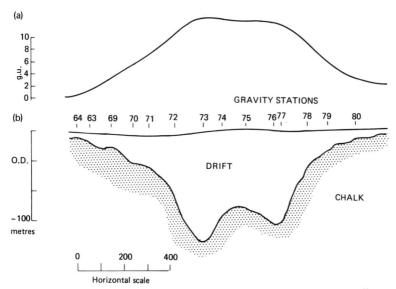

Fig. 8.32. (a) Typical gravity profile across Stour buried tunnel-valley and (b) interpretation

The density of the valley fill (boulder clay) was found to be significantly higher than that of the surrounding Chalk and so a series of eleven gravity profiles was measured across the valley at regular intervals between Wixoe and Long Melford. A typical profile corrected for various topographic effects is shown in Fig. 8.32(a). This profile can be interpreted in terms of depths to the valley floor and such an interpretation is shown in Fig. 8.32(b). Depth determinations from this type of survey are not very accurate. However, the precise location of the clay-filled valley was thought to have been achieved successfully between Wixoe and Long Melford. Profiles east and west of these points did not detect a buried valley, possibly either because the valley was filled with gravel and not the denser boulder clay or because the channel had become very shallow.

Later drilling showed that although the thickness of clay was correctly predicted using the gravity technique, deposits of gravel associated with the valley sides were not delineated. For this reason the sites of several proposed boreholes were studied with the resistivity sounding technique. A comparison between gravity and resistivity interpretations is shown in Fig. 8.33. The resistivity surveys have confirmed the position of the clay-filled valley and indicated that here 10 to 20 m of gravels underlie the surface boulder clay where the Chalk is shallow.

Detailed resistivity surveys of this nature require access to farmland and can only be undertaken conveniently during autumn, winter and early spring months. Gravity measurements, however, can be made along roads and tracks at all times of the year.

11. INVESTIGATION OF GRAVEL DEPOSITS

Gravels may normally be differentiated from adjacent rocks using the resistivity

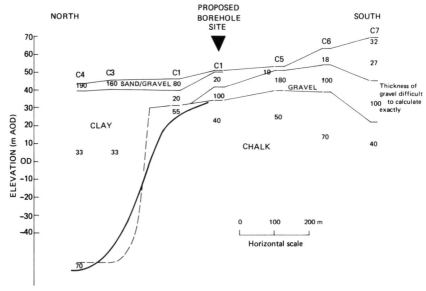

Fig. 8.33. Comparison between gravity and resistivity interpretations across Stour buried tunnel-valley

technique because of the high resistivities characteristic of sand and gravel deposits. The gravity and seismic techniques may sometimes be successfully employed, especially if the sands occur as infill to a buried valley. However, as Table 8.VI illustrates, the seismic refraction technique will not often be successful in delineating beds of gravel occurring between beds of glacial clay.

Because gravels normally exhibit electrical properties vastly different from those of the underlying and surrounding rocks, the location of gravel deposits or areas of thickest gravel may often be carried out rapidly and efficiently using a modern portable electromagnetic system such as the Geonics EM-31. An example of the use of this instrument is presented in Example 6 in Section 13.

TABLE 8.VI.   **Comparison of Properties of Gravel with those of Clay and Compact Sedimentary Rock**

	Sand and gravel	Clay	Sedimentary rocks
Resistivity (ohm-m)	100–5000	<100	50–300
Seismic velocity (m/ms)	0.5–2.1	1.0–2.0	2.0
Density (t/m³)	2.00	1.80–2.20	2.20–2.60

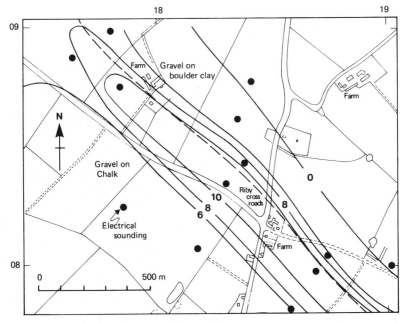

Fig. 8.34.   Gravel isopachs measured with resistivity soundings near Riby, Lincolnshire (after University of Birmingham[28])

EXAMPLE 3. GRAVEL DEPOSITS IN LINCOLNSHIRE

This example illustrates the efficient use of geophysical surveys for siting boreholes accurately. To study the flow of water through gravel deposits overlying the Chalk of Lincolnshire it was necessary first to sink a borehole in a relatively thick sequence of gravels. This borehole could then be pumped to determine the properties of the gravels. From the available geological maps and borehole information, eight sites where thick gravel deposits were expected were selected for further study.

Between five and ten electrical resistivity soundings were conducted at each possible location, a single site being examined in much less than a day. Only two of the sites had a suitable thickness (8-12 m) of sand and gravel and in both cases the thickness of sand was confirmed (to within 10 per cent of the predicted depth) by later drilling. Fig. 8.34 shows the thickness of sand measured at one of these sites. In this example the site finally chosen for the borehole was not that which would have been drilled first, if all the sites had been investigated by drilling alone. Thus considerable expense was avoided by preliminary low-cost geophysical investigations.

12. LOCATION OF FRACTURE ZONES

Fracture zones in karstic and crystalline rocks may be located with profiling techniques using seismic refraction, gravity, resistivity and electromagnetics. Where space allows, as is normal in underdeveloped countries, constant separation resistivity traversing is quick and effective. Curves such as that shown in Fig. 8.35, obtained on a recent survey in Africa, can normally be obtained. Electromagnetic profiling is also becoming more widely applied in this type of survey.

Where roads and buildings do not allow continuous electrical profiling, seismic refraction and gravity methods may be considered.

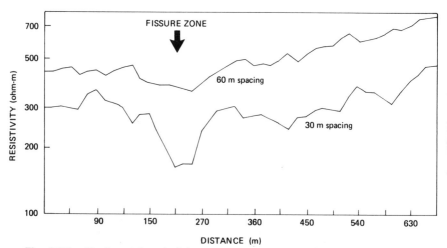

Fig. 8.35. Horizontal resistivity traverses across weathered dolomite in Zambia

13. GROUNDWATER SALINITY PROBLEMS

Water, sometimes carrying a large amount of salt in solution, is the rock component most important in defining the bulk resistivity of sedimentary rocks. In fact the rock resistivity is generally proportional to the saturating water resistivity, which is itself determined by the water salinity. Fig. 8.36 illustrates graphically the relationship between water resistivity, conductivity and salinity.

The diagram shown in Fig. 8.37 shows the general relationship between water resistivity and formation resistivity for different types of unconsolidated sediments. This diagram shows that it is not possible to differentiate sands and gravels bearing saline water from clays and marls containing fresh water. If the seismic velocity of a formation is also known, the determination can, however, often be made.

Formation Resistivity Factor

It has long been known that in a fully saturated clay-free granular formation the rock resistivity, ϱ_o, is related to the resistivity of the formation water, ϱ_w, by an expression of the form:

$$\varrho_o = F.\varrho_w \qquad \cdots \qquad \cdots \qquad \cdots \qquad \cdots \qquad \cdots \qquad \cdots \qquad \cdots \qquad \cdots \qquad (17)$$

where F is the formation resistivity factor or, simply, the formation factor.

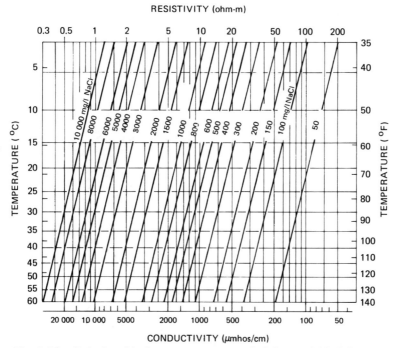

Fig. 8.36.   Relationship between water resistivity, conductivity and temperature for different concentrations of sodium chloride

When conductive minerals such as clay are present, the conduction, instead of being purely ionic, is partly the result of the mobility of weakly bonded ions in the clay structure. In this case the ratio ϱ_o/ϱ_w is a variable termed the apparent formation factor, F_m. A correction for this "matrix conduction" has to be made to obtain a true value of F.

In the two principal aquifers of Britain, the Triassic sandstone and Chalk limestone, the linear relationship between ϱ_o and ϱ_w is not found to hold to hold. In both cases the relationship is described by the Patnode and Wyllie[31] equation:

$$\frac{1}{\varrho_o} = \frac{1}{F} \cdot \frac{1}{\varrho_w} + c \quad \dots \quad \dots \quad \dots \quad \dots \quad \dots \quad \dots \quad \dots \quad (18)$$

where c is a constant and F is the true or corrected formation factor.

Archie's Law

The formation factor of a water-bearing rock is a function of the amount of water in the rock and the manner in which the water is distributed through the rock. The amount of water in a rock is usually determined by its porosity—the amount of void space in a rock which may be filled with water. In some rocks, particularly consolidated sediments, porosity is intergranular in origin, being the space left over between grains when the rock was formed. In compact igneous and other rocks porosity occurs in the form of fissures and joints.

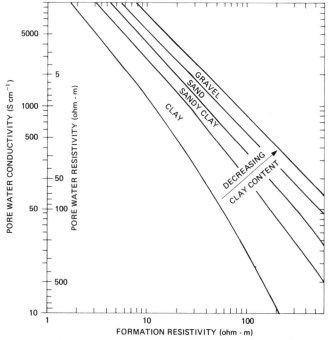

Fig. 8.37.   Relationship between formation resistivity and pore water resistivity for different rock materials (after Barker[37])

Pore spaces must be interconnected and filled with water for a rock to conduct electricity. Void space may comprise two types: larger voids, which act mainly as storage pores, and finer connecting pores. Most of the resistance to current flow is provided by the connecting pores because of their smaller cross-sections. A rock with a high ratio of storage pore volume to connecting pore volume will have a higher resistivity for a given porosity than a rock in which the ratio is low.

The formation factor, F, is related to the effective porosity, ϕ of a clay-free, granular formation through an equation of the form:

$$F = a/\phi^m \quad \ldots \quad \ldots \quad \ldots \quad \ldots \quad \ldots \quad \ldots \quad \ldots \quad \ldots \quad (19)$$

where a and m are assumed constant within a formation or section of a formation. This relationship is often referred to as Archie's Law[32].

Archie's Law can also be applied to rocks containing conductive minerals if the corrected formation factor is employed. Many laboratory results have indicated the relationships shown in Table 8.VII.

TABLE 8.VII.   Archie's Law Determined from Laboratory Measurements on Samples of Sherwood (Bunter) Sandstone and Chalk

Equation number	Area	Equation**	Source
(8)	Sherwood Sandstone, Lancashire	$F = 1.05\phi^{-1.47}$	Barker[33]
(9)	Sherwood Sandstone, Nottinghamshire	$F = 1.53\phi^{-1.12}$	Finch[34]
(10)	Sherwood Sandstone, Shropshire	$F = 0.83\phi^{-1.35}$	Finch[34]
(11)	Sherwood Sandstone, Vale of Clwyd	$F = 0.43\phi^{-2.13}$	Worthington[35]
(12)	Sherwood Sandstone, West Cumberland	$F = 1.04\phi^{-1.58}$	Worthington[35]
(13)	Sherwood Sandstone, Vale of York	$*F = 1.48\phi^{-1.66}$	Zaafran[36]
(14)	Chalk, Lincolnshire	$F = 1.80\phi^{-1.28}$	University of Birmingham[28]

Note: **F is the true formation factor; *F is the apparent formation factor determined using a saturating electrolyte with a resistivity of 0.18 ohm-m.

Geophysical Investigations of Salinity

Geophysical surveys are often employed to locate areas of saline groundwater and to define accurately the extent of such areas. Only rarely are quantitative estimates of salinity required and then the effects of porosity and matrix conduction must be taken into account. The following examples illustrate the various techniques which can be applied.

EXAMPLE 4. SALINE GROUNDWATER IN STAFFORDSHIRE

Three water supply boreholes had been sunk in the Sherwood Sandstone in the Shugborough Park area east of Stafford (Fig. 8.38). Two of these, at Milford and Shugborough pumping stations, supply fresh water while that at Essex Bridge yields highly saline water (15 000-20 000 mg/l Cl⁻). Clearly, there was a need to identify the extent of the saline groundwater in the area, while at the same time studying the subdrift geology and determining the positions of major faults.

The Triassic rocks in this area are covered by the thick sands and gravels of the Trent River Valley. These deposits, together with underlying faults, were thought likely to have an important controlling influence on the distribution of the saline groundwater.

To locate the body of saline groundwater, 58 soundings were conducted in and around Shugborough Park. The presence of high salinity groundwater was clearly recognised from the low resistivities obtained from many of the sounding curves between Essex Bridge and Tixall. Bedrock resistivities as low as 3 ohm-m were recorded in many places. The extent of the saline groundwater may be seen on the map of bedrock resistivity (Fig. 8.38), where the area of strongly saline groundwater is approximately defined by the 10 ohm-m contour. Saline ground-water occurs in the whole region between Tixall Farm and Essex Bridge and extends northwards along the valley of the River Trent. Careful quantitative interpretation of the resistivity soundings also yielded useful information concern-ing the thickness of surface sands and gravels, the Triassic geology and the positions of the important Tixall Fault.

In this example geophysical surveys have provided considerable insight into the problem of saline groundwater in the area. To obtain the same information by drilling observation boreholes would have proved enormously expensive.

EXAMPLE 5. GEOPHYSICAL SURVEYS IN HUMBERSIDE

In the region of Skitter Ness, Humberside, the Chalk is completely covered by

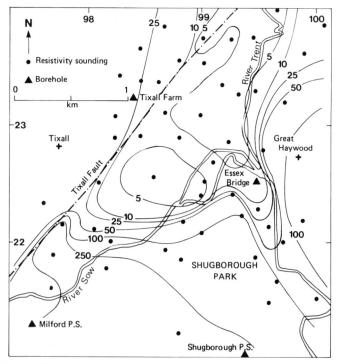

Fig. 8.38.   Map of bedrock resistivity near Shugborough Park

glacial clays and recent estuarine deposits. Here resistivity surveys[37] provided a cheap means of studying the drift lithology and thickness and also the nature of the groundwater saturating the Chalk.

A typical geoelectrical section (Fig. 8.39) clearly shows the presence of two drift lithologies (boulder clay in places overlain by estuarine silt) resting on Chalk. The boulder clay exhibits a fairly constant resistivity (24-35 ohm-m) over the whole area as does the estuarine silt (5-15 ohm-m). The Chalk resistivity varies as a function of the salinity of the groundwater between 20 ohm-m and 150 ohm-m. A contour map showing this resistivity variation more clearly is presented in Fig. 8.40.

Laboratory measurements have shown that the resistivity of the Chalk is related to that of the saturating groundwater through the Patnode and Wyllie relationship. In addition, Archie's Law in this case was determined as relationship (14) in Table 8.VII. A value for c in the Patnode and Wyllie equation may be obtained by substituting the value of water resistivity measured on samples of fresh water obtained from areas where the Chalk resistivity is known to be around 140 ohm-m. The groundwater resistivity in these places is around 20 ohm-m (i.e. conductivity 500 μS/cm or salinity 30 mg/l Cl⁻). In the Skitter Ness region the true formation factor of the Chalk is known from sampling to be fairly constant at around 8.5 (i.e. porosity = 30 per cent). Substituting these values in the Patnode and Wyllie equation (Eqn. 18) yields a value for c of 0.0013.

Using the calculated value for c it is now possible to compute groundwater salinities from surface-measured Chalk resistivities. Along the geoelectrical section, for example, the Chalk resistivity varies from 140 to 16 ohm-m. This is equivalent to a variation in groundwater resistivity from 20 to 1.9 ohm-m or a variation in salinity from 30 to 2 000 mg/l Cl⁻.

Estimates from surface geophysical surveys of groundwater resistivity may be compared with values of water resistivity obtained from measurements on borehole samples. Fig. 8.41 shows the results of applying this technique to eight wells in the

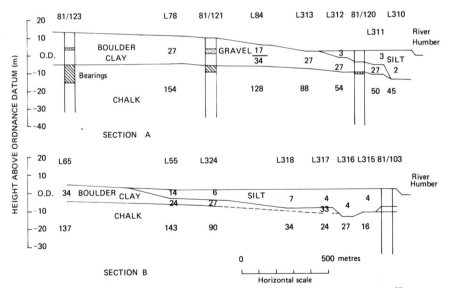

Fig. 8.39. Geoelectrical sections near Skitter Ness (after Barker[37])

Skitter Ness region. Here the geophysical estimates of water salinity are in very good agreement with measurements made on water samples.

The success of this technique in the Skitter Ness region suggests that surface

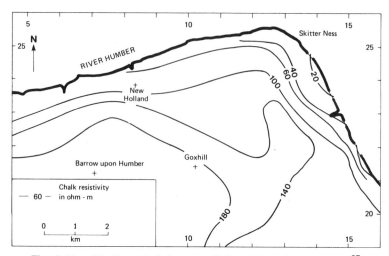

Fig. 8.40.   Chalk resistivity near Skitter Ness (after Barker[37])

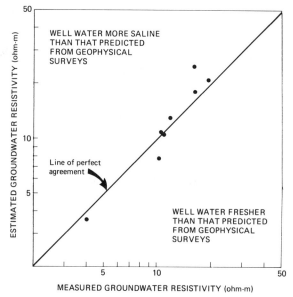

Fig. 8.41.   Comparison of borehole-measured groundwater resistivities with values estimated from surface resistivity surveys (after Barker[37])

measured resistivities could be used in other areas of the Chalk to estimate groundwater salinity fairly accurately.

EXAMPLE 6. RAPID DELINEATION OF AREAS OF SALINE GROUNDWATER

Areas of shallow saline or contaminated groundwater of local extent may be delineated quite rapidly using electromagnetic techniques. The Geonics EM-31 or EM-34 instruments are ideal in this respect as they give a direct readout of ground conductivity. Measurements can be made while walking over the region and areas of high conductivity can be noted. Fig. 8.42 shows a single profile across an area of shallow saline groundwater located along the coast in Sussex. The measured resistivity decreases rapidly over the saline area.

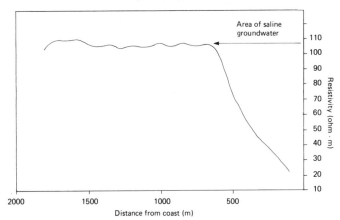

Fig. 8.42. Example of the use of the EM-31 to delineate an area of shallow saline groundwater on the south coast of England

14. WATER TABLE DEPTH

The depth to the water table can be successfully determined using seismic refraction[38] or resistivity techniques only where the water table is a truly free surface and where it occurs in an otherwise homogeneous formation. It follows that in the British Isles conditions are rarely suitable for this type of study, much of the country being covered by glacial drift and the groundwater being held at least partly under pressure.

15. REFERENCES

1. Roy, A. and Apparao, A. 1971 *Geophysics*, 36, 943, Depth of investigation in direct current methods.
2. Barker, R. D. 1979 *Geophys. J. R. ast. Soc.* 59, 123, Signal contribution sections and their use in resistivity studies.
3. Kunetz, G. 1966 "Principles of direct current resistivity prospecting" Geoexploration Monographs, Ser. 1 No. 1, Gebrüder Borntraeger, Berlin.
4. Edwards, L. S. 1977 *Geophysics*, 42, 1020, A modified pseudosection for resistivity and induced polarization.
5. Barker, R. D. 1981 *Geophysical Prospecting*, 29, 128, The Offset system of electrical resistivity sounding and its use with a multicore cable.

6. Mooney, H. W. and Wetzel, W. W. 1956 "Potentials about a point electrode and apparent resistivity curves for a two-, three- and four-layer earth", University of Minnesota Press, Minnesota.
7. Compagnie Générale de Géophysique, 1955, "Abaques de sondage électrique" (*Geophysical Prospecting, Supp. No. 3*), EAEG, The Hague.
8. Telford, W. M. *et al* 1976 "Applied Geophysics", Cambridge University Press, Cambridge.
9. Keller, G. V. and Frischknecht, F. C. 1966 "Electrical methods in geophysical prospecting", Pergamon Press, Oxford.
10. Koefoed, O. 1979 "Geosounding principles, 1: resistivity sounding measurements", Elsevier, Amsterdam.
11. Ghosh, D. P. 1971 *Geophysical Prospecting*, 19, 769, Inverse filter coefficients for the computation of apparent resistivity standard curves for a horizontally stratified earth.
12. Sumner, J. S. 1976 "Principles of induced polarization for geophysical exploration", Elsevier, Amsterdam.
13. Bertin, J. and Loeb, J. 1976 "Experimental and theoretical aspects of induced polarization", Geoexploration Monographs, Ser. 1, No. 7, Gebrüder Borntraeger, Berlin.
14. Vacquier V. *et al* 1957 *Geophysics*, 22, 660, Prospecting for groundwater by induced electrical polarization.
15. Ogilvy, A. A. 1970 *Geological Survey of Canada, Economic Geology Report*, 26, 536, Geophysical prospecting for groundwater in the Soviet Union.
16. Collar, F. A. and Griffiths, D. H. 1976 *Q. J. eng. Geol.*, 9, 57, A laboratory study of the relationships between induced polarization, permeability and matrix electrical conductivity in Bunter Sandstones.
17. Griffiths, D. H., Barker, R. D. and Finch, J. W. 1981 'Recent applications of the electrical resistivity and induced-polarization methods to hydrogeological problems' in "A survey of British hydrogeology, 1980"
18. Davis, A. M. and Schultheiss, P. J. 1980 *Ground Engineering*, 13, 44, Seismic signal processing in engineering site investigation—a case history, The Royal Society, London.
19. Griffiths, D. H. and King, R. F. 1981 "Applied geophysics for geologists and engineers" Pergamon Press, Oxford.
20. Hagedoorn, J. G. 1959 *Geophysical Prospecting*, 7, 158, The plus-minus method of interpreting seismic refraction sections.
21. Bamford, S. A. D. and Nunn, K. R. 1978 *Geophysical Prospecting*, 27, 322, *In situ* seismic measurements of rock anisotropy in the Carboniferous Limestone of N.W. England.
22. Hammer, S. 1939 *Geophysics*, 4, 184, Terrain corrections for gravimeter stations.
23. Nettleton, L. L. 1939 *ibid*, 4, 176, Determination of density for reduction of gravimeter observations.
24. Parasnis, D. S. 1952 *Mon. Not. R. Ast. Soc. Geoph. Suppl.* 6, 252, A study of rock densities in the English Midlands.
25. Mesko, C. A. 1966 *Geophysics*, 31, 606, Two-dimensional filtering and the second-derivative method.
26. Talwani, M., Worzel, J. L. and Landisman, M. 1959 *J. Geophys. Res.* 64, 49, Rapid gravity computation for two-dimensional bodies with applications to the Mendocino submarine fracture zone.
27. Bott, M. H. P. 1960 *Geophys. J.* 3, 63, The use of rapid digital computing methods for direct gravity interpretation of sedimentary basins.
28. University of Birmingham, 1978 "South Humberbank Salinity Research Project", Final Report to the Anglian Water Authority.
29. Lennox, D. H. and Carlson, V. 1967 *Geophysics*, 32, 331, Geophysical exploration for buried valleys in an area north of Two-Hills, Alberta.
30. Woodland, A. W. 1970 *Proc. Yorks. Geol. Soc.*, 37, 521, The buried tunnel valleys of East Anglia.
31. Patnode, H. W. and Wyllie, M. R. J. 1950 *Trans. Am. Inst. Min. Metall. Eng.* 189, 47, The presence of conductive solids in reservoir rocks as a factor in electric log interpretation.
32. Archie, G. E. 1942 *ibid*, 146, 54, The electrical resistivity log as an aid in determining some reservoir characteristics.
33. Barker, R. D. and Worthington, P. F. 1973 *Geoexploration*, 11, 151, Some hydrogeophysical properties of the Bunter Sandstone of northwest England.
34. Finch, J. W. 1979 "The further development of electrical resistivity techniques for determining groundwater quality". PhD Thesis, University of Birmingham.
35. Worthington, P. F. 1976 *Geophysical Prospecting*, 24, 672, Hydrogeophysical properties of parts of the British Trias.
36. Zaafran, Z. M. 1975 "An investigation of the utility of resistivity and seismic refraction techniques in groundwater problems", Unpublished PhD Thesis, University of Leeds.
37. Barker, R. D. 1982 *Proc. Yorks. Geol. Soc.*, 49, 119, Geophysical surveys near Goxhill, South Humberside.
38. Emerson, D. W. 1968 *Civ. Eng. Trans. Inst. Engrs. Australia*, 2, 15, The Determination of groundwater levels in sands by the seismic refraction method.

Chapter 9

DOWNHOLE GEOPHYSICS

1. INTRODUCTION

THE drilling of boreholes and sinking of water wells is expensive and for this reason alone it is important to obtain the maximum amount of information about the geological formation and the groundwater flow regime. Geophysical logging is a means of obtaining such information from a well or borehole. Its cost may be only a small fraction of the total cost of drilling.

Geophysical logging techniques are widely used in the evaluation and development of groundwater resources (Batt[1]). For example, extensive well logging was carried out for the Shropshire, Thames, Great Ouse and Vale of York groundwater schemes. Downhole methods have been employed to ascertain the extent of saline intrusion (Monkhouse[2]), to investigate fissure flow (Tate[3]), as well as to solve hydrogeological problems relating to the contamination, condition and performance of water wells (Fleet[4]).

REASONS FOR GEOPHYSICAL LOGGING

There are several reasons for geophysical logging:

(1) It provides information about the sub-surface which is often unobtainable from surface methods or from samples.
(2) It can be of considerable value in interpreting surface geophysical surveys.
(3) Physical measurements of borehole characteristics are made *in situ*.
(4) Measurements can be repeated accurately, allowing time lapse measurements to observe changes in well construction, fluid and formation.
(5) Continuous objective data are obtained, unlike sampling.
(6) Often logging is the only means of obtaining information from existing wells for which there are no data.
(7) Geophysical logs can assist in the efficient selection of suitable sampling points.
(8) Valid logs can aid in the design and location of water wells.
(9) Logging also permits vertical and horizontal extrapolation of data derived from drill holes.
(10) Geophysical measurements supplement geologists' and drillers' logs.

2. A BRIEF HISTORY

Some of the first well logs were probably derived from temperature measurements made by Hallock (1897) in the USA. By 1918 Van Ostrand[5] had designed borehole temperature instrumentation with a sensitivity of 0.01°C. The "depth temperature curves" showed anomalies caused by flowing water. Van Ostrand suggested that these curves might "afford a means of determining the relative water content of rocks *in situ*". A continuous temperature log was in operation by 1933. Today temperature measurements are one of the most useful and widely used methods in water well logging.

Electrical resistivity measurements were first made in 1927 by Schlumberger[6] in an oil field in France. The electric log of the 1930s was run commercially in several countries and consisted of a single point resistivity curve and measurement of the natural potential (spontaneous potential). Throughout the 1930s different elec-

315

trode arrays were developed and continuous recording of data became possible with photographic techniques. From 1945 there was a substantial increase in electric logging of water wells.

Investigation of flow conditions in boreholes was attempted in the 1920s; Fielder[7] describes the use of a low velocity deep well current meter designed by C. H. Au. Skibitzbe[8] developed a thermal flowmeter in 1955. Since then various forms of thermal flowmeter have been developed for low flow measurements (Dudgeon et al[9]).

Between 1940 and 1960 major developments were made in other downhole measurement techniques, notably radiometric and sonic methods. By using neutron and gamma-ray producing sources determinations of porosity and density were possible. Sonic methods were extensively developed by the petroleum industry but to date have seen little application or use in groundwater studies in the UK. In fact, up to the 1960s the oil industry was reponsible for the development of most of the logging equipment and interpretative methods (Segesman[10]).

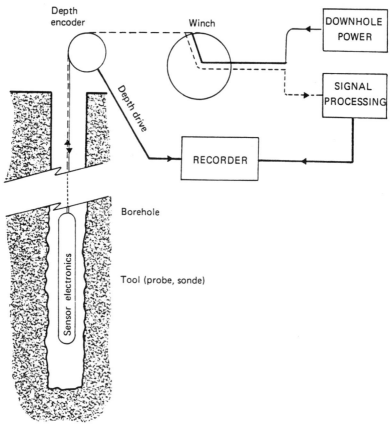

Fig. 9.1.   Basic geophysical logging system

3. THE PRESENT SITUATION IN THE UK WATER INDUSTRY

Although most oil well logging techniques may be used for hydrogeological studies, modifications to equipment and interpretation techniques are necessary because of environmental as well as economic differences. Some "oil" tools are specifically designed for relatively narrow diameter boreholes and have restricted use in large diameter water wells (up to 3 m). Some interpretative techniques differ owing to the fact that most oil wells are drilled with mud whereas most water wells use the formation water. Interpretation of water well geophysical logs has been mainly qualitative and in many cases this has been sufficient. Estimates of permeability are possible where there is good correlation between core sample data and resistivity measurements (Worthington[11]).

In the UK water wells are rarely deeper than 300 m and the tools used are not subjected to high temperatures and pressures as in oil wells. Consequently the costs of equipment and services are much lower. With the increased reliability and miniaturisation of electronics, logging tools have not only become more sophisticated but the simpler ones relatively cheaper. Customised low cost logging sets have been made specifically for hydrogeological use (Keys[12], Robinson[13] and Tate[14]).

A block diagram of a well logging system is shown in Fig. 9.1. Logging sets can be in the form of portable hand-winched units offering several basic logs (typically temperature, conductivity, flow, caliper, resistivity and gamma) operating to 200–300 m (Fig. 9.2). The costs of such units are in the range £13 000–£20 000*. Vehicle mounted systems offer, additionally, more sophisticated logs, such as the sonic and radiometric types but with power winching to greater depths (Fig. 9.3). The cost of these, excluding the vehicle, starts around £40 000*. Both systems are easily operated by one man. A basic set of logs, which could enhance well design or troubleshoot downhole problems in existing wells of average depth, could be carried out comfortably within a day.

Today the majority of water authorities have some form of logging equipment capable of running basic logs. More sophisticated logging is offered by several service logging companies (generally from the oil and mineral industries) or central research organizations.

Charges for such work vary considerably; the cost of a typical day's logging on one borehole may start at between £300–£1 000, and is generally a function of the log type and depth of run.

Table 9.1 lists the common water well applications of geophysical logs, which can be arranged into three categories—construction, fluid and formation logs.

4. CONSTRUCTIONAL LOGGING

Casing Collar Locator

Property Measured

Changes in magnetic flux due to presence of metal.

Log Applications

  (a) Location of casing base, collars and breaks.
  (b) Location of other magnetic hardware such as pumps, rising mains and foreign bodies.
  (c) Control log for other logs affected by casing presence.

The values given are only included to suggest a broad indication of equipment costs and operating prices in the UK during the Summer of 1982.

Method of Measurement

This device can be relatively simple and inexpensive, consisting of a permanent magnet inserted in a coil. Changes in the magnetic flux caused by moving magnetic material result in an induced emf in the coil. The log is run at constant speed; greater speed increases the magnitude of the emf. Sharp changes in the recorded emf indicate casing collars, or mass changes in the magnetic material. Casing collar locators are easily added to other tools and commonly run with the radiometric sondes. If interpretation is not clear a second, possibly faster, run should be made.

Calibration

The output is generally measurable in millivolts. Calibration as such is normally not necessary other than accurate depth measurement.

Fig. 9.2.   Portable logging unit

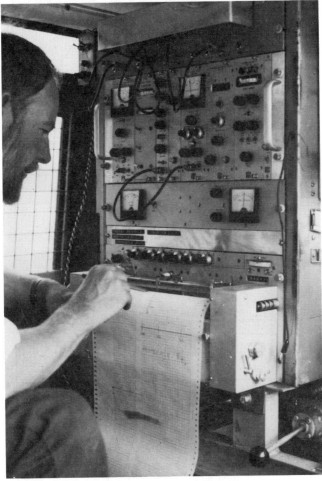

Fig. 9.3. Vehicle mounted logging unit

TABLE 9.I   Geophysical Logging—Common Waterwell Applications and Limitations

Log	Measurement Unit	Construction									Fluid			Formation						Limitations						
		Casing features	Casing location	Cement bonding	Cement location	Collapses	Dip and orientation	Diameter	Fissures	Obstructions	Borehole fluid quality	Fluid movement	Formation fluid quality	Bed boundaries	Bed thickness	Bed type	Bulk density	Permeable zones	Porosity	Air filled hole	Fluid filled hole	Lined hole	Open hole	Clean water	Radioactive method	Quality reduces with diameter increase
Acoustic Televiewer	°&mm	*	*			*	*	*	*	*										*	*	*	*			*
Casing Collar	mm	*	*			*		*	*	*										*	*	*	*			*
Caliper	µS&mv	*	*			*			*	*										*	*	*	*			
Cement Bond	°C		*	*	*																*	*	*			
Television	µS/cm				*																*	*	*			
Temperature	mm/s										*	*									*	*	*			
Conductivity	Ωm										*	*									*	*	*			
Flow	mV								*			*						*			*	*	*	*		
Tracer	APIcps		*									*									*		*			
Resistivity	API								*				*			*		*	*		*		*			*
Spontaneous Potential	gm/cc												*	*	*	*		*			*		*			*
Natural Gamma	API%Φ				*									*	*	*		*			*	*	*		*	*
Gamma-Gamma									*					*	*	*	*		*	*	*		*		*	*
Neutron-Neutron									*					*	*	*			*	*	*		*		*	*

Interpretation and Example Logs

Interpretation is quite simple. An example is shown in Fig. 9.4. Joins in the casing are indicated by marks in the log at 8, 13, 18 and 27 m. An adit entrance (a gap in the casing) occurs between 33.5 and 47 m. The log trace is featureless between these depths, as there is no metal presence.

More sophisticated devices using this principle have been used to locate areas of corrosion and calculate possible total metal loss (Edwards and Stroud[15]).

Limitations and Extraneous Effects

- (i) *Tool position:* position of the sonde in the hole affects the magnitude of the signals.
- (ii) *Hole size:* in large diameter holes the tool should be run close to the side of the well.
- (iii) *Logging speed:* changes in speed or direction give spurious marks on the log.
- (iv) *Noise:* the log can be susceptible to electrical noise, particularly if electric pumps are operating in the immediate vicinity.

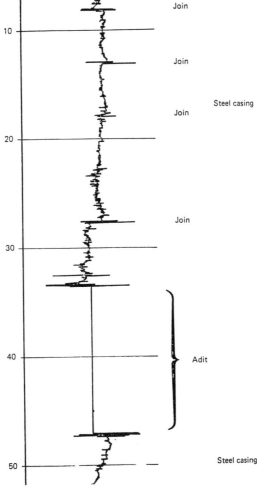

Fig. 9.4. Casing collar locator log

CALIPER LOGGING

Property Measured

This log is generally a continuous record of the mean diameter of the borehole. Some acoustic tools, such as the acoustic borehole televiewer, will give a radius measurement at the four points of the compass.

Log Applications

(1) Diameter changes within the borehole.
(2) Location of fractures/fissures and other openings, such as casing breaks.
(3) Identification of hard and soft formations.
(4) To provide information to correct formation logs that are affected by diameter changes.

Method of Measurement

The majority of calipers consist of 1 to 4 spring-loaded arms or feelers which are

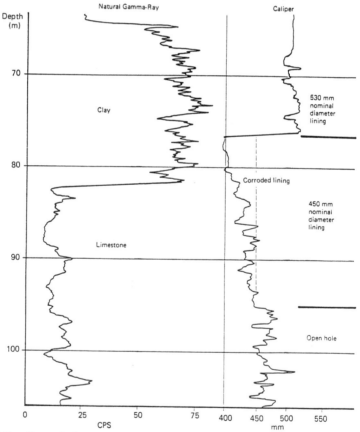

Fig. 9.5.   Corroded casing and formation squeezing into hole (caliper and gamma logs)

pressed against the well wall, any movement of these arms being transduced to a suitable electronic signal which is passed up the logging line. The arms are so arranged to give a mean diameter response or to give two orthogonal diameters, as with the X-Y caliper.

The tool is lowered to the lowest depth of interest and the arms are opened by remote control, usually by a motorised gearing mechanism. The log is then obtained on an upward run. Certain acoustic tools measure the transit time of an acoustic pulse reflected from the well wall which can be converted to the borehole radius.

Calibration

This is carried out using jigs or cylinders which enable an arm to be set at different radii. The log chart is then directly calibrated in millimetres. The difference and necessary correction between the jig and cylinder calibration for some tools should be established and checked periodically. A calibration is normally made before and after the log as a check on instrumental drift. It is often preferable when logging an open hole to run at least 5-10 m into the casing, if possible, as a further check on the calibration.

Interpretation and Example Logs

Interpretation of caliper logs is self evident, but more often than not they are used in conjunction with other logs. This aspect is shown by the following examples:

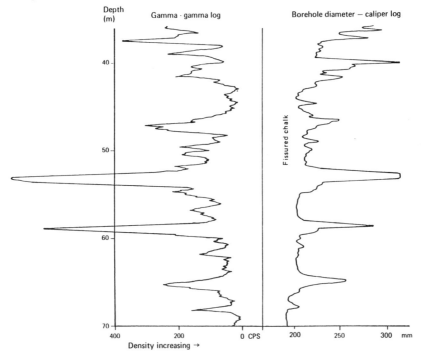

Fig. 9.6.   Borehole diameter effects—gamma-gamma log

(*a*) In Fig. 9.5, the borehole was originally lined with steel casing to 95 m; there was a diameter reduction at 76 m (530 to 450 mm). The caliper log is very rough between 68 and 95 m suggesting corroded or absent casing. The reduced diameter between 76 and 82 m is attributed to clay squeezing into the hole (see gamma log).

(*b*) The example in Fig. 9.6 shows how diameter changes (caliper log) affect a gamma-gamma (density) log. Fissures correlate with density "lows".

(*c*) Gaps in well linings can be detected using a caliper. In Fig. 9.7 a resistivity log was also run to distinguish between steel and plastic lining. The gap was in the plastic lining.

(*d*) Fig. 9.8 illustrates an acoustic televiewer log of a limestone borehole. A standard three-arm caliper log is compared with acoustic caliper logs for the four points of the compass.

Limitations and Extraneous Effects

(i) *Tool position:* decentralised single arm calipers may not give a true picture of an asymmetrical hole.

(ii) *Borehole fluid:* sonic tools must be used in fluid filled holes.

(iii) *Mud cakes:* can prevent arms from reaching the well wall.

(iv) *Casing:* compass control of sonic calipers is not possible in steel lined holes.

(v) *Obstructions:* the presence of rising mains, pumps or other hardware in a well will give erroneous caliper logs. Silts, muds and sands can prevent the caliper arms from opening.

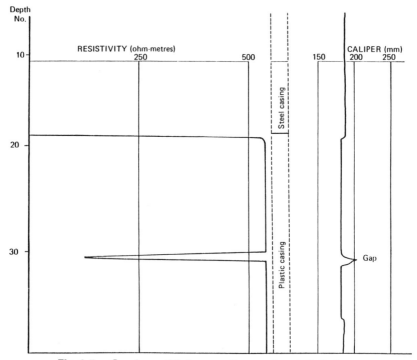

Fig. 9.7.   Gap in well lining—caliper and resistivity logs

TELEVISION LOGGING

Closed circuit television is a very qualitative inspection tool, used for viewing the condition of wells and boreholes.

Under favourable conditions casing and formation features can be identified. A crude indication of water quality and flow may be obtained. Most underwater television cameras are customised for borehole inspection work and supplied with a selection of lenses of different focal lengths and lighting attachments. It is common practice to use a wide-angle forward view lens for the first or reconnaissance run down the borehole. Side-viewing attachments are then used for close-up or more detailed inspections at selected points. Fig. 9.9 shows the use of both the forward and sideview lenses. This particular survey detected holes in the well screen which permitted the gravel pack to enter the borehole.

Limitations and Extraneous Effects

(1) *Hole size:* the quality of pictures tends to fall off with increased well diameter.
(2) *Borehole fluid:* the clarity of water affects the quality of the TV pictures. Light scatter from suspended materials in the water can also be a problem.
(3) *Interpretation:* difficulty in interpreting pictures often requires other geophysical logs to clarify the situation.

SONIC LOGGING

To date it has been mainly the cement bond and acoustic televiewer logs that have been run in UK waterwells rather than conventional sonic velocity logs.

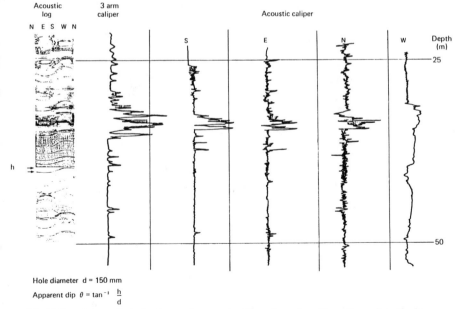

Hole diameter d = 150 mm

Apparent dip $\theta = \tan^{-1} \dfrac{h}{d}$

Fig. 9.8.   Acoustic televiewer log and caliper logs in a limestone borehole

Property Measured

Amplitude and transit (travel) time of refracted/reflected acoustic pulses.

The cement bond and televiewer logs measure the amplitude of the returned sonic signal. The acoustic caliper facility on the televiewer measures the travel time of the sonic pulse between the tool and borehole wall.

Fig. 9.9.   Holes in 380 mm diameter well screen as seen on borehole TV

CEMENT BOND LOGGING

Log Applications

(a) Amount of bonding between the cement grout and steel casing, or degree of channelling.

(b) Location of cement grout behind steel casing if bonded.

Method of Measurement

A cement bond tool consists of an acoustic transmitter and receiver spaced a fixed distance apart (typically 1 m). Steel casing suspended freely (unbonded) in a fluid-filled well transmits elastic energy at a velocity of 5200 m/s with very little attenuation over the transmitter-receiver spacing. When cement is present and properly bonded around the casing the elastic energy is dissipated before reaching the receiver. The received amplitude is therefore a function of the bonding (Grosmangin et al[16]).

Calibration

At 100 per cent bonding the signal amplitude should be zero and this calibration point can be obtained electronically. The 0 per cent bond line can be obtained by setting the tool in a freely suspended length of casing.

Interpretation

This is straightfoward and an example is shown in Fig. 9.10.

Limitations and Extraneous Effects

(i) *Borehole fluid:* to permit acoustic coupling to the casing the device must be used in fluid filled holes.

(ii) *Casing:* can only be used inside metal cased holes.

ACOUSTIC TELEVIEWER LOGGING

Log Applications

(1) Measurement of borehole wall phenomena such as fissures, fractures, and holes in casing.

(2) With orientation control, dip and direction of such features can be obtained.

Method of Measurement

This tool consists of a rotating (typically 3 rev/s) acoustic transmitter-receiver. The amplitude of the reflected signal is displayed on an oscilloscope as the sonic beam sweeps around the borehole at the same time as being drawn slowly up the hole at 1-3 m/min. Thus an acoustic picture of the borehole wall is built up line by line on, say, a polaroid film. Orientation control is provided by a flux-gate compass. The method is more fully described by Zemanek et al[17].

The amount of acoustic energy reflected by the borehole wall is a function of the physical properties of the surface. Smooth surfaces reflect better than rough ones; hard better than soft; a surface perpendicular to the tool better than skew. Generally speaking any irregularities will reduce the amplitude of the reflected signal.

Resolution of the device can be as good as 1 mm (Zemanek et al[18]).

Calibration

(a) Caliper section as described in Section 2.

(b) Accurate depth control is essential.

Interpretation

This again is straightforward as shown in Fig. 9.8, where bedding features and fissures in a limestone borehole are clearly seen.

The apparent dip of features can be calculated using:

$$\Theta = \tan^{-1} \frac{h}{d}$$

where h is the maximum-minimum depth of the feature and
   d is the hole diameter

The direction can be read directly from the compass scale.

Limitations and Extraneous Effects

(i) *Tool position:* must be centralised.

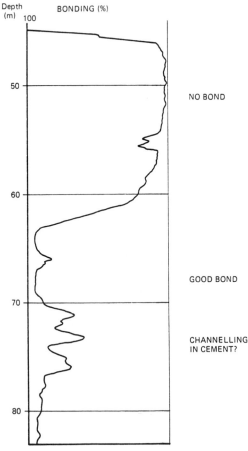

Fig. 9.10.   Cement bond log

(ii) *Hole size:* cannot be used in very large diameter wells; the tool has been successfully used in wells up to 550 mm in diameter.
(iii) *Borehole fluid:* must be used in fluid filled holes to permit acoustic coupling.
(iv) *Casing:* no compass control is possible in steel lined wells.
(v) *Logging speed:* a slow and constant speed is essential.
(vi) *Interpretation:* relies on the operator's experience in selecting appropriate arrivals in wave train.

5. FLUID LOGGING

The main methods involve the measurement of the temperature, conductivity and velocity of borehole fluids. Derivatives of these are the differential methods, tracing and sampling.

TEMPERATURE LOGGING

Property Measured

A temperature log is a continuous record of temperature of the fluid surrounding the probe in the borehole.

The geothermal gradient is a function of the result of a balance between the heat produced in the centre of the earth and the heat radiated from the surface. This gradient varies with the thermal conductivity of the geological formation. Under no-flow conditions temperature logs can be used to identify the formation. However, in most wells the fluid temperature is not in equilibrium with that of the formation and there is usually a vertical fluid flow so that the geothermal gradient is not well developed.

Log Applications

(1) Ascertain fluid movement.
(2) Identify zones of inflow/outflow (including casing leaks).
(3) Location of cement grout behind casing.
(4) Formation identification, under no-flow conditions.
(5) Data for correction of other logs such as conductivity.
(6) Indication of water quality.

Method of measurement

There are various forms of suitable sensor but the most common is probably a heat sensitive resistor (thermistor). Temperature changes result in a proportional resistance change which can be used in a variety of electronic circuits to give a suitable calibrated output signal to a recorder. Differential temperature can be obtained by measuring the difference between two temperature probes a set distance apart or electronically using a single probe and measuring the change with depth or time (at constant logging speed). The sensitivity of this technique is a function of the differential spacing (typically 0.25-2.5 m) and logging speed (typically 1-10 m/min). Obviously for least disturbance of the fluid the log should be run slowly.

Differential temperature logs are particularly useful as gradual changes in temperature are sharply accentuated. Repeatability of differential logs is good for major disturbances.

Where temperature logs are used to determine the location of grout outside the casing after cementing, the well should be filled with water to a level considerably above the expected top of the grout. Ideally the log should be run within 24 hours of cementing, although it is possible to detect grout for several days after cementing.

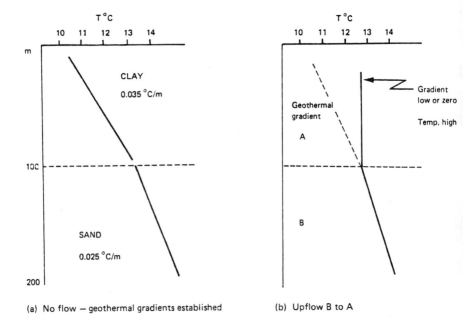

(a) No flow — geothermal gradients established

(b) Upflow B to A

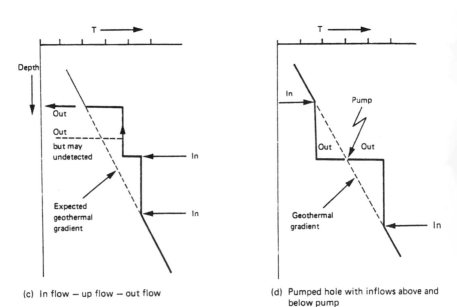

(c) In flow — up flow — out flow

(d) Pumped hole with inflows above and below pump

Fig. 9.11.   Idealised fluid temperature logs

Calibration

From time to time the temperature probes should be calibrated in a fluid bath against an accurate thermometer. The electronic system should also be checked and standardised values used, such as degrees centrigrade.

Interpretation and Example Logs

Where there is no groundwater flow, the temperature gradient in an isotropic formation under equilibrium conditions is linear with depth. Geothermal gradients encountered in British aquifers are around 1°C per 35 m. Vertical flow of groundwater can be estimated from temperature measurements (Bredehoeff and Papadopoulos[19]).

Fig. 9.11 shows idealised temperature logs for various flow patterns. These examples assume only movement of the formation water that is in equilibrium with the formation.

Fig. 9.12 shows very distinct differential temperature, temperature conductivity and resistivity responses due to inflowing saline water at specific horizons in a borehole.

Fig. 9.13 is an example of temperature and conductivity logs where warm poor quality water is entering the borehole via fissures (see Caliper Logging, Section 4).

Limitations and Extraneous Effects

(a) Hole size: this log can be run in all sizes of borehole although in large diameter holes thermal instability may affect the results (Diment[20] and Samuel[21]) and can cause significant disturbances to the geothermal gradient.

(b) *Borehole fluid:* the borehole fluid is disturbed during logging. Two sensor differential probes can be inaccurate because the first sensor disturbs the thermal environment. Consequently fluid temperature and fluid conductivity logs should be run down the holes before any other logs. For this reason temperature and differential temperature should be run simultaneously. If more than one log is run, the first-down log should be considered most representative of equilibrium conditions. If temperature logs are to be repeated, time must be allowed for the fluid to re-settle. Drilling, cementing (Gretener[22]) and pumping disturb the thermal environment of a borehole fluid and considerable time may be necessary for equilibrium to be attained.

(c) *Casing:* sometimes a temperature anomaly is observed at the base of casing which cannot be attributed to fluid flow but is due to the difference in thermal conductivity between the lined and open hole.

(d) *Logging speed:* with time function type devices errors are introduced if the logging speed is not constant.

(e) *Instrumental effects:* thermal lag, self-heating and drift of electronics can cause significant errors in the interpretation of temperature logs.

CONDUCTIVITY LOGGING

Property Measured

Fluid conductivity is a measure of the electrical conductivity of the borehole fluid. This log is essentially a fluid quality log as the conductivity is related to the total dissolved solids content.

Log Applications

(i) Ascertain borehole fluid quality.
(ii) Location of zones of differing water quality.

Method of Measurement

The simplest form of conductivity tool (probe) is one utilizing two closely spaced electrodes and measuring the electrical resistance between them. Normally these electrodes are in the form of rings made from an inert metal, such as gold or silver, and are fitted in a non-conductive tube. Four-electrode systems are commonly used but require a multi-conductor logging cable. By using alternating current electrode polarisation effects are reduced.

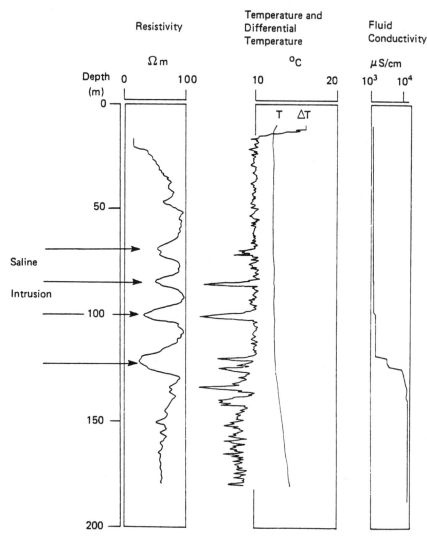

Fig. 9.12.   Inflow of saline water: fluid temperature, conductivity and resistivity logs

An alternative probe uses an inductive method. In this case the probe consists of two coils (transformers) spaced a fixed distance apart. One coil is energised by low frequency alternating current; the induced emf in the other is a function of the coupling between the coils, which is governed by the conductivity of the borehole fluid. This log may run in all sizes of borehole.

Calibration

Conductivity is normally expressed as micro-siemens per centimetre (μS/cm). Calibration of the fluid-conductivity probe should be done in fluids of known conductance and corrected to standard temperature.

Once the response of the instrument to conductivity changes has been established, field calibrations can be carried out using a resistance decade box. Calibrations should be repeated from time to time as the contact resistance of the electrodes changes.

Interpretation and Example Logs

Often water quality is discussed in terms of total dissolved solids, but there is no direct way to calculate the concentration of specific dissolved ions in water from conductivity. However, for a given fluid conductivity and temperature the electrically equivalent sodium chloride concentration can be estimated from the graph in Fig. 9.14. If for a given aquifer pore-water samples analysed in the
· laboratory indicate a consistent relation between dissolved solids and specific conductance, the correlation may be useful in interpreting regional water quality patterns from logs. The relation of the borehole fluid to the formation fluid depends on the fluid flow regime in the borehole and the permeability of the strata

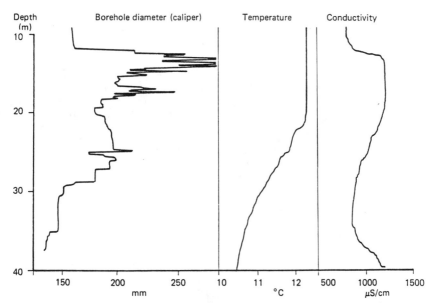

Fig. 9.13.   Poor quality water entering upper sections of a borehole (caliper temperature and conductivity logs)

penetrated by the borehole. The conductivity log should always be interpreted in conjunction with the other logs, especially temperature and flow logs.

A simplified example of a conductivity log is depicted in Fig. 9.15. Assuming the flow quantities Q_1 and Q_2 can be determined from flow logging, the conductivity (K_2) of the formation fluid can be determined from:

$$Q_1 K_1 + Q_2 K_2 = (Q_1 + Q_2) K_3$$

If more inflows are apparent this process has to be repeated at each inflow level, working down current. By this means small quantities of highly conductive water can be detected, which might otherwise pass unnoticed from a casual interpretation.

Fluid conductivity logs are often similar in character to temperature logs (Fig. 9.11). Also, differential techniques can be applied to conductivity measurements.

Limitations and Extraneous Effects

(1) *Borehole fluid:* disturbance of borehole fluid causes extraneous effects on conductivity logs. Well water may require months to attain chemical equilibrium with the surrounding rocks after drilling or cementing, unlike thermal equilibrium. Changes in

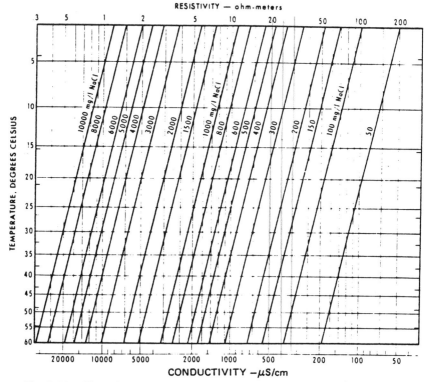

Fig. 9.14. Electrically equivalent concentrations of a sodium chloride solution as a function of temperature and conductivity

conductivity require movement of water or ions, so equilibrium may never be achieved if there is much water movement in the well.

(2) *Casing:* often in plain lined sections of boreholes low conductivities are observed. The reason for this is not clear, but it is thought that there is a chemical reaction between the water and the lining, resulting in the precipitation of dissolved solids and thus reducing conductivity values.

FLOW LOGGING

Property Measured

Measurement of fluid velocity within the borehole.

Log Applications

(a) Flow rates within the borehole.
(b) Identification of permeable zones.
(c) Location of casing leaks.

Method of Measurement

There are several means of measuring vertical flow in boreholes, dependent on

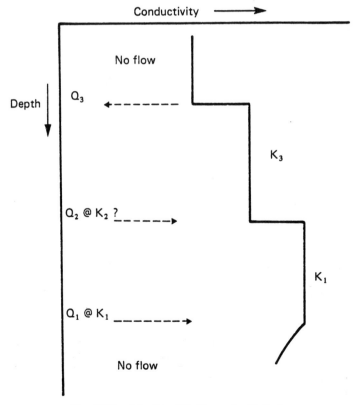

Fig. 9.15.   Idealised fluid conductivity log

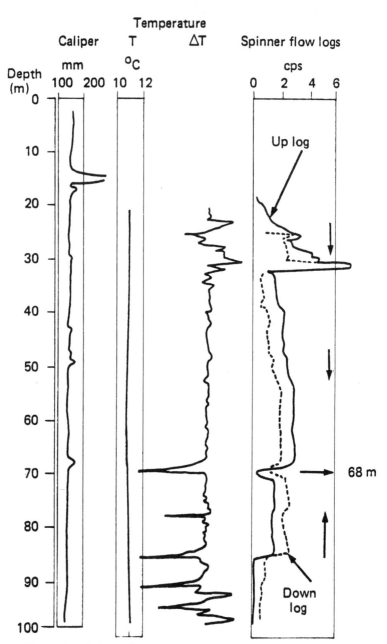

Fig. 9.16.   Spinner flowmeter log using the difference method

the magnitude of velocities anticipated (Pattern and Bennett[23]). The most common but least sensitive is an impeller type which consists of a turbine whose revolutions against time are measured.

Velocities lower than 30 mm/s may be detected using a spinner by applying the difference method, running the tool up and down the borehole at constant speed and noting the differences. When the tool moves against the flow the revolutions per minute increase and conversely when the tool moves in the same direction as the flow, the revolutions per minute are reduced. Deflections on one log not matched by deflections on the opposite direction log are likely to have been caused by logging speed variations, or the tool catching the borehole side.

A more sensitive flowmeter is the heat-pulse type (Dudgeon *et al*[9]). This tool consists of a heating grid on either side of which heat detectors are fixed. An electrical pulse to the grid results in a pulse of heat, the time taken by the heat pulse to reach a detector being a function of the fluid velocity. The sensitivity of such a tool can be as good as 1 mm/s.

For very low flows a variety of injection methods can be employed using radioactive or chemical substances. The basic downhole equipment consists of a device for injecting the tracer in the well and one or more appropriate detectors. The detectors may be held stationary or used to follow the slug of tracer up or down the hole to the point of exit. If very low velocities are encountered it will be necessary to re-log the hole periodically.

Calibration

Flow measuring tools should be calibrated in the size of hole in which they are to be used. Because of tool asymmetry these measurements should be made using upward and downward flows.

Interpretation and Example Logs

Open-hole flow logs should always be used with the caliper log so that fluid velocities can be converted to fluid flow by multiplying the velocity by the borehole cross-sectional area.

An example of a spinner flowmeter log using the difference method to obtain flow direction is shown in Fig. 9.16. There is an outflow at 68 m; above this depth the water flows downwards ("up" log velocity > "down" log velocity). Below 68 m the water is flowing upward ("down" log velocity > "up" log velocity). The differential temperature log clearly shows the inflow and outflow points, which are coincident with fissures as seen on the caliper log.

Limitations and Extraneous Effects

(i) *Tool position:* a common problem with flow metering is the apparent variation of fluid velocity with radial position within the borehole. In a smooth cylinder fluid velocity is lowest near the wall and at a relatively stable maximum across the central portion. Measuring velocity over a small cross-section of the total well can produce low results if it is near the well wall. It is, therefore, essential to use centralisers, channelling flanges or packers to improve the accuracy of the measurements.

(ii) *Instrumental:* discrepancies in the "up" and "down" responses of flow meters are apparent due to asymmetrical tool construction. Common disturbing effects to the heat-pulse flow tool method are turbulence at the point of measurement, convection cells being set up by too rapid "pulsing", and identifying correct heat-pulse, as this tool is also a very sensitive thermometer.

(iii) *Borehole fluid:* at very low velocities direction errors in tracer type measurements occur, due to specific gravity differences between water and tracer. It is essential to use slim tools in this sort of work as large diameter tools with respect to well diameter cause more vertical dispersion when passed through a tracer slug.

6. FORMATION LOGGING

RESISTANCE AND RESISTIVITY

Property Measured

Electrical resistivity of the formation around the borehole.

Log Applications

(1) Strata geometry and type.
(2) Strata correlation between boreholes.
(3) Determination of formation water quality.
(4) Determination of porosity.

Method of Measurement

A single point resistance measurement is the simplest electrical method. One electrode is lowered into the borehole fluid and a second electrode placed at the surface. The electrical resistance is measured between these two electrodes. The radius of investigation is small, 5 to 10 times the electrode diameter, and is also dependent on the borehole fluid conductivity. This log is suitable for qualitative interpretations only—that is, geological correlations, determinations of bed boundaries and lithological changes.

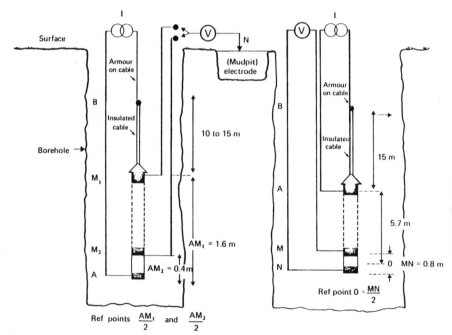

Fig. 9.17.   Resistivity electrode arrays

It is also useful for detecting fractures because the measurements are very susceptible to diameter changes. A variation of this log is the differential point resistance, where two downhole electrodes are used a short distance apart.

The use of multi-electrode probes enables resistance measurements to be made of a known or assumed volume of earth. Thus the resistivity can be obtained which depends only on the nature of the conductor and not its dimensions.

$$\text{Resistivity } \varrho = \frac{R\,A}{L} \qquad \text{(ohm-m)}$$

where R = earth resistance   (ohms)
       A = cross section area (m^2)
       L = length   (m)

Common electrode arrays used are shown in Fig. 9.17, where $AM_1 = 1.6$ m (long normal) and $AM_2 = 0.4$ m (short normal). A constant alternating current, I, is passed between electrodes A and B and the resulting potential, V, between N and M_1 or M_2 is measured. The resistivity for such an array is given by:

$$\varrho = \frac{V}{I}\,G$$

where G is the geometric factor specific to the array which in the above case is $4\pi AM$ m.

The radius of investigation is about 2AM, but it is also a function of the borehole fluid conductivity as well as the resistivity of the formation volume sampled and so constantly varies.

Long- and short-spaced normal arrays were originally introduced by oil logging companies, the short-normal to obtain the resistivity of the rock close to the borehole wall which had been disturbed by the mud invasion during drilling and the long-normal to obtain the resistivity of the remoter undisturbed rock. The short-normal has good vertical revolution, enabling bed boundaries to be well defined.

The lateral log (Fig. 9.18) was designed as a deep looking device and it gives best results in beds whose thickness is twice the electrode spacing (AO). The geometric factor for the lateral array is $4\pi(AO)^2MN$.

Focused current devices (such as the guard and laterolog) have been designed to measure relatively high formation resistivities through conductive borehole fluids (Doll[24]).

Calibration

This is achieved by attaching resistances of known values to the tool.

Interpretation and Example Logs

For a fully saturated formation Archie[25] defined a fundamental relationship as follows:

$$\text{Formation Factor } F = \frac{R_o}{R_w} = \frac{\alpha}{\phi^m}$$

where R_o is the resistivity of 100 per cent saturated formation;
       R_w is the resistivity of the pore water;
       ϕ is the porosity of the formation;
       m is the cementation factor, which usually ranges between 1 and 3;
and α is a constant determined empirically and is a function of the rock matrix

Generally satisfactory results are obtained using:

$$F = \frac{0.62}{\phi^{2.15}} \qquad \text{for sands and}$$

$$F = \frac{1}{\phi^2} \qquad \text{for limestones}$$

Hence porosity for a known rock type may be obtained from resistivity logs. R_o can be obtained from a wide-spaced resistivity log such as the 1.6 m normal. R_w may be obtained from the fluid conductivity log *only* if the water column adjacent to the formation can be assumed to be that of the formation water. Otherwise R_w must be obtained from the porewater samples taken from cores.

Conversely water quality (R_w) can be determined from resistivity logs if porosity (from neutron logs) and the relevant matrix information is available. In mud-filled holes the calculations are somewhat different, to take into account the effects of mud cake and invasion (Pirson[26]).

Fig. 9.18 shows several logs run in a Triassic sandstone borehole. The gamma, caliper, neutron (porosity) and resistivity logs all suggest clean and consistent sandstone, whose porosity is in the range of 32-39 per cent. These logs may be used to estimate the formation water quality; for example at 360 m, the neutron log gives a porosity value of 35 per cent and the 1.6 m normal resistivity gives a formation resistivity of 100 ohm-m. Using these values in the above equation for a sandstone:

$$F = \frac{0.62}{(0.35)^{2.15}} = \frac{100}{R_w}$$

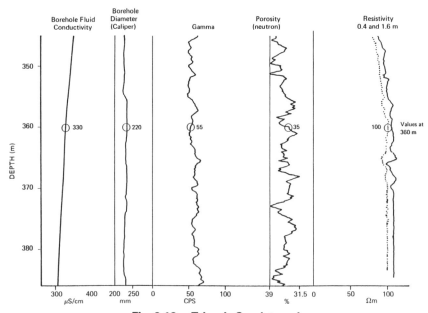

Fig. 9.18.   Triassic Sandstone logs

Hence $Rw = 17$ ohm-m. Or in terms of conductivity

$$\sigma_w = \frac{1}{17} \times 10^4$$

$$\sigma_w = 590 \ \mu S/cm$$

Note that this value is different from the borehole fluid conductivity at this depth (330 μS/cm).

The resistivity log shown in Fig. 9.12 illustrates the effect of high conductivity fluid (intruding sea-water) on the apparent formation resistivity—that is, increased porewater conductivity decreases the apparent formation resitivity.

Formation identification and correlations are possible from resistivity logs (Gray[27]). In Fig. 9.19 a resistivity log (with a gamma log) through the Chalk succession of Southern England is shown. It is apparent that different sections of the Chalk have unique electrical (and gamma) characteristics, which correlate over a wide area.

Limitations and Extraneous Effects

(a) *Hole size/borehole fluid:* increases in hole size/conductivity decrease the sharpness and definition of resistivity logs.
(b) *Noise:* the logs can be susceptible to man-made electrical noise and magnetic storms.
(c) *Instrumental:* polarisation of electrodes can cause errors but this is reduced by using alternating currents.

SPONTANEOUS POTENTIAL (SP) LOGGING

Property Measured

Electrical potentials caused by electrochemical differences between the salinity of the fluids or mineralogy of the formation or electrokinetic effects of fluid flow (Gondouin[28]).

Log Applications

(i) Formation water resistivity.
(ii) Bed boundaries.
(iii) Geological correlations.
(iv) Permeable zones.

Method of Measurement

A single electrode is run through the borehole fluid column and the potential difference measured between this electrode and one placed at the surface. Voltages are measured in millivolts.

Calibration

The system is calibrated using known potentials over the range of the logging instrumentation.

Interpretation and Example Logs

Where electrochemical differences between the borehole fluid (drilling mud) and formation water give rise to the spontaneous potential (SP), and NaCl is the dominant solute, the formation water resistivity may be calculated using:

$$SP = - K \log \frac{R_m}{R_w}$$

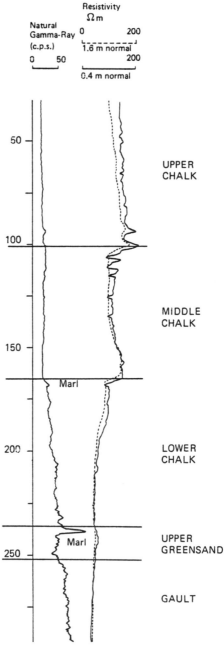

Fig. 9.19.   Gamma and resistivity logs of a borehole penetrating Cretaceous strata of Southern England

where K is 70mV for NaCl solutions;
      R_m is the borehole fluid resistivity;
and R_w is the formation fluid resistivity

In freshwater wells Ca^{2+} and Mg^{2+} are often the dominant ions. Alger[29] shows the above formula may be used for freshwater wells once the equivalent NaCl solution has been derived empirically from local chemical data.

Certain stratigraphic interfaces such as clay to sand and sand to hard rock give rise to electrochemical potentials. Electrical measurements may thus provide a means of identifying freshwater strata and permeable zones. An idealised example is shown in Fig. 9.20.

Limitations and Extraneous Effects

(1) *Casing:* active electrolytic corrosion of casing may give rise to spurious potentials.
(2) *Noise:* man-made noise from electrical cables and motors and magnetic storms may cause intense induced currents such that high voltage variations make logging impossible.

NATURAL GAMMA-RAY LOGGING

Property measured

The natural gamma-ray emission from rocks. The gamma radiation is a result of the disintegration of the radioactive elements uranium, thorium and potassium present in certain rocks, the rates of emission being statistical in nature.

Log Applications

Lithology identification, mainly used to distinguish between clay and marl (high gamma activity) and sandstones and carbonates (low gamma activity).

Method of Measurement

The most common gamma-ray detector used in hydrogeological work utilises a sodium iodide crystal which emits light when exposed to gamma radiation. A photomultiplier is used to detect and amplify this light. The crystal photomultiplier and further amplification circuits are housed in the downhole tool. The amplified signal is in the form of random pulses which are sent up the logging line to surface rate-meters.

The radius of investigation of a gamma log in water-saturated sands and limestones is approximately 30 cm. The presence of steel casing reduces the gamma-ray intensity by about 30 per cent due to energy loss, but logs are still obtainable. As a rule of thumb 50 per cent of the counts come from within 12 cm of the well bore. The borehole diameter has a very marked effect on the measurements. For this reason the tool should be run down the side of the borehole, and the logs of open holes should be interpreted along with the caliper log.

Calibration

In the water industry gamma logs are used for qualitative interpretations, so the surface recording equipment is often only calibrated in counts per second. Recognised standard calibrations such as those set down by the American Petroleum Institute[30] are commonly adopted by logging companies. These require the tools to be calibrated in pits of known radioactivity at Houston, Texas. A secondary means of calibration is to simulate these pit responses by radioactive sources placed a given distance away from the tool. Logs so calibrated do allow more accurate comparisons between logs from different companies.

Interpretation and Example Logs

The main use of gamma logging in UK waterwells is to identify clay and marl bands or determine the relative clay content of the chalk or sandstone aquifers. The gamma log in Fig. 9.19 shows marl bands at the top and bottom of the Lower Chalk, a persistent feature of the Chalk across southern England. The relative increase in the gamma count rate of the Lower Chalk with respect to the Upper and Middle Chalk is also a well recognised feature.

This very sensitive log permits good correlations to be made between boreholes, as illustrated in Fig. 9.21 which shows the gamma logs of three sandstone boreholes on the same site. Although there are no major "clay" peaks, there is good correlation between logs.

Limitations and Extraneous Effects

(a) *Hole size:* increases in hole diameter decrease the gamma log response.

(b) *Casing/Grout:* the sensitivity of the log is decreased by increases in the electron density of material surrounding the tool.

(c) *Instrumental:* size of the crystal and probe as well as the time constant (averaging period) of the counting equipment and logging speed affect the response and sensitivity of the log (see Section 7 on procedures).

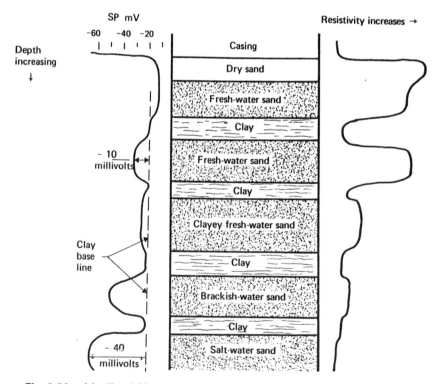

Fig. 9.20.   Idealised SP and resistivity curves through clays and sands

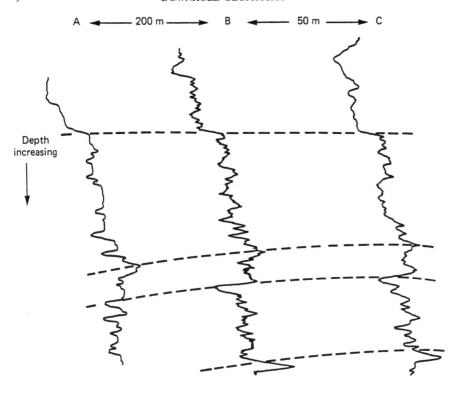

Gamma radiation increases →

Fig. 9.21. Correlation between three sandstone boreholes using natural gamma-ray logging

DENSITY (GAMMA-GAMMA) LOGGING

Property Measured

Attenuation of back scattered gamma radiation as a function of the electron density of the rock surrounding the borehole.

Log Applications

(i) Measurement of bulk density and porosity of rocks.
(ii) Identification of lithology.
(iii) Location of cavities and cement outside the casing of a well.

Method of Measurement

The probe contains a gamma radiation source such as Co-60 or Cs-137 placed a set distance from a detector. As the detector is shielded from the source most of the radiation detected is *via* the formation. Several processes may account for the degradation of radiation in the rock. The most signficant is Compton Scattering (Tittman[31]), in which a gamma photon loses some of its energy to an orbital electron. So the gamma radiation detected is proportional to the electron density of the material. The electron density is approximately proportional to the bulk density, although some corrections are required for certain materials which do not have the same ratio of atomic number to atomic mass of the calibration blocks. The radius of investigation is primarily a function of source-detector spacing and source strength. The count rate recorded on the log is inversely proportional to the bulk density. Some probes use two detectors to provide density measurements corrected for borehole effects such as mud cake and small irregularities in the well diameter (Wahl et al[32]). All tools are run down the side of the borehole, being pressed up against the well wall by either bowsprings or caliper type arms.

Calibration

The primary calibration standards for density tools are freshwater filled limestone blocks of accurately known densities and high purity. The secondary standards are large magnesium, acrylic and aluminium blocks into which the tool is inserted. The secondary standards are kept at the base office as their bulk makes them difficult to take into the field. At the well site a small radioactive test source and jig may be used to produce a signal of known strength so as to check the detection system.

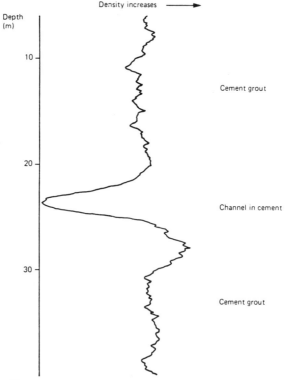

Fig. 9.22.   Channelling of cement grout behind steel casing—density (gamma-gamma) log

Interpretation

A calibrated density log should be viewed alongside a caliper log (Fig. 9.6). Corrections for diameter changes and casing presence should be made.

As well as lithological changes being apparent on the density log the porosity ϕ, of "clean" formations can be determined using:

$$\phi = \frac{\varrho_m - \varrho_b}{\varrho_m - \varrho_f}$$

where ϱ_m is the matrix density;

   ϱ_b is the bulk density, obtained from the log;

and ϱ_f is the formation fluid density

Common values for ϱ_m are 2.65 g/cc for sands and sandstones and 2.71 g/cc for limestones. Density logs can be run in cased holes but, without correction and calibration for the effects of casing, only qualitative interpretations can be made. Density measurements in cased holes have been used to locate cavities in the formation or channelling of the cement grout. This effect is illustrated in Fig. 9.22.

Limitations and Extraneous Effects

(1) *Hole size:* variations in borehole sizes due to cavings, fissures etc. cause loss of contact with the well walls (Fig. 9.6).

(2) *Bore roughness:* introduces a major source of error as it introduces a low density medium (fluid, mudcake, mud) between the tool and the formation.

(3) *Casing/grout:* the sensitivity of the log is decreased by increases in the electron density of material surrounding the tool (Fig. 9.23).

(4) *Instrumental:* same as for gamma-ray log (see also Section 7).

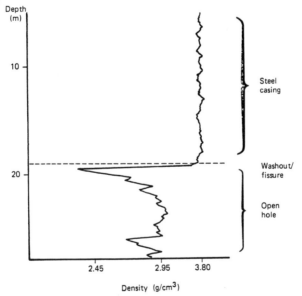

Fig. 9.23.   Effect of steel casing on a gamma-gamma log

NEUTRON-NEUTRON LOGGING

Property Measured

(a) Hydrogen content of the formation.
(b) Log applications:
    (i) delineation of porous formations;
    (ii) determination of porosity.

Method of Measurement

The neutron tool contains a source of fast neutrons (commonly americium-beryllium) with a thermal neutron detector at a fixed distance from the source (20-40 cm). Shielding prevents radiation from the source travelling directly to the detector. Increases in the hydrogen content within the area of investigation of the tool cause a reduction in the count level observed by the detector.

The emitted fast neutrons collide elastically with the surrounding elements. These collisions cause them to slow down and thermalize at some distance from the source, dependent upon the relative mass of the elements to the neutron. Neutron mass is essentially the same as hydrogen, hence collisions with hydrogen atoms cause maximum energy loss. In the presence of hydrogen the neutrons thermalize closer to the source and further away from the detector. In high porosity and high water content strata fewer collisions are required to thermalize the neutrons. This will take place within less than 30 cm of the source. So much of the neutron response comes from the first few cm of the formation. For this reason the tool is run down the side of the hole.

Calibration

The primary standard for calibration of neutron tools is the American Petroleum Institute, Neutron Pit in Houston (API[30]). Here the response of a logging tool is measured in a water-filled limestone with a porosity of 19 per cent. This response is then known as 1000 APINU. Calibrating sleeves are used for secondary (or field) calibrations.

However, it is recommended that the tools are calibrated empirically against laboratory porosity determinations on core samples for a given aquifer (Pirson[26]).

Interpretation and Example Logs

The neutron-neutron log must be interpreted with other logs, in particular caliper and natural gamma, so that hole diameter and lithology corrections can be made. Once corrected, porosity values are read directly from the new log (Fig. 9.18).

A common water well application for neutron logging in unconsolidated formations is to locate the high porosity sands behind drillers' casing so that well screens may be set at the best depths. In this instance gamma logging is also carried out in order to distinguish between high porosity sands and clays. An example is shown in Fig. 9.24, where zones A and B are the most ideal having low gamma counts (sand) coincident with low neutron counts (high porosity).

Limitations and Extraneous Effects

(1) *Hole diameter:* as the borehole size increases a greater number of neutrons are captured in the water column close to the source so that the intensity at the detector reduces. This effect gives rise to false porosity indications. Ideally, neutron logs should be run in small diameter boreholes (less than 30 cm diameter).

(2) *Casing:* this reduces the counting rate and porosity resolution of the tool (particularly plastic) and also holds the tool away from the formation. Two or more strings of casing give very poor resolution.

(3) *Grout:* has a high water content which masks the neutron curve.

(4) *Eccentricity:* much higher counting rates are obtained when the tool is against the well wall rather than in the centre of the hole.

(5) *Mud cake:* keeps the tool away from the well wall and introduces low density, high porosity material between the tool and formation. Corrections must be made to correct for the high porosities.

(6) *Instrumental:* same as for gamma-ray log (also see Section 7).

7. LOGGING PROCEDURE

PRIOR TO LOGGING

Before logging a borehole certain information, such as the basic geology, the well diameter and depth and casing details, should be obtained. Well records from the British Geological Survey, water authorities or drilling companies may also provide a valuable source of information. In the case of old boreholes, with no records, the required information must be built up during the course of logging (caliper, television and casing collar locator).

The aim of the logging should be clearly defined and limitations imposed by the wells' construction should be considered in order that the correct suite of logs is selected. For example it is pointless running fluid logs in only a few metres of fluid or nuclear logs in very large diameter wells. As may be realised from the previous sections, seldom is only one log run or interpreted without other "control" or correction logs.

ORDER OF LOGGING

Some logs may be carried out during or immediately after drilling. These are mainly formation logs to evaluate the lithology so that the final depth of the

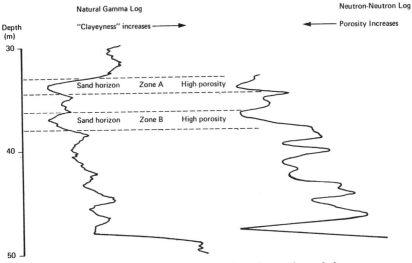

Fig. 9.24. **Gamma and neutron logs in sands and clays**

borehole may be determined or a decision made for optimum location of casing or well screen.

In the case of fluid information from downhole measurements, drilling or other fluid disturbing mechanisms, such as pumping, should cease at least 24 hours before logging. Also pumping rates of any nearby boreholes during the logging period should be noted. The order of logging is important, particularly for the fluid parameters. If the flow pattern in the well is to be determined temperature logs should be run first, if water quality is more important then fluid conductivity. Fluid logs may sometimes be carried out under pumped as well as non-pumped conditions, depending on the nature of the problem. Normally it is advisable to log in wells with pumps and rising mains removed but useful logs may sometimes be obtained through access tubes.

NUCLEAR LOGGING (GAMMA, NEUTRON ETC)

Since "nuclear signals" are statistical in nature these variations are smoothed by an electronic integrator, the time constant (averaging period) of which is selectable. During this period the tool will have travelled a given distance governed by the logging speed so the true radiation intensity of a bed can be determined only if the

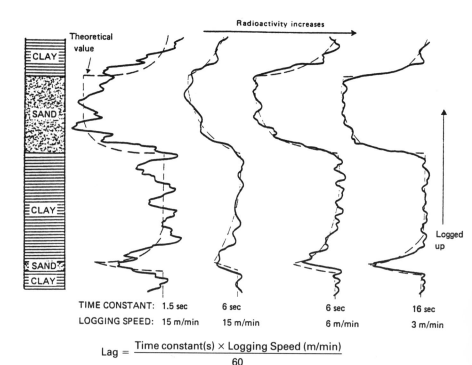

$$\text{Lag} = \frac{\text{Time constant(s)} \times \text{Logging Speed (m/min)}}{60}$$

Note: Lag correction is additive on upward logs

Fig. 9.25.   Effect of logging speed and time constant on statistical data

logging speed is less than the bed thickness divided by the time constant (Fig. 9.25). For example, if one requires a minimum detectable thickness of 0.3 m, using a time constant of 3 s the logging speed must be less than 6 m/min. The time constant is selected to give least statistical variation in the signal while the tool is held stationary in the borehole for 1 to 2 minutes. Conventional analogue time constants and integrating circuits are, however, being dispensed with as digital techniques are increasingly deployed. Repeat logging of small sections of the hole (10 to 30 m) serves as a check on the quality of the data.

Logging Speeds

Logging speeds and time constants of the instrumentation not only determine the resolution of some logs but also the time taken to complete the measurements, which can be significant if rig standing charges are being paid. Therefore speeds and settings may often be a compromise to minimise inhole time yet ascertain the required information.

Generally nuclear logs are run very slowly, typically 1 to 5 m/min. On the other hand resistivity and conductivity logs can be run fast, at 10 to 30 m/min.

The Final Result

Recorded on the log heading are the pertinent details of the borehole with special attention to features that affect its interpretation, such as casing, water levels and well diameters. Corrections to the logs are normally made back at base using standard charts (Schlumberger[33]).

Often in water well logging it is possible with experience to make preliminary qualitative interpretations on site thus permitting immediate action to be taken, such as screen setting, installation of pumps, renovation work or continued drilling.

8. REFERENCES

1. Batt, L. S. and Brereton, N. R. 1973 "The use of well logging techniques in water resources development", *Société pour l'Avancement de l'Interpretation des Diagraphies, Second Annual Symposium, Paris.*
2. Monkhouse, R. A. and Fleet, M. 1975 *Q. J. eng. Geol.*, 8, 291, A geophysical investigation of saline water in the chalk of the south coast of England.
3. Tate, T. K., Robertson, A. S. and Gray, D. A. 1970 *ibid*, 2, 195, The hydrogeological investigation of fissure flow by borehole logging techniques.
4. Fleet, M. and Oliver, D. 1976 Second International Conference on the Application of Geophysics in Hydrogeology and Engineering Geology, Brno, Czechoslovakia.
5. Van Ostrand, C. E. 1918 *West Virginia Geological Survey, County Reports of Barbour and Upshur Counties*, p66, Apparatus for the measurements of temperature in deep wells.
6. Schlumberger, C. and Schlumberger, M. 1929 *Min. and Metall*,. 10, 515, Electric logs and correlations in drill holes.
7. Fielder, A. G. 1928 *US Geological Survey Water Supply Paper*, 596-A, 24, The Au deep well current meter and its use in the Roswell artesian basin, New Mexico.
8. Skibitzke, H. E. 1955 *US patent* No. 2 728 225, Electronic Flowmeter.
9. Dudgeon, C. R., Green, M. J. and Smedmor, W. J. 1975 "Heat-pulse flowmeter for boreholes", Technical Report No. 4, Water Research Centre, Medmenham.
10. Segesman, F. F. 1980 *Geophysics*, 45, 1667, Well logging method.
11. Worthington, P. F. 1973 *Wat. and Wat. Engng.*, 77, 251, Estimation of permeability of a Bunter Sandstone aquifer from laboratory investigations and borehole resistivity measurements.
12. Keys, W. S. 1968 *Ground Water*, 6, 10, Well logging in groundwater hydrology.
13. Robinson, V. K. 1974 *Q. J. eng. Geol.* 7, 207, Low cost geophysical well logs for hydrogeological investigations.
14. Tate, T. K. and Robertson, A. S. 1975 *Water Services*, 79, 368, Logging equipment for water boreholes.

15. Edwards, J. M. and Stroud, S. G. 1964 *J. Pet. Tech.*, 16, 377, Field results of the electromagnetic casing inspection log.
16. Grosmangin, M., Kokesh, F. P. and Majani, P. 1961 *ibid*, 13, 165, A sonic method for analysing the quality of cementation of borehole casings.
17. Zemanek, J. *et al* 1969 *ibid*, 21, 762, The borehole televiewer—A new logging concept for fracture location and other types of borehole inspection.
18. Zemanek, J. *et al*, 1970 *Geophysics*, 35, 254, Formation evaluation by inspection with the borehole televiewer.
19. Bredehoeff, J. D. and Papadopoulos, I. S. 1965 *Wat. Res. Res.*, 1, 325, Rates of vertical groundwater movement estimated from the earth's thermal profile.
20. Diment, W. H. 1967 *Geophysics*, 32, 720, Thermal regime of a large diameter borehole.
21. Samuel, E. A. 1968 *Geophysics*, 33, 1004, Convective flow and its effects on temperature logging in small diameter wells.
22. Gretener, P. E. 1968 *J. Pet. Tech.*, 20, 147, Temperature anomalies in wells due to cementing of casing.
23. Patten, E. P. and Bennett, G. D. 1962 *US Geological Survey Water Supply Paper*, 1544-C, Methods of flow measurement in well bores.
24. Doll, H. G. 1951 *Trans. Am. Inst. Min. Metall. Eng.*, 192, 305, The laterolog, a new resistivity logging method with electrodes using an automatic focusing system.
25. Archie, G. E. 1942 *ibid*, 146, 54, The electrical resistivity log as an aid in determining some reservoir characteristics.
26. Pirson, S. J. 1963 "Hand book of well log analysis", Prentice-Hall, New Jersey.
27. Gray, D. A. 1958 *Bull Geol. Survey, GB*, 15, 85, Electrical resistivity marker bands in the Lower and Middle Chalk of the London Basin.
28. Gondouin, M. and Scala, C. 1958 *J. Pet. Tech.*, 10, 170, Streaming potential and the SP log.
29. Alger, R. P. 1966 "Interpretation of electric logs in fresh-waterwells in unconsolidated formations", CC 1-25, Seventh Annual Logging Symposium, Soc. Professional Well Log Analysts, Tulsa, Oklahoma.
30. American Petroleum Institute 1959 "Recommended practice for standard calibration and form of nuclear logs", RP 33.
31. Tittman, J. and Wahl, J. S. 1964 *Geophysics*, 30, 284, The physical foundations of information density logging.
32. Wahl, J. S., Tittman, J. and Johnstone, C. W. 1964 *J. Pet. Tech.*, 16, 1411, The dual spacing formation density log.
33. Schlumberger Well Surveying Corporation 1979 "Log interpretation charts".

Chapter 10

WATER TRACERS AND INVESTIGATORY TECHNIQUES

1. INTRODUCTION

TRACING techniques may be used to determine the direction of movement of groundwater, its dilution, spatial dispersion or residence-time distribution for a given pathway. At the outset of any investigation there are basically two strategies that may be used:

(1) Inject a tracer to obtain direct evidence of water movements. The substances used are chemicals, dyes, manufactured radionuclides and biological tracers, and these are discussed in Section 2.
(2) Investigate the distribution of substances which already exist in the aquifer, and deduce the behaviour of the groundwater by correlation techniques. These 'passive' studies are discussed in Section 3.

For direct injections, particularly when information is sparse on flows and dilutions in the aquifer, the investigator must make an estimate of the appropriate order of magnitude for the quantity of tracer to inject (see last part of Section 2). It is not uncommon for tracers to be lost, in the sense that they are never detected at the monitoring points. In some cases the reason will be that dispersion does not take place according to the predicted pattern—for example, the tracer may disperse to deeper strata and never reach the monitoring point. In other cases the dilution may be so great that the tracer is below the limit of detection, or the residence time so great that the tracer does not reach the monitoring site while it is in use. Patience and persistence often pay dividends, but there will be cases where the resources available cannot match the subterranean mysteries involved. The main factors to consider when planning a tracer investigation are given in Table 10.I.

The advantage of passive studies is that substances already in the system may indicate the behaviour of groundwater over a much longer period of time—decades or centuries—than is possible by injecting a tracer. Movements of the latter may be so slow that results not only take an unacceptable time to accrue but might be misleading, because the problem of introducing a tracer to simulate natural processes is often difficult to overcome. The purposes of this chapter are to indicate the relative merits of chemical, dye, radioactive and biological tracers, and to present information on techniques, which should prove useful to anyone planning tracer investigations. Some of the data have been obtained from pilot-scale experiments and these are often of great value, but the uncertain composition of natural strata means that field and model tests must always complement each other. Theoretical concepts are not dealt with since the physics of liquid dispersion through porous media and the hydrodynamics of groundwater movements have been described in Chapters 4, 5 and 6.

The public health aspects of using tracers in the environment must be considered for each investigation. Concentrations at sampling points generally present no hazard to the public but the quantities injected, prior to dilution, may be hazardous. Notification to interested parties is normal practice for radiotracer injections and the public relations aspects should not be overlooked for other types of tracer. In particular the local water authority and the public health department, or local medical officer of the area concerned, should be consulted. Where potable supplies are involved the potential risks to consumers must be balanced against the benefits of the information that will be gathered from the study. These aspects mean that the liaison and planning stages may take a long time. There are sometimes objections to the injection of any 'foreign' substance, irrespective of the type of tracer. The tracer is then considered a pollutant and it may be prudent for the sponsor of the investigation (or the site owner) to employ external tracer specialists, so that the user and the sponsor are not the same person or organization. This will be necessary in any case where specialised equipment or techniques are involved. In such cases the sponsor should still be involved in decisions on how the tracer is introduced, and on the nature and frequency of sampling.

TABLE 10.I   Factors to be Considered in Planning a Tracer Investigation

Check List	Action for Answers:	
	'Yes'	'No'
(a) Have tracers been used in the aquifer before?	List experiments and information obtained	List potential injection and detection points
(b) Is work on the aquifer possible without delay?	Investigate geology, water quality and hydrology	Gather background information on aquifer, or on similar systems
(c) Are tracer results wanted within a very restricted timescale?	List tracer types that can be used in time-span available	Assess use of passive methods*, models* and column tests*
(d) Can residence times be estimated to an order of magnitude?	(i) Radiotracers of much shorter half-life unsuitable (ii) If times are long, biotracers are of doubtful use	Plan preliminary experiments
(e) Can dilutions be predicted to an order of magnitude?	Estimate quantities and costs of optional tracers	Repeat preliminary experiments ($\times 10$ tracer quantity each time)
(f) Will most transport take place via fissures?	Consider dyes or biological tracers for economy	Chemical or radioactive* tracers probably necessary
(g) Have objections to the use of the proposed tracer been expressed?	Attempt to resolve issues by liaison (if objectors suggest alternatives, then consider them)	Assess what agreements exist (in case objections occur after injection)

Note: *The facilities and experience available at specialist laboratories may be required

2. INJECTION OF TRACERS

CHEMICAL TRACERS

Since mineral lattices are negatively charged, anions are obvious candidates for chemical tracers. In most groundwater investigations, fluoride, chloride and bromide ions may be considered of equal choice regarding their proven conservative properties, whereas iodide requires critical assessment. Fluoride and iodide concentrations down to about 0.1 mg/l are detectable by ion-selective electrodes under field conditions. The logarithmic response of electrodes over several orders of magnitude in concentration is reliable and new electrodes are being developed which promise greater stability or sensitivity. The state of the art, on a worldwide basis, was recently reviewed by Buck[1]. Ion-exchange liquid chromatography, coupled with ultraviolet absorption detection, may be used for simultaneous determination of Cl^-, Br^-, and I^- (also NO_3^- and SCN^-) at below mg/l levels in groundwater[2].

Chloride concentrations below 0.1 mg/l are readily detectable, but applications of chloride will be of little benefit where background levels are high or variable. Fisher[3] found levels in rainwater greater than 1 mg/l close to the Atlantic seaboard of the USA and levels greater than 0.5 mg/l in areas within about 160 km from the coast, with a steady decrease in concentrations inland. Levels of sodium followed a similar pattern in absolute terms, yielding a much higher ratio of sodium to chlorine than that found in sea water. Local variations of concentration in groundwater may be caused by the salting of roads during winter conditions.

Chloride may be useful for tests in small systems where the quantities of common salt (solubility 357 g/l at 0°C) are not inconvenient. Conductivity meters may be used to detect the tracer—the response should be linear in the range 0-50 mg/l. Temperatures must be recorded as the relationship between conductivity and concentration is strongly dependent on temperature. A chloride ion-selective electrode may be used over the range 0-350 mg/l provided serious interferences are not caused by other ions. Again, temperature corrections may be necessary, and standards should be made up with the groundwater being monitored. When common salt is used in bulk it may not be very pure but there will seldom be any reservations about its use. Density effects during the early dispersion stage should be considered.

Bromide may be considered the most suitable chemical in many cases because background levels are often reasonably stable. There is a good choice of analytical methods for its detection and few reservations about its use on safety grounds. Although it is not too costly (about £100 per 100 kg as KBr) considerable time may be involved in dissolving the chemical prior to injection (solubility 535 g/l at 0°C). Moreover, the process of injection, when large volumes of a dense tracer solution are required, may be lengthy because a constant rate of injection for several hours may be required to avoid false initial dispersion caused by density effects.

Iodide may be used in systems where the probability of losses caused by organic matter is low. As there will seldom be any objections to its use, it is a convenient tracer for simple 'time of travel' investigations, but doubts about its quantitative recovery may make its use for other purposes unsuitable. The solubility of KI is 1 275 g/l at 0°C and the tracer may be detected by ion-selective electrodes in the field, or in the laboratory. An automatic method using catalytic spectrophotometry has been developed[4]. Again, standards should be made up using background water from the aquifer.

Other chemical tracers which have been used include sodium dichromate (with a possible safety hazard) and manganese sulphate. Fluoride should be considered as it may be detected by ion-selective electrodes or by prompt *in situ* gamma-ray spectrometry simultaneously with neutron activation. The use of cations is probably limited to lithium, which is not readily adsorbed and may therefore be considered for use in aquifers where the clay fraction is very low. Adsorption losses will depend on the dimensions of the crystal lattice and the particle-size distribution of the deposits concerned, because of the larger specific surface areas of the smaller particles. An example was quoted by Levi and Miekeley[5] for adsorption of caesium (Cs-137) on vermiculite. The exchangeable fraction was found to be only 10 per cent for a specific surface area of 7 m^2/g but 51 per cent for an area of 43.5 m^2/g. They also found that lithium ions in the same apparatus exchanged to the extent of

10 per cent, whereas the figure for potassium ions was 40 per cent.

Although some pollutants may be modified by biological oxidation, some, such as phenol, can give reasonable indications of water-retention times, as shown in Fig. 10.1(b) and in Fig. 10.2 (Gaillard *et al*[6]), where phenol compares well with

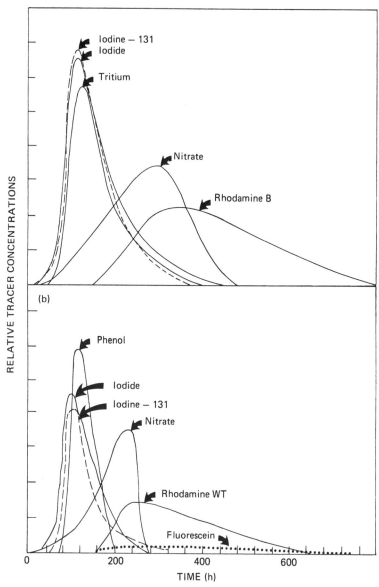

Fig. 10.1.   Comparison of residence times of various tracers and pollutants in alluvial deposits[19]

tritium and iodide. Dextrose also appears to be conserved (Fig. 10.3), whereas Lindane is delayed considerably (Fig. 10.2). These curves demonstrate that the residence-time of any particular substance cannot always be predicted from results using established water tracers. Where it is important to predict the fate of a particular substance in a given time then that substance, or a labelled form of it, should be used directly.

DYES

Fluorescent dyes radiating various colours are available, but the one most often used in hydrological work is fluorescein (or uranine). Since its fluorescent spectrum peaks at green wavelengths, where the colour response of the human eye is at its most sensitive, this dye is very suitable for direct observation in clear water. Where the intensity of daylight is low, or there is darkness, the fluorescence may be excited by ultraviolet lamps. Schwille et al[7] employed this technique to trace the course of the infiltration front continuously from the soil surface to the water table in laboratory columns. The uneven advance of the tracer fronts and their horizontal dispersion through the capillary zone, which in one case prevented the tracer from reaching the water table, were recorded in detail. Quantitative measurements may be taken with fluorimeters, provided with filters to accommodate dyes which fluoresce at different wavelengths. Some have facilities to allow a continuous flow to be monitored.

Quantitative work in fluorimetry needs close control of temperature and composition. For example, dilutions should be made up with the same water as that being traced. The use of chlorinated water, which may considerably quench the fluorescence, must be avoided. Fluorescence displays a negative temperature coefficient and the effect may be as high as several per cent per °C for the rhodamine dyes. Temperature correction data for rhodamine-B, pontacyl and fluorescein dyes have been given by Feuerstein and Selleck[8]. One advantage of fluorescein over the rhodamine dyes is that it has a temperature coefficient almost an order of magnitude lower. It suffers higher photochemical decay but this should not be important for subterranean tracer work. Rhodamine-B and fluorescein were found satisfactory over a range of pH values from about 5 to about 10 with rapid decrease in fluorescence below a pH value of 5. Pontacyl gave stable readings to a pH value of about 3. Feuerstein and Selleck investigated a range of environmental effects, including sorption by suspended solids and algae, and concluded that pontacyl was the most suitable choice since it displayed a negligible uptake by suspended solids.

It has been reported[9] that the cost ratio was about 3:2:1 for pontacyl, rhodamine-WT and rhodamine-B, while the adsorption tendency was in the ratio 1:1.5:4, respectively. Examples of the recovery curves of dyes passing through fine soils (Figs. 10.1 and 10.3) indicate that dyes may not give an accurate measure of the velocity of water flowing through such materials. A list of most of the dyes used in tracer studies is given in Table 10.II, with selected examples of alternative names.

The stability of 12 fluorescent dyes, under conditions of alternate saturated and unsaturated-zone conditions, was investigated by Reynolds[10] who concluded that pyranine was most suitable to trace drainage water in acid soils, provided a sufficient quantity was used to overcome lag effects. However, the dyes tested did not include pontacyl or rhodamine-WT. Pyranine was detectable for several months in a field test and was photographed in ultraviolet light to trace drainage profiles. In a series of laboratory and field studies Smart and Laidlaw[11] concluded

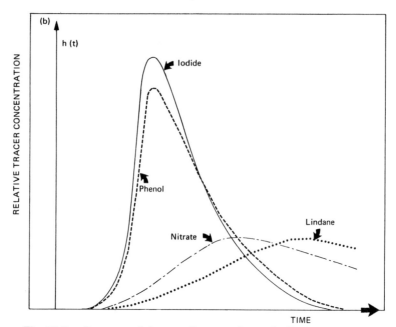

Fig. 10.2.   Passage of three pollutants through alluvial deposits compared with iodide[6]

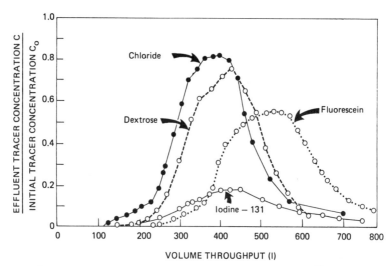

Fig. 10.3.   Passage of several tracers through loam[20]

(©1956, The American Water Works Association; reproduced by permission)

TABLE 10.II.   Dyes Used in Tracer Studies

Dye	Alternative names
Sulpho-rhodamine-B (CI Acid Red 52)	Pontacyl Brilliant Pink-B Lissamine Red-4B Kiton Rhodamine-B Acid Rhodamine-B
Sulpho-rhodamine-G (CI Acid Red 50)	Sulpho-rhodamine-G-extra Amido-rhodamine-G-extra Acid-rhodamine-G Lissamine-rhodamine-GP Kenacid-rhodamin-G
Rhodamine-WT	—
Rhodamine-B (CI Basic Violet 10)	—
Rhodamine-G (CI Basic Red 8)	(Pigment Red 82)
Eosin (CI Acid Red 87)	Tetrabromofluorescein-S Eosin -- (many single or double letter of alphabet)
Pyranine (CI Solvent Green 7)	D and C Green-8
Lissamine-FF (CI Acid Yellow 7)	Brilliant Acid Flavine-10J Brilliant Acid Yellow-8G Brilliant Sulphoflavin
Fluorescein (CI Acid Yellow 73)	Fluorescein Sodium-BP Resorcinol Phthalein Sodium Uranine A Extra Uranin
Amino G Acid	—
Photine-CU (CI Fluorescent Brightener 15)	—
Bromophenol (W) Blue	Tetrabromophenol Blue Albutest

that pyranine, lissamine FF and amino G acid were most resistant to adsorption while fluorescein, rhodamine-WT and sulpho-rhodamine-B had moderately high resistance. The dye eosin was not evaluated in any of these trials but has been found to exhibit low adsorption. Its favourable performance, compared with Br-82, is illustrated in Fig. 10.4 for a path of 40 m in glacial river gravels[12]. Another dye which has indicated low adsorption, even in clay, in recent tests[13] is bromophenol blue.

Fluorimeters are capable of detection in the range 1 to 10^{-4} mg/l and special techniques are available for greater sensitivity. White[14] optimised the design of a fluorimeter optical system to obtain sensitivity in the 10^{-3} to 10^{-6} mg/l range, and similar levels were reported by Imasaka et al[15], using a xenon lamp or various lasers. Advanced spectrophotometers may be used for the detection of two or three dyes in the same sample. Sub-aqua fluorimeters have been developed for continuous detection in remote locations.

Rhodamine-WT has been in widespread use in the USA and Canada and to date

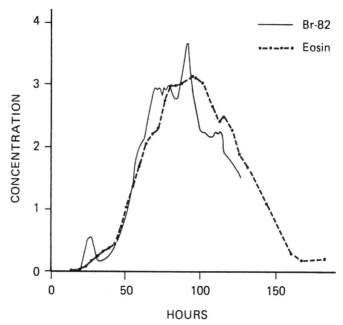

Fig. 10.4.   Eosin compared with Br-82 after passage through glacial river gravels (40 m) [12]

TABLE 10.III.   **Halide Radiotracers Suitable for Groundwater Investigations**

Radionuclide (stable product)	Half-life ($T_{1/2}$)	Use
I-132 (Xe-132)	2.3 h	Short-term connection tests. I-132 may be repeatedly generated in mCi quantities from Te-132 generator ($T_{1/2}$ 78 h). Excellent *in situ* detection.
Br-82 (Kr-82)	35.4 h	Studies lasting up to about 10d. Cheap in curie quantities. Systems over $10^8 m^3$ may be investigated. Excellent *in situ* detection.
I-131 (Xe-131)	8.0 d	Studies lasting up to about 6 weeks. Expensive in curie quantities. Fair *in situ* detection.
I-125 (Te-125)	60.2 d	Studies lasting to about 1 year. Available in pre-packed quantities of 1 to 30 mCi. *In situ* detection by flow-through plastic scintillation head (X-ray emitter)
Cl-36 (Ar-36)	3×10^5 y	Pilot scale studies. Recovery and re-use possible. Available in vials of 0.025-0.25 mCi. *In situ* detection by Geiger or flow-through plastic scintillation counter (Cerenkov counting possible)

Notes: One curie (Ci) = 3.7×10^{10} Bq (37 G Bq)
One becquerel (Bq) = 2.7×10^{-11} Ci = 27 p Ci

the only problem appears to be that residues from the degradation of rhodamine dyes can cause an astringent taste in chlorinated drinking water (Wright and Collings[16]). For groundwater studies in the USA with rhodamine-WT it is understood that application to the Geological Survey Headquarters is necessary, and if assessments predict a concentration greater than 10^{-2} mg/l at any water intake, the use of dye is not approved. Fluorescent dyes should be handled with great care by the user, who should wear protective clothing, and their use should be assessed on a benefit against risk philosophy. The fluorescein dyes have proved non-mutagenic in bacterial systems and are in general use in the UK. The rhodamine dyes were used in the UK during the 1970s but there are now considerable reservations about using them in any system used for, or which may lead to, potable supplies. Studies on rhodamine-B, WT and 6G have shown such dyes to be mutagenic in bacterial systems and in mammalian tissue culture[17]. It has also been shown that, under the conditions found in many natural waters, they can react with nitrite to produce a high yield of diethyl nitrosamine[18].

MANUFACTURED RADIONUCLIDES

The first radiotracers to consider for groundwater investigations are the halide ions; the possibilities, limited by availability, price and half-life, are shown in Table 10.III.

The use of iodide may be limited by its tendency to be adsorbed on organic matter so that results obtained in areas of unknown strata should be treated with caution. In pilot-scale tests at Grenoble, reported by Molinari et al[19], it was shown that I-131 and stable iodide behaved satisfactorily in comparison with tritium (Fig. 10.1(a)) over a 13 m path-length of a laboratory aquifer made with alluvial material and operated under saturated conditions. Kaufman and Orlob[20] stressed the importance of incorporating sufficient non-active form of tracer as a carrier (Fig. 10.5). If, as their data suggest, the concentration of carrier needs to be in the mg/l range then the carrier itself could be detected, as previously described, using an ion-selective electrode, making the need for the radionuclide questionable. However I-131 has the great advantage of being detectable in strata through which a borehole exists, as illustrated in Fig. 10.6. The crystal detector receives gamma-rays from a sphere, the radius of which depends on the energy of the rays. For a tracer uniformly distributed in the surrounding material, spherical volume shells beyond the 'infinite' radius will not contribute to the output of the detector, because of the shielding effect of the material. Experimental tests at the WRC indicated an infinite radius for Br-82 of 54 cm in water alone and 34 cm in sand saturated with water. Detection of the higher energy emitters might be more efficient, and more representative of the average tracer content in the bulk material, but if scans through the aquifer are made, then greater resolution of the tracer distribution would be obtained at lower energies. This concept of detection geometry and shielding is also important when scans are conducted, because variations in detector output may be due to shielding changes (e.g. due to changes in the minerals present or porosity of the strata), although the tracer content in the groundwater is constant. To compare the relative readings of the detection system in one position with other positions, samples of the water (or cores) should be taken at known readings, and counted under conditions of fixed geometry either at the laboratory, or using the same detection system fixed in a calibration assembly.

Radionuclides that may also be applied in anionic form are S-35 (as sulphate), Co-56, Co-58 or Co-60 (as cobalticyanide). S-35 ($T_{1/2}$ 87 d) is relatively cheap, but emits low-energy beta rays and must therefore be assayed by liquid scintillation counting. Co-56 ($T_{1/2}$ 77 d) is expensive, even at millicurie quantities, but is one of the most prolific gamma-ray emitters known and is thus highly suited to *in situ* detection. Co-58 ($T_{1/2}$ 71 d) is cheaper than Co-56 but less readily detectable. Co-60 ($T_{1/2}$5.3 y) is cheap at curie quantities and readily detectable *in situ*. Sternau *et al*[21] have reported that potassium cobalticyanide is not absorbed to any appreciable extent in formations containing significant amounts of clay or in limestone, but Baetsle and Souffriau[22] found that both this compound and I-131 (as iodide) travelled at a velocity 5 to 10 per cent lower than that of water. Cr-51 ($T_{1/2}$ 28 d) has been used (complexed with EDTA) but is a poor emitter of gamma rays. Most cations suffer ion-exchange delays but may be suitable where background carrier levels of the element are high, or where fissure flow is dominant. Some possible cationic tracers are listed in Table 10.IV.

TABLE 10.IV.   Cationic Radiotracers of Possible Use in Groundwater Investigations

Radionuclide	Half-life ($T_{1/2}$)	Use
K-42	12.3 h	Short-term connection tests. *In situ* detection. Cheap in curie quantities but considerable decay losses during transport.
Na-24	15.0 h	(As above)
Rb-86	18.7 d	Studies lasting up to about 3 months if adsorption problems not serious. Cheap in curie quantities. *In situ* detection.
Cs-134	2.06 y	May be useful for long half-life but adsorption probability limits period of study Cheap in curie quantities. *In situ* detection.
Na-22	2.6 y	(As above) Available in millicurie quantities

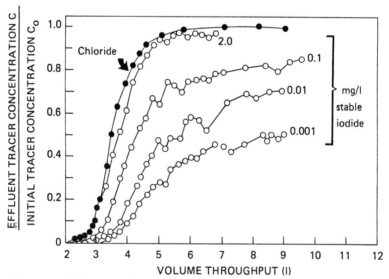

Fig. 10.5.   **Influence of stable iodide on the passage of I-131 through loam**[20]

(©1956, The American Water Works Association; reproduced by permission)

Radionuclides found unsuitable as water tracers, because of facile adsorption on solid surfaces, may be applied to indicate the direction of groundwater flow away from a borehole by location of the radial surface where the isotope has lodged. Suitable isotopes (for labelling solids), with data on their main radiation energies and costs, have been listed by White[23]; this publication also includes data for many of the aqueous-phase tracers considered above. The gamma-ray energy may be a criterion of tracer choice, because if it is probable that the tracer will adsorb within a few centimetres of the borehole wall, a low-energy emitter will be suitable, but a high-energy emitter would be necessary for reasonable detection over some distance, as discussed above (see Fig. 10.6).

To locate the direction in which the tracer has been transported an asymmetrical detection probe may be used. The crystal/photomultiplier assembly is placed on one side of the probe, with lead shielding to provide attenuation in other directions. The techniques have been described by Drost et al[24], who found that Au-198 ($T_{1/2}$ 65 h) was suitable in most cases because of its good 'fixability'. The advantage of this technique is that only small quantities of tracer are necessary. At shallow depth a torsion-free rod may be used to support the probe, to allow direct read-out of direction, but at greater depths an electronic compass in the probe will be necessary. Similar methods have been described by Fried[25] and by Halevy et al[26] in their review of borehole dilution techniques.

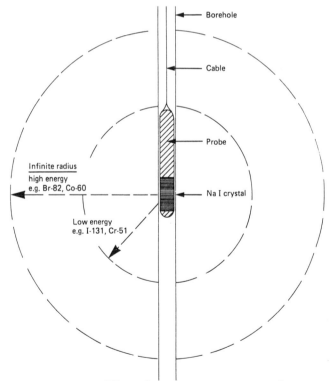

Borehole

Cable

Probe

Infinite radius
high energy
e.g. Br-82, Co-60

Na I crystal

Low energy
e.g. I-131, Cr-51

Fig. 10.6.   Effect of gamma-ray energy on the 'infinite radius'

The disposal of effluents containing radioactive waste to the ground, as practised at Hanford and Oak Ridge in the USA, and Chalk River in Canada, has provided a wealth of information on the relative behaviour, in various strata, of many radioelements. In particular Ru-106 ($T_{1/2}$ 1 y) has been shown to be worthy of consideration as a water tracer since it is difficult to contain in natural strata when released in the presence of nitric acid. This radionuclide is a waste product of nuclear reprocessing so could be available in quantity, but Ru-103 ($T_{1/2}$ 40 d), which

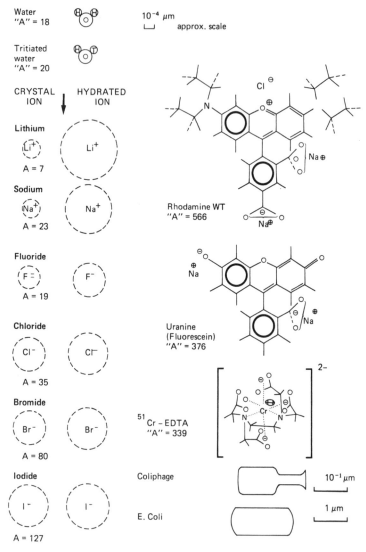

Fig. 10.7.   Comparison of the structure, mass and approximate scale of various tracers with the water molecule

is very readily detectable *in situ*, and cheap at millicurie levels, is also available as a stock item as the chloride or nitrosyl complex. At Chalk River, in 1952, about 5000 m^3 of water containing about 10000 curies of mixed fission products were piped into trenches in a sand dune formation. The rate of percolation of Cs-137 and Sr-90 was so slow that the plumes are still the subject of study decades later.

BIOLOGICAL TRACERS

Biological tracers may be suitable for applications where groundwater flow is predominantly by way of fissures, or the porosity is such that they will not be filtered out. They are massive tracers compared with ions (Fig. 10.7) and each organism is surrounded by a membrane with specific physical and chemical properties relating to the life or survival of the organism. The range of tracers includes bacteria, viruses, phages and spores. Their use, in concept, is attractive since it may be possible to isolate a single organism from a large volume of groundwater, yielding a dilution sensitivity which may exceed that possible with radionuclides. The selection of the organism will depend on the micro-organisms that occur naturally, or as the result of pollution, in the system under investigation.

Wherever waters have been polluted by sewage, the direction of flow can be inferred by the enumeration of micro-organisms, including coliform bacteria, which can contaminate wells a considerable distance from the source. In cases where the source of such pollution must be identified, a tracer organism such as *Serratia marcescens* may be used. Pike *et al*[27] used this tracer to identify individual sources in pollution studies of coastal waters. *Serratia* produces red, pigmented colonies which are readily identifiable and a bacterial strain was selected which has resistance to certain antibiotics, which were then applied to reduce the growth of other micro-organisms during incubation. It is possible to grow 10^{14} *Serratia* cells per day to a concentration of about 10^{13} per litre. Bacterial tracers need to be used with care, and while the risks to health are usually low, they should not be ignored. For example, *Serratia* has often been used for demonstrations in colleges but has been implicated in cases of septicaemia by Dobson[28].

Wimpenny *et al*[29] have pointed out that the specificity of a bacteriophage for its host means that different phages can be used as tracers simultaneously, to identify possible sources without any health hazard, as the organism is completely inert in the absence of its host. They compared *Serratia marcescens* with a lambda-like phage of *E. coli*, and two yeasts, for tracer work in the R. Taff, and found the phage to be the most suitable. This phage is produced at concentrations of 10^{16} plaque-forming units per litre and visible plaques are incubated in about 5 h, so that rapid appraisal of dispersion in a sampling programme is possible. As bacteriophages have a covering which makes them insensitive to chloroform, the latter may be used to eliminate more sensitive natural populations of micro-organisms in the samples.

Gerba *et al*[30] have reviewed the survival of wastewater bacteria and viruses in soil. They found that the survival period of bacteria increases with decreasing temperature and decreases with acidity of the soil. They may survive for several months (even multiply if organic matter is present) but the factor most difficult to predict is the antibiotic activity of other soil microfauna. In one case, coliforms in sewage pumped underground were isolated from observation wells up to 8 km away, for 3 months after they were introduced. The adsorption of bacteria and viruses was greater the higher the cation concentration, and the percolation of viruses through soil was no more reliable than that of bacteria, although the antibiotic effect of other microfauna was practically absent. In the range of pH values of most natural waters, enteroviruses retain a net negative charge.

One of the problems of using *Serratia marcescens* is that it must be cultured at the time of use, since storage is difficult for more than a day or two. However, the spores of another coloured organism (*B. globigii* or *B. subtilis* var *niger*) can be stored in a refrigerator for long periods, so may be used at short notice, when required. It is a coloured variant of *B. subtilis* and exists in large numbers in hay, straw and soil. Another possibility is *B. stearothermophilus* which exists on grass, and grows in piles of grass cuttings causing heat to be generated. It is used in some hospitals to test the efficiency of sterilisation equipment, such as autoclaves.

One of the simplest detection systems for tracer studies consists of a plankton net and a microscope. A suspension of dyed clubmoss *(Lycopodium)* spores may be used as the tracer. These have a diameter of about 30 microns and are only slightly denser than water. The use of these spores has been described by Smith and Atkinson[31] (in cavernous and fissured limestone) and by Gardner and Gray[32] (in karst regions).

Keswick *et al*[33] have reviewed the use of bacteria, spores, animal viruses, bacteriophages and yeasts (which in one of the studies moved through the aquifer faster than bromide or iodide). They concluded that bacterial viruses were most suited as groundwater tracers because of their small size, ease of assay and lack of pathogenicity. Kinnunen[34] found that practical dilutions in rivers of between 10^{-9} and 10^{-11} were possible with phage tracers, with the advantage that different phages could be used simultaneously in the same system (T7, F46, F52). However, phages (T7, F137) were lost by adsorption, in sand, in an artifical groundwater recharge plant. Survival of living cells depends, to some extent, on their ability to move towards, or stop at, sites presenting favourable nutrients, temperatures, surfaces etc. Blakemore[35] discovered in 1975 that some bacteria have lines of iron-containing cells, making them capable of magnetic-field detection and it was suggested that the purpose may be to enable them to 'swim' downwards where the supply of nutrients might be higher. Further studies were made by Frankel *et al*[36]. These considerations suggest that bacteria cannot always be regarded as impartial tracer units in the same way as lifeless tracers, particularly in groundwater where water movements may be too slow for turbulent action to carry the organisms along.

QUANTITY OF TRACER TO INJECT

When the questions listed in Table 10.I have been answered, the investigator will have an idea of which types of tracer it is possible to use, and an estimate of minimum time-of-travel possible (t_{min}) and the minimum dilution volume *en route* (V_{min}). In order to estimate the quantity of tracer to use for the first experiments, some assumptions must be made, working backwards from the proposed detection station, to the point at which the tracer is to be introduced.

The first step is to assess the background concentrations of tracer (e.g. in samples collected at the detection station). If the evidence is that background concentrations are reasonably constant then less tracer will have to be injected than if variations occur to such an extent that they might be confused with a tracer flow-through curve. As an example, assume that the limit of detection of the assay equipment is C_{lim} and the estimated background concentration is C_{back}. A decision must be taken on the concentration required at the detection station, C_{det}, to achieve significant results. A first estimate would be provided by the criterion:

$$C_{det} \geqslant 10 \times C_{back} - \text{where } C_{back} > C_{lim}$$

This would allow the tracer to be clearly identified relative to the background, even if the latter varied more than expected. The second criterion is that C_{det} must be below the maximum permissible concentration, C_{max}, as determined by the uses to which the water is put:

$$C_{det} < C_{max}$$

In most cases C_{back} will be much greater than C_{lim} and less than one-tenth part of C_{max} so the first criterion can be used. For *in situ* detection of radionuclides counting times and shielding effects will be important[23].

The second step is to decide the period for which C_{det} must be maintained for the tracer to be detected. If it is only possible to sample at intervals of 6 hours then it would be prudent to ensure that C_{det} existed, at the detection station, for at least 12 hours. Let this period be T_{det}. Then if the flow of water at, or past, the station is Q_{det} the minimum quantity of tracer that will be required will be M where:

$$M = C_{det} \times Q_{det} \times T_{det}$$

The period T_{det} can be ensured, in some cases, by injecting the tracer for this period of time. In other cases, where a gulp injection is used, evidence will be available that dispersion effects will ensure that the tracer does not come through in a shorter period. T_{det} may be much shorter when continuous detection and recording is possible.

The third step is to estimate the effects of t_{min} and V_{min}, using assumptions of what exists between the injection and detection points. In some cases it may be necessary to set both at zero, while in others V_{min} may be so great compared to the product $Q_{det} \cdot T_{det}$ that the quantity of tracer must be multiplied by a huge factor. (For a perfectly mixed volume V_x into which a quantity of tracer M_x is injected the outlet concentration will initially be $\dfrac{M_x}{V_x}$). The effect of t_{min} will be losses by physical decay in the case of radionuclides and by various other processes for the other types of tracer (adsorption, absorption etc.) The factor to estimate the effect of t_{min} and V_{min} is best expressed as an order of magnitude e.g. 10^n where n is the number of orders by which it is estimated that the tracer concentration will be less than the desired value for C_{det}. The quantity of tracer to use for the first experiment, M_i, will therefore be given by:

$$M_i = C_{det} \cdot Q_{det} \cdot T_{det}\, 10^{n_I}$$

If for example $C_{det} = 1$ mg/l, $Q_{det} = 0.1$ m^3/s, $T_{det} = 10$ hours and $n_I = 2$, then $M_i = 1 \times 100 \times 10 \times 3600 \times 10^2 = 36 \times 10^7$ mg = 360 kg.

3. PASSIVE STUDIES USING EXISTING TRACERS

The various elements, and substances, which exist in the hydrological cycle, from which the movement, and residence times, of groundwater can be deduced, may be grouped into three main classes as follows:

(1) nuclear bomb fallout, i.e. radionuclides with known injection profiles in time;
(2) natural radionuclides, of primordial origin or produced by cosmic rays;
(3) stable isotopes.

These classes and some of the detection techniques are discussed in the three sections below. Some chemicals in the environment may also be used for dating water, in a similar way to tritium dating e.g. 'Freon 11' (Thompson and Hayes[37]).

RADIONUCLIDES FROM BOMB-TESTING

The fallout from the testing of thermonuclear weapons in the 1950s and 1960s can still be traced in some groundwater samples. The Partial Test-ban Treaty meant that the cumulative deposition of the longer lived radionuclides, such as Cs-137 and Sr-90, reached equilibrium values in the late 1960s and has since been steadily decreasing. There have been further tests in recent years, carried out by the Chinese in the N. Hemisphere and the French in the S. Hemisphere. Recent fallout in the UK has mainly been that caused by the Chinese tests.

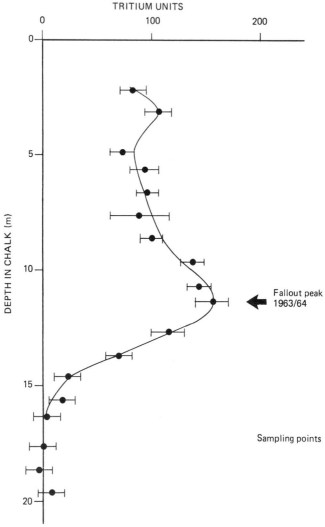

Fig. 10.8.   Tritium profile through a borehole in the Chalk aquifer of eastern England due to nuclear bomb fallout

The history of the deposition of radionuclides washed out of the atmosphere may be obtained from core samples taken from a range of sites including the polar ice caps. In favourable local circumstances groundwater and sediments can be dated. The radionuclides consist of fission products such as Cs-137, Sr-90 and 89, Zr/Nb-95, Ce-144, Ru-103 and 106, Sb-125 and activation products of bomb materials such as Pu-239, Mn-54 and Co-57, 58 and 60 but the latter are mostly at much lower concentrations. Tritium (H-3) is produced as a result of both processes, and is also a product of the bomb thermonuclear fusion process. Several of these radionuclides may provide tracer studies for specialised purposes but the two of most general use are probably Cs-137 for dating sediments and H-3 for dating water[38].

Tritium

Tritium exists in the environment predominantly as water, where one of the hydrogen atoms of the water molecule has been replaced by a tritium atom (H-3). The half-life of tritium, 12.3 years, is convenient for recent dating purposes, because it can be deduced that the age of water, which has a very low content of tritium, will be greater than a certain limit (i.e. about 50 years, but the limit will depend on the sensitivity of the assay method). When the concentrations of tritium from a series of samples from a borehole (Fig. 10.8) can be correlated with the variation of tritium in rainfall year by year, following the bomb-test programme (Fig. 10.9), then quite accurate dating and residence period information can be obtained. The results illustrated in Fig. 10.8 indicate that the rainfall in 1963/64, when tritium levels were at a peak has, at the time of sampling in 1982, percolated down through the unsaturated zone (chalk aquifer) to a depth of 11.5 m. Thus the average rate of percolation of rainfall at this site was about 0.6 m/yr.

For very low level assay of tritiated water electrolysis is used, as a pre-concentration procedure, prior to counting the beta rays emitted by tritium. It is possible, using long counting periods, to determine concentrations of tritium as low as about 10 TU without electrolysis, but after distillation in most cases (one TU is equivalent to 0.12 Bq/l or 3.26 pCi/l). Samples should be sealed in glass containers as soon as possible after sampling.

It was reported[39] several years ago that the period left for the determination of accurate date profiles using fall-out tritium was limited. The reason is illustrated by Fig. 10.9. The inventories of tritium in the environment from bomb-testing and natural processes, with their respective bands of uncertainty are shown, with the predicted quantities arising from nuclear power stations[40]. These indicate that concentrations of bomb tritium are now approaching natural levels, and that direct subterranean releases of waste tritium, e.g. to landfills, might interfere with profiles at particular sites. However the local correlation of tritium levels enables groundwater dispersion to be determined, and the enchanced levels in some rivers have been used to measure residence times of groundwater. A recent application was described by Hadzisehovic et al[41] relating to 'Ranney' wells in Yugoslavia. The residence times were established and the percentage contribution of river water to the wells calculated.

Tritium is used for a range of industrial purposes (luminous paint, warning signs, etc) and is a common radionuclide in both gaseous and liquid effluents from nuclear reactors. Speculative sampling may therefore, on occasions, reveal a transient concentration in the hundreds of thousands of TU range which might be worth following for hydrological information. Tritium released to the atmosphere as gas HT slowly transforms to tritiated water (HTO) over a period of several years[42].

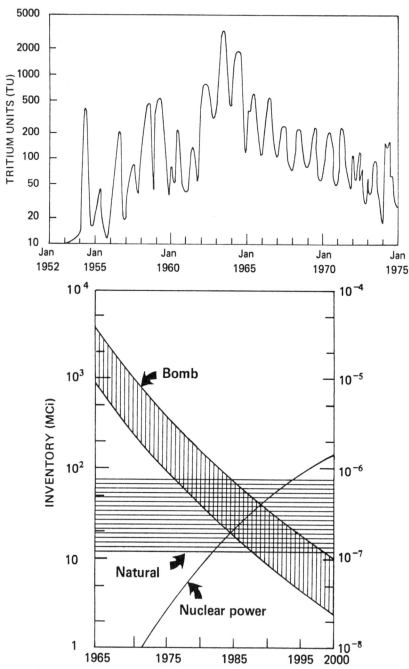

Fig. 10.9.   Tritium data: (*upper*) concentration in UK rainfall[54]
(*lower*) inventory in waters in the N. Hemisphere[40].

Tritium has always been a natural constitutent of rain, at a level of up to about 10 TU in mid-latitudes. Therefore, even if there had been no atmospheric bomb testing it would be possible to date some recent precipitation after the electrolytic enrichment of samples. Various assay techniques have been reviewed and compared elsewhere[43] and some novel methods were outlined at a recent international symposium[44]. The bomb testing conducted in the N. Hemisphere, by China, in the late 1970s has given rise to new peaks in the recent fallout pattern as shown in Fig. 10.10 (Cambray et al[45]).

NATURAL RADIONUCLIDES

Our environment and our bodies have always been permeated by naturally occurring radionuclides of primordial origin (K-40, U, Th, etc) or resulting from cosmic-ray bombardment (C-14, H-3, etc). Whereas the lighter species generally decay directly to a stable element, uranium and thorium decay by successive transformations via a series of "daughters". Since naturally occurring radionuclides, and individual daughters, can be identified by their characteristic type of radiation and energy it is possible to use them as environmental tracers, both of past events, and, in favourable circumstances, of current events. The decay products of uranium, which is widely distributed in the earth's crust, may be particularly useful and the decay series of U-238 to U-234 is shown in Table 10.V.

TABLE 10.V.   Decay Series of U-238 to U-234

Radionuclide	Half-life	Main radiation	Energy (MeV)
Uranium-238 ↓	$4.49.10^9$ y	α	4.19 (100%)
Thorium-234 ↓	24.1 d	β	0.10 (~35%) 0.19 (~65%)
Protoactinium-234 m ↓	1.18 m	β	1.50 (~10%) 2.31 (~90%)
Protoactinium-234 ↓	6.66 h	β	1.13
Uranium-234	$2.48.10^5$ y	α	4.72 (~30%) 4.77 (~70%)

Since U-234 is a decay product of U-238, with a much shorter half-life, it will exist in equilibrium with U-238 and, in an isolated system (inside "dry" rock), the activity ratio should be the same everywhere and equal to unity.

In a system which is not isolated the activity ratio can be changed in a number of ways. When an atom of U-238 decays there is mutual recoil between the alpha particle and the Th-234 ion. The recoil of the ions results in damage to the crystal lattice and the Th-234 atoms may be lodged in unstable lattice sites from which they may be preferentially leached in comparison with the leaching of parent U-238 atoms. The larger the surface area available for leaching the greater will be the U-234/U-238 ratio and the groundwater moving through fine-grain strata may show an activity ratio greater then 2, and values greater than 10 have been reported. The possibility therefore exists of identifying certain waters and their movements by this activity ratio[46,47]. The same philosophy may be applied to determining the effective depth of fissuring or weathering, and to tracing the origin and/or movement of sediment particles, which will mostly have a ratio of less than unity.

The method has been applied to investigate aquifers in many regions of the world. Details and case histories are presented in the extensive review by Osmond and Cowart[48]. Activity ratios of 1.8 were typical of shallow water in the Galilee-Jordan area, whereas Florida karstic terrain samples gave 0.85. The shallow groundwaters around the great lakes of N. America give 1.25. Deep groundwaters may have high ratios and low U concentrations and residence times may be estimated from the U-234 decay. In southern Nevada uranium isotope data indicated a source of recharge at a distance of 120 km. In other regions the contributions of tributaries and springs to mixed waters have been deduced.

One of the isotopes produced in the uranium decay series is Radon-222 which exists almost everywhere in the earth's crust and dissolves in groundwaters. Its half-life, of 3.8 days, makes it potentially useful for tracing where groundwater springs enter surface waters and for mixing studies in impounded waters[38]. Radon dissolved in groundwater can be assayed over a period of several days from the time of sampling. If some radium is also dissolved in the water then there will be an extra component to the "unsupported" radon, and this can be determined by regeneration to an equilibrium level several days after the radon has been released from the sample by aeration. Clearly it is important to use impermeable containers for samples, e.g. glass, to fill them completely, and to provide them with hermetically sealing caps. If the radon concentrations are high enough such sampling may not be essential because *in situ* detection of the radon decay products may be possible.

The cosmic-ray bombardment of the atmosphere continuously generates about 20 radionuclides as activation products of the gases and fine particulate matter

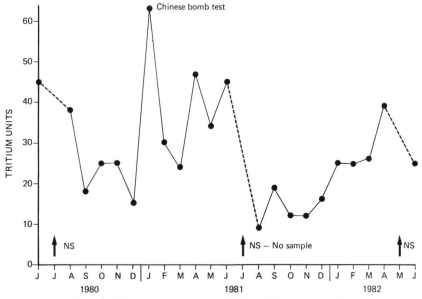

Fig. 10.10.   Tritium levels in rain at Milford Haven showing recent variations[45]

carried aloft. Complete absence of the longer-lived products in groundwater samples may indicate their isolation from infiltration for periods greater than that assessed by the particular half-lives. Young *et al*[49] collected large volumes of rain on plastic sheets. The chlorine isotopes were precipitated as silver chloride and the filtrate evaporated as preparatory steps to multichannel gamma-ray spectrometry. Rainfall at rates below 2 mm/h was found to be an order of magnitude more effective at scavenging radionuclides than heavier rain at rates above about 8 mm/h. Aircraft were used to determine the Na-24 radioactivity variation with altitude and an increase of three orders of magnitude was found between ground level and 20 000 m.

The detection of Ar-39 might be a most valuable method of dating water. Toosli and Oeschger[50] pointed out that whereas the ages of glacial cores, derived from Ar-39, had confirmed the technique, it was evident that large discrepancies (orders of magnitude in some cases) existed between Ar-39 ages for some groundwaters compared with ages derived by C-14 techniques, as illustrated in Table 10.VI. In some of these cases positive tritium concentrations tend to support the Ar-39 ages but in other cases the discrepancies cannot be explained. (Carbon exchange reactions may cause dilution of the C-14 which results in additional apparent decay and therefore age).

TABLE 10.VI.   Apparent Ages of Groundwater Derived from C-14 and Ar-39 Measurements[50]

C-14	Ar-39	C-14	Ar-39
37 900	600 ± 80	4 080 ± 110	490 ± 65
21 200	685 ± 100	3 470	275 ± 35
17 400	325 ± 35	1 810	85 ± 25
8 120	410 ± 40	870	<30
6 150 ± 150	390 ± 50	820	<55
5 715 ± 135	45 ± 35		

STABLE ISOTOPES

There are three isotopes of hydrogen, one of which is unstable (tritium) and seven isotopes of oxygen, four of which are unstable. The natural percentages of the three main species in standard mean ocean water (SMOW) are given below:

(H-1)$_2$ (O-16)	99.73 per cent 'Ordinary' water, H_2O
(H-1)$_2$ (O-18)	0.199 per cent
(H-1) (H-2) (O-16)	0.031 per cent (Deuterated water)

When water evaporates the vapour contains less O-18 and H-2 than the mean levels in the liquid phase, by a few parts per thousand, and a few tens of parts per thousand respectively. In the reverse process the heavier isotopes condense first and this means that the first rainfall, as damp air moves over land, will show the least deficit, and the deficit will increase as the lighter fractions condense i.e. usually much further inland. The deficits of the two isotopes will therefore be proportional to each other and waters may be characterised by the deficits of O-18 and deuterium. The deuterium contours across Germany [12] during 1980 are shown in Fig. 10.11. The worldwide distribution of mean O-18 deficits in precipitation is given in Fig. 10.12[51]. The ratios will be affected by the history of the water vapour and its cycles of condensation and evaporation. There will be altitude, seasonal and latitude effects, and possibly effects due to heating or freezing in the ground, but correlation of the values from one point to another will be a powerful tool in deducing the general trend of groundwater movements or to prove whether aquifers may or may not be connected. The H-2 and O-18 concentrations are determined by mass spectrometry, which tends to be expensive. The assay techniques will not be given here as they have been described fully in the references given above and at two international IAEA conferences during the 1970s[52,53], where numerous case histories of groundwater tracer studies were also given.

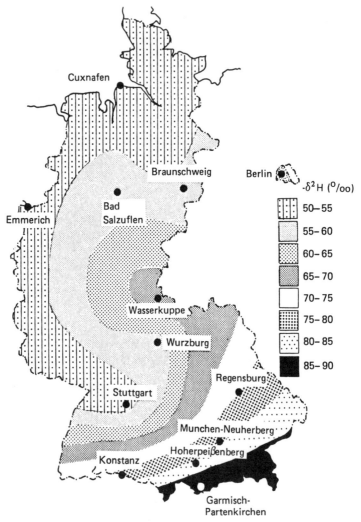

Fig. 10.11.   Variation of deuterium deficits across Germany in 1980[12]

Other stable isotopes can be used in a similar way, where a variation in concentrations has been caused—for example, there are two stable isotopes of carbon and the C-13 concentrations may be used, possibly to amplify, or correct, radioactive C-14 dating. Examples of such data, with corresponding deuterium and O-18 values, have been given by Lloyd[54]. Stable isotope ratios may be particularly valuable in tracking the fate of some pollutants. For various systems and situations it is possible to envisage that the stable isotopes of lithium, boron, nitrogen, magnesium, silicon, sulphur, chlorine, potassium and calcium could be of value.

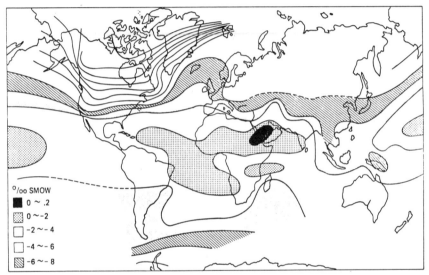

Fig. 10.12.   Global variations of O-18 deficits[51]

4. DISCUSSION AND EXAMPLES OF APPLICATIONS

The alternative strategies that may be used to investigate an aquifer are passive studies—detecting tracers present in the system—or active studies involving the injection of tracers, of which there are four main types. Passive techniques are often based on a single tracer, such as tritium, but there are cases where water movements may be deduced by correlation of the analytical results from a general examination of water samples taken at two locations. Evidence that water flows from one point to another will be stronger when the range of analytical techniques available is wide, so that a chemical and radionuclide 'fingerprint' of a sample can be produced, based on concentrations of ions, natural radioelements such as K-40 and U, Freon, trace elements determined by neutron activation analysis, and general water quality factors.

To investigate many aquifers both active and passive techniques will be necessary, since only the passive techniques can provide data relating to movements over sufficiently long time-scales. Where fissure flow is known to exist the choice of tracer is wide, but otherwise an assessment of the adsorption probability will be necessary. Adsorption losses will depend on the surface area (soil grain size and shape) and nature of the particles. Organic particles and some clays, such as montmorillonite, have high specific surfaces and high cation exchange capacities, whereas grains of quartz and feldspar have low cation exchange capacity. In most minerals the cation exchange capacity dominates relative to that for anions, one notable exception being kaolinite. In many systems therefore anions will be the first choice except where the water molecule itself incorporates the tracer (deuterium, tritium or O-18).

When deuterated water or tritiated water is used, one end of the water molecule is twice (DHO) or three times (HTO) its normal mass, respectively, and the modes of vibration will be more perturbed than when the central atom is heavier than normal (H_2O-18). Tritiated water in particular is less likely to represent the behaviour of normal water molecules in situations where evaporative losses are high, where near-freezing temperatures exist or where dispersion takes place by the movement of monomolecular layers of water. Kaufman and Orlob[20] compared the passage of tritium with chloride in sandy loam columns and their results (Fig. 10.13) serve as a caution in regarding any tracer as the optimum indicator of the transport of various substances. When differences are detected between tracers, the one which lags is usually considered to be suspect, not the leading tracer, and it might be considered prudent, whenever clay is present or suspected, to use at least two of the least-sorbable tracers available.

Relative tracer lag effects were also found in recent studies, at WRC, of the movement of tritiated water, anions and cations through solid core samples of porous (triassic) sandstone. The results were similar for five cores tested and for one set are shown in Fig. 10.14, where the considerable delay on the cations, including lithium, is indicated. Similar differences in residence time between

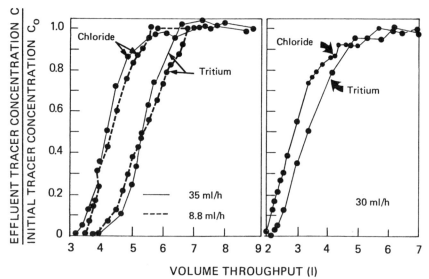

Fig. 10.13.   Passage of chloride and tritium through loam[20]

anions, and between tritiated water and the anions, have been observed at an aquifer recharge site as the recharge water breaks through to an abstraction borehole.

It is not surprising, on consideration of Fig. 10.7, that tritiated water molecules may be able to diffuse into micropores (also possibly into the crystal lattice) where other tracers cannot penetrate, or where they may by-pass the micro-pores because of the repulsion effects caused by static charges on the mineral surfaces. Biological tracers will be trapped more readily than other tracer types, and the potential losses of dyes must always be evaluated. Dye molecules may be more than two orders of magnitude smaller than phage particles but they are relatively massive compared with the simple chemical ions. Percolation rates may depend on environmental conditions, such as periods of frost, and results should give such conditions as well as the soil or matrix type.

It is important to emphasise that when passive studies are conducted, the form of the radionuclide should be established. In particular, bomb-fallout may retain its physical form, of sub-micron particulate matter, resulting from the condensation of vaporised bomb materials and other substances, including soil, in the vicinity of the detonation. However, the movement of the same radionuclide in ionic form may be entirely different. It is also important that whereas the appearance in groundwater of certain radionuclides may indicate that recent recharge has taken place, the converse may not be true because the non-appearance of a given isotope may be caused by adsorption or precipitation *en route* to the sampling point.

The International Atomic Energy Agency (IAEA) convenes a conference every four years or so on the subject of isotope hydrology. At the meeting held in 1978[53] it was clear that passive methods were being exploited in many parts of the world. The proceedings of that conference, and of earlier ones[52,55-57], are mostly compilations of case histories relating to regional investigations, the origin of groundwater, recharge studies, aquifer characteristics and the mining or civil engineering aspects of groundwater hydrology. Such examples, which are often outlines of long investigations, will not be summarised further here. Some examples of actual investigations have already been mentioned and a few case histories of tracer use are presented below to illustrate how some problems have been dealt with, and the quantities of tracer that have been released. Site specific factors, and the resources available to the investigator, will tend to dominate the choice of tracer.

AMENITY LAKE WITH SEWAGE WORKS NEARBY

In this application fluorescent dyes were used and one proved unsatisfactory. The effluent from the works percolated into the ground, which consisted of natural sand beds, and verification was required that the lake, used for potable supplies and swimming, etc., could not be contaminated. Aulenbach *et al*[58] reported that a preliminary study, using rhodamine-B, was unsuccessful because the dye could not even be recovered after passage through a few metres of the ground. However, rhodamine-WT reached the water table, at a depth of about 20 m, and the dye indicated an average percolation rate of 0.7 m/day in the unsaturated zone. The tracer could not be followed in the saturated zone, so a cocktail of rhodamine-WT with 0.1 Ci of tritium was injected direct into this zone. These tracers were not detected in any of the observation boreholes, so the injection was repeated with the same negative result. More observation wells were prepared and another injection made. The two tracers were then located and moved at the same rate, taking 60 days to reach an observation well about 100 m from the works. Sampling nearer the lake continued for 8 months without detection of either of the tracers.

LANDFILL POLLUTION PROBLEM

Pollution of a stream in a field, used by grazing animals, was causing concern, and evidence was required that the source of pollution was a landfill, in fissured sandstone. The landfill had been used for the disposal of industrial wastes for several years. It was considered that the complex nature of the landfill contents and the leachate were such that chemical or biological tracers would be inappropriate for proof of connection between the landfill and the stream. It was decided that a short-lived radiotracer should provide irrefutable evidence. A scintillation detector was placed in the stream, operated from electronics powered by a portable generator. A nominal one millicurie of Br-82 was injected into a pool on the side of the landfill site nearest to the stream. The tracer was first detected, above the background counts caused by natural radiation, four and one-half hours later. The readings increased steadily to a peak about six hours later and then decreased steadily over the following two days. Decay checks on samples taken from the stream confirmed the presence of Br-82 and the groundwater connection was proved.

FLOW PATHS IN A KARST FORMATION

In order to map flow paths, between sink-holes and resurgencies, dyed lycopodium spores were used by Gardner and Gray[32] in limestone regions of West Virginia. This tracer was successful, and acceptable in the locality because the spores are not harmful to water users, biota or industrial processes. For distances up to 8 km, and discharges up to 7 m^3/s, quantities of up to 5 kg of spores were used. Details of the procedure used to prepare the tracer in slurry form were given, and it was found possible to store slurry for more than a year prior to use. Plankton nets were used for sampling, over set periods of time, and the results appear in the form of a histogram of spore counts, from microscopic examination of samples, against time periods. This application demonstrates the advantages of a technique requiring no complex equipment, or specialist assistance. However, the preparatory stages and the sampling and analytical procedures may be rather labour intensive.

POTABLE SUPPLY BOREHOLE CONTAMINATION

A water supply became contaminated with bacteria and information was required on whether the pathway of contamination was directly from a nearby sewer, or from a suspected leakage zone in a stream close to the borehole, into which storm overflows from the sewer were diverted. The extent of the leakage zone, and even its exact location, were unknown so a tracer was required which could be added, over many hours, so that sufficient tracer-rich stream water would soak into the bed to make it detectable in borehole water. Several curies of Br-82 were injected, at constant rate, into the stream over a period of 3 days and nights. The tracer was detected *in situ* and the residence time was three days. The radiotracer dilution between the stream and the borehole was very variable, ranging from less than ten-fold to orders of magnitude. In such cases continuous recording of tracer concentrations is of considerable value. A phage tracer was used to check on the integrity of the sewerage system, and the possibility of direct fissure flow paths between sewers and boreholes.

HYDROLOGY RELATING TO A SPOIL HEAP

To assess the stability of a spoil heap, situated on saturated boulder clay and sandy beds, overlying faulted sandstone, the water flow pattern below the tip was required. Ten litres of a suspension of the type 2 phage of *Aerobacter aeruginosa* 243 (3.10^{14} phage/l) were used by Martin and Thomas[59]. Phage was detected at a number of positions, at distances up to 680 m, at times ranging from 3 days to 9 days after the injection of tracer. The water velocities ranged from 1.5 to 7.5 m/h and the general features of the water movements were established.

ARTIFICIAL RECHARGE EXPERIMENT

To evaluate direct injections of municipal effluents, as a strategy for producing reclaimed water in California, Hoehn and Roberts[60] reported two tests with Br-82 and tritium in a shallow aquifer of alluvial deposits, with a mean grain size of one mm, and containing a few per cent of silt-clay. The tracers were detected at artesian wells 7.6 m and 16.8 m from the injection well, where water was pumped in at a steady rate of 2.5 m^3/h. The results are summarised in Table 10.VII.

TABLE 10.VII. **Determination of Porosity of Aquifers by Direct Injection of Tracers[60]**

Tracer	Pore volume (m^3)	Mean residence time (h)	Average linear velocity (m/h)	Effective porosity (ϕ)
Br-82	47.5	14.1	0.54	0.15
H-3	54	20.7	0.37	0.17
Br-82	104	ca.40	0.42	0.08
H-3	117	ca.45	0.37	0.08

The porosities determined from the tracer studies compared with a value of 0.22 obtained from a core sample. Both tracer recovery curves exhibited lengthy 'tailing' and a two-domain model was applied to fit the observations. The tritium time lag was thought to be partly due to the lower flowrate out of the nearer well during the tritium test (the flow at the other was the same for both tests) but also due to anion repulsion effects by the negatively charged clay particles. Similar effects are illustrated in Figs. 10.13 and 10.14.

INTERWELL FLOW INVESTIGATIONS

The simultaneous application of relatively large quantities of different types of tracer was used in oil fields, to investigate reservoir heterogeneities that would lead to 'channelling' and inefficient use of expensive oil recovery fluids. Wagner[61] described five investigations; two are outlined briefly here to indicate the tracers and quantities selected. To find the interwell connections between ten wells on a 5 hectare site in W. Texas four tracers were injected during the waterflood of the area. Two outer injection wells were each dosed with 6 curies of tritium and two others with nitrate ('10 000 lb' of ammonium nitrate). One of the inner wells was injected with iodide ('1 400 lb' of potassium iodide) and another with ammonium thiocyanate. From the tracer breakthrough curves the effective pore volumes swept were estimated.

At a well site in Wyoming three wells were injected with different tracers to determine preferential flow trends, to delineate flow barriers and to decide if water injected into one formation was being lost to the overlying one. The first well was dosed with 100 Ci of tritium, the second with ethyl alcohol ('12500 gal' containing 50 ppm bactericide as a precaution against biodegradation) and the third with isopropyl alcohol ('12500 gal'). Times-of-travel to adjacent wells ranged from 9 days to 102 days and the preferential flow patterns were established (northeast-southwest direction).

In other tests bromide was used as a tracer but oilfield brines often contain high background concentrations of bromide and iodide so alternatives, such as those mentioned above, are used. Dyes are seldom used when the expected residence time exceeds 5 days because of adsorption problems, and quenching caused by ions in the groundwater.

DISCUSSION OF CASE HISTORIES

These case histories, with the information reviewed earlier, provide some guidance with regard to the selection of tracers for various media and various kinds of test. One aspect which must be kept in mind is that of care in using long-lived tracers, whether radioactive or otherwise, which have any doubt at all attached to them with regard to their safety in the local environment. There is doubt about the safety of some biological tracers, and fluorescent dyes, and the latter may be as long-lived as tritium in the ground. Fluorescent dyes and long-lived radionuclides should not be used in quantity unless preliminary tests give adequate evidence that a system of long residence-time is under study, and only then after checking with interested parties that long-term contamination will not cause problems later. There have been reports of the use of long-lived materials in systems having residence-times of only a few days, even hours in some instances, and such applications are not only unwarranted on environmental protection grounds, they can mean that contamination of the system may prevent further studies. The very short-lived radioisotopes are ideal for preliminary tests as they are completely

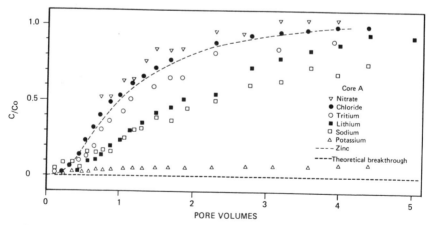

Fig. 10.14. Percolation of tracers through a solid sample of sandstone compared with the theoretical breakthrough curve (- - - -)

self-cleansing within the system. It may be prudent in some situations to carry out several preliminary tests using such tracers, increasing the quantity of tracer in stages. Otherwise, established innocuous substances such as common salt, bromide, iodide, fluoride, etc, should be used prior to the release of other types of tracer. Although rarely used, physical techniques may be of use in favourable circumstances. Heat, sound and air/vapour transport may be considered—for example, to investigate Karst systems when water levels are low or to establish where empty fissures exist. Keys and Brown[62] described the use of temperature logs to determine groundwater movements after artificial recharge from naturally warmed lakes. It is possible to envisage the use of warm water from power stations in a similar way.

5. CONCLUDING REMARKS

Information on groundwater movements may be obtained by detecting tracers already in the environment or by the injection of selected tracer substances, of which there are four types. Chemical, dye or biological tracers can often be used by engineers or scientists without specialist assistance, but this may be necessary for the application of small quantities of radiotracers, if no prior experience of handling radionuclides has been obtained. For short-term connection tests, or preliminary studies in aquifers, the short-lived radiotracers, particularly Br-82, are suitable because their trivial mass and self-cleansing properties leave the system exactly as it was, with no residual tracer to interfere with future studies. The most acceptable tracers to release in the environment are chemical ions such as chloride, bromide and iodide but background variations may restrict their effectiveness. Prediction of the residence time of some elements or chemical compounds in an aquifer may not be possible from the results of studies using water tracers alone (Figs. 10.1, 10.2, 10.3 and 10.14).

Groundwater tracer investigations are seldom straightforward and results may be gathered only with persistence and effort over much longer periods of time than originally envisaged. However, tracer techniques are often considered essential for the assessment of resources, the control of pollution and various other purposes such as civil engineering projects and mining. Data may be of lasting value and the investigation costs, even in protracted cases, will mostly be outweighed by the benefits possible from knowledge about the aquifer. Where it is impossible or impracticable to inject tracers, then the passive techniques outlined will often elucidate the movements of groundwater. In particular, the radionuclides that already exist in the aquifer can provide hydrological data relating to time scales which may vary from weeks to centuries or millenia. Such methods may become important for evaluating regions, or subterranean systems, for the disposal of toxic wastes, where containment over very long periods of time must be guaranteed.

6. REFERENCES

1. Buck, R. P. 1976 *Analyt. Chem.*, 48, 23, Ion selective electrodes.
2. Stetzenbach, K. J. and Thompson, G. M. 1983 *Ground Water*, 21, 36, A new method for simultaneous measurement of $Cl^-, Br^-, NO_3^-, SCN^-$ and I^- at sub-ppm levels in ground water.
3. Fisher, D. W. 1968 *US Geological Survey Water Supply Paper*, 1535-M, Annual variations in chemical composition of atmospheric precipitation, eastern North Carolina and southeastern Virginia.
4. Truesdale, V. W. and Smith, P. J. 1975 *Analyst*, 100, 111, The automatic determination of iodide or iodate in solution by catalytic spectrophotometry, with particular reference to river water.

5. Levi, H. W. and Miekeley, N. 1967 'Studies on ion diffusion in vermiculite' in "Disposal of radioactive wastes into the ground", Proceedings of Symposium, Vienna; International Atomic Energy Agency (IAEA), Vienna.

6. Gaillard, B. *et al* 1976 'Evaluation pratique par traceurs de caractéristiques de transfert de l'eau, vecteur de pollutants, dans la zone saturée des aquifères' in "The development of nuclear-based techniques for the measurement, detection and control of environmental pollutants", Proceedings of Symposium, Vienna: IAEA, Vienna.

7. Schwille, F., Lippok, W. and Weisflog, D. 1967 'Model experiments on fluid flow in the transition zone from unsaturated to saturated soil' in "Disposal of radioactive wastes into the ground", Proceedings of Symposium, IAEA, Vienna.

8. Feuerstein, D. L. and Selleck, R. E. 1963 *J. San. Eng. Div.*, ASCE, 89, SA4, 1, Fluorescent tracers for dispersion measurements.

9. Anon. 1971 "Fluorometry in studies of pollution and movement of fluids". G. K. Turner Associates, Palo Alto, California.

10. Reynolds, E. R. C. 1966 *J. Soil Sci.*, 17, 127, The percolation of rainwater through soil demonstrated by fluorescent dyes.

11. Smart, P. L. and Laidlaw, I. M. S. 1977 *Wat. Res. Res.*, 13, 15, An evaluation of some fluorescent dyes for water tracing.

12. Anon 1982 "Institut für Radiohydrometrie: Jahresbericht 1981", R.296, Gesellschaft für Strahlen- und Umweltforschung mbH, Munich.

13. Brown, L., Rhead, M. M. and Hill, D. 1983 *Wat. Res.*, 18, 1083, The use of bromophenol blue as a tracer in sewage works.

14. White, J. U. 1976 *Analyt. Chem.*, 48, 2089, Sample optics for increased sensitivity in fluorescence spectrophotometers.

15. Imasaka, T. *et al* 1977 *ibid*, 49, 667, Detection limit of fluorescein as determined by fluorometry with an Esculin laser source.

16. Wright, R. R. and Collings, M. R. 1964 *J. AWWA*, 56, 748, Application of fluorescent tracing techniques to hydrologic studies.

17. Nestmann, E. R. *et al* 1979 *Cancer Research*, 39, 4412, Mutagenic activity of rhodamine dyes and their impurities as detected by mutation induction in *Salmonella* and DNA damage in Chinese hamster ovary cells.

18. Abidi, S. L. 1982 *Wat. Res.*, 16, 199, Detection of diethyl nitrosamine in nitrite-rich water following treatment with rhodamine flow tracers.

19. Molinari, J., Rochon, J. and Gaillard, B. 1976 'Étude expérimentale des mécanismes de migration des substances pollutantes miscibles dans la zone saturée des aquifères' in "The development of nuclear-based techniques for the measurement, detection and control of environmental pollutants", Proceedings of Symposium, Vienna; IAEA, Vienna.

20. Kaufman, W. J. and Orlob, G. T. 1956 *J. AWWA*, 48, 559, Measuring groundwater movement with radioactive and chemical tracers.

21. Sternau, R. *et al* 1967 'Use of radioisotope tracers in large-scale recharge studies of groundwater' in "The use of isotopes in hydrology" Proceedings of Symposium, Vienna; IAEA, Vienna.

22. Baetsle, L. H. and Souffriau, J. 1967 'Fundamentals of the dispersion of radio-nuclides in sandy aquifers' in "The use of isotopes in hydrology", *ibid*.

23. White, K. E. 1974 'The use of radioactive tracers to study mixing and residence-time distributions in systems exhibiting three-dimensional dispersion' in "Mixing and centrifugal separation" Proceedings of First European Conference, Cambridge. British Hydromechanics Research Association, Cranfield.

24. Drost, W. *et al* 1958 *Wat. Res. Res.*, 4, 125, Point dilution methods of investigating ground water flow by means of radioisotopes.

25. Fried, Jean J. 1975 "Groundwater pollution: theory, methodology, modelling and practical rules, Development in water science, 4." Elsevier, Amsterdam.

26. Halevy, E. *et al* 1967 'Borehole dilution techniques—a critical review' in "The use of isotopes in hydrology", Proceedings of Symposium, Vienna; IAEA, Vienna.

27. Pike, E. B., Bufton, A. W. J. and Gould, D. J. 1969 *J. appl. Bact.*, 32, 206, The use of *Serratia indica* and *Bacillus subtilis* var. *niger* spores for tracing sewage dispersion in the sea.

28. Dodson, W. H. 1968 *Arch. Intern. Med.*, 121, 145, *Serratia marcescens* septicemia.

29. Wimpenny, J. W. T., Cotton, N. and Statham, M. 1972 *Wat. Res.*, 6, 731, Microbes as tracers of water movement.

30. Gerba, C. P., Wallis, G. and Melnick, J. L. 1975 *J. Irrig. Drain. Div.*, ASCE, 101, IR3, 157, Fate of wastewater bacteria and viruses in soil.

31. Smith, D. I. and Atkinson, T. C. 1974 'Underground flow rates in cavernous and fissured limestones' in "Groundwater pollution in Europe", Proceedings of Conference, Reading, (Ed J. A. Cole) Water Information Center, Port Washington.

32. Gardner, G. D. and Gray, R. E. 1976 *Bull. Assn. Eng. Geol.*, XIII, 177, Tracing subsurface flow in Karst regions using artificially coloured spores.

33. Keswick, B. H. 1982 *Ground Water*, 20, 142, The use of microorganisms as ground-water tracers: A review.

34. Kinnunen, K. 1978 "Tracing water movement by means of *Escherichia coli* bacteriophages" National Board of Waters, Helsinki, Publication 25, Water Research Institute, Finland."

35. Blakemore, R. 1975 *Science*, 190, 377, Magnetotactic bacteria.

36. Frankel, R. B., Blakemore, R. P. and Wolfe, R. S. 1979 *ibid*, 203, 1355, Magnetite in freshwater magnetotactic bacteria.

37. Thompson, G. M. and Hayes, J. M. 1979 *Wat. Res. Res.*, 15, 546, Trichlorofluoromethane in groundwater—a possible tracer and indicator of groundwater age.

38. White, K. E. 1981 *Wat. Pollut. Control*, 80, 498, Hydrological studies possible with radionuclides of bomb-test, primordial and natural origin to complement investigations using manufactured radiotracers.

39. White, K. E. 1977 'Tracer methods for the determination of groundwater residence-time distributions' in "Groundwater quality—measurement, prediction and protection" Paper 11, Proceedings of Conference, Reading; Water Research Centre, Medmenham.

40. Kelly, G. N. *et al* 1975 "The predicted radiation exposure of the population of the European Community resulting from discharges of krypton-85, tritium, carbon-14 and iodine-129 from the nuclear power industry to the year 2000", Document V/2676/75, Commission of the European Communities.

41. Hadzisehovic, M. *et al* 1982 *J. Radioanalyt. Chem.*, 74, 239, Characteristics of the tritium distribution in the Danube basin region in Yugoslavia.

42. Mason, A. S. and Ostlund, H. G. 1979 'Atmospheric H.T. and HTO: Distribution and large-scale circulation' in "Behaviour of tritium in the environment" Proceedings of Symposium, San Francisco; IAEA, Vienna.

43. Anon 1976 "Tritium measurement techniques: recommendations of the National Council on Radiation Protection and Measurements", NCRP Report No. 47, NCRP, Washington.

44. IAEA 1981 "Methods of low-level counting and spectrometry." Proceedings of Symposium, West Berlin; IAEA, Vienna.

45. Cambray, R. S., Playford, K. and Lewis, G. N. J. 1982 "Radioactive fallout in air and rain: results to the end of 1981", UKAEA Harwell, Report AERE-R 10485 HMSO.

46. Borole, D. V. *et al* 1979 'Uranium isotopic investigations and radiocarbon measurements of river-groundwater systems, Sabarmatic basin, Gujarat, India' in "Isotope hydrology", Proceedings of Symposium, Neuherberg; IAEA, Vienna.

47. Barr, G. E. and Carter, J. A. 1979 'Uranium disequilibrium in groundwaters of south eastern New Mexico and implications regarding age-dating of waters', *ibid*.

48. Osmond, J. K. and Cowart, J. B. 1976 *Atomic Energy Review*, 14, 621, The theory and uses of natural uranium isotopic variations in hydrology.

49. Young, J. A. *et al* 1970 'Short-lived cosmic ray-produced radionuclides as tracers of atmospheric processes' in "Radionuclides in the environment, Advances in Chemistry Series 93", American Chemical Society.

50. Loosli, H. H. and Oeschger, H. 1979 'Ar-39, C-14 and Kr-85 measurements in groundwater samples' in "Isotope hydrology", Proceedings of Symposium, Neuherberg; IAEA, Vienna.

51. IAEA 1981 "Stable isotope hydrology. Deuterium and oxygen-18 in the water cycle, Technical Report Series No. 210", IAEA, Vienna. ,

52. IAEA 1975 "Isotope techniques in groundwater hydrology 1974" (2 vols), Proceedings of Symposium, Vienna; IAEA, Vienna.

53. IAEA 1979 "Isotope hydrology", Proceedings of Symposium, Neuherberg; IAEA, Vienna.

54. Lloyd, J. W. 1981 'Environmental isotopes in groundwater' in "Case-studies in groundwater resource evaluation" (Ed. J. W. Lloyd), Clarendon Press, Oxford.

55. IAEA 1963 "Radioisotopes in hydrology", Proceedings of Symposium, Tokyo; IAEA, Vienna.

56. IAEA 1967 "Isotopes in hydrology", Proceedings of Symposium, Vienna; IAEA, Vienna.

57. IAEA 1970 "Isotope hydrology 1970", Proceedings of Symposium, Vienna; IAEA, Vienna.

58. Aulenbach, D. B., Hull, J. H. and Middlesworth, B. C. 1978 *Ground Water*, 16, 149, Use of tracers to confirm ground-water flow.

59. Martin, R. and Thomas, A. 1974 *J. Hydrol.*, 23, 73, An example of the use of bacteriophage as a groundwater tracer.

60. Hoehn, E. and Roberts, P. V. 1982 *Ground Water*, 20, 457, Advection-dispersion interpretation of tracer observations in an aquifer,

61. Wagner, O. R. 1977 The use of tracers in diagnosing interwell reservoir heterogeneities—field results.

62. Keys, W. S. and Brown, R. F. 1978 *Ground Water*, 16, 32, The use of temperature logs to trace the movement of injected water.

1 (left) **Cut-away section through typical borehole pump**
(upper right) **A range of pumps awaiting despatch**
(lower right) **Re-assembly of pump during overhaul**
(Courtesy of Emu Pumps (UK) Ltd)

Chapter 11

DESIGN OF BOREHOLES AND WELLS

1. INTRODUCTION

THE following distinction was drawn[1] in 1969 between wells and boreholes:

'A well may be defined as any shaft or excavation made for the purpose of intercepting groundwater, exceeding 1 m in diameter if made by men working in the shaft or exceeding 1.8 m irrespective of the method of construction. . . . A borehole may be defined as a shaft of any diameter up to and including 1.8 m constructed solely by a recognised method of boring'.

However, over the last two decades the distinction has become blurred, possibly because traditional methods of well sinking are no longer practised in the UK. The terms have become interchangeable and will be so used in this chapter.

Wells are most often used for abstracting groundwater from aquifers for water supply. However, they may also be used for exploration, as observation wells, for the disposal of liquid wastes, in pressure relief or drainage works and for the artificial recharge of aquifers. The design of a well will be governed by its proposed use, the quantity and quality of water or waste to be withdrawn or recharged, the hydrogeology of the aquifer and economic factors.

The Chalk and Permo-Triassic sandstones are the principal UK aquifers. At many localities these rocks have sufficient strength to stand unsupported and during the 19th and early 20th century many wells, possibly up to 3 m in diameter, were hand dug in these formations to depths of the order of 60 to 120 m. In some cases yields were improved by driving sub-horizontal adits, often hundreds of metres long, into the chalk and sandstones. Many of these wells are still in operation or on standby. Modern production wells are much smaller, seldom exceeding 1 m in diameter, and are bored rather than sunk to depths of up to 300 m.

2. SCREENS AND PACKS

The design of a well is governed by the hydrogeological conditions at the site and its intended use. There are therefore a great variety of screen and casing arrangements. Some typical examples are shown in Fig. 11.1 (see also Section 4, Chapter 13). The Chalk wells are almost always unscreened although the upper sections of the well are cased and sealed to prevent contamination of well water from surface or sub-surface pollution (Fig. 11.1a and b). The Permo-Triassic sandstones show much greater variability in their physical properties than does the Chalk. In some locations these sandstones are sufficiently strong to stand unsupported but in others weaknesses may be revealed either during drilling or hydraulic testing and screens or perforated casings, together with artificial sand/gravel filters, are needed. It is particularly important to monitor the sand/silt content of the pumped water during a well test. Even a small concentration of sand in the pumped water can, in time, lead to damage of the pumping equipment, instability of the well walls and possibly damage to the well head. At low abstraction rates the influx of sand may be negligible but at higher rates it could be significant and it is important therefore that

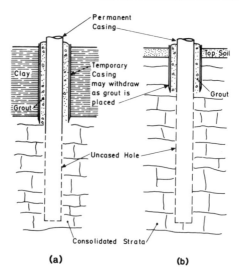

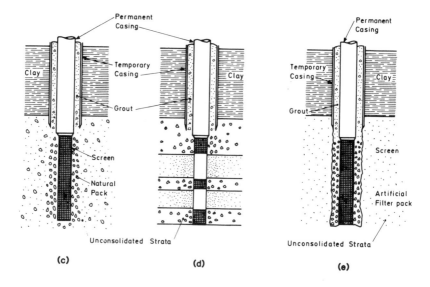

Fig. 11.1.   Typical arrangements for casing and screen designs

(a) Casing through soft impermeable strata over consolidated water bearing strata

(b) Casing installed to shallow depth to prevent pollution of consolidated water bearing strata

(c) Casing and screen in unconsolidated aquifer—natural pack

(d) Series of screens to coincide with high yielding horizons in an aquifer

(e) Casing and screen in unconsolidated aquifer—artificial pack

hydraulic tests on production wells are carried out at abstraction rates which will exceed the maximum proposed operational pumping rates.

Although wells in Chalk and Permo-Triassic sandstones may not need screens and packs, wells in unconsolidated or partially consolidated aquifers in the UK do.

The design of screens and packs will in this chapter be considered in relation to production wells. The principles, with some modifications, will be applicable to other situations—for example, observation wells, well points, recharge wells, etc.

The screens should be designed to allow groundwater to flow into the well with the minimum of hydraulic losses while at the same time preventing the entry of sand and giving structural support to the walls. The screen is often set at the bottom of the well with a blank casing extending from the top of the screen section to well head level (Fig. 11.1c). However, in some situations screens are set at selected levels to correspond with the most productive water-bearing horizons (Fig. 11.1d). The intervening sections of the well carry blank casings between the screens. Although the screens are primarily concerned with preventing the ingress of sand to the well they may also be used to support fractured aquifers, in which loose blocks would otherwise fall into the well damaging its construction, the pumps or casing.

Sand screens are used in conjunction with a "filter pack", an envelope of coarse sand or gravel in the annular space between the screen and the aquifer formation. The "filter pack" may be "*natural*" in that it is formed of the aquifer materials by pumping or surging the well so that the fine grained materials in the zone surrounding the screen are drawn into the well (see Section 5, Chapter 13). In this way a stable pack is formed. The fines are removed from inside the well by bailer or sand pump.

Some formations are unsuitable for development of a natural pack and in this case an "*artificial pack*" may be used (Fig. 11.1e). This pack is a carefully graded sand or gravel inserted from the surface into the annular space between the screen and the aquifer. Preformed artificial packs bonded to the outside of a suitable screen are also available.

When a well is being pumped the velocity of the groundwater flowing through the pores or fissures in the aquifer increases as it approaches the screen. The loss in hydraulic head also increases. A velocity may be reached at which the laminar flow conditions, which pertain in many aquifers, become turbulent. The transition from laminar to turbulent flow corresponds to a marked increase in hydraulic head loss. The provision of a sand or gravel pack coarser than the aquifer material increases the size of the pore space as the well screen is approached and contributes towards maintaining a laminar flow condition. The pack thus not only acts as a filter to prevent the movement of sand into the well but also reduces the head loss and thus increases well efficiency (see Section 2, Chapter 5).

SCREEN TYPES

The simplest form of screen consists of pipe sections with circular or, more commonly, slot perforations (Fig. 11.2a). As slot sizes are usually relatively large and the open area per unit area of screen is low, since cutting large numbers of perforations or slots would weaken the casing, they are not normally used in coarse-grained aquifers or with gravel filters. The degree of blockage in such screens is apt to be high. They are relatively inexpensive in comparison with other screens and can be made in metal, plastic or wood. They can be cut on site with a blow-torch or saw. Slots in metal screens may be cut vertically with a length of about 100 mm and a width of 10 mm. Generally there are about 8 slots per circumference. A wide range of slotted screens are available in PVC and fibreglass. Slot sizes may lie in the range 0.2 to 3.0 mm and may be vertical, horizontal or, in some fibreglass screens, at an angle to the axis of the pipe (Fig. 11.2b).

A development of the perforated screen is the factory made bridge-slotted screen in which the perforations are not completely pressed out (Fig. 11.2c). A bridge of metal is left over the opening. This forms a stronger screen than the simple perforated type and smaller slot-sizes are possible. The louvre or letter-box screen is formed by pushing out the metal so that a flap is left attached to the top edge of the screen. This forms a protective lip (Fig. 11.2d). The maximum open area of the bridge slotted and louvred screens is about 30 per cent of the surface area. The smallest slot sizes of both screen types usually lie in the range 2-4 mm.

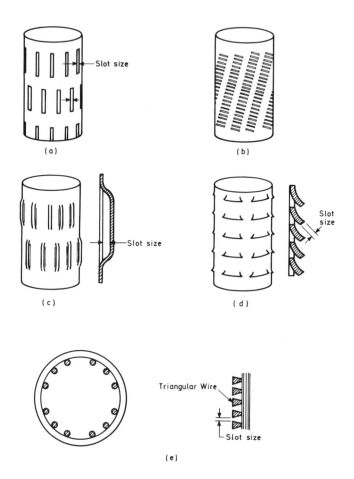

Fig. 11.2.   Typical examples of well screens
(a) Simple vertical slots (b) inclined slots of the type used in some fibre glass screens, (c) bridge slots, (d) letter box slots, (e) wire wound

Wire wound screens, in common use for many years, consist of mild steel or stainless steel wire wound around a number of longitudinal rods of the same material set on a circumference. The contact points of the rods and wire are welded, producing a screen with a continuous helical slot. The slot size is formed by the gap between successive turns of the wire, which is usually wedge shaped with the flat surface facing outwards (Fig. 11.2e). The triangular wire forms V-shaped slots that may reduce the tendency to blocking by sand and gravel and lower the hydraulic resistance. The open area of wire wound screens may vary from 10 per cent at the smallest slot sizes (0.25 mm) to 60 per cent with large slot sizes (3.8 mm). Continuous slot screens are expensive but are robust and hydraulically efficient and the slot size can be carefully controlled.

FILTER PACKS

The design of packs and screens for a productive well clearly depends on the grain size distribution of the aquifer. Samples should be recovered from a number of horizons to represent the range of lithologies present in the sequence of water-bearing strata. The grain size distribution of each distinct lithology should be determined by sieving the samples following the procedures of BS 1377[2]. In weakly cemented sandstone aquifers it may be necessary to degrade the samples mechanically prior to determining their grain size distributions. A grain size distribution graph called a grading curve is prepared by plotting the percentage of material passing each standard sieve. Typical grading curves for a well graded sand (A) and for a poorly graded silty sand with some gravel (B) are shown in Fig. 11.3. This type of curve permits rapid appreciation of the aquifer lithologies and the pack or screen requirements. The location of the screen sections in the aquifer may depend on the results of these analyses.

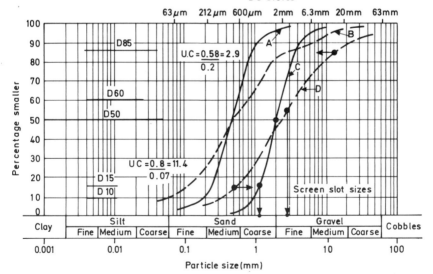

Fig. 11.3. Grading curves for a well-graded sand (A) and a poorly-graded silty sand with some gravel (B)

(Equivalent artificial uniform (C) and graded packs (D) are shown with the required screen slot sizes)

The grading curves may for the present purpose be categorised in terms of two elements, namely fineness and slope of the curve. The fineness is usually simply expressed as the aperture size of the sieve which would allow 10 per cent of the material to pass. This is referred to as the D_{10} or the *effective grain size*. The D_{60} is the sieve aperture size which would allow 60 per cent of the sample to pass and therefore would retain 40 per cent of the sample. The D_{60} is used with the D_{10} to define the slope of the curve in terms of the *uniformity coefficient* which is defined as follows:

$$\text{Uniformity coefficient} = \frac{D_{60}}{D_{10}}$$

Thus the lower the uniformity coefficient the better graded the material and the closer it will approach single size particles. Large values of uniformity coefficient represent a wide spread of particle sizes and generally less well graded materials.

Many criteria, based on well performance and field observations, have been suggested for use in the design of packs and screens. In general there is agreement on design principles but there are some differences in detail. The values chosen here are a compromise and follow closely those selected by Monkhouse[3].

A *natural graded pack* is formed from the constituent materials of the aquifer. Development of the well by pumping or surging draws the finer material into the well leaving the coarser in place. The method may be particularly advantageous in deep wells where placing an artificial pack could prove difficult. However, it may not be possible to develop a satisfactory natural pack in an aquifer with a substantial quantity of either fine or coarse grained material. The guiding principle is as follows. In an aquifer with an effective grain size (D_{10}) greater than 0.25 mm, D_{90} less than 100 mm and uniformity coefficient between 3 and 10, a natural graded pack can usually be produced without trouble. If the uniformity coefficient is less than 2 and D_{10} greater than 0.25 mm a suitable natural pack will form without the need for any development, although a thin uniform filter pack with a grain size similar to that of the aquifer may be used in the annular space between the aquifer and the well screen as a formation stabilizer.

If the aquifer grain size properties are such that an *artificial pack* is required, the grading curves will indicate whether a *"uniform"* or *"graded"* pack is needed. The uniform artifical pack should be selected for aquifers where the uniformity coefficient is less than 3. The material of the pack should have a D_{50} 4 to 5 times the D_{50} of the aquifer and the pack's uniformity coefficient should be less than 2.5. The grading for a uniform artificial filter to be used in a sandy aquifer (curve A) is given by curve C in Fig. 11.3. Graded artificial packs contain a wide range of grain sizes and are selected so that their uniformity more or less matches that of the aquifer. They are of particular value where there is a high proportion of fine material in the aquifer. The selection of the material to make up the graded pack is essentially based on the Terzaghi[4] filter rules such that:

(1) D_{15} pack is at least 4 times greater than D_{15} of the coarsest aquifer sample.
(2) D_{85} pack should be slightly less than 4 times the D_{85} of the finest aquifer sample.
(3) The curve of the graded filter pack should match the shape of the average grading curve obtained from a representative series of aquifer samples.

A filter, based on the above rules, to match the silty sand aquifer (curve B) in Fig. 11.3 is given by grading curve D.

Methods of drilling and installing casing and screens are described in Chapter 13. When a natural pack is to be used the well is gently surged so that the small annular space between the aquifer and the screen is filled with collapsed material from the aquifer. The surging must not be too heavy or damage by crushing of the screen may result. In some cases, particularly if the aquifer will form a suitable natural pack without development, a thin uniform filter pack is run in to stabilize the aquifer walls. Once the walls have collapsed surging followed by pumping is continued until no further sand enters the well.

In placing a uniformly graded artificial pack the sand is washed down pipes into the annular space between the screen and the aquifer walls. In an artificially graded filter "tremie" pipes are run to the bottom of the well and slowly raised during the placing procedure while keeping the pipes topped up to the surface with the filter material. Care is taken in washing the material into place that undue segregation of the fine and coarse components does not occur. Artificial filters are usually 75 to 150 mm thick. It has been shown that a smaller thickness would be effective but placing the material becomes a problem. With a filter thickness of 150 mm or more it may prove difficult to remove the drilling cake from the walls of the aquifer during development.

The uniform artificial packs require only limited development to remove any drilling cake whereas artificially graded packs require surging and pumping similar to that used for a natural pack.

SCREEN LENGTH AND SLOT SIZE

The length of screen needed will be governed by the required yield and the effective open area of the screen to keep the entrance velocity through the screen slots below a value that would lead to high hydraulic losses and/or encrustation of the screens. The effective open area is generally about one half to one third of the total area of screen slot openings, due to blocking by the granular aquifer or filter material. Mathematical analysis and laboratory experiments have shown that for most new wells the head losses across the screens are very small provided that the open area exceeds 10 to 15 per cent. However, once plugging starts the head loss will accelerate the potential for further encrustation.

It has been suggested that the maximum entrance velocity should not exceed 3 cm/sec but Walton[5] proposed that in nonreactive waters the entrance velocity (V_e) should be linked to the aquifer's hydraulic conductivity (k) in accordance with Table 11.I. If direct measurements are not available, the hydraulic conductivity of the aquifer may be estimated from the well-known Hazen relationship:

$$k = 1.0 \times D_{10}{}^2$$

where D_{10} is the effective grain size in mm and k has the units of cm/sec.

The relationship between the effective open area (A_e) per unit length of screen and the entrance velocity through the slots is given by

$$A_e = \frac{Q}{V_e \cdot L}$$

where Q is the discharge and L the screen length.

Thus for an aquifer with a natural pack having a D_{10} of 0.4 mm the estimated hydraulic conductivity based on the Hazen formula would be 0.16 cm/sec. From Table 11.I the optimum entrance velocity (V_e) through the screen would be about 4 cm/sec. If a well discharge of 2500 m³/d was required when the effective open area of screen is given by:

$$A_e \times L = \frac{2500}{86.4 \times 10^3} \times \frac{100}{4} = 0.72 \text{ m}^2$$

(Note that 1 m³/s = 86.4 × 10³ m³/d).

The actual open area of screen should be double the effective open area to allow for blockage. If it was proposed to screen 10 m of the aquifer with a 1 m diameter casing then the minimum percentage open area to be provided by slots will be as follows:

$$\text{Minimum slot area required} = \frac{0.72 \times 2 \times 100}{10 \times \dfrac{\pi}{4} \times 1^2}$$

$$= 18.3 \text{ per cent}$$

TABLE   11.I. Optimum   Screen   Entrance
Velocities (after Walton[5])

Hydraulic conductivity (cm/sec × 10⁻³)	Optimum entrance velocity through screen slots (cm/sec)
<23	1.0
23	1.5
46	2.0
93	3.0
139	4.0
186	4.5
232	5.0
278	5.6
>278	6.0

Where a groundwater has encrustation potential it is recommended that the entrance velocities in Table 11.I should be reduced by one third. If a gravel pack is used a common practice is to take the average of the recommended screen entrance velocity for the aquifer and pack calculated separately. As a useful approximation the hydraulic conductivity of artificial packs is usually 3 to 5 times that of the aquifer.

The size of the screen opening (slot size) is selected on the basis of the grading of the filter material or, if a natural pack is used, the aquifer. With an *artificial uniform pack* the slot size should be between the D_{10} and D_{20} pack sizes; in other words, the screen would retain 80-90 per cent of the material immediately behind it (see Fig. 11.3). With an *artificial graded pack* the slot size should be between D_{50} and D_{60}, thus retaining 40-50 per cent of the pack material (see Fig. 11.3). In the case of *natural packs* Walton[5] suggested that where these are heterogeneous, with a uniformity coefficient greater than 6, then the screen slot size should be selected to retain 50 per cent if the aquifer is soft and as little as 30 per cent if the aquifer is firm. In more homogeneous aquifers with a uniformity coefficient less than 3, 60 per cent should be retained in a soft aquifer and 40 per cent in a firm aquifer. If the zone of the aquifer to be screened shows a variability due to stratification or other causes then the D_{50} for the finest zone should be used to size the screen slots. If the

D_{50} for the coarsest material is more than 4 times the D_{50} for the finest then consideration should be given to sub-dividing the zones using screens with different slot sizes. If some of the zones are very fine it may be uneconomical to screen these and blank casing can then be used (see Fig. 11.1d).

Detailed information on screen types, materials and slot size availability will be supplied by screen manufacturers on request. Useful information is contained in Campbell and Lehr[6] and in Johnson[7].

3. BOREHOLE CONSTRUCTION MATERIALS

A wide range of materials have been used for casings and screens. Casing diameters range from 25 mm for observation boreholes to 1 000 mm or more for large production wells. Depths range from a few metres to almost 300 m. In general the highest loadings on casings and screens will occur from external pressures during the development of gravel packs where, due to the surging and pumping in the well, large differential water pressures may arise between the outside and the inside of the casing. In addition large quantities of sand and gravel either from the aquifer or in the pack may be in motion leading to high stresses on the screen. If clay horizons are encountered swelling may exert considerable pressure. In such cases it is not possible to give general guidance and each site would have to be separately assessed.

There are a number of equations which estimate the collapse resistance of pipes under external pressures. Campbell and Lehr[6] consider the most applicable to water wells to be that developed by Cleindeinst[8]. The equation for the external pressure (P_c) to give elastic collapse is:

$$P_c = \frac{2E}{(1-\mu)} \frac{1}{(\frac{d}{t})(\frac{d}{t} - 1)^2}$$

where E = modulus of elasticity
μ = Poisson's ratio
d = outside diameter of the pipe
t = wall thickness.

Tensile or bending forces may also contribute to wall collapse and it is suggested that the equation be used with a design factor of safety of 3 for wells in unconsolidated formations and 1.8 to 2 in consolidated rock. The wall thickness estimated on this basis would be increased to match the nearest standard pipe size.

METAL CASINGS

Moss[9], using an equation of the type given above and making an allowance for installation and development stresses, recommended steel casing wall thicknesses as a function of pipe diameter and depth as shown in Table 11.II. In BS 879[10] the thicknesses of casing recommended for both screwed and socketed butt joints and butt welded joints (Tables 11.III and 11.IV) meet the requirements given in Table 11.II except for some of the smaller diameter casings at depths over 600 ft (183 m).

Steel is in wide use for casing and screens but prior to selecting it the degree of aggressiveness of the groundwater should be considered. It may be that a small increase in wall thickness or some protective coating could appreciably extend the life of the well. In particularly aggressive waters it may be necessary to choose another material. Stainless steels have high strength and durability and are now widely used for casings and screens in corrosive environments. Their durability is such that wall thickness needs only to meet the loading criteria and no allowance need be made for corrosion.

TABLE 11.II.   **Suggested Minimum Thicknesses for Steel Water Well Casing** (after Moss[9]) (in US standard gauge and inches)

Depth of single casing (feet)	Diameter (inches)										
	6	8	10	12	14	16	18	20	22	24	30
<100	12	12	12	10	10	8	8	8	8	8	3/16
100-200	12	12	10	8	8	8	3/16	3/16	3/16	3/16	1/4
200-300	10	10	8	8	8	3/16	3/16	3/16	1/4	1/4	1/4
300-400	10	8	8	3/16	3/16	3/16	1/4	1/4	1/4	1/4	5/16
400-600	10	8	3/16	3/16	3/16	1/4	1/4	1/4	5/16	5/16	5/16
600-800	3/16	3/16	3/16	3/16	1/4	1/4	1/4	5/16	5/16	3/8	3/8
>800	3/16	3/16	3/16	1/4	1/4	1/4	5/16	5/16	3/8	3/8	7/16

Note: Values above stepped line are in US standard gauge; values below line are in fractions of an inch

CORROSION AND DEPOSITION

The quality of groundwater must be taken into account in the choice of materials for casing, screen, pumps and rising main. Corrosion and encrustation are complex processes and many agents both chemical and biological may contribute. It is only possible here to suggest the factors that should be looked for and if there would appear to be a problem then specialist advice should be sought.

The indicators of corrosion potential are:

(a) pH less than 7;
(b) dissolved oxygen (which will accelerate corrosion even in slightly alkaline waters);
(c) the presence of hydrogen sulphide;
(d) carbon dioxide exceeding 50 mg/l;
(e) total dissolved solids exceeding 1000 mg/l;
(f) chlorides exceeding 300 mg/l; and
(g) high temperatures

Corrosion may cause wear on the pumping unit and can lead to an enlargement of the screen openings causing sand or silt to be carried into the well with possible damage to the pump. In an extreme situation the screen or casing may disintegrate. A range of corrosion control measures have been applied to casings and screens including cathodic protection, but if the groundwater is aggressive the best approach would appear to be to use a corrosion resistant material. Johnson[7] lists metals in order of decreasing corrosion resistance as follows: monel, stainless steel, everdur, brass, low carbon steel. Monel would resist high sodium chloride water (sea water concentrations) including dissolved oxygen. Stainless steel is suitable for widespread use in water supply wells. Mild steel will not resist aggressive waters but has proved satisfactory where the water is non-corrosive. Other materials to be considered include PVC and GRP.

If the groundwater conditions are suitable then encrustations on the screens and in the aquifer will occur regardless of the material used in the screen or the type of

TABLE 11.III.   **Dimensions of Casing for Screwed and Socketed Butt Joints**

Outside diameter (mm)	Thickness (mm)	Nominal inside diameter (mm)	Weight per metre of plain tube (kg)
114.3	6.3	101.7	16.8
168.3	8.0	152.3	31.6
219.1	8.0	203.1	41.6
273.0	9.5	254.0	61.7
323.9	9.5	304.9	73.7
355.6	9.5	336.6	81.1
406.4	9.5	387.4	93.0

Source: BS 879, Part 1, 1985*

TABLE 11.IV.   **Dimensions of Casing with Butt Welded Joints**

Outside diameter (mm)	Nominal wall thickness (mm)	Nominal internal diameter (mm)	Weight per metre of tube (kg)
114.3	5.4	103.5	14.5
139.7	6.3	127.1	20.7
168.3	6.3	155.7	25.2
193.7	6.3	181.1	29.1
219.1	7.1	204.9	37.1
244.5	7.1	230.3	41.6
273.0	7.1	258.8	46.6
323.9	8.0	307.9	62.3
355.6	8.0	339.6	68.6
406.4	9.5	387.4	93.0
457.0	9.5	438.0	105.0
508.0	9.5	489.0	117.0
559.0	9.5	540.0	129.0
610.0	9.5	591.0	141.0
660.0	9.5	641.0	152.0
711.0	9.5	692.0	164.0
762.0	9.5	743.0	176.0
813.0	9.5	794.0	188.0
914.0	9.5	895.0	212.0
1016.0	12.5	991.0	309.0
1118.0	12.5	1093.0	341.0
1220.0	12.5	1195.0	372.0

Source: BS 879, Part 1, 1985*.

well construction. The encrustation may consist of hard cement-like deposits, soft sludge or bacterial slimes. The principal indicators of the encrustation potential of a groundwater (Walton[11]) are:

(i) pH greater than 8.0;
(ii) total hardness greater than 330 mg/l;
(iii) total alkalinity greater than 300 mg/l, and
(iv) iron content greater than 2 mg/l.

Encrustations are most often formed of calcium and magnesium carbonate, thrown out of solution as the pH of the water is lowered on entering the well. This reduction in acidity is caused by a decrease in dissolved carbon dioxide in the water due to a drop in hydrostatic pressure. Oxidation of soluble ferrous and manganese oxides may lead to formation of brown or black deposits on the screen. Iron bacteria may also contribute to this process. A high entrance velocity through the slots may accelerate the accumulation of such deposits. To prevent loss of yield from a well, routine maintenance of screen and pumps is required and the need for this should be recognised at the design stage. Acid treatment to loosen or remove the carbonate scale may be aided by surging or jetting. Chemical additives such as polyphosphates may loosen other encrustations and hypochlorite or other disinfecting agents will kill bacterial growth and loosen slimes.

Non-metallic Casings

Plastic casings have been used for well screens for more than 25 years. The range of products and the quality of the material have steadily improved. PVC was initially used for small diameter, relatively shallow, observation wells. However, casing and screens are now available for installation in suitable ground conditions up to depths of about 100 m in 600 mm diameter and to depths of about 250 m in 300 mm diameter. A wide choice of slot sizes from 0.2 to 3 mm is available. The percentage open area tends to be small, ranging generally from about 3 per cent with an 0.2 mm slot to 14 per cent with a 3 mm slot. The hydraulic performance of some makes of screen is improved by the use of closely spaced vertical ribs running the length of the pipe, or similar arrangements, which act as a bridge to the sand and protect the slots. PVC casings and screens for high temperature applications, up to 80°C, are also available but in a more restricted range of diameters.

The smaller size of PVC casings and screens, because of their light weight, corrosion resistant properties and relative cheapness have proved their value in shallow observation wells. While the specifications for the larger sizes suggest that they may be installed in deep wells, these are based on uniform external loading conditions. Stress concentrations resulting from collapses of a borehole wall or pressure from swelling clays or other geological causes may possibly lead to deformation. Long term creep must also be a concern. Particular care should therefore be taken in assessing the pressures likely to develop on the casings and screens before these larger PVC pipe sizes are specified for very deep wells.

In the 1960s fibre reinforced epoxy casings and screens were developed. They were widely used in Pakistan for a major tubewell installation where corrosion resistant materials were a requirement. They are easily handled, being less than a quarter of the weight of an equivalent steel pipe and about half the weight of PVC. Standard sizes are available in 150, 200, 250 and 300 mm diameter and two weights of pipe are offered. In the standard range they can be installed to depths of up to 100 m. Slot sizes range from 0.75 to 3.0 mm with open areas from 7 to 15 per cent respectively. The manufacturers will offer thicker walled pipes as 'specials' to meet high surging and pumping pressures during well development or for particularly deep wells. As the pipe thickness is increased, however, the cost will rise and stainless steel or other corrosion resistant materials may then become economically competitive.

4.   OBSERVATION BOREHOLES AND RECHARGE WELLS

Observation boreholes may be used to measure the seasonal variation of water level in an aquifer, the change in water level during pumping tests, the *in situ* measurement of water quality or for the collection of water samples for chemical or biological analysis. Discussion on the location of observation wells in pumping tests, water resource assessment or groundwater quality studies is covered elsewhere in this volume.

To measure the water level in consolidated aquifers such as the Chalk or the Permo-Triassic sandstones, the borehole will be cased to below the water table and will be in open hole thereafter (Fig. 11.4a). The water level may be measured manually by an electrical dipper attached to a graduated tape or automatically by a float attached by a wire passing over a continuous chart recorder drum to a counterweight in the borehole. An accuracy of a few millimetres can be attained with float recorders. The borehole must have a minimum diameter of about 200 mm so that the float does not stick on the well sides and to give adequate room for the counterweight arrangement. A small (vandalproof) kiosk is required to house the recording drum directly above the borehole head.

Electrical pressure transducers have been increasingly used for water level measurements over the last 15 years. The transducer units may be quite small (20 mm diameter × 100 mm long). The transducer is located below the minimum groundwater level likely to occur in the borehole. It is attached to the surface by a waterproof cable and may record data directly into a small portable data logger which can be programmed to take readings at pre-set intervals. Modern data

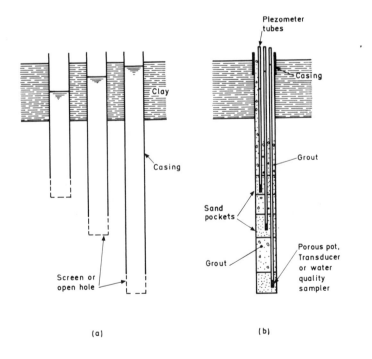

Fig. 11.4.   Arrangements for (a) individual and (b) multiple observation boreholes

loggers are small, portable units which may be left unattended for several months and when recovered can output their data through a computer in tabular or graphical form. The water level measurements from a transducer unit may be less accurate than those from a float recorder but because of the ease of data collection and the smaller diameter of the borehole required they are being increasingly used. However, one major advantage of a larger (200 mm diameter) observation borehole is that a small submersible pump may be used to recover 'fresh' samples for water quality analysis.

If the aquifer to be monitored is thick there may be changes in the piezometric head with depth. In this case it may be necessary to have two or more boreholes set at different depths in the aquifer (Fig 11.4a). This is a costly arrangement and with care it is possible to record water levels at two or three separate horizons in a 150 mm diameter hole. This is achieved by running two or three small diameter tubes (25 mm) to individual porous elements set in sand pockets adjacent to the horizon at which measurements are required. The open hole between the piezometer pockets is sealed with clay or cement grout (Fig 11.4b). Care is required in placing the sealing materials so that they do not enter and block the sand pockets. A layer of fine sand is often placed below and above each pocket to prevent entry by the grout. Water levels at the pockets may be measured manually by dipper or electric transducers with associated data loggers may be installed. A similar arrangement may be used for collecting and recovering water quality samples using an *in situ* device of the type developed by the Water Research Centre[12].

If a single observation point is required in unconsolidated strata then a screen will be required to support the observation borehole walls. Slot sizes should be selected using the principles for water well design described above. If multiple water level or quality sampling points are needed then no screen will be required but great care should be taken in withdrawing temporary casing so that the piezometers or sampling units are not disturbed.

It has been suggested[13] that a recharge/abstraction well should carry a screen and artificial pack of similar design to that for a water supply well. The suspended material in the recharge water will, through time, reduce the permeability of the pack. Wells have therefore been designed and constructed to include a number of small diameter vertical tubes in the annular space between the pack and the screen. These can be pressurised and used to back-wash the filter material. The recharge main arrangements must be such that cascading of water into the well is avoided as this leads to air bubbles being trapped in the filter causing a reduction of recharge capacity. The recharge main should therefore discharge below the well water level.

5. PUMPING EQUIPMENT

The number of artesian or free-flowing wells in the UK has reduced markedly with the extensive development of groundwater over the last 150 years. In most wells the static water level is now below ground level so that wells must be equipped with pumps. These are mainly of the impeller type and usually driven by electric motors, but on some smaller installations pumps may be directly driven by petrol or diesel engines. Jet, airlift, bucket pumps etc are sometimes used for small domestic supplies. They operate at small flows and low efficiencies. They will not be considered further here (see Chapter 13). The maximum theoretical suction lift is 10 m but in practice it is usually considerably less than this due to head losses in the intake strainer and suction pipe. So unless the water level in the well is close to the ground surface, the pump unit is placed below the water level in the well.

The pump may be driven by either a vertical shaft placed at the centre of the discharge main or by a submersible pump where a completely submerged motor is coupled to the pump (Fig. 11.5a and b). With a vertical spindle pump the driving motor is at ground surface and the pump may be 20 to 30 m down the well. The drive spindle is held in a tube of 75-125 mm diameter and located at the centre of the rising main. Capital and installation costs are high and considerable skill and time are required if repair is necessary. A 6-8 day delay could result in removing and replacing the pumping unit. However, they are robust with high efficiency and long life and can operate at variable speed. A building is required at the surface to house the drive unit. In contrast, submersible pumps are of fixed speed only, but are designed to operate at a wide range of duty. They are cheap and can be installed or replaced, if a spare pump is available, in a matter of hours. The associated electrical switch gear and control systems can be contained in a relatively small

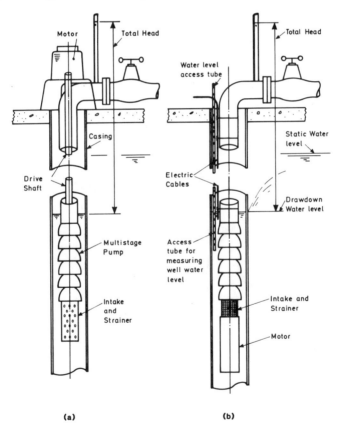

Fig. 11.5.   Borehole pumping arrangements with (a) a spindle and (b) a submersible pump

weatherproof cabinet at the surface so no building is required at the well head. The power supply is fed to the motor, which is usually below the pumping unit, by waterproof cables attached to the rising main. Submersible pumps can be installed in a small diameter hole and the verticality specification for the borehole is less than that for a vertical spindle pump. Submersible pumping units have become the preferred choice in almost all major groundwater developments in the UK.

IMPELLER PUMPS

The action of the pump is through a rotating impeller consisting of several narrow spiral-shaped blades set between two metal discs (Fig. 11.6a). The impeller may rotate at speeds between 1800 and 3600 rpm. A hole (the "eye") at the centre of one of the discs is connected to the water supply. The water enters the "eye" and is thrown radially outwards. It is collected in a spirally shaped housing and leaves through the discharge pipe. In some pumps a series of stationary diffuser vanes are introduced in the housing so as to reduce energy losses due to turbulence (Fig. 11.6b). With good design the efficiency of an impeller pump is usually close to 80 per cent but for special applications efficiencies up to 90 per cent are possible. The design and size of a centrifugal pump vary considerably according to the quantity of water that has to be pumped and the operating head; the combination of these is commonly referred to as the pump's "duty". The total head that the pump supplies is the sum of the following:

(1) The vertical height from the water level in the well to the ground surface. Note that this is the pumping level in the well under operational conditions and not the rest water water level.
(2) Frictional loss through the pump screen and rising main.
(3) The static pressure head inside the discharge pipe at the top of the rising main.
(4) The velocity head ($v^2/2g$) in the discharge pipe.

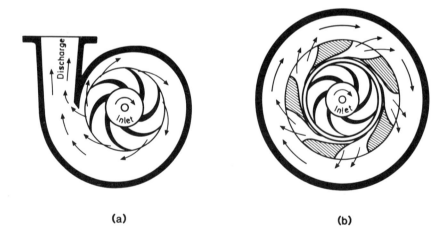

(a)   **(b)**

Fig. 11.6.   Impeller pumps: (a) volute type; (b) turbine pump
(Water leaves the impeller and moves through diffuser vanes and vertically upwards to the next impeller stage)

In most situations the water velocity in the discharge pipe and the rising main is small and consequently the head losses under (2) and (4) are usually small in relation to (1). The total head can therefore in most cases be estimated as the height from the water level in the well during pumping to the piezometric level at the well head discharge main. The latter may be the additional head necessary to convey the water through pipes to a treatment plant or surface reservoir.

The rate of water delivery, Q, of an impeller pump operating at constant speed decreases as the total head increases. A typical relationship (Fig. 11.7) is called the *pump characteristic*. The characteristic curve depends on the geometry of the impeller and diffuser design. The total head when the discharge is zero, the "shut-off head", represents the maximum pressure head the pump can generate with the outlet valve closed. Under such circumstances the impeller would rotate but damage may eventually result from heat generation.

At a given speed the total head a pump can produce increases approximately with the square of the impeller diameter. However in a borehole the diameter of the pump and hence the impeller is restricted and consequently this would appear to limit the head that can be developed. This is overcome by mounting a number of impeller stages in series, the discharge from one impeller being guided to the "eye" of the impeller above it. This multi-stage pump arrangement may have up to 20 or more impellers mounted one above the other in the pump bowl. The total head that a multi-stage pump can generate is the sum of the heads from the individual units. The quantity pumped is governed by the diameter of the individual impellers. The diameter of the well must be significantly larger than the pump bowl so that the

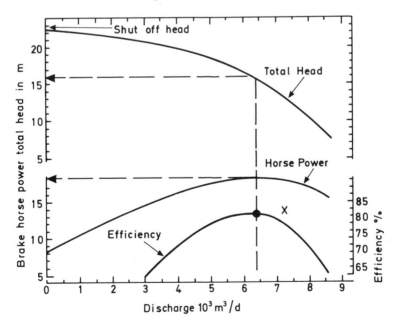

Fig. 11.7. Typical relationship between pump discharge, total head, efficiency and brake horse-power

pump does not bind on the well sides and to reduce the hydraulic head losses in the annular space. A guide to the pump bowl and associated borehole diameter in relation to the pumping rate Q is given in Table 11.V. The pump must be positioned in the well at a depth such that its intake is sufficiently below the operational well water level to prevent air being drawn through the pumping unit. The casing diameter may be reduced below the level of the pump (Fig.13.13b) but an allowance should be made so that the pump can be lowered to accommodate any predictable reduction in regional groundwater levels.

TABLE 11.V   Suggested Casing and Pump Bowl Diameters in Relation to Discharge

Pumping rate $(10^3 m^3/d)$	Pump bowl diameter (mm)	Casing or well diameter (mm)
0.5	100	150
1.25	125	200
2.5	150	250
4.0	200	300
6.0	250	300
8.0	300	400
12.0	360	510
20.0	400	610
20.0	460	760

When a submersible pump is switched off the water in the rising main flows back into the well, causing the impeller to run backwards. If the power were briefly interrupted the motor on restarting would be operating against a backward running pump, which could overload and damage the unit. Protection is provided by building in a time delay, possibly of several minutes, before the unit restarts. Commonly on spindle pumps but also on some submersible pump systems a flap valve ('foot valve') is placed at the end of the suction main to prevent this backward flow of water. Foot valves need to be designed so that their hydraulic losses are small and be well maintained so they do not stick. If a submersible pump intake is in a section of borehole adjacent to a filter/screen or to soft strata in an open hole, circumferential shields (shrouds) should be fitted adjacent to the pump intake strainer to prevent local erosion of aquifer or filter material.

The power input to operate the pump at a given head for a given flow is called the *brake horse-power* (bhp). The bhp required to drive the pump at a fixed operating speed is not a constant but varies with the discharge. The bhp is usually lowest at zero discharge (the "shut-off head") as it only has to overcome the resistance of the impeller rotating and there are no friction losses due to water flowing through the pump or in the rising main. As the flow increases the bhp reaches a maximum and then begins to decline (Fig. 11.7). The output power in terms of the flow and the total head necessary to lift the water the required height is the *water horse-power* (whp). A horse-power is the power required to lift 76 kg through one metre every second and hence:

$$whp = \frac{Q \times \text{total head in metres}}{0.076 \times 8\,6400}$$

where Q is the pump discharge in m³/day. (Note that the metric horse-power is 75 kg/m/sec and therefore slightly smaller than the horse-power). The whp is always less than the bhp due to friction and other energy losses in the pump. The pump efficiency (E_p) is defined in percentage terms as the ratio of the whp to the bhp

$$E_p = \frac{whp}{bhp} \times 100 \text{ per cent}$$

The E_p is not a constant but varies with the discharge. A maximum value of E_p is obtained only at one value of flow and head for a particular pump (Fig. 11.7). Ideally, pumps should therefore be selected so that the "duty" (as specified by flow and total head) under which they operate is at the maximum efficiency. That is point X in Fig. 11.7. In practice, wear on the pumping unit, a blockage of the pump screen, or a combination of flow and head other than that originally selected means that the pumping may take place at less than maximum efficiency.

CHOICE OF PUMP

Section 2, Chapter 5 describes the conduct of a pumping test which leads to the production of a yield versus drawdown curve for a well. A typical relationship is shown by curve A in Fig. 11.8. The total head the pump needs to generate will be the sum of the drawdown, the lift from drawdown water level in the well to ground

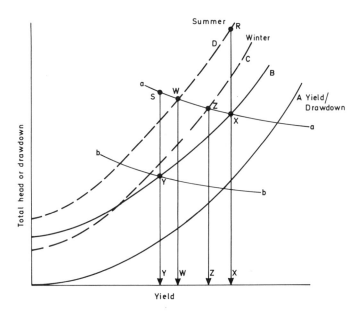

Fig. 11.8. Typical yield versus total head (drawdown) curve (A) for a well and pump characteristic curves (aa and bb)
(The fall in pumping efficiency that may result as the well yield versus head relationship changes with time is shown in curves C and D)

surface, head losses in the pump screen, rising main or subsequent pipe system, plus any additional pressure head to pump the water to a high level tank. The relationship between total head and yield may be represented by curve B. Once the maximum yield required from the well has been selected, say at X, then the pump may be chosen so that its characteristic curve (aa) passes through X at peak efficiency. If the well is required to operate over a range of flows from say X to Y and a fixed speed pump was chosen with a characteristic curve (aa) then the pump will be matched to its "duty" at X but the pumping rate will have to be restricted at Y by throttling the outlet valve to increase the head. The head to be lost by throttling will be by YS.

If a variable-speed pump is used (bb) will represent the characteristic curve at the lower speed of rotation. The variable-speed pump will give lower running costs as a head is not being dissipated against a partially closed valve, as with a fixed-speed unit. However, the capital costs of the variable-speed pump will be higher and variable-speed pumps should generally be avoided. Fixed-speed pumps may be chosen which have a flat efficiency versus flow relationship over the required operating range. In this case only limited throttling will be needed to give the reduced flows. Multi-stage pumps may carry dummy stages which can be replaced by additional impellers as the "duty" increases with time.

The choice of the most appropriate pump may be further complicated by variations in the yield-drawdown curve with time. The original yield versus drawdown curve will be established for the groundwater level prevailing during the test period. This relationship will change with time due to:

(a) Decrease in well efficiency caused by encrustation of well screens or filters.
(b) Regional long term lowering or raising of the water table. This may be particularly important in conjunctive use groundwater developments of the type described in Chapter 14, or in situations where over-development of groundwater is occurring.
(c) Seasonal variation in water levels. For example, in some aquifers the water level may vary from winter to summer or from year to year by 30 m or more.

The modified yield versus total head curves which may result from such variations and long term changes are shown by curves C and D in Fig. 11.8.

The fixed-speed pump with characteristic curve (aa) while meeting the demand requirements during the early life of the well would not be able to cope with the increased total head XR once deterioration in well performance had taken place. Using the original pump the yield would be reduced to W or Z for summer and winter operating conditions respectively.

OPERATIONAL PUMPING COSTS

The pump may be driven by an electric motor or by an internal combustion engine. Electric motors generally have efficiencies (E_m) in the range 80 to 95 per cent while the engines are much lower at 15 to 35 per cent. Considering firstly an electrically driven pumping system, a horse-power (76 kg m/s) is equivalent to 745.7 watts. Therefore the electrical power requirement is given by:

$$\text{whp} \times \frac{100}{E_p} \times \frac{100}{E_m} \times 745.7 \text{ watts}$$

As an example the cost (C) of raising water at a rate of 4 500 m^3/d against a total head of 90 m over a period of 1 000 hours, where E_p = 80 per cent, E_m = 90 per cent and p is the unit price of electricity per kilowatt hour (kwh) can readily be calculated as follows:

$$\text{whp} = \frac{4500 \times 90}{0.076 \times 86400} = 61.7$$

$$C = 61.7 \times \frac{100}{80} \times \frac{100}{90} \times 0.736 \times 1000 \times p$$

$$C = 63000\,p$$

As a rule of thumb 1 whp is equivalent to 1 kwh.

The electricity supply industry ideally prefers a steady or predictable demand for electricity and consequently any consumers who impose heavy intermittent and unpredictable demands are penalised through the electricity tariff system. Therefore, it is important, in reducing operating costs, for the ratio of the average to peak power required during a given operating period, of say a month, to be as high as possible (the pumping unit should run at a high 'load factor'). The duty of pumps, the number and size of the standby units, the working hours and the availability of storage must all be considered in relation to the prevailing electricity tariff structure so that operating costs can be minimised. Even short duration trial runs of a few hours to test newly installed pump units may cost several hundreds of pounds and consequently should be planned with care in relation to the tariff structure.

Turning now to pumps driven by engines, the fuel requirements of a diesel or other internal combustion engine may be calculated by using the calorific value of the particular fuel and the relationship that 1 horse-power equals 178 cals/sec. Thus taking the example given above but on this occasion driving the pump by a diesel engine the cost (C) for 1000 hours of operation may be calculated as follows. Assume that the efficiency of the pump remains the same at 80 per cent but that the engine efficiency is only 21 per cent. Take the diesel to have a calorific value of 10000 k cal/kg, a specific gravity of 0.813 and a price q per litre. As in the previous example the water horse-power is 61.7. The calorific requirement of the fuel over the 1000 hours, taking into account the efficiency of the pump and engine, is thus:

$$C = 61.7 \times \frac{100}{80} \times \frac{100}{21} \times 178 \times 1000 \times 60 \times 60$$

$$= 2.35 \times 10^8 \text{ k cals}$$

$$C = \frac{2.35 \times 10^8}{10000 \times 0.813} \times q$$

$$= 28947 \times q$$

In this example 1 whp is equivalent to a fuel consumption of 0.47 l/hour, ie 28.9/61.7. As a general rule of thumb one whp is equivalent to a consumption of diesel fuel at the rate of 0.25 to 0.05 l/hr.

It must be noted that higher electric power and fuel requirements than those indicated above will result from worn or badly maintained pumping sets.

6. REFERENCES

1. Institution of Water Engineers 1969 "Manual of British water engineering practice, Vol. II, Engineering practice", IWE, London.
2. British Standards Institution 1975 "BS 1377, Methods of testing soils for civil engineering purposes", BSI, Milton Keynes.

3. Monkhouse, R. A. 1974 *Water Services*, 78, 939, The use and design of sand screens and filter packs for abstraction wells.

4. Terzaghi, K. 1943 "Theoretical soil mechanics", John Wiley and Sons, New York.

5. Walton, W. C. 1962 "Selected analytical methods for well and aquifer evaluation", Illinois State Water Survey Bulletin No. 49.

6. Campbell, M. D. and Lehr, J. H. 1973 "Water well technology", McGraw-Hill, New York.

7. Johnson, E. E. Inc. 1972 "Groundwater and wells", Johnson Division, Universal Oil Products, St. Paul, Minn.

8. Cleindeinst, W. V. 1939 "A rational expression for critical collapse of pipe under external pressure", API Drilling and production practice.

9. Moss, R. 1964 "Design of casings and screens for production and injection wells", API Pacific Coast District biennial symposium; 'Treatment and control of injection wells', Anaheim, California.

10. British Standards Institution 1985 "BS 879, Part 1, Water Well Casing", BSI, Milton Keynes.

11. Walton, W. C. 1970 "Groundwater resource evaluation", McGraw-Hill, New York.

12. Edworthy, K. J. and Brown, S. L. "An *in situ* groundwater sampling device", ILR No. 611, Water Research Centre, Medmenham.

13. Monkhouse, R. A. and Phillips, S. 1978 "The design, construction and maintenance of recharge wells", Technical Note No. 25, Central Water Planning Unit, Reading.

Chapter 12

CONTRACT SPECIFICATIONS FOR DRILLING AND CONSTRUCTION OF WATER WELLS

1. INTRODUCTION

WATER WELL drilling contracts are essentially the same as most other forms of contracts used in civil engineering works. However, because of the specialised nature of well drilling, several modifications to existing standard forms of conditions of contract are often required, together with technical specifications tailor-made to suit the peculiarities of water well construction. Three main differences between well construction and other types of construction works have been cited[1]:

(1) Each well, or group of wells, can be said to be unique even though underground conditions at different locations seem to be similar.
(2) Much of the well structure cannot be inspected visually either during drilling or after completion.
(3) The owner is likely to be unfamiliar with the construction methods—particularly the special skill and techniques involved in successful well drilling.

Recently, with the development of the borehole televiewer camera, it has become possible to visually inspect casings and screens in most lined wells and the walls of boreholes constructed in crystalline rock. Even so, much of the knowledge of the well structure and the condition of the hole is obtained only by indirect evidence from geophysical and penetration rate logs, drilling data and the visual inspection of cuttings and cores. Also, the widespread activities in recent years in the search for oil and water in many countries have generally increased the awareness and understanding of well drilling and construction techniques. So, although it is perhaps fair to say that private owners may not be familiar with well construction methods, most government departments in the UK and overseas are becoming increasingly aware of at least the basic methods of well construction.

In the UK, a comprehensive specification for water well drilling and construction is sadly lacking. The NWC specification[2] includes a section on wells and boreholes but, although the proposed specification could be used as a general guide for the preparation of drilling contracts, it is too incomplete and sketchy to form a basis for a specification of well construction—particularly where deep production wells are required.

The AWWA standard[3] is an excellent guide to the preparation of contract documents for well construction. The USEPA manual[4] provides a sound and detailed basis for preparation of drilling contracts. The manual incorporates both conditions of contract and technical standards, together with information for selecting casings (including PVC), on developing and pump-testing wells, and geophysical logging and sampling.

Because of the existence of these two excellent guides, the aim of this chapter is to present a commentary on some of the more important aspects of technical specifications and their relation to contractual procedures—together with an outline of tendering procedures and contract supervision. It is hoped that it will, when read in conjunction with the two publications cited, provide a better understanding of contracts on water well construction.

2. DEFINITIONS

CONTRACT

The word "contract" in civil engineering usually means the signed agreement between the two parties (employer and contractor) which refers to and incorporates the conditions of contract, specification, drawings, schedules of particulars and priced bills of quantities, together with any addenda issued during the tender period, subsequent communications between the parties, minutes of any meetings held to discuss the tender, and the employer's letter of acceptance.

TENDER DOCUMENTS

Documents issued for the purpose of obtaining tenders, known as "Tender Documents", normally include the following sections:

- (*a*) Instructions to Tenderers
- (*b*) Form of Tender and Appendix to Tender
- (*c*) Conditions of Contract
- (*d*) Specifications
- (*e*) Drawings
- (*f*) Schedule of Particulars to be completed by the Tenderer
- (*g*) Unpriced Bill of Quantities and/or a Schedule of Items against which the Tenderer inserts rates or prices.

Instructions to Tenderers

These consist of a set of instructions and explanations issued to guide tenderers in preparing their tender. The instructions normally include information as to how, where and by what date tenders should be submitted, the language of the tender, the submission of alternative tenders, the procedure for evaluation of tenders, the period of validity of tender, tender guarantees and the currency of tender. Normally, instructions to tenderers do not form part of the subsequent contract.

Form of Tender and Appendix to Tender

The form of tender and appendix to tender form part of the tender and eventually the contract. The form of tender is a statement signed by the tenderer confirming that he will undertake the works and comply with all the stipulations of the contract for a stated sum of money and that he will execute the works within a certain period of time.

The appendix to tender contains items to be completed by the tenderer relating to the times of mobilisation and completion of the works, amounts for insurance, amounts for performance and maintenance guarantees, liquidated damages, retention monies and the like.

Conditions of Contract

These essentially consist of a list of general conditions governing the obligations and the rights of the parties entering into the contract and including the duties and powers of the engineer appointed by the employer to supervise the works to be constructed under the contract. There are several published standard conditions of contract for civil engineering works which may be used for water well construction. For contracts in the UK, the ICE Conditions of Contract[5] are widely used, whereas abroad those of the Fédération Internationale des Ingénieurs-Conseils (FIDIC)[6] are being adopted to an increasing extent.

There are other standard conditions and, for a particular project, special conditions may be considered appropriate. However, the use of standard conditions, and particularly the two mentioned above, probably serves best the interests of both the employer and contractor who have become familiar with them. During recent years precedents and court decisions have been established which have resulted in a better understanding of the various clauses; the lesser used forms do not have this advantage. However, due to the specialised nature of well construction, certain matters need particular consideration and are usually covered by special conditions (or by conditions of particular application). Some of these are discussed in later sections of this chapter.

Specifications

Essentially, specifications are a set of instructions to the contractor regarding methods of construction, standard of workmanship and the types of well structure to be constructed. The approach to the preparation of the specification and the degree of detail required are dependent upon the selected method of bidding, the type of contract, the purpose of the wells to be constructed and on any special features peculiar to the project. These aspects are discussed in Section 6.

Drawings

The drawings should include typical designs of the wells to be constructed and maps showing both the sites of the wells and the extent of the area in which the work will be located. They may also include geological maps, existing borehole logs and other pertinent site details.

Bills of Quantities

A bill of quantities consists of a list of items giving brief identifying descriptions and estimated quantities of the work comprised in a contract. The ICE Civil Engineering Standard Methods of Measurement (CESMM)[7] contain a standard bill of quantities for the measurement of works in site investigations; this includes "Trial holes and shafts, boreholes, wells, samples, tests and instrumental surveys". Although the standard is suited to geotechnical work it is considered inappropriate for use in water well construction. A proposed typical format for water wells, summarising the main items that could be included in a bill of quantities and which can form a basis of measurement is presented in Appendix A.

Bills of quantities should relate to the specification in such a manner that all works to be undertaken by the contractor can be measured and paid for. Where uncertainties exist as to the exact nature of some of the works to be executed, or where part of the work is to be executed by a sub-contractor (for example, laboratory core analyses and geophysical logging), the bill of quantities should contain an appropriate provisional sum or sums. A schedule of rates is sometimes included with the bill of quantities to enable variations of the work to be priced readily. This is particularly useful in projects where geological conditions can vary. Obviously, the scope and extent of variations that can be covered by the schedule have to lie within the general framework of the specification.

Schedule of Particulars

The schedule of particulars comprises a list of items which should be completed by the tenderer and which relate to the plant, equipment, materials and personnel to be used or employed under the contract. It is always prudent for the schedule to be as detailed as possible so that the capability of tenderers can be judged with reasonable accuracy. A proposed format is included in Appendix B.

3. TENDERS AND TENDERING PROCEDURES

TYPES OF TENDER

Three types of tender are in general use:

   (i) unit price;
  (ii) lump-sum; and
 (iii) guaranteed yield.

In many cases the unit price and lump-sum methods are combined so that parts of the work, such as mobilization and demobilization, are priced as lump-sum items and the drilling and construction works in unit price form. Guaranteed yield tenders are uncommon in cases where large organizations such as government agencies require significant water supplies. They are often still used in the private sector, where owners of farms and factories find it convenient to commission contractors to provide an individual guaranteed groundwater supply.

Unit Price Tender

The AWWA standard[3] recommends that this method is most suitable where the extent of the work, depth of wells and other conditions are not well known. It enables the estimated quantities to be changed significantly during execution of the work. Because of the variable nature of subsurface strata, even within the small area of a wellfield, the great majority of tenders fall within this category. Hydrogeologists or engineers experienced in preparing contract documents can normally estimate the extent of the works reasonably confidently after careful consideration of the geological and hydrogeological evidence. Where, however, the extent of the work may have to be changed, it may be necessary for the bill of quantities to be varied. In the FIDIC conditions of contract[6] a maximum variation of 10 per cent of the contract sum is recommended, within which the unit rates shown in the bill of quantities remain fixed. For an increase or decrease in work greater than 10 per cent of the contract price, the amount of the contract price is normally agreed between the engineer and the contractor; failing this it is fixed by the engineer who takes account of all relevant factors, including-the contractor's site and general overhead costs. In some cases, where the quantities cannot be estimated within the 10 per cent margin, engineers tend to increase this to 15 or 20 per cent and the contractor prices his offer accordingly. Variations exceeding 20 per cent are considered unreasonable and should be avoided.

Some employers, who need the works executed within a given budget, insist that the engineer should obtain their prior approval before authorising expenditure in excess of the contract sum. It is important that this is made known to the contractor by introducing an appropriate clause in the conditions of contract.

It is important that major variations which may invalidate the rates in the bills of quantities should be viewed in relation to individual items in the bill. In extreme cases, an overall increase or decrease of 10 per cent as applied to the contract sum may imply a variation of 100 per cent or more for a particular item. Thus, although the contract sum may not be exceeded or reduced beyond the limits permitted by the contract, the contractor would still have to provide services or materials substantially different in scale from those intended under the contract. Under such circumstances it might be appropriate to issue a variation order which would include rates different from those entered in the bills.

In order that tenders can be adjudicated properly, it is important that items in the bill of quantities should relate as closely as possible to the specification—and that there are no tests or works described in the specification which the contractor has not been asked to price in the bill. The AWWA standard[3] recommends that separate unit price and measurement forms should be used for consolidated and unconsolidated formations. The distinction between the two types is somewhat unnecessary as the type of formation, and the appropriate construction, should have been made clear in the specification. Experience has shown that a bill of quantities with the appropriate preamble forms a sound and clear basis for pricing and measurement. The items to be included in the bill depend upon the required well construction and tests.

It is recommended that none of the rates in a unit price tender should be entered on the forms by the engineer or the employer. This contrasts with the AWWA recommendation[3] for pricing the item for "setting up and removing equipment". It is felt that fixing this price in advance restricts the competitiveness of bids and is therefore unfair to the employer. Furthermore, in international tenders where tenderers may come from different parts of the world, it would be difficult if not impossible for the engineer to determine a realistic sum for this item. For other items relating to the construction, development and testing of wells, lump-sums should be avoided and tenderers asked to enter unit prices.

Uncommon units such as "bags of cement" for grouting, or lump-sum prices for items like pump-testing and development, should be avoided.

Lump-Sum Tender

The AWWA[3] recommends that this type of tender is the most suitable in cases where the conditions of construction and the extent of work are known with reasonable accuracy. In water well drilling this is seldom the case, except perhaps during the construction of production wellfields following completion of a detailed exploratory programme. Normally, the contractor is asked to tender a sum for construction of the whole of the works as specified, any additions or extra work being paid for on a unit price basis. It is always wise to provide for circumstances that may cause either a decrease or an increase in the amount of work. Such provision can be made by having the tenderer enter unit rates for items likely to change. It is generally considered unwise for the engineer or the employer to fix such unit prices as this may give rise to claims if the prices become unrealistic during the currency of the contract.

In general, lump-sum tenders should be avoided as they are usually prone to misunderstandings and claims during the execution of the works because often the interpretation of the specification by prospective tenderers may not coincide with the intentions of the engineer or employer.

The adjudication of tenders of this type can be difficult and not always successful as the engineer or employer cannot have the benefit of comparing the pricing of individual items by the tenderers (as is the case in unit price tenders) nor in assessing whether the tenderer has followed the specification properly.

Guaranteed Yield Tender

The guaranteed yield method of obtaining tenders involves the contractor undertaking to provide the employer with a certain quantity of water. This type of contract has been rightly criticised, as follows[1]:

"While appearing to warrant the production of a certain quantity of water many guaranteed yield contracts for wells really do not provide an absolute guarantee. Most such contracts have the effect of setting a price for the quantity said to be guaranteed which becomes a reference figure for negotiating a settlement at a lower price if the quantity is less than anticipated.

There seems nothing wrong with this—except where the contractor claims that the guarantee he offers is absolute, when, in fact, it may not be so. Neither the contractor nor the well owner can beat nature".

The guaranteed yield contract is not recommended for use either by government or other authorities requiring large quantities of water. If for special reasons this form of contract is adopted, then the conditions of contract should include an appropriate clause which clearly states the intentions of both parties entering into contract and the limits imposed as to the quantity to be procured by the wells from the formations to be penetrated. Such a clause will form a basis for an equitable agreement among the parties if the wells do not perform as intended by either party. A final point on this type of contract is that the employer or engineer cannot stipulate the method of construction as this has little meaning when the contractor takes upon himself the responsibility for producing the required quantity of water.

TENDERING PROCEDURES

Procurement of Tenders

There are two methods in general use for procuring tenders:

(1) by direct invitation from a list of firms, known to and approved by the employer;
(2) by national and/or international advertisement.

In both methods, the employer provides brief particulars of the scheme as regards its location, size, depth, diameter and number of wells, timing and any special circumstances.

In the first method, invited firms are supplied with the tender documents with a time limit for their return. In the second method, the employer can either issue tender documents to all companies who express interest (open tender) or he can follow a prequalification procedure leading to the preparation of a short list which will include those tenderers that the employer deems capable of undertaking the work. Only those tenderers on the short list are subsequently issued with tender documents.

In prequalifying tenderers the following procedure is normally followed:

(a) All firms who express interest in tendering for a project are asked to provide financial and other information on their company; a list of projects previously undertaken (with a brief account of their nature, location and value); projects in hand; experience on projects similar to that advertised; type and availability of plant and where at present deployed; previous and current employers and engineers to whom reference may be made; bankers and insurers; and any other details relevant to the project.
(b) On receipt of this information and on checking the references supplied, the employer and/or engineer will prepare a short list of companies (normally about six) to whom tender documents will be issued.

Obviously, obtaining tenders by direct invitation is the least time consuming and is the simpler of the two methods. Procuring tenders through a prequalification procedure can take up to six months or more but has the advantage of attracting a wider spectrum of companies and enhancing the competition. Where possible, open tendering should be avoided as it can lead to a large number of diverse tenders often prepared by companies not in fact capable of undertaking the work.

Adjudication of Tenders and Award

The general procedure and criteria employed to adjudicate tenders are normally made known to the tenderers in the "Instructions to Tenderers". In general, the following criteria are used:

(i)   Plant and equipment
(ii) Previous experience of similar projects
(iii) Experience of proposed personnel
(iv) Construction period
(v)   The competence displayed in preparing tender
(vi) The tender sum.

Because price is an important factor, which can often influence adjudication, it is always advisable that tender evaluation is carried out in two separate stages—a technical assessment followed by a financial assessment. This leads to a "two envelope system" where tenderers are asked to submit their technical and financial proposals separately. In such cases, the technical offer is evaluated first and a short list of contractors drawn up (usually three in number). The financial offers of only those tenderers on the short list are then opened, and the award made to the lowest if it is considered that all tenderers on the short list are equally capable on technical grounds.

Insofar as one tenderer cannot have exactly the same capability as another, the "two envelope system" suffers from the disadvantage that the award may be made to the least competent contractor whose price may be only marginally lower than that of the most competent. Nevertheless, the method provides a fair basis to all parties, providing the technical assessment has been as detailed and as rigorous as possible.

The "two envelope system" is normally used when tenders are procured by invitation or prequalification. However, in some cases the law of the country, or regulations within the government body inviting the tenders, may require that the award is made to the lowest tenderer.

When tenders are procured by "open tender" the frequent diversity of tenders, and the lack of knowledge of the capability of all interested companies, make it unwise to be committed to making an award to the lowest bidder or to any bidder. Clearly the employer should make this clear to prospective tenderers, the normal phrase being: "The employer is not bound to accept the lowest or any tender received". This method of bidding should be avoided where possible as not only does it have the disadvantage of creating a large number of bids, many of which may be from irresponsible or inexperienced contractors, but it also causes responsible contractors to spend time and money with perhaps little chance of success.

4. CONDITIONS OF CONTRACT

ASPECTS CONSIDERED

Most standard conditions of contract contain a large number of clauses (about seventy) which define and explain the duties and responsibilities of the employer and contractor, and of the engineer appointed by the employer to supervise the work. Experience has shown that these standard conditions adequately cover most, if not all, of the needs of water well construction contracts. Because, however, of the special nature of water well construction, some aspects may need modification. In the following sections, some of these are discussed in detail, namely:

(1) Engineer's representative
(2) Site
(3) Inspection of site
(4) Responsibility for site conditions
(5) Adverse physical conditions

(6) Accuracy of estimated quantities
(7) Period of maintenance and maintenance of works
(8) Work by day and night
(9) Health and safety

Naturally many other matters—such as assignment and sub-letting, insurance, commencement time and delays, claims, arbitration and liquidated damages—are important but as these are common to all civil engineering works they are not discussed in this chapter.

Engineer's Representative

The engineer's representative is normally defined as the person appointed by the engineer and notified in writing to the contractor to watch and supervise the construction, completion and maintenance of the works on his behalf. The conditions of contract stipulate his duties and responsibilities, and the engineer may delegate certain of his duties to him dependant upon all the circumstances. Normally, the engineer's representative has no authority to vary the works or order any work outside the contract. In well construction, however, minor changes to the specification (such as well depth and duration of pump-testing) may need to be carried out urgently with no time available to obtain prior approval of the engineer or employer. It is therefore always in the interests of the project for the engineer's representative to be delegated authority to act under such circumstances so that unnecessary delays and risks to wells are prevented.

Site

The "site" is normally defined as the lands and other places on, under, in or through which the works are to be executed and any other lands or places provided by the employer for the purpose of the contract. This definition is perfectly adequate for the drilling of water wells. However, proposed borehole locations are sometimes marked on a drawing without clear definition of what constitutes the site. Often in the development of wellfields, or in exploratory drilling, the location of individual boreholes (which often evolves during the execution of the work) cannot be accurately known in advance. It is therefore wise to define the site as an area within which drilling operations could take place rather than as points on a map or drawing.

Inspection of Site and Responsibility for Site Conditions

Under the conditions of contract issued by FIDIC[6], "Inspection of Site" is dealt with as follows:

"The Employer shall have made available to the Contractor with the Tender documents such data on hydrological and sub-surface conditions as shall have been obtained by or on behalf of the Employer from investigations undertaken relevant to the Works and the Tender shall be deemed to have been based on such data, but the Contractor shall be responsible for his own interpretation thereof. The Contractor shall also be deemed to have inspected and examined the Site and its surroundings and information available in connection therewith and to have satisfied himself, so far as is practicable, before submitting his Tender, as to the form and nature thereof, including the sub-surface conditions, the hydrological and climatic conditions, the extent and nature of work and materials necessary for the completion of the Works, the means of access to the Site and the accommodation he may require and, in general, shall be deemed to have obtained all necessary information, subject as above mentioned, as to risks, contingencies and all other circumstances which may influence or affect his Tender".

The wording of the clause is fair to all parties and has been generally found workable. The emphasis in the second paragraph given by the wording ". . . and to have satisfied himself, so far as practicable . . " is particularly relevant in water well drilling where the nature of the sub-surface conditions cannot be accurately known by the contractor prior to actually drilling at the site.

Since sub-surface conditions cannot be accurately known, contractors must base their tender prices on existing information made available to them, or that they have collected through their own researches or obtained by visual inspection and measurements of rock outcrops and existing wells.

Since sub-surface conditions cannot be accurately determined without the contractor undertaking his own exploratory drilling—which is unreasonable—it would be generally unfair to hold a contractor responsible for conditions which cannot be reasonably foreseen by either the engineer or the employer.

However, Section 1-1.4 of the AWWA standard specification[3] suggests the type of information that should be given to tenderers and then continues to state:

"This information regarding sub-surface conditions is intended to assist the contractor in preparing his bid. However, the owner does not guarantee its accuracy, nor that it is necessarily indicative of conditions to be encountered in sinking the well to be constructed thereunder, and the contractor shall satisfy himself regarding all local conditions affecting his work by personal investigations, and neither the information contained in this section nor that derived from maps or plans or from the owner or his agents or employers shall act to relieve the contractor from any responsibility hereunder or from fulfilling any and all of the terms and requirements of his contractor."

In addition to the above, engineers often add:

"The contractor is required to drill through all kinds of strata actually encountered".

This type of clause is unreasonable and contradictory and leaves the contractor in doubt as to the reliability and value of any of the information given by engineer or employer. Moreover, the additional requirement that "the contractor shall drill through all kinds of strata actually encountered" does not relieve the employer from paying the contractor, if he encounters strata having significantly adverse properties that could not be reasonably foreseen.

Therefore, to avoid ambiguity, the employer or engineer should state as clearly as possible the basis on which the contractor is expected to price. There are two clear options:

(a) The contractor is informed that it is entirely his responsibility to assess the sub-surface conditions and that he shall price accordingly; the employer will not accept any claims due to any conditions encountered by the contractor. If this approach is adopted, the employer should be willing to accept a higher tender as the contractor will have to cover himself for all contingencies.

(b) The engineer or employer will make available to the contractor all existing information and accept that, if adverse physical conditions and artificial obstructions are encountered during the execution of the works that could not have been reasonably foreseen by an experienced contractor he will be entitled to receive additional payments. This approach is considered fairest to all parties and generally results in the procurement of reasonably priced tenders.

Adverse Physical Conditions Relating to Sub-Surface Strata

Adverse or unforeseen (or unexpected) physical conditions in relation to underground strata are often difficult to define owing to variable lithologies encountered even within the same group of rocks. Experienced drilling contractors accept this and their tenders include for the range of physical conditions normally encountered within a given rock type. For example, if the rock to be penetrated were a karstic limestone, an experienced contractor would expect fissures and perhaps caverns and loss circulation zones and would price his bid accordingly. Under normal circumstances, a contractor who drills through such a formation and encounters loss of circulation, could not reasonably claim "unforeseen or unexpected" conditions. Similarly, an experienced contractor asked to drill through alluvial sediments would assume that these sediments would be generally unconsolidated and that sands, clays and mixtures of these lithologies might be encountered. Therefore he would tender to include for any appropriate drilling fluid and perhaps temporary lining to combat any hole instability. Other drilling problems such as stuck-pipe or stuck-casing, normally form a part of the risk that the experienced drilling contractor includes in his offer.

Conditions that can be considered as unforeseen may arise when lithologies are encountered which have significantly different properties from those indicated by available data and where such conditions will necessitate the contractor changing his methods of work, plant, equipment and materials. For example, if in an extreme case all the data and information had indicated the presence of alluvial sediments, whereas the contractor actually encountered granitic basement rock, in such circumstances most of his equipment such as bits, drill collars, and even drilling rigs might have been inappropriate. The contractor would then be justified in claiming for additional payment on the grounds of unforeseen physical conditions.

It is always wise and fair to all parties concerned that the tender document should describe as clearly as possible the conditions the contractor is likely to encounter. It is also important that responsible contractors interpret the information given by the engineer in the light of geological conditions that might be variable and not in the narrow context of strict lithological interpretation. For example, if the rock to be penetrated were described as a "sandstone" in fact and the contractor encounters a clayey or ferruginous or calcareous sandstone, such a variation should not be interpreted as "unforeseen conditions" unless it imparted properties to the rock that resulted in a significant modification of the drilling techniques and equipment which the contractor had intended to use.

Names of formations should generally be avoided as they normally do not give the correct impression of the lithology of the rock unless the tenderers have a particular knowledge of the formation. Thus, descriptions such as "Wealden Clay" or "Carboniferous Limestone" or "Nubian Sandstone" are in themselves insufficient. The engineer should, however, direct the tenderer to the particular source of his information or he should clarify that, for example, "Wealden Clay" is clayey sand rather than clay. Also, statements such as "the contractor shall drill through igneous rock" are generally uninformative since the term "igneous rock" covers a wide range of rock-types varying from lavas (basalts, rhyolites etc.) to plutonic rocks (gabbros, granites etc.) which may or may not be significantly weathered and fractured.

Much controversy and fruitless effort can be avoided if engineers, employers and contractors seek the advice of experienced geologists and hydrogeologists in preparing and pricing tender documents and in resolving differences as to what might constitute "unforeseen conditions".

Accuracy of Estimated Quantities

In well drilling it is often difficult to estimate accurately the works even in areas where the geology is reasonably well known. The thickness of aquifer, grain size distribution of sands within aquifers and location of permeable zone in fissured aquifers, are all often difficult to predict. Thus the quantities entered in the bills of quantities must necessarily be estimates, the accuracy of which is inherently less than normally experienced on civil engineering construction contracts. Providing that additional work on any item does not necessitate the use of plant other than that intended to be used for the execution of the work as originally specified, and that the additional work done does not increase the time for completion, then the scheduled rates normally apply and no variation order need be issued.

Period of Maintenance and Maintenance of Works

It is always difficult to estimate the period of maintenance, which is normally calculated from the date of substantial completion of the works. Some employers like to specify long periods of maintenance, perhaps hoping that if the well does not perform as intended then the contractor will have an obligation under the contract to repair it. It is also often customary for payments of up to 10 per cent of the contract price to be retained and payment to be made after the expiration of the period of maintenance. In borehole contracts, long periods of maintenance are usually unwise as they tend to make tender prices unacceptably high. In overseas contracts it is often impracticable and uneconomic for a contractor to keep plant in the country for long periods to make good any defects that may come to light during operation of the wells. In practice long periods of maintenance imply inflated tenders and a temptation on the part of the contractor to write-off any retention money due to him after the expiration of the contract.

It is important that writers of drilling contracts are clear in their minds as to what they desire to achieve during the period of maintenance. Basically, the objectives of maintenance are twofold:

(i) That during the maintenance period the contractor is obliged to finish any outstanding work and carry out any repairs and make good any defects. In other words that the works are delivered to the employer in the condition required by the contract. Usually, the period required for such works is fairly short, being only two to three months.

(ii) That the employer may require maintenance of the wells subsequent to the takeover, which would involve periodic cleaning, disinfection, removal of incrustation and perhaps replacement or repair of screens and casings. The period for such maintenance is usually quite long (a few years at least) and may span the life of service of the wells. Inclusion of this type of maintenance in a borehole construction contract is not recommended. Nevertheless, if it is required then it should take the form of a separate agreement between the employer and the contractor.

There are many cases, especially relating to urban supply schemes, in which quite long periods of maintenance after takeover are stipulated, but the maintenance period often expires before the wells are commissioned, because the civil engineering works required to place the supply scheme into service often commence after the water well source has been proven. In such cases the employer may incur significant expenditure whilst the wells are standing idle awaiting commissioning.

Under normal circumstances, it is considered that the period of maintenance should be kept within the time limit required for repairs and making good any defects. Providing that supervision of the works during construction is carried out competently and diligently, most defects become apparent during construction and testing and are rectified on the spot before the contractor moves to a new borehole. Close supervision and the recording of all operations are therefore imperative in determining whether a borehole does not perform as intended because of defects, poor workmanship, poor design or poor aquifer characteristics. It is apparent therefore that, because of the underground location of the borehole structure and the difficulty of visual inspection, a contract which holds the contractor responsible after takeover does not make poor workmanship good, cannot replace competent supervision, and yet adds to the cost of the works.

Work By Day and Night

In normal civil engineering construction the contractor is required to give notice of his intention to carry out works during the night and locally recognised days of rest. In water well drilling, the contractor can only work economically if he is allowed to work continuously by day and by night. Certain operations, such as drilling through unstable formations, running casing and screen, and gravel packing, warrant continuous and speedy work if caving-in and collapse of borehole walls is to be avoided. Also, pump-testing should not be interrupted if the results are to prove amenable to analysis. For these reasons the contractor should be allowed to work by day and by night and on locally recognised holidays.

HEALTH AND SAFETY

During construction the safety aspects of the well site rest with the contractor. He is responsible under the contract for initiating, maintaining and supervising all safety precautions and programmes in connection with the works. Therefore he is obliged to take all necessary precautions for the safety of all employees and other persons, and for the prevention of damage, injury and loss to the works and all materials, property and equipment whether on or off the site.

Statutory regulations regarding health and safety on construction sites exist in many countries at both local and national level. In the UK the Health and Safety at Work Act 1974 has been designed to protect all workers as well as the health and safety of other persons affected by those at work. The objects of the Act have been described[8] and its implications for the drilling industry set out[9]. The latter document also details the duties of the employer, employees and manufacturers, together with the precautions to be undertaken at drilling sites. Other publications are also relevant, such as those prepared by the ICE[10], the Australian National Water Well Association[11] and the BSI[12].

Standard conditions of contract contain several general clauses relating to health and safety on construction works sites. Additional clauses may be included in a contract concerned particularly with water well drilling and dealing with such aspects as:

(1) the transportation of drilling rigs and other heavy equipment:
(2) the presence of underground or overground electric cables and other services;
(3) the use of corrosive and radioactive materials, welding and cutting equipment, explosives, wire ropes and lifting equipment;
(4) the risk of fire; and
(5) the encountering of gas or water under high pressure.

To minimise such risks the contractor may be asked to provide special first aid, safety and fire-fighting equipment and monitoring equipment for gas or radioactivity. More generally he may be requested to ensure that the site is provided with adequate lighting, ventilation, fencing and fire breaks together with suitable washing and toilet facilities. In water well drilling operations it is also often required that the contractor takes adequate measures to prevent pollution of the well and to disinfect the well after completion.

5. CONTRACT SUPERVISION AND RESPONSIBILITY

CONTRACT SUPERVISION

Contractor's Superintendence

All standard forms of contract require the contractor to provide the necessary superintendence during execution of the works and as long thereafter as necessary. In water well construction, the supervisory personnel should be experienced and knowledgeable in the drilling, construction and testing of boreholes and any other peripheral specializations such as mud control, gravel packing and well development.

Specialised contractor's personnel normally required on site are:

(*a*) Tool pushers
(*b*) Drillers
(*c*) Assistant drillers
(*d*) Rig mechanics
(*e*) Casing-screen welders
(*f*) Geologists
(*g*) Logging technicians.

The contractor should appoint to the site an authorized agent or representative who will be in charge of the works and the safety of all operations and to whom the employer or the engineer can issue directions or instructions.

Engineer's Supervision

In most contracts an engineer is appointed by the employer to supervise the works, and his power and duties are defined in most standard forms of contract. In general the engineer's role is:

(i) to ensure that the works are carried out in accordance with the contract;
(ii) to measure the work executed by the contractor;
(iii) to issue payment certificates; and
(iv) to vary the nature, quality and quantity of the work (depending on the authority vested in him by the employer).

In supervising the contract within these defined limits, the engineer is acting as an agent of the employer in ensuring that the work is being carried out in accordance with the contract. The engineer has other roles to play in the contract, such as deciding disputes, where he acts independently and not as an agent of the employer. In this capacity it is crucial that he is seen to be scrupulously objective and impartial between the employer and the contractor.

In most contracts the engineer is represented on site by the engineer's representative, whose powers are defined in the conditions of contract. Dependent upon circumstances, the engineer may delegate certain of his powers to his representative by notice in writing. One of the most valuable and effective contributions that engineer's site supervisory staff can make lies in keeping a comprehensive record of all events during the currency of the works. This is best achieved by daily completion of a standard diary form with entries for the numbers of machines and men working or idle during the day, with operations on which they were engaged, weather conditions, visitors, actual drilling depths achieved, accidents, delays to progress (with causes), matters discussed with the contractor's agent and the like.

In drilling contracts, the contractor will normally be required by the terms of the specification to complete a regular series of forms. These should be signed by the contractor and then endorsed by the engineer's representative. Such information will be conclusive historic evidence as to the conditions encountered and the progress made, and will prove invaluable in resolving disputes that may arise. For this reason both signatories should ensure that the forms are carefully scrutinised before signature. Should the engineer's representative not agree with the record presented, he should clearly state this on the form, together with his own version of the situation. The engineer will receive copies of the reports in due course and should be informed immediately of any such disagreements. Continuing disagreements between the engineer's representative and the contractor must be resolved without delay by an effective intervention of the engineer. Continued disagreement despite such intervention is often best resolved by replacement of personnel.

The engineer must keep the employer informed of the progress of the works and of the financial position, preferably by routine reports in an agreed format. The employer must be informed as soon as possible of any likely additional costs. These may be due to urgent additional work found to be necessary, or to unexpected circumstances which will lead to claims for additional costs by the contractor. Where possible, the employer's prior approval should always be obtained for additional expenditure arising from extra work.

In water well drilling, it is quite common for unforeseen conditions to be encountered and an experienced and competent engineer's representative is of great value to all parties to the contract. Changed conditions may need variations in the works; clear instructions to the contractor for the required variations must be given as soon as possible.

As in the case of the contractor's personnel, the engineer and his supervisory staff should not only be experienced in the drilling, construction and testing of water wells but also have adequate knowledge of contract procedures and conditions. Therefore, a team comprising civil engineers (with knowledge of contracts) and hydrogeologists (knowledgeable in water well construction) will often best serve the interests of both the employer and contractor.

RESPONSIBILITIES UNDER THE CONTRACT

Contractor's Responsibilities

Normally, full responsibility for construction, maintenance and safety of the works rests with the contractor. The contractor, save insofar as it is legally or physically impossible, should execute and maintain the works in strict accordance with the contract and the employer's or engineer's instructions.

However, the contractor cannot be held responsible for either the design or specification of permanent or temporary works which have been prepared by the employer or the engineer. Also, unless expressly stated otherwise in the contract, the contractor has no responsibility for the performance of wells in terms of yield, drawdown and specific capacity, providing that they have been constructed in accordance with the designs and specifications and with the engineer's subsequent instructions.

Engineer's or Employer's Responsibility

The engineer and employer are responsible for the specification and design of the temporary and permanent works provided they have been prepared by them, and the contractor has been instructed to construct these accordingly. The engineer and employer are not responsible for the performance and safety of the work.

As regards methods of construction—in water wells this means methods of drilling, running casing screens, gravel packing and development—responsibility will rest either with the contractor (if the specification requires the contractor to adopt any method of his choosing but to the approval of the engineer or employer) or the engineer or employer (where the specification requires a given method or methods for constructing and completing the wells). It should be noted that approval or consent by the engineer or employer to the contractor's proposed methods of construction does not normally relieve the contractor of any of his duties or responsibilities under the contract. This aspect is discussed further in Section 6.

6. TECHNICAL SPECIFICATIONS AND BILLS OF QUANTITIES

APPROACH

Specifications can vary from a detailed set of instructions describing the methods to be used for constructing the wells to a simple description of the requirements of the employer. In "guaranteed yield" tenders, the specifications may consist only of a typical drawing showing the construction of the permanent well required by the employer, together with a brief description of the material for the linings. In the "unit price" and "lump-sum" methods, specifications are generally more detailed.

The Well Drillers' Association of the UK recommends[13]:

"(1) That the Client could reasonably be expected to define his requirements as fully as possible but not necessarily the methods to be used to achieve them unless there is some special need to do so.
(2) That the Specification and Bill of Quantities should:
    (a) be relevant to the work in hand and should not be standard documents possibly containing inessential and misleading items. On the other hand it would appear desirable that there should be as much standardisation as possible so as to provide optimum ease of preparation and understanding.
    (b) be completely inter-related and set out so that all the requirements of the Specification can be clearly seen and associated with items in the Bills.
(3) That the Bills of Quantities should contain all foreseeable items required to complete the contract to Specification, including provisional items where areas of uncertainty exist. A Schedule of Rates should always be included to enable variations to be made to extend or reduce the work covered by the Bill items"

All three basic concepts are sound but, contrary to paragraph (1), in many cases the methods of construction should also be defined by the employer or the engineer as fully as possible. It is in the nature of well drilling that most temporary works which lead ultimately to the completion of the well exercise a profound influence on the utility and proper function of the final product. There are many occasions in well drilling when the method of construction and the techniques used to overcome drilling problems may subsequently prove to be detrimental to the performance of the completed well. Furthermore, as the methods to be adopted often influence not only the final product but also the cost of the works, tenders cannot be properly adjudicated unless the methods of construction are clearly defined. Moreover, clear and detailed specifications tend to safeguard employers from irresponsible and incompetent bidders who, in different circumstances, may procure the contract by virtue of the lowest price and then can often proceed with disastrous results.

A typical format, found to be generally successful, is presented below. Under each heading the engineer or employer should state clearly and concisely what is required of the contractor. When clearly set out the proposed format can provide the means by which the desired result can be achieved; also, misunderstandings during the execution of the works can be avoided.

The format can be modified to suit particular circumstances or hydrogeological conditions. If coring is called for under the contract, a special section can be inserted which details the type of coring, size of cores, recovery and storage, and other relevant matters. Care should be taken that the specification complements and does not contradict the conditions of contract or any other sections of the contract documents.

TYPICAL TECHNICAL SPECIFICATION FORMAT

Section A — General

Description of works
Purpose of works
Location of works
Existing information (including hydrological, geological and drilling conditions)
Safety measures
Units of measurement

Section B — Borehole Drilling

Method of drilling
Drilling plant and equipment (including drilling rigs, mud pumps, drilling assemblies, fishing tools, compressors etc)
Drilling fluids

Section C — Borehole Construction

Typical designs of the boreholes to be constructed
Schedule of construction
Gravel packing (if required)
Cementation

Section D — Materials

Casings and accessories
Screens and accessories
Centralizers
Reducers, hanging tools, packers etc
Gravel pack
Cement

Section E — Well Stimulation

Development
Use of mud dispersants
Acidification, hydraulic fracturing etc (if required)

Section F — Tests

Verticality and alignment
Sand analyses
Geophysical logging
Pump-testing and recovery
Chemical analyses of water (if required)

Section G

Sampling (geological, water samples etc)
Recording and reporting

Brief Guide to Preparation of Technical Specifications

Borehole Drilling

The engineer should specify the method or methods of drilling acceptable to him but should also make it clear to the contractor that he may put forward other methods for the engineer to consider. Such alternative proposals should be embodied in a letter accompanying the contractor's bid. This approach safeguards against unbalanced bids and ensures that the plant proposed by the tenderers is appropriate to the job. There have been instances where, because of a low tender price, engineers have accepted a method of drilling and types of plant which were not appropriate for the work—with disastrous results.

The engineer has a clear and responsible role to play in specifying drilling methods and should not withdraw from his responsibility by inviting clauses such as: "The contractor shall use drilling rigs, plant etc to the approval of the engineer". Although engineers often tend to seek protection under Clause 14 (7) ICE[5], which states that " . . approval by the engineer of the contractor's programme . . . and the consent of the engineer to the contractor's proposed methods of construction . . . shall not relieve the contractor of any of his duties or responsibilities under the contract", it would not be in the interests of the employer for the engineer to approve, even reluctantly, any plant he may consider unsuitable. It is important that the engineer takes the initiative in specifying the method which he considers most suitable for the conditions; at the same time, however, he should not take an inflexible approach by rejecting out of hand any alternative proposals submitted by tenderers.

It is not normally necessary to stipulate the make, capacities and properties of drilling rigs and plant but in the "schedule of particulars" the contractor should be asked to state the make, model and major specifications of his plant (such as rigs, mud-pumps and compressors). This information is of paramount importance in evaluating the major items of plant proposed by the contractor, in judging whether he can successfully achieve the degree of workmanship stipulated by the specification, and whether he can overcome ordinary drilling problems with the minimum of delay and effort. In assessing such plant the engineer should bear in mind whether:

(i) The rig can drill the hole at the specified diameters and depths with reasonable ease and speed.
(ii) The rig has sufficient capacity to install the string of casings and screens of the weights and dimensions specified.
(iii) The rig has sufficient capacity to free stuck pipe or casing as normally encountered in drilling operations.
(iv) The rig can handle a drilling string (including drill pipe, drill collars, stabilizers etc) of such weights and dimensions to ensure reasonable penetration with the minimum of misalignment.
(v) The mud-pumps are of sufficient capacity to ensure sufficiently high annular velocities for proper and efficient cleaning of the hole during drilling. (Similar considerations apply to the size of compressors in air/air-foam and down-the-hole hammer drilling techniques).

Details of the drilling assembly are not normally specified unless special conditions are expected, such as steeply inclined strata, substantial fissuring with cavernous horizons, and interbedding of very hard and very soft layers. Engineers should ask for specific assemblies if the formation to be penetrated will present problems of hole deviation. The use of proper assemblies suitable for the rock to be penetrated is in the interest of both the contractor and the employer. On one hand, the contractor would gain by encountering fewer problems in running casing and logs and also less chance of enduring stuck pipes and drill pipe fatigue, etc. On the other hand, the employer would be assured that within the limitations of the geological conditions to be encountered he would have a straight hole, a smooth string of casing, a good cement bond and a good gravel pack.

If the holes are to be rotary drilled (see Chapter 13, Section 12), the types of drilling fluids to be used should be specified. Bentonite fluids tend to damage the aquifer through invasion and formation of a mud cake, whereas organic polymers, water and air-foam fluids are proving successful under a wide variety of conditions. One notable exception is that these low density fluids cannot be used where artesian pressures are expected. The circulating drilling fluid should be monitored during drilling operations so that its properties remain consistent with good drilling practice and cause least damage to the aquifer. Parameters to be monitored should include: mud weight, viscosity, filter loss, sand content, electrical conductivity and pH value.

Standard instruments for measurement of these parameters are readily available. Monitoring and interpreting mud data provide proper mud control which can save both the contractor and employer time and money in the long run.

Borehole Construction

Typical designs of the boreholes to be constructed should be provided to the contractor. The designs should show clearly the various components of the boreholes and should include diameters, depths, wellheads and positioning of casings, screens, gravel pack, cement grout and any other items of the permanent structure. When temporary works (such as a pilot hole which is to be enlarged) precede the permanent works, they should be clearly shown on the drawing and stated in the text. Because these drawings are often only typical presentations of the final construction, a clear indication should be given to the contractor of likely variations from the typical design.

It is always advisable to include in the specification a schedule of construction which should briefly describe the sequence of operations in constructing and completing the boreholes. The schedule not only conveys information to the contractor regarding the time interval between operations (which will assist him in pricing and planning) but also ensures that important operations such as gravel-packing and development are carried out efficiently and promptly with minimum delay.

Gravel packing can be undertaken using a variety of methods, depending upon the depth and construction of the borehole. The most common method is by means of a tremie-pipe although more sophisticated methods such as the use of a cross-over tool may be employed under special circumstances. Similarly, cementation of the annular space can be carried out by a variety of techniques either through the casing or through the annular space. In both cases the method of emplacement should be clearly defined as this will influence the quality and cost of the work. The nature and gradation of the gravel-pack should also be clearly specified.

For cementing operations the type and mix of cement and cement additives should always be described—preferably by reference to international standards such as those published by the BSI, American Petroleum Institute (API) or American Society of Testing Materials (ASTM).

It is often desirable to specify the method of installation of casings and screens—particularly in deep wells or where different sizes are joined together or where special assemblies are required—so that the contractor can price accordingly.

Casings and Screens

It is always prudent to define the material to be used by reference to an international standard, and to provide accurate information as to the dimensions, wall thickness, weight and type of joints etc of the casing or screen required. Failure to provide this information or vague statements such as "the casings shall be 400 mm steel pipes" always create confusion and prejudice proper tendering. Fortunately, international standards published by API[14,15,16], ASTM[17], BSI[18] and other bodies apply to most materials in use for water well casing. The most commonly used materials are ordinary steel, stainless steel, GRP, PVC and ABS.

Unfortunately, there are no international standards for screens and therefore more care should be exercised in defining the requirements accurately. It is always important to state the type of screen required (slotted pipe, bridge slot, louvre, wirewound etc), the column and external collapse strength, the open area, the slot width, the type of material, dimensions, type of joints and lengths.

In specifying the type of material to be used, the likely formational pressures should be estimated so that material of sufficient strength can be selected.

Well Stimulation

Well development (see Chapter 13, Section 5) is the most frequently used method of well stimulation. Being an important aspect of well completion it merits a comprehensive description of the operations required; these in turn depend upon the type of well construction. There are a number of techniques (mechanical surging, surging and backwashing with compressed air, jetting and overpumping). The selected methods should be clearly specified so that the contractor can procure appropriate plant and equipment. As the operation is often time-consuming—requiring the installation, removal and the frequent insertion and withdrawal of tools (air pipes, eductor pipes and jetting tools)—it is advisable that the contractor is made aware with reasonable accuracy of the procedures to be adopted so that he can price accordingly.

Other forms of well stimulation such as acidification are normally used in carbonate rocks. Hydraulic fracturing is rarely used in water well construction. Again, a clear description of what is required should be included in the specification. Because of the specialist nature of the techniques (particularly hydraulic fracturing) it is often prudent to ask contractors to describe in detail the methods and procedures they propose to adopt. It is sometimes prudent to arrange discussions during the period of adjudication so that any necessary clarification may be obtained.

Verticality and Alignment

Boreholes and well linings should be as true to vertical as possible, and should not be misaligned or have dog-legs, corkscrews or bends. The drilling of a perfect hole is always difficult, and the most that should be expected from a contractor is the construction of a hole which will permit the screens and casings to be properly installed—and the pumps to be inserted readily and to operate satisfactorily. Misaligned holes are more problematical than holes out of plumb, as the former frequently cause severe pump wear and stuck casings, screens and drill pipe.

The amount of deviation permitted will depend upon the purpose for which the borehole is designed—for example, deviation in small diameter observation boreholes is not crucial—on the type of pump to be installed and on the strata to be penetrated. In specifying verticality limits, these factors should always be borne in mind if tolerances either too lax or too strict are to be avoided.

Methods of testing for deviation in lined wells have been described by the AWWA[3]. In open holes mechanical drift indicators can be used. It is important that specifications describe the methods to be used for testing for verticality and alignment and also stipulate acceptable tolerances.

Geophysical Logging

In specifying geophysical logging (see Chapter 9) the specification should make clear the suite of logs to be run, the standard of logging required and the manner in which the results are to be presented. Where the logging is to be carried out by the employer or by a specialist logging company, this should be so stated and appropriate standing times incorporated in the bill of quantities or schedule of rates. In water well construction, it is normal for the drilling contractor to carry out the logging himself except where special logs are needed.

Pump-Testing and Recovery

This operation (see Chapter 5) needs to be described in some detail, particularly as regards the anticipated discharge rates, the expected pumping depths, the required method of discharge measurement, frequency of measurement of water levels, and disposal of the water abstracted. Such information will assist the contractor in pricing and procuring all necessary equipment and personnel. It is always advisable to state under what conditions the test will be rejected by the employer or engineer. Normally, a test is rejected when the measurement, collection and recording of data are unsatisfactory or when the test is interrupted because of plant failure.

Sampling and Reporting

The specification should include for the collection, labelling and storage of geological samples by the contractor. These are normally taken at specified depth intervals.

The form in which the sampling work should be presented should also be stated. The following reports are normally needed:

  (1) Daily drilling report
  (2) Drilling string and assembly
  (3) Bit record
  (4) Casing and screen tally
  (5) Lithology log and penetration rate
  (6) Geophysical logs
  (7) Sieve analyses and gravel pack
  (8) Verticality and alignment
  (9) Well development
 (10) Pump-testing and recovery.

7. REFERENCES

1. Edward E. Johnson Inc. 1975 "Groundwater and wells", Johnson Division, UOP Inc., St. Paul, Minnesota 55165.
2. National Water Council 1978 "Civil engineering specification for the water industry".
3. American Water Works Association 1966 "Standard for deep wells, A100-66".

4. Environmental Protection Agency 1975 "Manual of water well construction practices, EPA-57019-75-001", US Office of Water Supply.
5. Institution of Civil Engineers—Association of Consulting Engineers—Federation of Civil Engineering Contractors 1979 "Conditions of contract for works of civil engineering construction".
6. Fédération Internationale des Ingénieurs-Conseils 1977 "Conditions of contract (international) for works of civil engineering construction".
7. Institution of Civil Engineers and the Federation of Civil Engineering Contractors 1976 "Civil engineering standard methods of measurement".
8. British Safety Council 1975 "Health and safety—the new law".
9. British Drilling Association 1980 "Surface drilling—Part 1 of Code of safe drilling practice", Brentwood, Essex.
10. Institution of Civil Engineers 1972 "Safety in wells and boreholes".
11. National Water Well Association of Australia 1976 "Drillers' training and reference manual".
12. British Standards Institution 1978 "Safety precautions in the construction of large diameter boreholes for piling and other purposes, BS 5573".
13. Well Drillers' Association of the United Kingdom 1982 "Proposed specifications and bills of quantities for water boring and allied operations". (Water Research Centre and Water Authorities Association 1985).
14. American Petroleum Institute 1976 "Specification of casing, tubing and drill pipe, API 5A".
15. American Petroleum Institute 1976 "Specification for thermoplastic line pipe (PVC and CPVC), API 5LP".
16. American Petroleum Institute 1976 "Recommended practice for care and use of reinforced thermosetting resin casing and tubing, API RP 5A4".
17. American Society for Testing Materials 1943 "Standard specification for black and hot-dipped zinc coated (galvanised) welded and seamless steel pipe for ordinary uses, ASTM 120-73".
18. British Standards Institute 1967 "Specification for water well casing, BSS 879".

Additional Bibliography on Contract Administration

1. Wallace, D. I. N. 1974 "The international civil engineering contract", Sweet and Maxwell, London.
2. Wallace, D. I. N. 1979 "The ICE conditions of contract: A commentary", Sweet and Maxwell, London.
3. Abrahamson, J. M. W. 1979 "Engineering law and the ICE contracts", Applied Science Publishers, London.

APPENDIX A. TYPICAL FORMAT OF BILL OF QUANTITIES
Notes Forming Part of the Bill

(a) The Bill of Quantities is not and does not purport to be either exhaustive or explanatory of all the obligations and duties of the Contractor and in making his Tender and pricing the items of the Bill the Tenderer must cover himself and shall be deemed to have covered himself for:

   (i) All services and materials which according to the true intent and meaning of the Contract Documents may be reasonably inferred as necessary for carrying out in a good and workmanlike manner the Works shown upon the Drawings and described in the Specification whether expressly mentioned therein or not, and
   (ii) All the duties, obligations, liabilties and responsibilities which any of the Contract Documents places upon the Contractor in connection with or in relation to this Contract.

(b) The Tenderer shall insert against each item in the Bill such rates and prices as he may deem necessary to cover the above requirements. Items shall not be bracketed together, and where no rate or price is inserted against any item in the Bill the cost thereof shall be deemed to have been included and spread proportionately over all items priced by the Tenderer.

(c) All measurements in these Quantities are taken strictly net. The principle of net measurement shall apply to all works executed under this Contract. The Bill of Quantities will form the basis of measurement.
All quantities measured for payment will be measured by the Engineer on the basis of actual quantities in place of accepted permanent work performed according to the principle of net measurement.

Note: Insert any other relevant points.

Bill of Quantities

Item No.		Quantity	Unit	Rate	Amount
1.	Mobilization of all necessary plant, equipment, personnel, office and store accommodation, ancillary works and services for drilling, construction, development, testing etc of (no.) boreholes at (location) in (country)	LUMP	SUM		
2.	Demobilization at completion of contract	LUMP	SUM		
3.	Set up and dismantle rig, plant, equipment etc; include for rigging down and for transport between boreholes (per borehole)	—	No.		
4.	Clear and reinstate sites (per borehole)	—	No.		
5.	Supply and install (material) conductor pipe of .....mm diameter to be set .....m below ground level; include for drilling hole to accommodate and cementing in place (per metre)	—	m		
6.	Drill hole to a diameter of .....mm:				
	From .....m to ......m (insert depth intervals as required)	—	m		
	Note: Repeat 6. for other hole diameters and rock types as required				
7.	Supply, install and withdraw temporary casing as specified				
	From .....m to .....m (insert other depth intervals as required)	—	m		
8.	Enlarge (or under-ream hole) to a diameter of .....mm				
	From .....m to .....m	—	m		
	Note: Repeat 8. for other diameters and rock types as required				
9.	Supply, join and install .....mm nominal diameter casing of the type, weight and dimensions specified:				
	From .....m to .....m	—	m		
	Note: Repeat 9. for other diameters, as required				
10.	Supply, join and install .....mm nominal diameter screen (or slotted casing) with .....mm slot width and of the type, weight and dimensions specified	—	m		
	From .....m to ......m (insert other depth intervals as required)				
	Note: Repeat 10. for other diameters and slot widths				

Bill of Quantities (contd)

Item No.		Quantity	Unit	Rate	Amount
11.	Supply and install centralizers of the type specified at .....m depth intervals for:				
	(a) .....mm diameter casing	—	No.		
	(b) .....mm diameter screen	—	No.		
	(insert other screen/casing diameters as required)				
12.	Supply and install as specified:				
	(i) Reducers	—	No.		
	(ii) Hangers	—	No.		
	(iii) Packers	—	No.		
	(iv) Casing shoes	—	No.		
	(v) Sealing plates etc	—	No.		
	(Use as appropriate)				
13.	Supply and place gravel pack (or formation stabilizers) in annular space as specified (per m^3 of gravel pack emplaced)				
	(a) Between .....mm hole and .....mm screen				
	From .....m to .....m	—	m^3		
	(insert depth intervals as required)	—	m		
	(b) As in (a) but for other annular spaces				
14.	Carry out cementation of annular space; include for supplying cement and additives, mixing and emplacing cement grout, all as specified (per m^3 of cement grout emplaced)				
	(i) Between .....mm hole and .....mm casing				
	From .....m to .....m	—	m^3		
	(ii) As in (i) but for other annular spaces	—	m^3		
15.	Carry out, measure and record verticality and alignment tests (per survey)				
	(a) In open hole	—	No.		
	(b) In cased/screened hole	—	No.		
16.	Carry out borehole geophysical logging as specified (per log run)				
	(i) SP–Resistivity	—	No.		
	(ii) Gamma ray-neutron	—	No.		
	(iii) Caliper	—	No.		
	(iv) Conductivity–Temperature	—	No.		
	(v) Other	—	No.		
17.	Develop boreholes as specified (include for installation and withdrawal of any equipment used for development and supply and use of dispersants) (per hour development)				
	(a) Circulating with water	—	hr		

Bill of Quantities (contd)

Item No.		Quantity	Unit	Rate	Amount
	(b) Mechanical surging	—	hr		
	(c) Surging with compressed air and air lifting	—	hr		
	(d) Developing by pump	—	hr		
	(e) High velocity jetting	—	hr		
	(f) Other	—	hr		
18.	Carry out test pumping as specified; include for installation, withdrawal of pump and setting up all ancillary plant and equipment and all measurements and records (per hour of pumping)	—	hr		
19.	Carry out recovery tests as specified; include for all measurements and records (per hour of recovery)	—	hr		
20.	Supply and install discharge pipeline for disposing a discharge of up to .....l/s (i) From borehole to .....m	—	m		
21.	Disinfect borehole as specified; include for provision of all materials and tests (per borehole)	—	No.		
22.	Provide and fix tamper-proof cap and well head as specified (per borehole)	—	No.		
23.	Carry out sieve analysis; include for all measurements and records (per sample)	—	No.		
24.	Take and store water samples during development and testing as specified (per water sample)	—	No.		
25.	Take and store geological samples at .....m depths intervals as specified (per sample)	—	No.		
26.	Prepare and deliver in bound form full report in .....copies for each borehole containing all measurements, records, data, graphs, as constructed drawings, logs etc all as specified (per borehole)	—	No.		
27.	Standing time (rate only per hour of standing)	—	hr		

APPENDIX B. PROPOSED FORMAT FOR SCHEDULE OF PARTICULARS

(a) The Tenderer shall complete the schedule giving particulars of plant, equipment, materials and personnel he intends to use or employ for the execution of the Works under the Contract.

(b) The Tenderer shall include in the Schedule the names of manufacturers and suppliers of plant, equipment and materials. He shall also state whether he owns or he intends to buy or rent any of the plant, equipment and materials included in this Schedule.

(c) Failure to complete this Schedule will preclude consideration of the Tender by the Employer.

1. DRILLING RIGS

Number of rigs...

Rig No.	1	2	3	4
Identification				
Type				
Make				
Model				
Hook load capacity (kg)				
Drill string				
Running casing				
Date bought				
Date inspected				

2. MUD PUMPS

Number of mud pumps ....
State whether integral with rig or not:
Number of stand-by mud pumps:

Mud Pump No.	1	2	3	4
Identification				
Type				
Make				
Liner size (mm)				
Stroke (mm)				
Efficiency (per cent)				
Displacement				
Volume (l/min)				

3. DRILL STRING

Drill Pipe

String No.	1	2	3	4
Nominal size				
Weight per metre				
API grade				
Length of string (m)				
Tool joint size and style				
Tool joint OD (mm)				
Date of last inspection				

Drill Collars

String No.	1	2	3	4
Quantity				
Max. OD (mm)				
Min. bore (mm)				
Average length (m)				
Approx. string weight (kg)				
Tool joint style and size				

Stabilizers

String No.	1	2	3	4
Quantity				
Max. OD (mm)				
Min bore (mm)				
Average length (m)				
Approx. string weight (kg)				
Type				

4. Auxiliary Equipment*

(i) Mud tanks (mud pits)

State whether: Mud tanks or mud pits are to be used

....

Number	Size	Capacity each
....	....	....

(ii) Mud mixing equipment

Pumps...

Prime mover...

*Note: In Sections 4 to 10 of this schedule as printed the number of blank ("stringer") lines has been restricted in the interests of space. In practice, sufficient lines should be provided to accommodate all the information required.

Mud agitating equipment ....

(iii) Shale shakers and desanders (if any)

Describe ....

(iv) Generators

Number	Make	Model	Type	Capacity (KW)
....	....	....	....	....

(v) Generators and prime movers

Number	Make	Model	HP or KW
....	....	....	....

(vi) Lighting system

Describe ....

(vii) Transport vehicles

Number	Make	Model	HP	Load capacity
....	....	....	....	....

(viii) Water tankers

Number	Make	Model	Capacity
....	....	....	....

(ix) Welding equipment

Make	Model	Type
....	....	....

(x) Fishing tools (list type)

....

(xi) Grouting equipment

Pumps

Make	Type	Pressure (kN/m^2)	Displacement volume (m^3/min)
....	....	....	....

Grout pipes

Quantity	ID (mm)	OD (mm)	Type
....	....	....	....

5. COMPRESSORS FOR DRILLING AND WELL DEVELOPMENT

Number	Make	Type	Intended use
1 etc	....	....	....

Compressors	1	2	3	4
Free air delivery (m^3/min)*				
Normal effective working pressure (kN/m^2)				
Max effective working pressure (kN/m^2)				

*At normal working pressure

6. PHYSICAL AND GEOPHYSICAL TESTING EQUIPMENT

(a) Measurement of penetration rate (state whether or not a geolograph is to be used; describe proposed method if geolograph is not to be used)

....

(b) Deviation survey equipment (state number, make, model and type of drift indicators)

....

(c) Mud testing equipment including sand content measuring equipment (state make, model, type and instruments to be included)

....

(d) Contact gauges (dip meters) for water level measurement (state number, make, type and length of tape)

....

(e) Flow measurement device (state whether orifice weir or V-notch or rectangular weir; give number of measuring devices)

....

7. Development and Pump-testing Equipment

(i) Development

Air line

String No.	1	2	3	4
Nominal size (mm) Length of string (m) Type				

Eductor Pipe

String No.	1	2	3	4
Nominal size (mm) Length of string (m) Type				

Jetting tools (state number and diameter and number of nozzle)
....

Other Development Tools (describe)
....

(ii) Test well pumps

Include details of gate valves, pressure gauges, types and rating curves of pumps etc:
....

(iii) Prime movers for pumps (engine drive for generators)

Number	Make	Model	HP or KW
....	....	....	....

Pump No.	1	2	3	4
Type Make Model Discharge (l/s) Head (m) Max. diameter (mm)				
Diameter rising main (mm)				
Length rising main (m)				

8. Materials

(a) Drilling muds and mud dispersants (describe)

(b) Sand pack (origin and gradation)
....

(c) Cement

Type: ....
Manufacturer: ....
Commercial name: ....

(*d*) **Cement additives** (if any)

....

(*e*) **Casings and screens** (give details if alternative to specification). State manufacturer and quantity (m)

....

(*f*) **Cement baskets** (type and number, state manufacturer)

....

(*g*) **Packers, hanging tools, reducers etc** (describe):

....

9. ALLOCATED PERSONNEL (Curricula vitae to accompany offer)

Personnel	Number	C.V. needed (tick)
Project Manager		
Tool pushers		
Drillers		
Assistant drillers		
Mechanics		
Welders		
Geologists		
Logging Technicians		
Drivers		
Roughnecks		

10. INSURANCES (name(s) and address(es) of insurer(s) who will provide cover as required by the contract)

....

Air/foam rotary drilling in the Yemen Arab Republic
(Courtesy of George Stow & Co Ltd)

Chapter 13

DRILLING AND CONSTRUCTION METHODS

1. INTRODUCTION

DEEP boreholes have been drilled for several thousand years, perhaps initially by the Chinese some 3000 years ago. The methods used have become increasingly more sophisticated, particularly during the last hundred years or so.

In the UK, water well drilling is now a continuous activity, for several decades subject to no appreciable growth nor decline. The only notable change has been the demise of hand-sunk wells in favour of mechanically drilled boreholes, about 200 of which are constructed annually. This very small output is balanced by the average diameter being of 610 mm, taken to an average depth of 90 m. Figures for industrialised north-west European countries are proportionately similar and few individual dwellings possess a borehole.

An entirely different situation is found in North America where it is the rule rather than the exception for householders to own and operate a private borehole, statistics indicating that some 9400 contractors drill more than 850000 boreholes annually at an average diameter of 100 mm to about 70 m average depth.

Geology strongly influences drilling procedures in Britain. There are few comparable countries where such a wide variety of formations have been compressed into so small an area; this requires a contractor to hold equipment and personnel capable of dealing with all likely drilling conditions, which results in a versatility unmatched elsewhere. However, it is also true that a contractor specialising in small diameter repetition drilling in an area overseas can attain a level of productivity unheard of in this country.

The above extremes call for very different approaches to the choice of drilling methods. It must also be borne in mind that the developing countries—encouraged by United Nations agencies—are providing an expanding market for drilling rigs and tools, often orientated towards 'low-cost' and 'appropriate' technology. This has a beneficial effect on the equipment range in that simple plant with its inherent reliability and rugged versatility is still being manufactured. At the other end of the scale, highly sophisticated specialised rigs supported by adequate service can provide formidable drilling efficiency in the hands of skilled operators.

In Section 2 the range of drilling methods available will be fully described and discussed.

2. RANGE OF METHODS AVAILABLE

CABLE-TOOL (PERCUSSION) DRILLING

In this technique, a string of tools is suspended on a steel wire rope passed over a rubber-cushioned crown sheave at the top of the drill rig and down under a spudding sheave at the end of a beam. It then passes up and over a heel sheave at the fulcrum end of the beam. The rope finally leaves the heel sheave to coil in storage on a braked drum—the bull reel or main reel (Fig. 13.1)*.

Note: Figs. 13.1 to 13.7 and the accompanying text are based on "A review of water well drilling methods" (Cruse, K. 1979, Q. J. eng. Geol., 12, 79) and are reproduced by kind permission of the Geological Society of London.

A connecting rod transmits motion from a variable-stroke crank to the free end of the beam, which imparts a reciprocating action to the rope and suspended tools.

The string of tools consists of a bit (chisel) surmounted by a drill stem (sinker bar), perhaps drilling jars, then a swivel rope socket containing a mandrel into which is secured the wire rope (Fig. 13.2).

Bits, forged from high-carbon steel, are required to penetrate, crush, mix and ream. Bits for hard formations have a blunt angle of penetration, a large cross-sectional area (to give strength), and small 'flutes' or waterways in the sides; bits for soft clay have a sharp edge, generous clearance angles, and large waterways coupled with a small area to allow rapid reciprocation through a viscous slurry.

Originally nearly all cable-tool rigs were equipped with a blower to provide air to a forge for bit sharpening and reforming, but most outfits are now equipped with portable electric welding plant with which a moderately hard build-up can be applied to the working face.

The drill stem is located above the bit to provide weight plus directional stability. Also, by its pumping action, it moves the cuttings upwards, away from the bit.

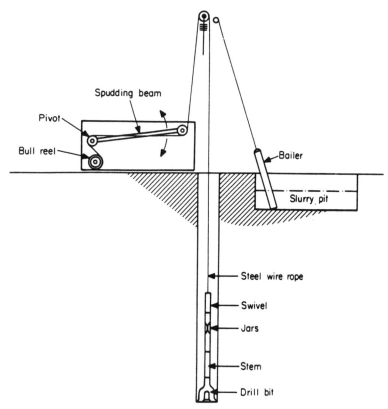

Fig. 13.1. Cable-tool or percussion drilling

Drilling jars must be fitted above the stem when there exists the risk of pieces of rock falling in and trapping the tools in the hole; they are for jarring stuck tools out of the hole. Jars in no way aid the drilling function; rather they add to the list of mechanical weakness points and for this reason are often omitted by the driller when prudence should have prompted their inclusion. They are in effect sliding links giving some 150 mm of free vertical movement, designed to be of a diameter only a little larger than the stem. They are usually operated by exerting a powerful continuous pull on the cable and stuck tools. At the same time a coaxial weight (a jar bumper) is run down the drilling cable. A blow on the top of the rope socket momentarily closes the jars which snap back smartly to give a positive upward blow.

The topmost item in the tool string is the swivel rope socket. This has the dual function of attaching the wire rope (drilling line) to the tools and imparting a continuous rotation. Inside the socket is a mandrel into which the drilling line is secured. The top shoulder of the mandrel consists of a smooth, hardened surface which is located inside the rope socket and carries the full weight of the tool string.

The drilling line is of non-preformed, left-hand lay, steel wire rope. When drilling begins, the weight of tool unwinds the rope with a clockwise rotation and transmits this torque through the socket/mandrel face to the tools, countering any tendency for the right-handed tool joints to unscrew. The tools thus slowly begin rotating, moving the bit to a new position on each stroke and ensuring a circular borehole.

Depending on several factors, such as viscosity of cuttings, tautness of line, weight of tools, etc., the drilling line eventually resists this unwinding process and returns to its natural 'lay', and it does this by momentarily breaking the friction

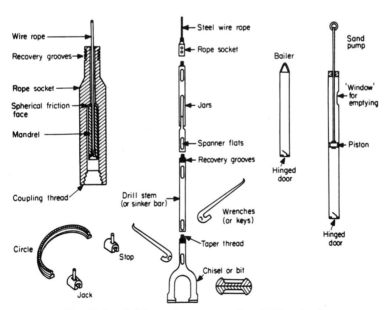

Fig. 13.2. Cable-tool or percussion drilling tools

between mandrel and socket. This occurs during each stroke or as infrequently as 60 or more strokes at greater depths. The slowly rotating mass of tools is, of course, unaffected by this sudden line reversal, which is felt by the driller with his hand on the line.

There is now a column of tools weighing between 300 and 4 000 kg reciprocating at 40-80 times per minute at a stroke of between 1.2 and 0.4 m, and slowly rotating. At this stage the driller makes two vital adjustments to his rig controls; firstly, the blows per minute are set so that the tool string is just—and only just—able to keep up with the motion imparted to it by the reciprocating spudding beam without causing a violent snatch in the drilling line, and secondly the drilling line is paid off the bull reel until the bit *just* reaches out and gives a sharp, clean blow to the bottom of the borehole. The reaching-out and rapid withdrawal is assisted by the rubber-cushioned crown sheave and, especially at depth, the natural spring in the drilling line.

The above two settings are absolutely critical and leave little margin for error. Too slow a rate and the bit will make little progress; too fast a rate and the rig will be seriously damaged; too slack a line invites verticality problems and poor progress; too tight a line produces a vertical hole but little footage and the swivel may not function, thus halting rotation of the tool.

Water is fed to the borehole in small quantities until such time as a natural supply is reached. The purpose of the water is to produce a slurry out of the cuttings and to suspend this material above and away from the bit face. Lesser functions are to cool and lubricate the tool string.

With the tools correctly striking the bottom of the hole, the depth of the borehole will increase and this will alter the two critical relationships just discussed. The driller then adjusts the secondary or 'fine' control on the brake of the bull reel until the reel begins to creep round and so pay off a fraction of drilling line at every stroke.

The drilling rig is now in operation and, assuming no change of stratum, will continue until the driller feels, literally, that the thickening slurry is retarding the tools. He will then either slow the rig blows to keep in step with them for a while, or he will clean the hole out, an inevitable operation sooner or later.

A bailer (or shell) is used for this purpose (Fig. 13.2). The tools are withdrawn and the bailer run into the borehole on a separate line called the sand line. The bailer consists of a steel tube with a hinged door or clack on the bottom. The slurry fills the bailer and is hoisted to the surface and tipped into the slurry pit (Fig. 13.1) the operation being repeated until the hole is clean.

When drilling hard rock the driller may leave a little slurry in the hole so that the rock chips are in suspension. He may even introduce a little clay for the same purpose.

A sand pump (Fig. 13.2) is similar to a bailer but incorporates a piston within the tube and the piston rod is attached to the sand line. When lowered in the extended position the tube comes to rest on the bottom of the hole. Further lowering allows the piston to travel to the bottom of its stroke with its disc valve open. Rapid withdrawal draws the piston with closed valve up the tube which sucks the slurry through the bottom door. At the top of the stroke the piston reaches its retainer and lifts the complete sand pump to the surface.

When drilling begins, a short guide tube or conductor pipe is always drilled or hand-sunk into the ground. This tube is essential to stabilize the ground around the working area and has to be placed in a truly vertical alignment to start and maintain a vertical hole.

In chalk or firm sandstone with little overburden, it may only be necessary to drill for, and place, some 15 m of permanent tubes as a seal against surface-water contamination. The remainder of the borehole would be drilled open-hole and present no problems.

The opposite is the case in unconsolidated material, especially if interbedded with hard strata. Under these circumstances it is sometimes necessary to start at large diameter and insert several tiers of intermediate temporary tubes. In any case, if the drilling engineer is anticipating problem conditions, such as boulders, he may opt to start at an extra large diameter, if only to be able to gain some freedom with regard to verticality when inserting the permanent tubes. This may, of course, introduce an undesirable element in that a large annular space would require more cement grout, but this is usually compensated by the fact that the greater diameter provides more scope for 'swallowing' boulders and placing emergency tubing.

Two or three decades ago, it was common practice to drive tubes down to their required depth if they became tight, and indeed the standard schedule of percussion drilling tools includes for this facility. The tubes were provided with 'drive-heads' and 'drive shoes'. Heavy jacks were standard tools but as most of the tubes were socketed there were many cases where recovery was impossible and boreholes were completed incorporating several columns of unnecessary tubes.

The use of flush-jointed temporary tubes and the realization of the need to keep tubes on the move by 'surging' resulted in the application of persuasion instead of force to the tubes, and their recovery is now the rule rather than the exception.

In the past, horses were used in Europe and America to power some of the early rigs and eventually steam power was applied, especially where the greater depths required considerable power to raise the combined weight of wrought iron rods and the bit assembly. At depths greater than 300 m the weight ot the falling rods on each stroke caused tool and rig damage, so a sliding joint and trip-release device was introduced at a point above the chisel. This permitted a free-fall action for the tools while the rods reciprocated down quietly to pick them up again. Rotation was achieved by another device near the chisel consisting of a pair of ratchets actuated by the vertical motion of the tools. Drilling feed was provided manually by a turn-screw between the uppermost rod and the beam. Sometimes wooden rods with iron fittings were used to reduce weight.

The main drawback to the above system was the wasteful proportion of time taken to withdraw the rods in order to clean out the hole. In an attempt to overcome this problem, hollow drilling rods were tried and water was passed through them with the aim of raising the cuttings to the surface.

ROTARY DRILLING

Direct Circulation

In this system a fluid, usually clay-based, is mixed in a mud pit or tank and delivered by a pump at high pressure through a flexible hose to the top of a rotating column of tools called the drill string. It then flows through the tools to the bottom of the borehole and returns to the surface and back into the mud pit (Fig. 13.3).

At the bottom of the drill string the bit is either of the roller cutter type or, less commonly, the plain drag bit type. A roller rock bit carries three or four hard steel toothed cutters, free to run on bearings. The body of the bit has passage ways to conduct the flow of fluid which cools and lubricates the rollers, cleans the teeth and carries away cuttings.

The bit is applied to the bottom of the hole and rotated at speeds of 30-300 rpm—depending on diameter and strata—and weight is applied within a range of 250-2750 kg per 25 mm of diameter.

In hard rock the line contact of the teeth causes the formation to fail due to overloading; in softer rock the rollers are skewed slightly to add a twisting action and, for soft rock, the teeth are formed to impart a tearing action.

Drag bits carry no rollers. They have three or four hard-faced blades and cut soft strata in a manner similar to a wood auger. They drill rapidly in very soft conditions but tend to stress the drill pipe and over-tighten the tool joint if used through hard bands where chatter can occur.

The same verticality and straightness constraints for percussion-drilled holes apply equally to rotary boreholes, but the latter technique suffers from a disadvantage in that a continuous weight must be placed on the bit and therefore gravity has less effect on the tool column. However, a kink-free hole is generally achieved due to the rigid influence of the drill collars.

Drill collars (Fig. 13.3) are extra heavy pipes fitted above the bit to provide the essential weight and assist straight drilling by their stabilising influence. In addition, as they are of large diameter relative to the borehole, a smaller annulus results, causing an increased fluid velocity which rapidly carries away the cuttings from the bit vicinity. Ideally, most of the tool string length should be in tension from the crown wheels of the drilling rig but this is not always possible and weight is sometimes added by a hydraulic or chain mechanism known as a 'pull-down'.

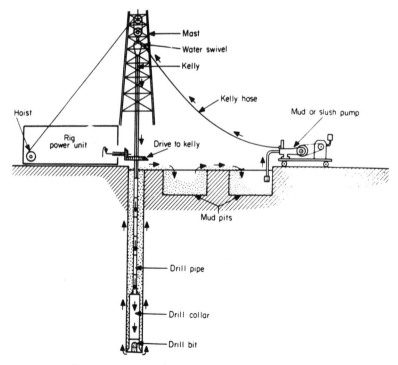

Fig. 13.3.   Normal direct circulation rotary drill

The main length of the drill string consists of drill pipes (Fig. 13.3) added as depth increases; they extend from the top of the drill collar to the surface. They are usually in lengths of about 3-10 m and the diameter is selected to suit the drilling conditions, e.g. the clear diameter through the pipe and joints must be such as to cause minimum head loss on the descending fluid and the drill pipe must be large enough to promote a reasonable rising fluid velocity for a given mud-pump size.

The uppermost length of pipe, of special construction, is called the kelly. Its purpose is to transmit rotary drive from the rotary table and it is therefore of a square, hexagonal, or round section with grooves or flutes to fit into a corresponding aperture in the rotary table. This permits free vertical movement and allows the kelly either to feed off down the hole as drilling proceeds or to be withdrawn.

The swivel is located at the top of the kelly. It contains a bearing assembly which carries the complete weight of the tool string. It also has an entry for the drilling fluid, passing up from the mud-pump through the kelly hose, and a suitable gland to control the passage of the fluid from the static swivel to the rotating kelly.

As drilling proceeds, and cuttings are brought to the surface, the kelly will travel down through the rotary table until the swivel unit reaches the table. Feed off is then stopped, rotation may be slowed, and the circulating fluid allowed to continue for a short time to carry the most recent cuttings up and away from the bit and drill collars. The pump is then stopped, the kelly withdrawn and unscrewed from the drill pipe, while the latter is suspended in the rotary table slips. Another drill pipe is added and lowered with the drill-pipe column until it is at table level, when the kelly is again attached and circulation re-started. Rotation is engaged and finally the bit applied once more to the bottom of the hole. The above procedure is repeated until such time as final depth is reached or the tools withdrawn to change bits.

Reverse Circulation

This method differs from the more common 'direct circulation' system in that the drilling fluid is circulated in the reverse direction. Basically the equipment is similar in general arrangement (Fig. 13.4) but considerably larger, e.g. the water way through the tools, drill pipe, swivel, and kelly is rarely less than 150 mm in diameter. The minimum practical drilling diameter is in the order of 400 mm while sizes in excess of 1.8 m are not unknown.

Conventional tricone bits within the above diameter range would be impractical and it is, therefore, usual to fit a composite roller rock bit. This consists of a sturdy bed plate, to the underside of which are fitted a number of toothed rollers so arranged that the full face of the borehole is tracked. The bed plate incorporates short passages which rise to a common bore at the coupling flange. Material dislodged by the drilling action is drawn up through the bit centre and rapidly carried to the surface.

A full diameter flanged-fitted tube, bolted above the bit, contains a central tube of the same bore as the drill pipe. Apertures in the end of the outer tube allow the downward-flowing clean water to pass unrestricted. This assembly, a stabilizer, restrains lateral wandering of the tools.

A composite bit requires weight to provide penetration and this is achieved, as in other methods, by incorporating drill collars in the drill string. These may be of a considerably smaller diameter than the borehole. Under some conditions the sequence of stabilizers and drill collars may be rearranged. The bits described above are suitable for unconsolidated strata, soft clay, and soft rock. Stiff clay would call for a drag bit.

Drill pipe for reverse circulation work must have couplings which present an unrestricted inner bore and are therefore normally of the flanged type. They are also relatively short in order to employ a corresponding short kelly to avoid high suction lifts above ground.

Suction pumps, attached to the kelly hose outlet, used to be of the centrifugal 'paddle' type which drew out the full flow of water containing all the cuttings. As a flow of 4.5 m³/min through a 150 mm system generated a velocity of nearly 213 m/min and debris with a diameter of 140 mm or more was pumped, the pump had a short life. It is now usual to combine the centrifugal pump with a venturi unit producing a suction in a circuit separate from the pump. A few rigs use compressed air only as the vacuum induction circuit above ground.

Water and cuttings are discharged into a large temporary lagoon the size of which is determined by the 'rule of thumb' that the volume should not be less than three time the volume of the drilled hole. A 750 mm borehole drilled to 60 m would require a lagoon 12 m long, 8 m wide, and 1 m deep, the spoil from which takes up additional area. This is but one of several factors to consider when selecting the system of drilling and these will be discussed later.

The lagoon is often divided or 'baffled' to encourage settlement of the cuttings in one area well away from the channel returning the clean water to the borehole.

Mud is seldom used because one of the advantages of reverse-circulation drilling is that relatively clean water is imposed upon the aquifer and therefore there is no invasion of the formation. In the event of clays being drilled in the upper section of the hole, the lagoon may be cleaned out and refilled with fresh water before proceeding into the aquifer.

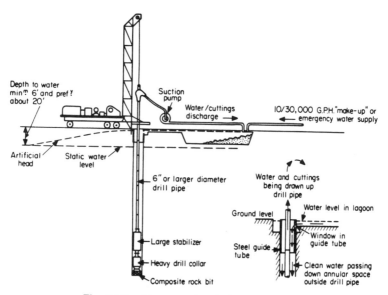

Fig. 13.4.   Reverse circulation rotary drill

The main advantage of this method is the very rapid rate of drilling at large diameters, especially in unconsolidated sands and gravels. Boreholes are sometimes drilled and lined within 24 hours as no cleaning is necessary (development is a different phase) and indeed, speed is essential in unconsolidated strata as the driller may be relying upon only 1 or 2 m of head surcharge in the hole to prevent collapse and possible loss of tools.

It will be apparent that the imposition of a head of clean water upon an unconsolidated stratum will involve some water losses. In view of this, one of the prerequisites of reverse-circulation drilling is the close availability of a substantial supply of water for make-up. This is often quoted as 45 m³/hour and in practice can amount to between 9 and 70 m³/hour.

While the average reverse-circulation system utilises suction as the motive power behind the circuit, there are circumstances, such as pipe friction at greater depths, low water table etc., when suction is insufficient and, therefore, most drilling rigs have provision for introducing an air-lift into the system. This is accomplished by incorporating air pipes in the drill pipe lengths, either concentrically or paired on the outside, with a mixer jet arranged to discharge inside the drill pipe at a suitable level.

Under ideal conditions penetration rates of 0.6 m/min have been recorded and average rates of 12 m/hour are quite common. It should be noted that the flanged-and-bolted drill pipe connections most commonly used involve time-consuming handling and there appears to be room for technical improvement here. Rotational speeds are within the 8-50 rpm range; drilling depths average 120 m and occasionally 300 m are obtained.

Drilling Fluids

The first recorded drilling fluid, water, was directed through hollow rods on percussion drilling rigs in an attempt to remove cuttings without having to withdraw the tools—a time-consuming operation. Clay was sometimes added to increase viscosity and density to aid the lifting of rock chippings and gravel.

One of the basic principles of rotary drilling is the use of a circulating fluid and for some 50 years this has been a clay-based mud.

Clay or Bentonite. A natural clay or bentonite mud is the most common drilling fluid for oil and water wells. Its functions are to:

(1) remove cuttings from the face of the borehole and transport them to the surface;
(2) lubricate and cool the bit and tool string;
(3) promote suspension of cuttings in the borehole whilst adding further drill pipe;
(4) allow settlement of fine cuttings to the bottom of the mud pits;
(5) consolidate the formation by build-up of a "wall-cake" and so reduce loss of fluid into the formation;
(6) control subsurface pressures (artesian flow); and
(7) provide some buoyancy to long strings of tools or casing in deep boreholes.

Cleaning the bore face is essential to ensure maximum bit life and optimum drilling efficiency. The mud then rises to the surface at a calculated velocity, depending upon pump capacity and speed, borehole size and drill pipe size. The cuttings, however, will not rise at this velocity because they tend to sink under gravity. This 'slip velocity' must never be greater than the annular mud velocity to ensure transport of the cuttings to the surface. If the borehole has partially collapsed in any section, it will there be of larger diameter and the mud velocity will be correspondingly lower. The geometry of the system must therefore be known and the mud flow carefully controlled if cuttings are to be effectively transported to the surface. In addition to velocity, other factors that influence the removal of cuttings are the density and size of the cuttings, and the viscosity and density of the fluid. The viscosity determines the lifting power of the mud and depends on the properties and dispersal of the suspended solids in it, while density affects the carrying capacity of the mud through buoyancy, expressed in weight per unit volume of mud.

There is a close relationship between the factors controlling mud behaviour, requiring careful consideration when making any changes. To overcome cuttings-slip, the viscosity may be increased, but in so doing pumping pressures may be raised to an unacceptable level. An increase in density may have beneficial effects down the hole but when the mud reaches the mud pit it may fail to drop the fine solids, recirculation of which would cause excessive wear of the pumping plant, especially if the cuttings were abrasive.

Wall-cake buildup is an essential function of the drilling mud. When drilling in a formation with a pore size which prevents ingress of mud particles, the water portion of the fluid filters into the formation, leaving behind a 'filter cake' of mud solids. This remains on the borehole wall and controls loss of further water into the formation.

The hydrostatic head exerted by the mud column acts upon the wall-cake and enables drilling to continue through loose sands and gravels without resort to the insertion of temporary casing. Too thin a cake and the walls may be broken down by the rotating tools, and heavy water losses can occur which might aggravate the condition. A very thick cake will make drill string removal difficult and even cause collapse of the hole due to the swabbing effect of the bit.

Another important property found in natural and commercial clays is gelling, gel strength being governed by the thixotropic character of the mud. When actively in circulation, the mud has a given fluidity which is substantially reduced when it comes to rest. This feature is used to full advantage when shutting off the flow to add further drill pipe and it is vital to retain debris in suspension; if the solids fall onto the shoulders of the drill collars and bit, the latter may become fast in the hole. Considerable additional pump pressure is required to disturb the thixotropy when circulation begins again and a very heavy mud may overload the system in addition to preventing fall-out of fines in the mud pit.

Very many additives are commercially available for the treatment and control of drilling mud, ranging from ground walnut shells and shredded leather to complex chemical compounds. Drilling mud is a science in itself and the high pressures, temperatures, and great depths associated with oil-well drilling demand technology to cope with them. Water-well drilling, on the other hand, can be and often is carried out using no more mud control than the experience of the driller on the rig, using sight and 'feel' as his only instruments.

Organic Polymers. Although an essential mud property is that of forming a wall-cake, under some circumstances not only will the water phase of the mud invade the formation but the clay content as well. It can be extremely difficult, if not impossible, to remove all mud from the formation; in fact such mud frequently remains *in situ* between the screen and the formation for many years, even in a regularly pumped borehole, and many boreholes have been labelled as dry only because the aquifer has been 'mudded off'. This is particularly so where there are several poor aquifers at different levels in a well, the combined yields of which may have provided a useful supply. Proprietary dispersant chemicals are not always capable of removing clay particles, even if forming part of the well-development programme.

To overcome this objection, organic polymers were introduced. Polymer powder is mixed with water to form a drilling mud performing the basic functions of conventional bentonite but with one vital difference. It has a limited life, after which it breaks down to a water-like consistency and is easily drawn out of the formation. In addition, it has only a mild thixotropic property and releases solids more readily.

Obviously, some boreholes may take a considerable time to drill, so chemicals such as formalin are used to prolong mud life. Some polymer muds can be stabilized indefinitely. To break down the mud at a specific time, an additive such as chlorine (in heavy dosage) can be used, but this should not be confused with the light dosage given to combat soil bacteria.

An early problem was failure of the mud under conditions of varying pH value. It is now recognized that maintenance of a high pH value within a fairly close limit will ensure stability. Most manufacturers provide their own brand name additives to control mud flow according to specific drilling requirements.

A few years ago engineers were reluctant to permit the use of organic polymer drilling muds but it is now quite common to find contract clauses banning the use of bentonite mud and specifying a polymer mud by name. Caution is still advisable, particularly where a contractor offers an unfamiliar brand name. Furthermore, one well-known mud product has recently been subjected to close scrutiny following problems with bacterial growth.

Foam. A foaming agent has been developed to cope with a situation where:

(*a*)   mud cannot be circulated due to losses or water supply problems; and
(*b*)   insufficient annular air velocity is available to clean the hole adequately.

Under certain conditions a complete borehole may be drilled using foam. Other circumstances may call for only partial application. The introduction of additives into the air system is not new; detergent was used by air drillers some 20 years ago to overcome the aggregation of cuttings in a 'weeping' borehole.

A decade later saw the injection of a bentonite-foam slurry which provided a measure of support to the formation but still relied on a fairly high velocity and compressor capacity. It was found that increased quantities of formation water could be lifted, probably because the slurry caked the wall and provided a smoother borehole.

Recent development has produced a stable foam which requires quite moderate air quantities, a 'starting guide' being 0.3 m³/min per 25 mm of bit diameter. No mud pit or lagoon is required, the fluid being mixed in a tank and injected by a pump into the air supply system. It travels down the drill pipe under pressure and passes through the drill bit and lubricates and cools its. Expansion and foaming activity then takes place and sufficient support is developed to carry the cuttings up the annular space at a low velocity, say 12-20 m/min. The foam is similar to aerosol shaving cream in consistency and often appears at the surface with a surging pulse, a characteristic believed by some to assist in cleaning the borehole. The foam breaks down in 30-45 minutes, releasing its cuttings in the process. It is conducted away from the well head by a collector ring and horizontal pipe.

A typical fluid consists of 450 l of water to 4.5 l of foam and 1/1.5 kg of stabilizer; it is injected at a rage of 5-7 l/min. Holes of 150-650 mm diameter may be drilled

using foam and a special fluid is available for use with down-the-hole hammers
when provision must be made for lubrication.

Finally, although guide lines for the use of foam exist, it is a system which is still
the subject of development through experience. Therefore it is the responsibility of
the drilling engineer to adjust the settings to give optimum results under prevailing
conditions.

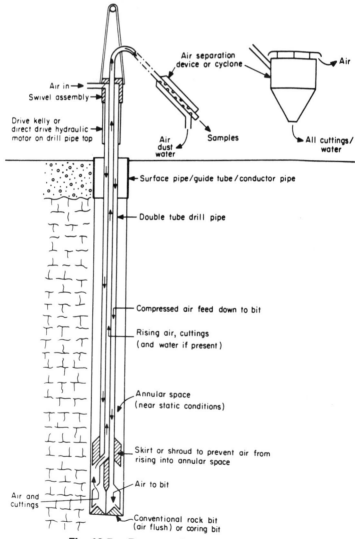

Fig. 13.5.   Reverse circulation air drill

AIR DRILLING

Direct Circulation

The use of compressed air as a drilling fluid has led to the development of specialised equipment in the rotary drilling field, permitting very high rates of penetration.

Air was applied to drilling by the quarrying and mining industries to resolve the problems of water haulage and freezing conditions. It was successful and, under favourable conditions, revealed additional advantages.

The engineering equipment is basically similar to that used for mud drilling but departures in detail are found, for example, in drilling bit design, where passages are modified to provide air to the bearings; also, the water swivel packing must be capable of dry rotation. Obviously considerable compressor capacity must, in most cases, be available.

Drilling bit life is extended because the cuttings are removed very rapidly, reducing lost time on 'round trips' to change bits as well as saving on bit costs. The cuttings arrive at the surface a few seconds after being produced and are representative of the formation being drilled at that time and depth.

Firm rock is an ideal drilling material in which to apply this method and fissured zones can be penetrated without the fear of lost circulation associated with water-based muds. There is also no risk of sealing off an aquifer with a wall-cake and normally no drilling water is required. The 'fluid' is expendable and as no mud pit or surface tanks are required this reduces the setting-up time for the rig and tools.

A disadvantage is that air cannot support a caving formation, where it may be necessary to insert temporary tubes or change to foam drilling. Problems also arise when small inflows of water tend to aggregate the cuttings and it is sometimes necessary to inject water into the air supply to produce a manageable slurry. A greater inflow of natural water can be airlifted out of the borehole and it is sometimes possible to evaluate the potential of an aquifer while actually drilling. However, depending upon the volume and pressure of the air, drilling efficiency falls off with increase in depth below water.

Reverse Circulation

One problem to be faced when drilling with air, especially as the diameter increases, is the need to produce a rising air velocity of not less than 925 m/min. To obtain this figure in, say, a 375 mm hole using standard 112 mm drill pipe would require air at a rate of some 100 m³/min, which is impracticable.

In an attempt to overcome the problem, some drilling has taken place using twin concentric drill pipes (Fig. 13.5). Air is fed through the annular space between the outer and inner pipes and released around the special bit. A shroud or skirt prevents undue escape of air into the annulus outside the rotating drilling tools and forces most of the air across the bit and up through its passages, whence it travels at high speed through the inner drill pipe to the surface, carrying the cuttings with it.

An interesting variation has been the application of this double-tube layout to small-diameter coring work. Water is pumped down the drill pipe annulus, carried across the coring crown and conducted up the inner drill pipe. There is no core barrel as such; instead, a special core-breaking device allows the rising water to propel short sticks of core to the surface, together with the fine particles of cuttings.

This arrangement obviates the need to remove a conventional core barrel for emptying and permits uninterrupted drilling. Here again, it can be applied only under favourable drilling conditions.

'Down-the-Hole' Hammer Drilling

The introduction of the hammer drill marked a significant step forward in the development of drilling tools suitable for hard ground.

An air-actuated single piston hammer, working on the same principle as the familiar road drill, is fitted beneath a string of drill pipe. A tungsten carbide-set bit is attached to the hammer (Fig. 13.6).

The complete assembly is rotated at 20-50 rpm and lowered towards hard rock. The rotation is primarily to change the position of the bit on the bottom of the hole and any 'drilling' benefit is of secondary importance.

The piston, before the tool touches the bottom of the hole, is 'idling' in its cylinder and nearly all the air is exhausted through the bit and, where fitted, additional ports in the tool body. This is because the anvil carrying the bit is in suspension and free to hang extended out of the tool bottom where it cannot be struck by the piston. This feature is built in to provide extra cleaning facilities when running in to the hole or to expel excessive accumulations of cuttings.

When the tool lands on the bottom of the hole the suspended bit/anvil assembly is pushed up into the tool body where it meets the oscillating piston which can now strike with a frequency of between 250 and 1000 blows per minute. At the same time the air, previously being exhausted, is directed to drive the piston and is released through ports in the bit only when most of its energy has been expended. The air now cools the bit, clears the cuttings and propels them up the annular space to a collecting box on the surface.

Hammer drills of 50-450 mm diameter are available and tools to drill up to 750 mm are being developed. Lifting the dust and cuttings to the surface is a technical problem with large annular spaces, but may be overcome in part by positioning an open-topped collector tube immediately above the tool which is raised and emptied periodically. Alternatively, a shroud and reverse air method might be considered.

The down-the-hole hammer system has vastly improved penetration rates through hard rock. For example, drilling in basalt in Mauritius, at a nominal 150 mm diameter, an early model (1960) hammer drilled 3 m/h compared with only 0.1 m/h for a cable-tool rig.

As with all specialised drilling techniques, there are disadvantages and/or problems. The hammer will not operate in unconsolidated ground or clays, and water may defeat it. A seepage of water will cause the cuttings to congeal and stick to the walls, although this can be relieved by injection of detergent into the air supply. A heavy flow of water, however, will be ejected as in 'air-lift' pumping, until a depth below water is reached when all the air power is expended on pumping, whereupon the hammer is stifled.

Higher working pressure tools were introduced to overcome, in part, the latter problem. Double-tube drill pipe and reverse-air circulation can also help, but not many water drilling companies possess, or have access to, this drill pipe.

OTHER DRILLING METHODS

Hydraulic Tube Racking (Casing Oscillators)

Where there is a requirement for relatively shallow wells with large diameters in loose gravels, sand, boulders, etc, a hydraulic tube racking device in conjunction with a rig or crane may be suitable.

In this method a short guide tube is hand-sunk into the ground and the first of a column of permanent tubes lowered within it. The bottom edge of the column is serrated and the tubes drilled, perforated, or slotted as required.

A hydraulically-clamped spider, supported on two vertical cylinders, is locked on to the tube a short distance above ground level. Long horizontal rams, attached to two diametrically opposite 'ears' on the spider, impart a very slow but powerful oscillating torque to the tube column. At the same time, the two vertical cylinders control downward feed and apply thrust if required.

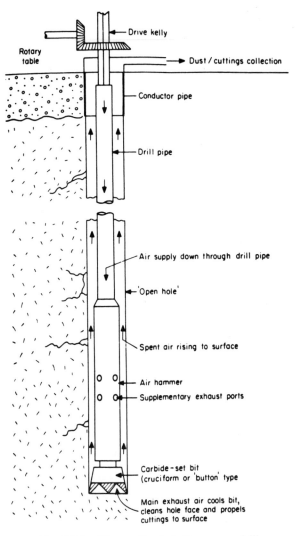

Fig. 13.6.   'Down-the-hole' hammer drill

Under this force the tubes travel down and spoil gathers inside them; this is removed by a grab until the top of the first tube is close to the spider table, when the next tube is placed upon it and the joint welded.

The essential principle underlying this system is the maintenance of a 'fluidity' of formation around the contact area of the tubes and it is quite common, therefore, to weld the next tube joint without halting the oscillation.

Tubes of 0.45-1.2 m can be worked down to 30 m or so under the right conditions, the advantage of this system being that both the need for temporary tubes (in percussion drilling) and large lagoons (in rotary drilling) can be dispensed with and there is no contamination of the aquifer by drilling fluids.

Auger Drilling

Auger drilling first appeared over 75 years ago when horses were used to power the machines. The deepest wells recorded were in the 100-110 m range, the auger being taken down until a caving formation was reached, whereupon an iron or steel 'shoe' topped by masonry was introduced, the weight of which cut a clearance hole for further masonry added at ground level.

Auger drilling is rarely used in the UK for water wells, but is worth considering in cases where, for example, a number of holes have to be drilled through a firm clay overburden overlying a stratum more amenable to the usual techniques. In such a case, an auger might produce a hole in 15 minutes against as much as one and a half days with a normal rig.

Essentially an auger bucket is rotated into the ground on the end of a long kelly and withdrawn frequently for emptying. Apart from the exceptional cases mentioned above, depths were restricted in the past by the need to have a kelly of transportable length, but when telescopic kellys were introduced this extended the reach and 25-30 m holes were possible. Another refinement is the use of solid drill rods with an inclined plane wound along them. These 'continuous flight' augers carry the spoil to the surface during rotation and it is unnecessary to remove the auger bucket.

Equipment is available covering diameters from 200 mm-3 m, the larger sizes finding more favour in parts of the USA where a combination of soft cohesive ground and weak aquifers may permit a cheap well offering a reservoir feature for intermittent pumping.

Scow Drilling

A 'scow', used in cable-tool drilling, combines the cutting edge of a chisel with the handling capacity of a bailer. It consists of a heavy thick-walled tube at the bottom edge of which is a hardened female bevel; it may also carry a bevelled cross-bar.

Inside the tube, a few cm from the bottom, a pair of hinged doors opens upwards. At the open top of the tube, there is a swivel connection for attachment to the drilling line.

In operation, the scow is run into the hole and the normal reciprocating action applied. Water for drilling is added if not present naturally. Material is dislodged by the cutting edges, and swept into the body of the scow by the 'pumping action' set up by the non-return feature of the doors. A size of tool is selected that will almost fill the diameter of the temporary tubes in use, thereby helping to 'swallow' boulders and enhance the pump effect. The scow is removed for emptying periodically.

Scows are used in loose, troublesome strata, especially where coarse gravel and boulders occur, and have the advantage of dislodging and lifting the materials rather than expending time and power on crushing, as with a normal bit.

A secondary factor is the shock effect of the water-hammer caused by the rapidly slamming doors. This results in a pulsating vibration throughout the tube-column and positively advances them down into unconsolidated ground. A disadvantage is that the drilling rig and cable must be in good condition to withstand the heavy loading created by scow drilling.

Diamond Drilling (Coring)

The application of diamond rotary drilling to water-well work is restricted mostly to small-diameter exploration drilling of 33-75 mm diameter, although there is an occasional geological requirement for a larger intermittent core sample during the drilling of abstraction boreholes.

With this system a tube 3-6 m long is rotated into firm ground at 200-900 rpm while a small supply of clean water is fed down to it through drill pipes. At the bottom of the tube, called the core barrel, a diamond-studded ring is fitted. This is the crown, and the diamonds are arranged across the bottom face with a few located both within the bore and on the outer periphery. The first 50 mm or so inside the crown are machined at a taper and a tapered, split, conical sleeve fits into this.

When the crown meets the rock, the diamonds scratch an annular groove and the tools travel downwards leaving a column of uncut rock within the tube. When the core barrel is full, rotation is stopped and a firm pull taken. The loose cone (core spring) jams in the taper and grips the core which is snapped off and brought to the surface inside the barrel. Cuttings consist of powder which is carried up with the circulating water. A bentonite or organic polymer mud may be used, or air can be applied very successfully under the right conditions.

With the aim of reducing the time required to empty the core barrel, a variation of the method was developed. This, the wire line method, employs a thicker crown, cutting a correspondingly smaller diameter core for a given hole size. The rising core is directed into an independent sleeve within the core barrel which, when full, is caught by a weighted 'spear' run down inside the drill pipes on a wire line. The sleeve is drawn rapidly to the surface, detached, and an empty sleeve lowered down into the core barrel while the full one is emptied at leisure.

Chilled Shot Coring

This system was commonly in use during the first half of the present century when boreholes, particularly of large diameters, were required in solid rock. It is rarely used now due to the relatively slow progress, which raises labour costs, which in turn are no longer outweighed by the attraction of simple low-cost equipment.

The method employs rotary equipment of either the portable type, or a sectional derrick and table assembly which powers the drill pipe, to the bottom of which is fitted a core barrel (Fig. 13.7).

The lower two-thirds of the barrel are open to accept the core, while the upper third is open-topped to receive the cuttings, the two portions being divided by a disc into which the hollow drill pipe fits.

The bottom of the barrel is thickened to form a crown which cuts a hole of sufficient size to accommodate the barrel above and produces a core which passes freely into the barrel. The crown has two or more slots across the face for the passage of water.

Unless firm rock is encountered at the surface, it is necessary to drill or hand sink through the overburden, whereupon the core barrel assembly is inserted and just touched-down on the bottom of the hole. At this point a relatively small flow of water is pumped down the drill pipe and some chilled steel shot introduced into the flow. These spherical shot of 8 to 3 gauge, selected according to well diameter, fall to the bottom of the hole where they become trapped under the rotating crown.

A relatively light loading is applied but as only a few pieces of shot are supporting it, the point loading is heavy and the rock fails under the face of the crown. Only sufficient water to lubricate and cool the crown, and raise the mud-like cuttings is necessary; too much would wash out the shot and could cause jamming at the outside of the crown. Flows of the order of 1.5-23 m^3/h are usual, depending on the diameter of the hole.

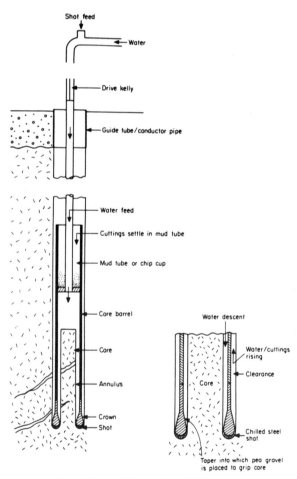

Fig. 13.7.   Chilled-shot drilling

The shot itself is worn away and must be replaced periodically by adding more to the water feed. Eventually, the core barrel contains a full stick of core and at this point, the driller stops rotation and inserts a small quantity of pea-gravel or chippings through the drill pipe. These come to rest within the annular clearance taper inside the crown and provide the jamming agent necessary to enable the crown/core barrel unit to grip and break off the standing core. The unit is then drawn to the surface for emptying.

Depths to 300 m or more can be drilled by this method with diameters ranging from about 150 mm to 1.2 m. One problem frequently encountered is that of fissures, the interception of which is the main goal in firm rock. These result in loss of shot and one may have to change to a crown bearing tungsten-carbide teeth to cross such a zone. Fissures above the water table may be dealt with by filling with a light mix of cement and ashes.

Jetting

In Britain this method is rarely used for water supply but is useful with well-points for dewatering.

The term 'Jetting' is often loosely applied to any small diameter system of hole making of about 50 mm bore although strictly speaking they may be driven, washed, speared, suction-bored, hollow-rod drilled or percussion jetted. There is even a do-it-yourself kit for a garden water supply.

Essentially, the equipment for straight jetting comprises a column of hollow rods—which sometimes form the permanent lining—to the bottom of which is fitted a bladed bit (Fig. 13.8(c)). A high pressure pump draws water from a settling pit and forces it up to a rotary swivel and down the drill pipes to the bit, where drilled ports direct strong jets of water into the formation. Basic rotation is applied with a simple rotary head, chain tongs or tillers and, as the soft ground is dislodged, the column is lowered. As in direct circulation rotary drilling, the cuttings are washed up the annular space to discharge into the settling pit.

In the event of firm ground being encountered above the desired depth, penetration may be achieved by raising and dropping the column in a light percussive manner.

Unstable ground would call for the insertion of temporary casing and this may be carried down concurrently with the drilling tools—or may even be washed down by fitting a cap to the casing above ground and applying water pressure. There are several combinations of this procedure; some involve the incorporation of screen sections and detachable non-return valves down the borehole.

Driven wells are constructed by driving a pointed screen directly into the aquifer, pipe being added as depth increases. The hammer blows may be applied on a drive head attached to the pipes above ground or, in some cases, through rods within the pipes, thus imparting a pull down force.

Another common method is 'hollow rod' drilling. Tooling similar to that for jetting is used, but a non-return valve is fitted inside the rods just above the bit. The water-ways in the bit are relatively large and, as the diameter of the drill hole is usually within the 50–100 mm range, a considerable pumping effect is generated by the reciprocating tools. This feature, aided by the non-return valves, causes an upward flow of water and cuttings within the hollow rods and these are discharged through a tee above the surface and into a settling pit. Water is at all times maintained in the hole at or near surface level. Although usually associated with shallow drilling, depths of 75 m are not uncommon using this method.

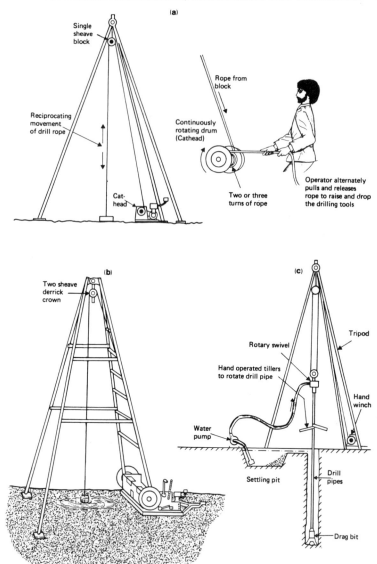

Fig. 13.8.   (a) Lightweight winch and tripod drill (slip rope drilling)
(b) Medium weight winch and derrick drill (friction winch drilling)
(c) Manual rotary drill

Turbine Drilling

Turbine drills, sometimes called 'down-hole-motors', were the subject of experiments soon after World War II, considerable funds being expended in the UK alone, especially on the gas turbine type.

In this system a conventional rotary rig is used but the drill pipe is not rotated. Instead, the pipe is used solely to conduct drilling fluid down to an axial flow multi-stage turbine motor which directly drives a tricone rock bit, the spent mud from which carries out its normal functions in the hole and recirculates.

Both the oil and water industries have used these drills but they are best suited to the drilling of inclined-hole oil wells where rotating drill strings had frequently failed. None the less, turbines are just returning to favour in North Sea drilling, where their efficiency at high rotational speeds can be matched to advantage with non-coring diamond crowns.

West German water well contractors consider turbine drills uneconomical at depths less than 500 m and the cost of mud cleaning apparatus rules out more general use.

A variation of this theme is found in a drilling machine powered by submersible electric motors mounted within a device which can either be lowered on reverse circulation drill pipes or on flexible hoses and steel wire ropes. In the latter arrangement there is provision for directional corrections by remote control from the surface.

Vibratory Equipment

More attention has been given in recent years to the application of vibration to tube columns. Originally this was 'borrowed' from the piling industry, mainly as a form of percussion to move tubes seized in deep soft ground, often simply to recover them. A facility for vibration is now being incorporated into drilling rigs and the latest rigs include the standard mechanisms of rotation and downthrust with vibration and percussion added. They also incorporate double-tube drill pipe to give direct or reverse circulation of any fluid, or even dry drilling (Fig. 13.9).

Basically, the system can be divided into small-diameter exploration drilling and large-diameter production drilling. The former method employs the outer drill pipes as the temporary casing and, as the drill bit does not cut a clearance hole, there is no annular space either in unconsolidated or cohesive formations. Using normal methods of drilling, this situation would result in the tubes being firmly seized into the ground, but the vibration facility produces a state of fluidity within the material immediately adjacent to the outer tubes. This separation of rock particles almost eliminates lateral friction, thus allowing the drill pipe to move down.

The drilling medium is normally air, conducted down between the outer and inner tubes, across the bit or crown, and returned up the inner drill pipe, carrying with it all the cuttings, plus natural water, if present from that zone only (there is no annular space to conduct water or material from a higher level).

An exploration hole drilled in this way, in any strata, can attain a depth of about 150 m at an effective diameter of between 75 and 150 mm, this being the open size of the inner drill pipe. The actual drilled diameters would be about 125 and 200 mm respectively.

In a consolidated stratum a trial air-lift yield test may be carried out by raising the drill string a few metres. This would be impracticable in a loose formation, in which case a short length of 75 or 150 mm screen pipe should be positioned within the drill string and the latter withdrawn a suitable distance to expose the screen to the aquifer. This temporary screen is withdrawn using a special overshot tool. Should it be necessary to line the exploration borehole permanently, this may be accomplished by running permanent tubes inside the drill pipe and vibrating the latter out of the ground leaving the permanent column behind, hence the earlier mention of 'effective' diameter.

Production drilling using this sytem is sub-divided into two types of borehole:

(i) In unconsolidated ground, boreholes up to 300 mm effective diameter are drilled, using air in reverse circulation and drill strings of 350 mm external diameter. Boreholes up to 600 mm effective diameter may be drilled to about 150 m, using a mud fluid and reverse circulation. Where the overburden is not very thick and consists of fine material, it is usually possible to insert a guide tube by vibration and percussion without any fluid circulation or a rotational element. In fact, in some applications tubes have been dry-drilled to 20 or 30 m in this manner.

(ii) A consolidated formation permits more efficient use of the forces available and a finished borehole of up to 700 mm diameter can be achieved, this actually being the drilled diameter.

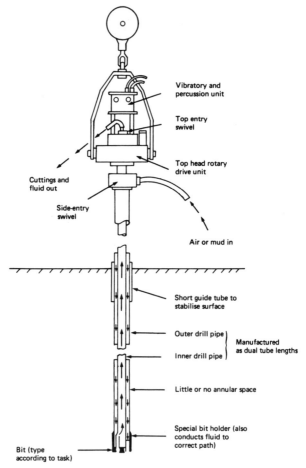

Fig. 13.9.   Vibro-percussion rotary drilling

Double-tube drill pipe conducts air down to, and across the bit, and then up to the inner pipe at a higher velocity, entraining the cuttings to be discharged at the surface. Obviously it would not be possible to use full-gauge drill pipe at these diameters, so an annular space is produced while drilling. However, the annulus contains relatively static air or water only, as a special bit holder, fitted between the bit and drill pipe, acts as a packer and prevents loss of air up to, or water from, the annular space. It also has the function of conducting air through the correct circuit in the immediate vicinity of the bit.

The vibratory and percussive forces are generated by rotating weights in a state of imbalance within a special assembly fitted above the rotary swivel. As the swivel is mounted on the drill pipe the vibration is transmitted down to the bit.

The amplitude of the vibrator assembly is restrained by strong springs and vertical guides and thus operates within a given travel. If, however, a percussive force is required, an 'anvil' is hydraulically raised to meet the vibrating hammer device above it, and rapid blows are delivered downward. Conversely, to apply upward percussion, an alternative anvil is lowered to meet the hammer.

Very rapid progress through all types of ground is claimed by the rig manufacturers and at 150-160 mm diameter the following figures are quoted:

(1)	coarse alluvium	20-30 m/h
(2)	marls	20-60 m/h
(3)	hard, compact sandstone	7-12 m/h
(4)	solid gneiss and quartzite	4-6 m/h

This system, introduced recently, is in the right drilling conditions undoubtedly very efficient. It would be interesting to compare progress with and without the percussive element as it is difficult to visualise an effective blow being received at the bit after travelling through the swivel assembly and drill pipes. Some of the first air-hammers used in quarrying were mounted at the top of the drill string but were almost ineffective compared with placing the same capacity unit 'down-the-hole'.

COMPARISON OF AVAILABLE METHODS

By critical assessment of the advantages and disadvantages of available methods it should not be too difficult to select the correct method for the work envisaged. Unfortunately, this is not always true. There may be difficulties in providing an adequate water supply—and this not only in arid developing countries. Other factors, too, have to be considered—for example, the site area and the proximity of dwellings. The use of acid or of explosives will be far from welcome in some areas.

Generally speaking, a heavy cable-tool rig or a standard rotary rig will offer the widest versatility whilst the specialised rigs provide maximum efficiency— especially for repetition drilling.

Nor must it be forgotten that a drilling rig is only as efficient as the driller using it; the more sophisticated the equipment the more critical this relationship becomes.

Cable-Tool (Percussion) Drilling

Of all the drilling methods available, cable-tool offers the greatest versatility in range of depths, diameters and ability to make the hole. Such a rig and tools can be sent anywhere in the world in the knowledge that drilling will take place—albeit with extreme inefficiency in some areas.

Cable-tools will penetrate all ground, with widely variable rates of progress—this being governed by the physical conditions of each stratum rather than the diameter and depth of hole, which has less influence on speed of penetration.

The most rapid drilling rates are achieved in soft stable rock and at larger diameters this method is the best available (unless certain conditions favour reverse circulation). The equipment is of relatively low capital cost, running costs are minimal and repairs can be undertaken by any plant engineer. Mild misuse by the operator may be absorbed by the rugged simplicity of this equipment, usually without serious result.

Obviously, hard rock can slow the penetration rate down dramatically—to as little as 1.0 m per day. There would also be bit changing and dressing to consider. Prior knowledge of geological conditions may rule out this method unless, for example, the drilling of hard material was tolerated just to prove basement in the bottom of the borehole.

Clay will also slow progress due to its adhesive properties which impede the fall of the tools and also cause energy loss whilst mixing the clay cuttings into a slurry.

Boulders are a source of trouble to most types of drilling and cable-tools are not excepted. At small diameter drilling it may be possible to carry casing down as depth is made so as to pass between and 'line out' the boulders. At large diameter work it is sometimes possible to remove boulders with a grab or perhaps with a scow tool.

A borehole drilled in soft unstable strata presents problems, especially if required to go to considerable depth. The penetration rate at any one time may be very rapid but, unless closely followed by a column of temporary protective tubes, periodical or total collapse will occur. The very fact that the tubes may be temporary places a restriction on their use, as the driller has to bear in mind that it is easier to insert tubes whilst drilling than to subsequently remove them against their own weight and skin friction and without the benefit of drilling tool vibration. It is therefore preferable to encourage the downward movement of temporary tubes by 'surging' rather than outright driving.

The point will be reached when the column becomes tight in the hole and, unless this coincides with a stable formation, it will be necessary to install a further column of temporary tubes of reduced diameter. This is a major disadvantage of the cable-tool method as it is not unknown to insert as many as five telescoped tiers of casing in a caving hole in order to reach the desired depth. All these tubes have to be transported, inserted, and may be required to be withdrawn again, so provision must be made for damage and the possibility of them becoming irretrievably fast. A further point is that the large annular space thus remaining will in most cases have to be filled with cement—certainly the upper portion as a seal against contamination.

On the credit side, it is almost immediately apparent when the drilling has entered an aquifer in a stable formation and this is a particularly important asset when drilling in an area bearing scant hydrogeological data. The tools may be removed and a bailer run into the borehole quickly to establish the presence or otherwise of natural water. Similarly, a stratum sample may be taken which is generally representative of the ground being drilled at that depth, although it will be pulverised and occasionally may be 'contaminated' by some minor infall from higher up.

The cable-tool rig normally requires very little water to drill the dry portion of the hole. This can be as low as 400 l/day—a factor of considerable importance when drilling in arid zones.

Rotary–Direct Circulation–Mud Drilling

The outstanding advantage of this method is that apart from a short length of conductor pipe at the surface it is generally possible to drill to great depths at rapid rates of penetration without having to insert temporary tubes. Unstable ground is retained in place by the hydrostatic head exerted by an internal column of drilling mud which may have a specific gravity of 1.1 to 1.3 and gelling properties to limit loss into the formation. In the event of light fissuring, which might cause some fluid loss, it may be acceptable to plug these with lost-circulation material. Heavy fissures would not respond to such treatment and indeed, if water bearing, any plugging operations would defeat the object of the drilling. In these circumstances an alternative method of drilling would have to be applied; air, for example.

Rotary–Reverse Circulation–Water Drilling

This is the most rapid method of drilling large diameter boreholes in gravels, sands and soft rocks. As the bit dislodges material rather than reduces it, the power is used efficiently to remove the cuttings with a 'vacuum-cleaning' flow of water. These cuttings are truly representative as minimal fines are recirculated and samples arrive at the surface a few seconds after being dislodged. It is a feature of this system that the downflow of clean water—although of high volume—is accommodated in a large annular space, so there is minimal erosion of the borehole wall. Cascading is avoided by maintaining the water level in the borehole at or close to that of the lagoon.

Mention has been made of the cleanliness associated with this type of drilling, but many apparently clean aquifers contain a proportion of very fine particles, some of which will travel back down the borehole and form a thin skin on the wall. This does not constitute an invasion of the aquifer and the skin is removed within a few minutes of initial clearance pumping. In fact this temporary wall plaster can aid the driller by reducing water loss into the aquifer.

Notwithstanding this, there is often an enormous loss of circulation water which has to be made good. This is a major deterrent to the more general use of reverse circulation drilling.

On the credit side, as with direct circulation, it is usual to drill the borehole without resort to temporary tubes, an advantage in itself as these rigs require a spacious site and there may not be adequate room for the handling of both temporary and permanent tube columns of the large sizes associated with reverse circulation drilling.

Problems are occasionally encountered with clays and shales which, when wetted, tend to swell and cause constriction in the borehole during construction. At the large diameters usually associated with reverse circulation drilling this problem may be compounded by the infall of large slabs of formation. The introduction of an acceptable commercially available chemical into the drilling water will control the situation by reducing wetting.

Rotary–Air Drilling

The advantages and disadvantages of air have been described in some detail earlier in this chapter, and also mentioned in relation to foam.

Generally speaking, in Britain there are no large areas where the exclusive use of air can be applied to water well drilling. This is in sharp contrast to some other countries and accounts for the world-wide proliferation of rotary rigs equipped with air to drill small diameter (by UK standards) boreholes at a high rate of production.

This is not to say that air drilling should not receive consideration when selecting the method of drilling, but rather that the small amount of drilling carried out in the UK, and the wide variation in diameters and geology to be found here, do not invite the application of large-scale air drilling. However, in hard rock at the smaller diameters the extremely high performance of a down-the-hole hammer drill makes it the first choice.

General Comments on Drilling Methods

Despite the swing away from percussion towards rotary methods there are disadvantages with the latter, apart from equipment costs—which are some three times greater.

The earlier serious and valid objection to the use of a clay-based mud has largely been overcome by the change to organic polymers; however, the problem of identifying the aquifer remains. The introduction of a heavy column of fluid into the borehole masks the presence of an aquifer—unless under the rare state of considerable artesian pressure—and consequently an aquifer can only be recognised with confidence if the water-bearing formation is known in advance and the drilled samples used in confirmation. But differential slip of the cuttings during their journey to the surface can often blur their accuracy, especially at high penetration rates. It can be argued that comprehensive geophysical logging of the borehole will fill the information gap. Although of undoubted value such logs will not indicate the potential of the aquifer nor the standing water level. This can be ascertained only by removing the drilling mud—which would in most cases cause the borehole to collapse.

Water will be required for drilling and as the quantity will be many times that consumed by a percussion rig this may be an important factor. It is difficult to quote firm figures because so much depends on the ground and the size of the borehole. A circulating volume of three to four times the borehole volume is a fair demand, to which must be added any losses of fluid into the formation.

The heavy pounding of a cable rig may not be acceptable in a built-up area, where the quieter motion of the rotary system would then make this the more suitable method.

3. VERTICALITY

INTRODUCTION

The ideal borehole is both vertical and straight and it is in the interests of the client and the contractor to aim for this ideal.

Factors which influence the attainment of a true bore include the:

(a) method of drilling employed;
(b) level of skill of the driller;
(c) nature of the ground being drilled;
(d) rate of penetration;
(e) type of tubes being used.

Effect of Drilling Method

Each drilling method shows a different behaviour regarding verticality. A borehole is biased towards the vertical by the force of gravity and it follows that any string of tools maintained in tension for most of its working cycle will tend to generate a vertical hole.

As cable-tools are operated at a precisely set speed and 'tautness' which avoids uncontrolled slack in the steel wire rope, this ensures optimum verticality and it is usual to obtain acceptable figures. A cable-tool drilled borehole is therefore reasonably vertical although the general alignment may be staggered through alternating beds of hard and soft ground.

Most rotary drilling involves the use of a roller rock bit which requires weight rather than torque to effect penetration—in fact, within certain limits, the more weight applied the greater the drilling rate and the lower the bit wear. There is a mechanism on most rotary rigs for using part of the weight of the rig to provide additional loading above the bit, especially when starting to drill. This of course has a negative effect on the drilling of a vertical hole and to relieve the situation (in part) it is customary to install heavy drill collars immediately above the bit and to try to maintain in tension the drill pipe string above the collars. Guidance is also provided at the surface by a carefully aligned conductor pipe which assists the vertical commencement until sufficient depth is made for the insertion of drill collars.

Generally speaking, a direct circulation rotary-drilled borehole will be straighter and suffer less sudden deviation than a cable-tool drilled borehole but the overall displacement from true verticality is often greater.

Where reverse circulation systems are used, verticality is usually within a close tolerance. This is due partly to application in soft ground where the column of tools is held in restraint to avoid cuttings congestion, and partly to the design of the drill collars/stabilisers which can be of an outside diameter large enough to almost completely fill the borehole, the down-flow of water being directed through special passages between the central pipe and outer sleeve. It is also customary to rotate at very low speeds. Occasional verticality checks can be carried out without removing the drilling tools. This is accomplished by passing a 125 mm plumbing cage down the 150 mm bore of the tool column.

The drilling method which maintains the closest accuracy is the down-the-hole hammer drill. Little or no weight is applied to the bit as it is only necessary to close the sliding joint against air pressure between the hammer body and the bit for the tool to start drilling.

Effect of Skill of Driller

The skill and attention of the driller is vital in ensuring a straight hole, in detecting any indication of deviation, and in taking measures to rectify an error.

More hole can be made per shift by allowing a fraction more feed per blow with cable-tools, but if this leads to severe deviation the driller will lose any time gain if he finds it difficult or impossible to insert a tube column in a winding hole. Throwing all available weight on to a rotary bit will in most cases result in a substantial increase in the penetration rate. This is quite in order (assuming that other factors allow) but not if the verticality figures are made unacceptable.

A driller constantly observes his cable position relative to the centre of the borehole at the surface and will inspect the tools above the top tube for a few seconds each time the bailer is run. Any rig settlement will be shown by the latter check whilst a mean lateral displacement of the cable during drilling will signify a deviation. In addition, undue wear on the cable, evidence of polishing on the side of the tools and an unsatisfactory drilling blow are all pointers requiring investigation.

Effect of Strata

Soft rock such as chalk offers ideal drilling conditions so far as alignment is concerned and it is only where flint beds occur, or fissures, or a dipping bedding plane is met, that the drilling tools are likely to be diverted. Dipping strata occur across the greater part of Britain and are a major cause of deviation during borehole construction.

Non-cohesive ground can be drilled vertically provided due care is taken. The presence of boulders causes problems depending on their size relative to the diameter being drilled.

Some of the worst possible conditions prevail where igneous rocks are interbedded with soft ash and blow-holes. Similarly, cavernous limestone throws most drilling tools seriously out of alignment and it is not uncommon to resort to the use of explosives to blast an obstruction in a large borehole.

Remedial Procedures

If the driller observes that his chisel or bit is not concentric with the mouth of the borehole when suspended above it, it is only necessary to re-align the drilling rig. However, should the actual borehole be crooked, steps must be taken immediately to implement corrective measures down the hole.

These can take several forms, depending on the severity and depth of the deviation, and the formation being drilled. A slight error in soft ground at shallow depth may respond to moving the drilling rig across in the opposite direction to the error and drilling for a few metres at that setting. Another method—particularly at larger diameters—is to drill a pilot hole at one side of the borehole bottom in the true axis; this to encourage the full size drilling to shift back into alignment. Yet another approach is to ream out at larger diameter (existing tubes permitting) to provide lateral freedom for a column of temporary pilot tubes placed vertically as a guide.

Where a smooth kink occurs in hard rock it is very difficult to erase the error and break into new ground. In such a case—more especially when cable-tool drilling—it is essential to backfill the borehole with material somewhat harder than the formation being drilled. This is primarily to slow down drilling to concentrate the reaming effect of the bit in one area so that a 'step' is formed. A secondary benefit is the abrasive property of the harder backfill which assists in eroding away the wall. It is quite common to backfill with broken pieces of cast iron when straightening a hole in hard rock.

Sometimes, if the deviation is sudden and severe and does not respond to immediate corrective measures, a small diameter rotary borehole may be fitted with a 'whipstock', a long device commencing in tube section and terminating as a blade. It is placed down the borehole in the direction required and acts like a 'shoe horn' to deflect the tool string.

In the worst cases a borehole may have to be abandoned.

SPECIFIED TOLERANCES

The most common verticality (plumbness) tolerance specified in the UK is 1 in 300 (100 mm per 30 m of depth or 4″ per 100′). Straightness (alignment) is not so clearly defined.

This tolerance is a legacy from earlier times and is sometimes adhered to quite unnecessarily at a cost of extra time and money. A suitable limitation should be applied, taking into consideration the purpose of the borehole, the diameter relative to the pumping plant, the size of any float recorder (in observation holes), the type and depth of pump, and the nature of the formation.

A century or more ago, steam-powered reciprocating pumps were used extensively to lift water from wells. The mechanism involved 'sucker rods' in tension guided at intervals up the well, so a crooked well would create increased wear in the guides.

Gas and oil engines were used eventually to power vertical-spindle submerged turbine pumps and again it was necessary to apply fairly strict limits to straightness to avoid spindle flexion and early failure of the centralising bearings.

Electric motors superseded most of the engines and were finally developed as submersible units, avoiding the use of shaft drive. Most modern electric submersible pumps can operate at any angle and, indeed, may be incorporated horizontally as boosters in a pipeline.

Notwithstanding the above, it is desirable to aim for a vertical and straight hole within reasonable tolerances and in fact vital where observation boreholes are to be installed with sensitive water level recorders relying on light floats connected by a wire and counterbalance to a chart recorder at ground level. Any marked deviation would cause the float or the wire and the counterbalance to adhere to the lining tube, thus impeding the response to small changes in water level.

Some water engineers require close control of verticality so that a submersible pump will hang truly central in the borehole. This may be to lessen the velocity of water movement immediately adjacent to a sand screen, to reduce possible wear at the point of contact, or to avoid electrolytic action in the presence of stray currents in water of low pH value. However, some pumps do tend to 'orbit' round the borehole and it might be worth introducing a short length of plain casing at the pump-setting depth if this falls within a screen section. Another method is to hold the pump centrally by means of rubber-covered spacers attached to the unit.

In some countries a deviation of one degree (525 mm per 30 m) is permitted whilst in others only 75 mm is allowed, this being applied down as far as the pump setting depth. A much looser clause calls for the contractor to drill a borehole of sufficient verticality and straightness to permit insertion of any temporary and/or permanent tubes and screen and to allow for satisfactory installation and running of the pumping plant. In the USA specifications usually require that a 'dummy' be run down the borehole. This takes the form of a piece of pipe 12 m long and of a diameter some 13 mm smaller than the borehole, if of 250 mm diameter or less. Boreholes of 300 mm or more require a dummy of 25 mm less than the diameter of the borehole to be measured. Verticality should fall within a maximum limit of two-thirds the smallest inside diameter of that part of the well being tested per 30 m.

Method of Measurement

Whilst there are several sophisticated instruments for measuring the degree and direction of inclination in boreholes, these are mostly used in small diameter exploration holes, especially at greater depths. Water wells, on the other hand, lend themselves to the application of a simple effective method commonly used in the UK and many countries overseas.

Basically a plumbing test is carried out by suspending a close-fitting cage in the centre of the borehole at ground level and lowering it down to the bottom. The cage is stopped at regular intervals and measurements taken to ascertain if any lateral deflection of the plumbing wire has occurred at ground level (Fig. 13.10).

The cage may be of a diameter some 12 mm less than the borehole diameter for small holes whilst the larger sizes of cage are usually provided with 25 mm clearance.

A steel wire rope of about 4 mm diameter is ideal as it possesses the strength to carry a heavy cage and yet is light enough to overcome the lateral curvature or 'sag' found in the deflection of a heavy cable, which would cause false readings.

The cable should be suspended from as high a point as possible and be run through a readily adjustable guide to facilitate setting the cage centrally in the top of the borehole.

Having centralised the cage just below the top of the guide tube or casing, a wire frame or cross cords are arranged so that lateral movements from zero may be measured (Fig. 13.11). Alternatively a scribed and slotted plastic disc or sheet is used. It is useful to arrange the cross wires in a N.S.E.W. configuration so that directional reference might be made to any specific deviation.

Although a high suspension aids accuracy, the long length of exposed cable is subject to wind pressure during unfavourable weather. This condition can be relieved by either threading the cable through a pipe above ground or by suspending a plank to windward of the cable.

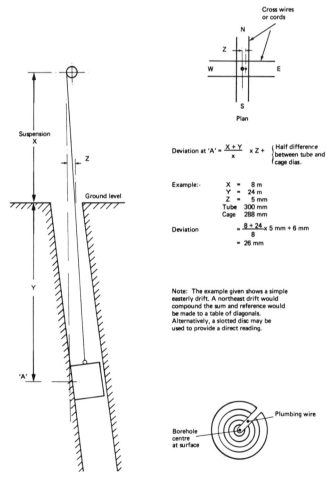

Cross wires or cords

Plan

$$\text{Deviation at 'A'} = \frac{X+Y}{X} \times Z + \begin{cases} \text{Half difference} \\ \text{between tube and} \\ \text{cage dias.} \end{cases}$$

Example:-

X   =   8 m
Y   =   24 m
Z   =   5 mm
Tube   300 mm
Cage   288 mm

Deviation $= \frac{8+24}{8} \times 5 \text{ mm} + 6 \text{ mm}$

= 26 mm

Note: The example given shows a simple easterly drift. A northeast drift would compound the sum and reference would be made to a table of diagonals. Alternatively, a slotted disc may be used to provide a direct reading.

Suspension
X

Z

Ground level

Y

'A'

Plumbing wire

Borehole centre at surface

Fig. 13.10.   Method of measuring borehole verticality

Fig. 13.11 shows that a severe deviation may cause the plumbing wire to touch the wall of the borehole, particularly one of small diameter and/or where the upper section of the borehole is vertical. It may be necessary to tilt the suspension point across in the opposing direction to obtain a clear path for the line under such circumstances and make allowance in the measurement. However, a crooked hole sometimes winds across in the opposite direction, in which case true readings may once more come into view.

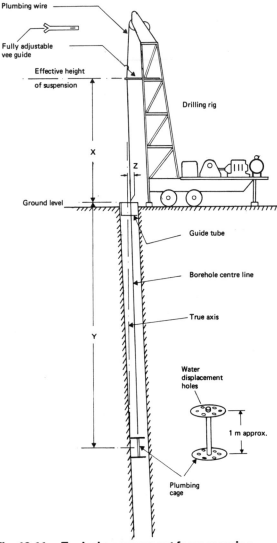

Fig. 13.11. Typical arrangement for measuring borehole verticality

Finally, some boreholes originally constructed straight and vertical have been checked in later years and found to be seriously crooked. The explanation for this unusual behaviour may be that sand has been pumped over the years, causing some lateral displacement. In volcanic areas overseas it is not unknown for borehole alignment to change overnight.

4. TYPICAL INSTALLATIONS

CASING AND SCREENS

Plain tubes are either permanent or temporary, the latter type usually being flush jointed, offering least resistance to insertion and subsequent removal during construction. The cost of screwed, flush-jointed tubes is rather higher than similar diameter welded joint tubes because the former have to be of sufficient thickness to bear male and female threads. However the lighter welded tubes require welding equipment to join them and gas cutting facilities to cut and reface them upon removal. If substantial thread protectors are available and the lengths fairly short it is preferable to use screwed, flush-jointed, temporary tubing.

For permanent plain tubes in smaller sizes, screwed-and-socketed casing may be used—even if only for the reason that it is readily available. The cheapest mild steel casing is the plain ended variety.

One of the many considerations is whether or not the tube column will be driven down into the ground. The practice of driving tubes is viewed with disapproval by modern drillers; it is preferable to surge gently several telescoped tiers through caving formations rather than force one column to a great depth. However, where vibration equipment is available it may be acceptable to run a long column if the tubes are sound.

Mild steel plain tubes for the upper section of a well are very common and, if surrounded by good cement, will provide long service even in an aggressive water. For diameters below 375 mm tubes made of plastics, glass-reinforced resins or laminated wood might be considered. Recent oil price increases have in some cases made plastic products costly but, even so, a very aggressive water may decide the issue and the cost would still be lower than stainless steel. Where borehole design permits high head differentials between the inside of the plastic lining and the annular space, consideration must be given to the safe working pressure of the lining before collapse.

As mentioned in Section 2, all systems require insertion of a guide tube to give stability at ground level and a true guide to the drilling tools to follow, which are usually from 12 to 25 mm less in diameter.

If the formation below the guide tube is stable, drilling will recommence and continue until such time as the full depth of the borehole has been reached or sufficient depth has been drilled to receive the first column of permanent casing.

Where unstable ground is present below the guide tube, the next step will be dictated by several factors—for example, the method of drilling, whether the permanent tube column incorporates screen tubes, and the design (drop-set screens, full diameter from top to bottom, telescoping etc.).

Taking a firm stratum as a simple example, drilling would continue down to the setting depth of the permanent casing, the tools be removed, a provisional verticality test carried out (if the hole is suspect) and the casing installed.

Water well casing is manufactured to British and American standards and nominal bore increases by increments of 50 mm up to 300 mm diameter and thereafter by 75 mm. It is usual to drill at least two increments larger than the bore of the casing to be inserted, the size being governed by whether the tubes are socketed or plain, the specified thickness of the cement grout, the possibility that the nature of the ground might cause verticality problems, and possibly an allowance for insertion of emergency temporary tubes.

Having installed the permanent casing, it is suspended from the rig and gently lowered on to the bottom. A verticality test is now carried out and any slight error extinguished by corrective movement of the casing at the surface. A cement plug is placed in the bottom of the borehole and the tubes carefully raised and lowered to allow the cement to flow out into the annular space to form a seal. After sufficient time to allow the cement to set, the annular space is filled through tremie pipes to the surface or, if the construction calls for a head chamber, to the invert.

Another method of cementing the casing—particularly at smaller diameters and greater depths—is to pressure grout, where a measured volume of cement grout is forced down inside the borehole followed by a separating packer driven down the hole by a column of clean water. The casing is suspended just clear of the bottom during this operation and is lowered off when the cement grout appears in the annular space at ground level. This method sometimes involves a disposable non-return valve at the base of the tube.

Yet another approach for large diameter casing is to fix a pair of steel elbows inside the tubes just above the level of the initial cement plug. The elbows are fitted with non-return valves attached to a left-hand joint and grouting takes place through grout pipes which are subsequently rotated to detach them. When the grout is sufficiently set a drilling tool is run down the borehole to snap off the elbows.

In structurally firm chalk, sandstone or limestone, it may be necessary only to drill 'open-hole' below surface anti-pollution casing to the required depth to complete the borehole (Fig. 13.12(a)). If the rock is fractured and unstable, a heavy wide-slotted tube to give structural support will be needed (Fig. 13.12(b)).

A different approach will be required when drilling in loose sand and gravel. Rotary drilling involving mud, water flush or foam will normally permit penetration to the full depth of the borehole, and where a gravel pack is incorporated, may call for some under-reaming—all of which would be carried out without the insertion of temporary tubes, borehole stability relying upon the superimposed head of fluid. At the smaller diameters without a gravel pack a complete column of screen and plain tubes would be installed. The method of cementing the plain section may consist of fitting a 'grout ring' on the outside of the lowest plain tube to provide a ledge in the annular space (Fig. 13.12(c)). A little sand is placed on this ledge, followed by an initial small quantity of cement grout. When this is sufficiently hard, grouting is continued up to the surface.

If the sand/gravel borehole is drilled by percussion methods it will be necessary to take two or more tiers of temporary tubes down as drilling proceeds, the final tier going to the designed depth.

The permanent screen and plain column would then be installed and the temporary tubes withdrawn to expose the screen to the formation (Fig. 13.13(a)). Natural slumping would be permitted whilst withdrawing the tubes until a level is reached where cementation is to commence, whereupon the driller will check the freedom of his remaining temporary and guide tubes to avoid the possibility of grouting them in.

Where a deep borehole is to be installed with a single column of screen and plain tubes care must be exercised to prevent damage to the screen by crushing, especially where a relatively short screen lies below heavy plain steel tubes.

Some boreholes—particularly those where a shallow pumping water level is anticipated—employ relatively large diameter plain tubes in the upper section in which the pump is suspended (Fig. 13.13(b)), whilst the lower section carries screen tubes of an appreciably smaller diameter. This effects a saving in cost on screens with little or no reduction in borehole performance; the actual drilled hole will have been at the larger diameter and the void between this and the small screen will either have been 'developed' from the natural formation or packed with a graded gravel.

The lower column of screen is sometimes continued up to the surface as plain tubes inside the larger casing to act as a gravel reserve (Fig. 13.14(a), (b)) or may be terminated with an overlap of several metres up inside the larger plain casing. In the latter case the lower column is known as a 'drop set' and it will be necessary to arrange both for a method of lowering them and for forming a seal between their uppermost part and the existing plain casing into which they overlap. The former can be achieved either by extending the screen column to the surface, employing temporary pipes attached to a left hand joint, or by using a horizontal hanger bar on pipes which fit into a bayonet slot. When the screen is resting on the bottom, the pipes and hanger bar are lowered a few centimetres further and turned clockwise; this disengages the bar from the slot and frees the pipe column for removal (Fig. 13.15(a)).

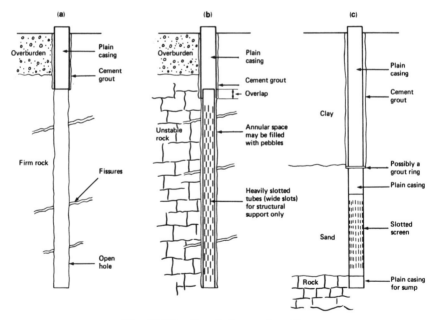

Fig. 13.12. Borehole construction
(a) Firm rock—open hole
(b) Unstable rock—casing for structural support
(c) Unconsolidated sands and gravels—slotted screen

This now leaves a space round the top of the screen column where it lies within the overlap of the plain casing. This space can be sealed with a lead packer or perhaps a composition seal. A lead packer consists of a parallel skirt extending upwards from the top of the screen. After installation, a swedge is driven into the skirt which causes it to expand into the bore of the plain casing, sealing the annular space. The swedge is then removed (Fig. 13.15(b)).

Another method of lowering the screen is to have a bail (or eye) attached inside the bottom closing plate and to suspend the column on steel wire rope with a release device at the point of attachment. This method would be used only within a clear bore such as inside temporary tubes.

Where a screen is to be surrounded by a gravel pack it is essential that it should be installed concentrically within the drilled bore or temporary tubes to ensure that the gravel thickness is uniform throughout. To this end, the screen tubes—and any plain tubes above them forming a gravel reserve—must be fitted with centralising spiders (Fig. 13.14). It is also important that the gravel be placed through pipes, preferably together with a flow of clean water, to ensure its arrival at the specified level without risk of 'bridging' in the annular space.

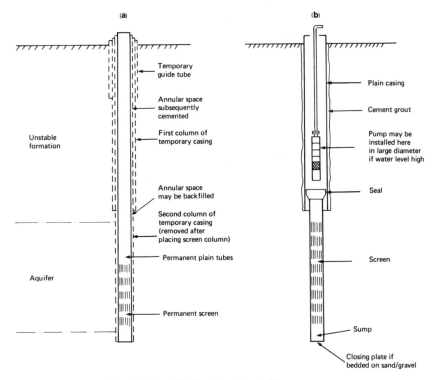

Fig. 13.13. Methods of installing screens
(a) 'Pull back' method; (b) Drop set screen

Pumps and Rising Mains

Airlift

Whilst pumps used in the UK both for testing and supply are almost without exception electric submersibles, there are circumstances where a persistently 'dirty' borehole will have to be pumped initially by airlift (Fig. 13.16(a)).

The efficiency of this system is low, but several small gains made during installation are sometimes neglected due to the simplicity of this method.

The bottom of the airpipe should be closed off and adequately perforated across the lower half-metre or so to facilitate rapid aeration of the water. The annular space between the eduction pipes (rising mains) and the borehole lining at the surface must be left open to atmosphere. To provide a steady discharge of water it is preferable to erect a long stand pipe above the tee which allows separation of most of the air from the water. Whilst a concentric airlift is easier to assemble—and may be the only option in a small diameter borehole—a separate string of airpipes alongside the eduction pipes and entering them just above the bottom offers less restriction to the rising column of water/air. Where the eduction pipes are carried down almost to the bottom of a deep borehole in order to draw out all the incoming solids there is little to be gained by inserting the airpipes lower than a depth giving 60 per cent or more submergence at maximum output; indeed, the extra sockets in a concentric assembly would increase resistance to the rising fluid.

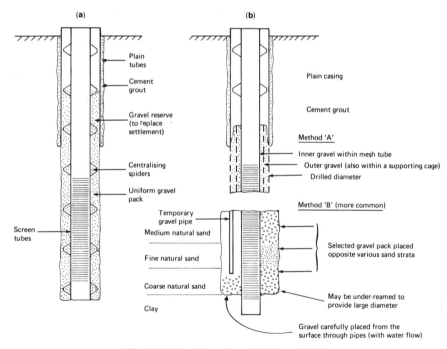

Fig. 13.14.   Gravel packed boreholes
(a) Simple system; (b) Multiple pack

The correct ratios of eduction pipes, airpipes and air pressure/volume must be selected; where BSP is used it must be of heavyweight quality.

Electric Submersible Pumps

When received on site these pumps may or may not be filled with coolant. It is most important to check this straight away with the makers' instructions as damage can occur even before installation due to frost or, in some cases, hot sunlight.

Early submersible pumps were filled wtih soluble oil and water, others with straight mineral oils; then most of them required distilled water. Latterly it has become standard practice to use clean tap water, although a few pumps despatched from the makers contain a glycerine mixture.

Older pumps tended to expel some fluid from the shaft-entry gland due to temperature expansion and breathed in replacement water (and contaminants) upon cooling. Modern pumps allow for temperature changes by a rubber diaphragm incorporated in the motor base.

The weakest part of the pump unit is the casting connecting motor to pump and through which the water enters. As it lies in the centre of two heavy assemblies and must offer the least restriction to incoming water it is of necessity skeletal and consequently vulnerable to careless handling in a horizontal plane.

Another point where care must be observed is at the entry of the power cable into the motor. Some cables change from circular to flat section alongside the pump and may be covered by metal trunking. This protects them whilst in the borehole

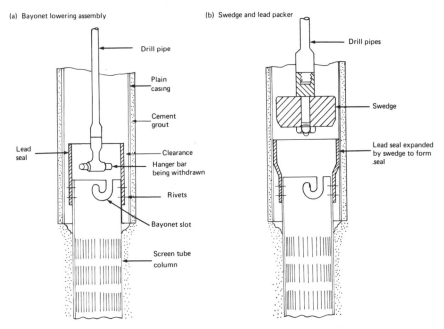

Fig. 13.15.   Method of lowering screen (a) and forming seal between screen and plain casing (b)

but the cable is still liable to severe kinking when erecting the pump on site prior to insertion.

It is advisable to check the resistance across each phase and the insulation resistance value to earth with a megger before lowering the pump. The principal dimensions should also be recorded, together with any matching piece between pump and the rising main.

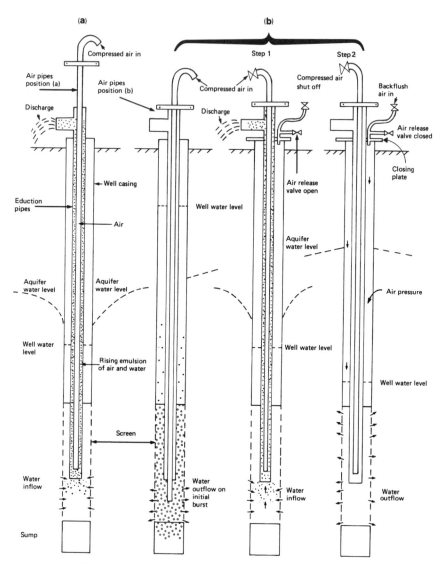

Fig. 13.16.   Well development by airlift pumping
(a) 'Blowback' air lift; (b) 'Closed head' air lift

There are conflicting opinions on the desirability of fitting a non-return valve above the pump. The sudden back-flush of water down the rising main when taking recovery levels during test pumping may interfere with the test data. On the other hand, if the pump is stopped just after commencement of pumping a dirty borehole, entrained solids will settle back on the valve and may cause it to jam in the closed position.

Some small pumps incorporating a pressure vessel delivery system rely upon the surge of air from the empty rising main to maintain air pressure in the vessel and must not carry a non-return valve above the pump. It would be quite in order, however, to fit one into the surface pipe work.

In pump installation, the makers' instructions will be followed and the work is straightforward where adequate clearance exists between the unit and borehole wall. Test pumps are generally attached to screwed rising mains as these are much quicker to assemble and provide greater clearance for insertion of instruments. It is important to ensure that the first two lengths or so of rising mains are screwed together securely as the torque reaction upon starting might twist the pump unit. It is also an advantage to maintain the cable in vertical alignment on one side of the main by cable clips rather than allow a spiral to develop, thus ensuring the maximum clearance. It is of course vital to apply sufficient tension and strapping to the cable to prevent slack loops—which could easily cause destruction of the cable when removing the pump from a borehole of restricted clearance.

Low-level and high-level control electrodes are often fixed to rising mains during installation. Where some changes in levels and output are envisaged it might be better to suspend the electrodes from the well head to allow adjustments without disturbing the pump.

It is usual to install a column of 'dipper pipes' in the borehole to a level just below the pump to facilitate insertion of an electric water level probe and protect the probe from recording any cascade or leakage from above the true pumping water level. The pipes may or may not be perforated.

Permanent submersible pumps are less likely to be suspended on screwed casing—unless the water is particularly non-aggressive—as it is difficult to provide adequate thread protection against corrosion inside the pipe joints. Although more expensive, flanged rising mains are stronger and lend themselves to the application of protective coatings more readily. However, their flanges may rule out their use in smaller diameter boreholes, even allowing for flange cutaways to accommodate the cable.

5. WELL DEVELOPMENT METHODS

GENERAL

Early water wells were considered complete as soon as the final depth had been reached, the permanent lining inserted, and any temporary tubes withdrawn. A pump was installed and the yield accepted as the actual output of that well.

Since those days, experience and modern technology have shown that further work will be beneficial to well or borehole performance and, in some cases, can increase the yield many times over. This additional phase of work—well development—can take from several hours to a week or more, depending on the strata.

The procedure consists of altering the conditions around the completed bore to allow the most effective inflow of water—by a variety of methods, ranging from injection of acid to rearrangement of the particles in sand formations.

The methods described are used in new boreholes but some may be applicable to improvement of yield in old boreholes.

SAND/GRAVEL BOREHOLES

Basically there are three types of sand screen construction:

(i) natural pack, where the sand or gravel formation is allowed to slump against the screen tubes;

(ii) *in situ* pack, where a gravel-packed annular space is formed between the screen tubes and the formation during borehole construction; and

(iii) pre-formed pack, which consists of widely slotted tubes surrounded by a uniform envelope of epoxy-resin coated gravel grains.

All three types require a development phase, although reverse circulation drilling, with a gravel pack, usually requires very little further work to be done.

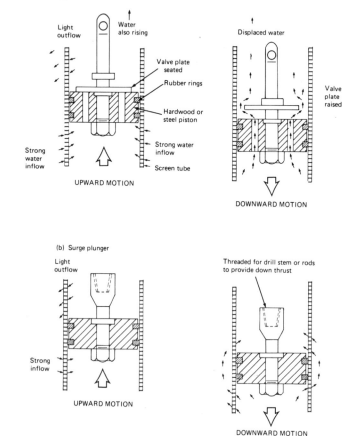

Fig. 13.17. Development of sand or gravel aquifer
(a) Using swab; (b) Using surge plunger

Bailing

The simplest method of developing a well—especially of small diameter—is to use a large bailer. This is initially operated gently in the upper part of the well to promote an incoming movement of water without inviting the problems later described. Measurement of both the quantity bailed and the draw-down will serve as a 'datum' from which to observe improvement in yield as bailing progresses.

It is important that the first period of bailing is confined to careful removal of solids from within and immediately without the screen tubes. If the motion is too rapid there is a risk of slabs of clay, silt, or drilling mud (where present) being drawn hard against the screen. Of greater danger is the real risk of screen collapse whilst vigorously withdrawing a close-fitting bailer up a mud-filled hole. This is caused by the head differential between the diminished pressure under the rapidly rising bailer and that of the static mud column outside the screen.

Bailing is continued at a faster rate until no more sand enters the borehole but it is stressed that this method is not necessarily a complete well development.

Swabbing

In this operation a swab is lowered into the borehole and drawn up through the water with the object of inducing an inward flow of water beneath it (Fig. 13.17(a)). A secondary and lesser outward flow occurs above the swab. As sand is drawn in it falls to the bottom of the borehole, whence it is periodically removed by a bailer or sandpump.

The aim of swabbing—and all the following methods used in sandy boreholes—is to re-arrange the formation particles so that fines are displaced and drawn into the borehole and coarser particles encouraged to build up outside the screen. By applying the proper technique it is sometimes possible to influence the natural formation some 100 mm or more radially from the drilled diameter of the borehole.

For a given abstraction of water from a borehole the inflow through the aquifer accelerates the nearer it approaches the centre line of the borehole. The greater the proportion of fine material in the formation the greater the resistance—or head loss—to this inflow. It follows that if the fine sand and silt around the screen or pack can be removed there will be a corresponding increase in water flow into the borehole for any given pumping level. However, whilst vigorous passage of water through the screen will certainly draw in fines, this by itself is not sufficient. Premature bridging of the formation particles can occur, which gives the quite false impression of a developed sand-free borehole.

To overcome the above condition it is necessary to ensure that a rapid flow is applied through the screen in *both* directions.

Surge Plunger

Whilst a swab is strongly active on the upward stroke and fitted with by-pass valves for downward travel, a surge plunger is often solid and used below a suitable heavy weight to create an effective back-flow on the down stroke as well as the upstroke (Fig. 13.17(b)).

The surge plunger, widely used by well drillers, is an effective tool. Some restraint is called for under certain circumstances, especially the risk of screen collapse mentioned above. Also, indiscriminate removal of sand in the presence of clay layers can cause structural problems and slumping. An abnormal inflow of sand may be due to an incorrect choice of screen for the formation, but this should have been calculated at the design stage.

Some drillers operate the surge plunger only in the plain tubes above the screen but this is not very efficient and may have been resorted to when using a wire-wound screen, where the vertical bars rule out effective use of a plunger.

Air-Lifting

Whilst air-lifting as a method of pumping water is inefficient, it is frequently used as an initial pumping device in a new borehole, where the presence of solids would damage a conventional submersible or turbine pump. It is also used specifically to develop boreholes. In all applications the governing criterion is that the borehole should possess a high water level relative to depth so that the system can function.

Surging by air-lift may be carried out in two ways: the 'blow-back' and 'closed-head' methods (Fig. 13.16(a)), (b)). In the former a conventional air-lift arrangement is installed, i.e. eduction pipes placed near the bottom of the borehole and air pipes a metre or so up inside them. The pump is at first operated with caution if drilling mud has been used (to avoid collapse of the screen) and then run at maximum duty. Output is shut off and the water allowed to recover to near normal level; in the meantime the air pipes are lowered to extend *below* the eduction pipes. Full air pressure from the air receivers is now passed through the air pipes and causes the standing water to be flushed outwards through the screen. This process is repeated until the water is sand-free and may be operated stage by stage up the full length of the screen—although again this would depend on the submergence factor.

The closed head method is similar, but differs in that the air pipes remain up inside the eduction pipes throughout the operation, and the space between airlift and well casing is sealed by a closing cap, carrying an air hose connection and air-release valve.

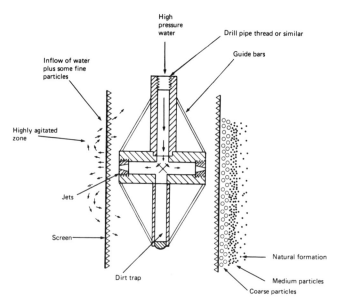

Fig. 13.18.   Jetting head

The air-lift is at first operated as a normal pump, then, after allowing time for recovery (displacing air through the valve) the compressed air is blown rapidly into the annular space *via* the cap connection. This causes the borehole water to be flushed out through the screen and the cycle is repeated.

'Over-Pumping'

This method of development is sometimes used with a measure of success. In essence, the borehole is pumped at a maximum rate in excess of the permanent pumping requirement and some stopping and starting cycle may be introduced to backwash the borehole, the theory being that if the borehole will perform satisfactorily—free from sand and structurally stable—under excess abstraction it should give reliable service under a less demanding duty. The permanent pump would not of course be used for this work as, apart from risk of damage by sand, it should not have the excess capacity to overpump if correctly selected in the first place.

The most suitable pump for this purpose is the vertical spindle turbine type because operating clearances can be adjusted quickly from the surface (providing larger clearances at the commencement and fine clearances for greater efficiency when the water is sand free); the speed can often be varied, and the water allowed to flush straight down through the pump intake to create a backwash when stopped. A disadvantage is the necessity to carry a somewhat complicated pump for this work. Also, despite initially large clearances, there will be wear when first pumping in a sandy borehole and in extreme cases the pump can become sand-locked.

Jetting

Strictly speaking there are two categories of jetting; the relatively low pressure method used for development of newly constructed boreholes, and the very high pressure system associated with rehabilitation of old boreholes.

Although a wire-wound screen cannot accept a swab or surge plunger it is ideally suited to the application of a water jet. Other types of screen will also benefit from jetting but, depending upon the design, with less effect.

The jetting tool usually carries three or more jets positioned radially in a head screwed to a column of drill pipes or similar (Fig. 13.18). The drill pipes are suspended from a water swivel to which is attached a kelly hose which feeds water from a pressure pump on the surface.

The tool is lowered to the bottom of the screen and the water turned on. Slow rotation is now applied whilst the tool is gradually raised up the screen section. The jets of water pass through the screen apertures and activate the formation, dislodging drilling mud, clay particles, silts and natural fines. Ideally an air-lift or other type of pump should be installed above the jetting tool to draw the displaced material out of the hole. If this is not possible the tool should be removed periodically and a sandpump or bailer used to clean out this material.

If the screen is surrounded by an *in situ* gravel pack it is debatable whether the jetting turbulence will reach through to the wall of the borehole and activate the natural sands. *In situ* packs are usually in the order of 50 to 100 mm thick and of various gradings—some of which may totally impede the water jet. However, jetting will certainly help clean a wire-wound screen and pack and combined with a flushing method should result in a fully developed borehole.

Very high pressure jetting has been introduced quite recently as a method of re-activating or improving an existing borehole. It consists of a jetting head for application inside the screen and, where a gravel pack is present, a lance for introduction into the annular space.

The equipment operates at pressures of 300 atmospheres or more and subsequent television inspection reveals that most of the deposit is removed from metal tubes, leaving a polished surface and clear slots. Where non-metallic screens are employed care must be taken to avoid damage under the localised loadings and this same caution should be exercised if metal screens are thought to be wasted through corrosion or external erosion through 'swirl'.

The lance for jetting within the annular space carries both downward and rearward facing jets—the latter to facilitate removal of the lance which is inserted at a number of points radially and as close to the screen as possible.

Internal jetting may require some 100 l/min of water whilst lancing at, say, 200 atmospheres would take about 60 l/min.

Again, provision must be made for removal of debris.

Chemical Treatment

When mechanical cleaning of a well cannot entirely remove silt, clay and mud particles, chemical treatment may be needed.

Apart from hydrochloric acid, reagents such as chlorine and ammonium salts, detergents, and *Calgon* (sodium hexametaphosphate) are used. The latter product is probably most commonly used, although drilling mud manufacturers market a number of 'own brand' dispersants.

The chemical is mixed with water and either poured down the borehole or directed through pipes into the screen area. It is left to stand for an hour or so, after which water is added to wash the fluid into the aquifer or gravel pack. Some mechanical agitation is beneficial at this stage to loosen the particles and may take the form of light swabbing or air-lifting. Any discharge of fluid at the surface should be allowed to settle before the fluid is returned to the borehole. This cycle of operations may be repeated over many hours and terminated when surge pumping no longer dislodges any more particles.

It must be stressed that only approved chemicals should be used in water supply wells.

BOREHOLES IN ROCK

Due to the prominence given by screen manufacturers to sandy borehole development work it is sometimes overlooked that large areas of the world are supplied with water from boreholes drilled into solid formations. Screening as such is rarely required and any tubes needed for structural support in the aquifer are usually widely-slotted heavy casings, sometimes surrounded by a pack of large pebbles.

The yield of a borehole in rock is dependent on the interception of fissures, solution holes, bedding planes and other apertures. The pores of a sandstone or chalk may be saturated but there will be little transmission of water into a borehole without joints or fissures.

Drilling is bound to introduce some material into these spaces whether through the fluid head of rotary drilling or the plastering effect of cable-tools; furthermore, the meandering passages will very likely contain natural deposits of silt. Surge-pumping and 'overpumping' rather than reverse-flow should be applied in these conditions to encourage the washing process.

Certain sandstone fissures tend to erode away under the influence of high-speed water and no amount of development will prevent the ingress of some sand. This condition can be relieved by pumping at a lower rate but the answer may be to pump gently from several boreholes rather than strongly from one.

Acid Treatment

Over the last 30 years boreholes into chalk would be drilled and test-pumped and, if the yield was poor, acid treatment would be applied. The results were from fair to dramatic and most present-day chalk borehole specifications include for acid treatment before pumping as a matter of course. This saves the expense of installing the pump a second time but no longer provides 'before and after' figures for yield comparison and this seems a loss. The response to acid injection varies enormously—even in boreholes of similar construction—and it is rare to find a behavioural pattern developing in a group of boreholes in one area.

Hydrochloric acid reacts with chalk according to the equation:

$$CaCO_3 + 2HCl = CaCl_2 + CO_2 + H_2O$$

One tonne of commercial acid ($32°$ Tw, SG 1.16, 31.52 per cent HCl by weight) will dissolve 0.43 tonnes chalk and generate approximately 0.49 tonnes $CaCl_2$, 77 l water and 0.19 tonnes CO_2, equivalent to 96 m^3 at STP. However, since CO_2 is readily soluble in water the volume released as gas will be less (**Caution:** This gas can be lethal—see later).

By dissolving chalk, acid treatment will increase the cross-sectional area of fissures, permitting freer flow, and will effect further improvement in flow by dissolution of drilling slurry and cuttings.

As a rough guide, not less than 6 tonnes of acid are likely to be required to treat 40 m of chalk borehole of 600 mm diameter.

Opinions vary on the most effective method of using acid, but it seems that pressure injection is marginally superior to gravity flow. Injection of acid into a borehole between two packers—a development from oil well technology—is claimed to give more effective treatment of selected fissures.

Inhibitors are frequently used when acidising boreholes lined with mild steel tubes. If correctly applied, an inhibitor will prevent acid attack by depositing a protective film upon the steel tubes.

Finally—but of primary importance—the matter of safety. Hydrochloric acid itself is not one of the more dangerous acids and copious supplies of water will cope with most accidents.

On the other hand, carbon dioxide can be lethal. This heavy gas is colourless and odourless and does not indicate its presence. On a still day it will linger in a hollow—a headpit especially—long after acidising works have ceased, so that extreme care must be exercised.

Furthermore, it is not always appreciated that carbon dioxide can be released from some formations into a borehole or well during a period of low barometric pressure—and that this has caused a number of fatal accidents.

Acidising works should never be begun unless there is a designated responsible and experienced person in total charge of the operation who will check all safety equipment, acquaint all personnel with the location and use of such equipment, and will fully explain the programme to ensure that everyone involved fully understands his duties.

Explosives

Some harder limestones and sandstones respond to the use of high explosives for improvement to fissuring. Gelignite is normally used but to be really effective the charge is often of such size as to endanger the well structure.

A more satisfactory approach is to use an RDX/TNT explosive moulded into a special canister (a 'shaped-charge') giving it directional effect; most of the blast may be then applied to selected zones by lowering the canister on wire line, or in thin square tubes, where directional accuracy is required.

6. TEST PUMPING—SITE PROCEDURE

PUMPS

Estimation of the probable performance of a new borehole is based on sound hydrogeological evaluation and local experience—but in some cases on wishful thinking. All boreholes are different—even when adjacent—their character being formed more by the quirks of nature than the skill of the design engineer or driller, so it is difficult to specify beforehand the exact duty required of the test pump. In some countries it is customary to install a vertical spindle turbine pump for testing a borehole and as this usually employs an i.c. engine for motive power, it has the advantage of variable speed and output.

Notwithstanding this, the type of aquifer, depth to water level, diameter and depth of borehole and the distance to discharge point are all considered and the contractor is usually called upon to provide the largest pump to meet all foreseen conditions. In practice this may present problems. A submersible pump of sufficient duty may be of such large diameter as to restrict the incoming water, and whilst a large pump might be acceptable for a permanent installation, it would be undesirable for a test pumping programme where one or more strings of conductor pipes are lowered past the pump to allow for unrestricted passage of logging instruments.

As mentioned earlier, installing a submersible pump near the bottom of the borehole invites the risk of a burnt-out motor, if sufficient solids accumulate beneath it to prevent a flow of cooling water, but a deep pump setting may allow the maximum amount of water to be drawn out of the borehole in the short term.

However, over the longer term it is important that the pumping water level is not depressed to a point where any screens—or fissures in unlined boreholes—are exposed to cause cascading. This would encourage entrainment of air bubbles which can damage pump impellers and falsify readings on some flow meters—apart from introducing other undesirable side effects. A further point is that in endeavouring to operate the test pump at the deepest level the additional pipe friction may cancel out any hoped-for gain in output. Also, the weight upon temporary headworks must not be overlooked as a long column of rising main full of water receives little buoyancy from a deep pumping water level.

Where conditions are favourable the preferable position for a pump is as high as possible and, ideally, just inside the lower end of the plain casing.

Before installation it is good practice to refer to the verticality test figures for the borehole, especially if a very large diameter pump relative to the borehole is being inserted, as it may be necessary to observe particular caution at certain depths. Most contractors are reluctant to fit foot valves to test pumps because it is often necessary to shut off the pump a few minutes after the initial run (for example, to change rotation or to fill a weir tank or just to close a leak in the pipework) and this could cause a sand-locked pump and/or the foot valve to stick if particles settle back on it. A disadvantage with the absence of a foot valve is that at the end of a test period the first minute or two of recovery will be influenced by the backflush of the full rising mains—especially where the pumping water level has been depressed down a deep borehole.

SURFACE PIPEWORK

A 90° bend fitted with a head gauge and sampling cock is attached to the top of the rising mains, followed by a gate valve and delivery pipework to the flow measuring device. The gauge should be fitted with a shut-off cock to isolate it from the hydraulic vibration usually found in the head assembly. The sampling cock is used to release air trapped between the closed gate valve and rising column of water upon initial start-up; it then serves to monitor water quality as close to the source as possible, rather than taking a sample from the end of a long pipeline which might not be truly representative—for example, when looking for sand content. The output control valve must be in first class condition as it will be required to adjust the output across a number of steps, the first two or three being against high pump pressure.

It is useful to include a short length of flexible hose in the pipework after the gate valve as this allows some movement to accommodate stresses set up during different stages of pumping—especially when pumping against a considerable head. As most test pumping pipework is temporary and includes mechanical joints, adequate thrust blocks and/or staking must be provided where substantial changes of direction occur.

Where a pipeline is laid across undulating terrain and pumping comprises short daytime stages in winter it is very important to make provision for draining any low-lying sections. Under freezing conditions the pipeline can quickly become blocked and even if some flow is regained the next morning the pieces of ice can be a hazard to metering devices and a nuisance in a weir tank.

FLOW MEASUREMENT EQUIPMENT

It is common knowledge that most types of flow meters should be installed in a straight length of pipework with full flow through them and away from valves, bends and sudden changes of section and figures are quoted recommending the length of such approach pipe. Practical experience shows, however, that these theoretical guide-lines are rarely adequate and it is worth while taking extra care to position meters where they can obtain information of sufficient accuracy.

A spiral meter of fixed diameter may be called upon to measure a wide range of flows during step-testing—and will usually do so, but it can hardly be expected to work accurately when bombarded by a high velocity jet of water from a partially open valve three metres upstream.

An orifice meter will operate reliably under reasonable conditions but will give misleading figures when asked to cope with air bubbles. It will also show a very steady flow rate if frozen solid.

The former situations can be avoided if steps are taken to prevent cascading in the borehole and to check for intake of air through leaking joints in the surface pipework. It is not always appreciated that water passing at high velocity across a faulty joint can induce air into an otherwise pressurised line.

The frost hazard may be overcome by providing the orifice meter/recorder with an electric or bottled gas heater and some protection from the weather.

There is little to go wrong with weir tanks if the design is correct in the first instance. Where errors do occur these are usually due to irregular settlement of the tank after the recorder or hook gauge has been set at zero. The weir tank must be placed on the level, with adequate support for the weight of water when full, and this level must be checked periodically whilst pumping. Where solids are deposited in the tank these should not be allowed to build up to a point where passage of water through the baffles is impeded.

If floats and hook gauges are positioned in the main tank compartment well back from the weir it is preferable to surround them with a perforated tube to 'still' the surface of the water. Ideally, the float may be suspended in its own small tank adjacent to, and connected with, the main tank. The connecting pipe should be well above the bottom of the main tank to avoid closure by silt.

For taking readings and making flow adjustments it is convenient to place the weir tank near to the borehole being tested, but where the pipeline is long and the route climbs, it is necessary to position it at the top of the rise or at the discharge end of the pipeline. Problems of communication between well head and weir tank, to make adjustments to flow rate, may be overcome by using small transceiver radios or field telephones.

Chapter 14

DEVELOPMENT OF GROUNDWATER

1. INTRODUCTION

THE development of a groundwater reservoir may be considered to pass through three stages:

(1) Abstraction is a small proportion of average recharge or storage and wells can be sited as and where water is required.
(2) Demand upon the aquifer increases as more wells are drilled. The abstraction-recharge ratio increases and reduction of groundwater discharge from the aquifer becomes apparent because of low river flows during dry periods. Steps must be taken to maintain river flows to meet demands on the river system.
(3) Abstraction exceeds recharge and mining of water storage occurs. If this is unacceptable, artificial recharge must be introduced to restore the balance between input and output.

In the UK, the river basin is the basic hydrological unit that must be considered in resource development. A groundwater basin or an aquifer is a natural underground reservoir which is an integral part of the hydrology of a river basin. Development of the groundwater in the reservoir will affect river flows not only from the river basin containing the source but in some cases also from adjacent basins.

Because of this, optimum development of an aquifer during stages (2) and (3) requires conjunctive use of groundwater with the surface water resources of an entire river basin. In the UK, groundwater development is strongly influenced by the fact that most streams and rivers are perennial and have considerable environmental value both as fisheries and for amenity. Many rivers with a significant groundwater component are committed to existing water supply schemes that involve direct abstraction of river water. It is now recognised that there is a need to maintain acceptable river flows, if necessary by regulation with groundwater, so that all demands on the river system can be met.

Groundwater resources are replenished by infiltration of rainfall and at one time the yield of an aquifer was considered equal to the infiltration into the aquifer's outcrop. However, as development increased, it became apparent that there is no fixed "safe" yield from an aquifer. Rather the safe or acceptable yield depends upon the method of developing the water resources of a river basin and upon the management objectives, which are likely to include consideration of, not only the amount of recharge but, *inter alia*, economic, social, legal and water quality aspects.

Groundwater is a renewable resource but only up to a limit constrained by the need to maintain a hydrological balance which satisfies all the various demands for water in a river basin.

The continued and extensive development of groundwater in the main aquifers of England, principally the Chalk and Permo-Triassic sandstones, led to the control of abstraction, by a licensing system under the Water Act 1945, in areas where over-development of resources had occurred or was threatened. While the decline of water levels and interference between wells led to the 1945 legislation, it was the reduction of river flow, particularly of rivers fed by the Chalk, that became one of

I.W.E.S., Groundwater: occurrence, development and protection, 1986, Chapter 14

the factors leading to the Water Resources Act 1963. Reduction of river flows was particularly apparent in the dry summer of 1959, despite the fact that it followed a winter of average infiltration.

In the late 1950s and early 1960s problems were arising with the licensing of new groundwater sources. It was difficult, if not impossible, to prove that a new well would have an effect on the river draining the basin in which the well was situated. This problem was increasingly hindering realistic working of the Water Act 1945. The consequences of abstracting increasing quantities of groundwater by industry and public authorities were disputed at public inquiries as it was not possible at that time to present convincing, acceptable evidence of the close relationship between groundwater abstraction and river flow. Licences were issued with time-limits attached so that the consequences of abstraction could be evaluated before licences were confirmed. But establishing the consequences was usually impossible because the additional groundwater abstraction represented only a small increment to total abstraction and there was, in any case, no independent organization charged with the responsibility of assessing the consequences.

This situation was corrected by the Water Resources Act 1963 which created the Water Resources Board and the river authorities with responsibility, *inter alia*, for managing the water resources of England and Wales. At this time the advantages of combined use of groundwater and surface water resources were being realised. It was these two events that led to the modern approach to groundwater development in the UK, incorporating river regulation by groundwater and conjunctive use of surface and groundwater sources[1].

2. RIVER REGULATION WITH GROUNDWATER

INTRODUCTION

The gradual increase in groundwater abstraction from the Chalk and Triassic sandstones began to have a serious impact on river flows in the 1950s, particularly during dry periods.

The uneven seasonal distribution of natural groundwater discharge from these aquifers, together with the fact that they still contained large volumes of water in storage below the level of natural outlets, even in dry periods, led to the suggestion that groundwater could be developed for direct supply and also pumped into rivers to maintain adequate river flows, and that it could be practicable to develop groundwater during the summer in areas sufficiently distant from the river so that groundwater flow to the river would not be affected immediately[2]. As long ago as 1949 G. and C. Allsebrook (Water Engineers, Reading) had proposed that the River Thames could be augmented by pumping groundwater from the Chalk into the river[3]. In 1956 the Thames Conservancy appointed Herbert Lapworth Partners to investigate the proposal and, after they reported to the Conservancy in 1957 and 1964, the Conservancy announced, in 1965, proposals to develop groundwater in the Chalk of the Berkshire Downs in this manner[3]. In the same year proposals were published[4] for development of the water resources of the Great Ouse Basin, which included regulation of the tributaries of the main river with groundwater from the Chalk. The Water Resources Board encouraged the Thames Conservancy and the Great Ouse River Authority to promote pilot studies to demonstrate the validity of the proposals beyond all reasonable doubt. This led to the pilot schemes in the Lambourn Valley (Upper Thames Basin) and in the Thet Valley (Great Ouse

Basin) described later. During the course of these and other schemes (Fig. 14.1) much information was obtained about the hydrogeology of the Chalk and Triassic sandstones and the factors influencing their development on a regional scale for river regulation. This information has been summarised by Downing et al[5,6] and the remainder of this section is derived mainly from these papers.

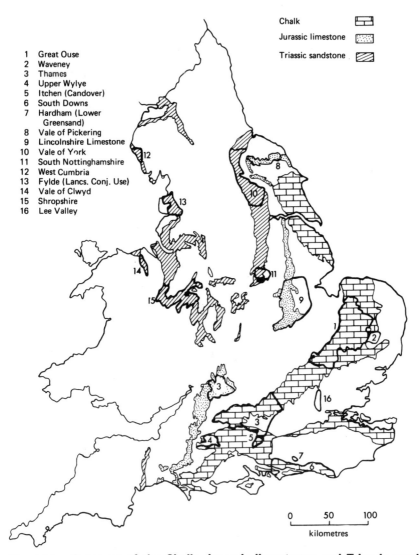

Chalk

Jurassic limestone

Triassic sandstone

1   Great Ouse
2   Waveney
3   Thames
4   Upper Wylye
5   Itchen (Candover)
6   South Downs
7   Hardham (Lower
     Greensand)
8   Vale of Pickering
9   Lincolnshire Limestone
10 Vale of York
11 South Nottinghamshire
12 West Cumbria
13 Fylde (Lancs. Conj. Use)
14 Vale of Clwyd
15 Shropshire
16 Lee Valley

0   50   100

kilometres

Fig. 14.1.   Outcrops of the Chalk, Jurassic limestones and Triassic sandstones showing the location of major groundwater schemes.

PRINCIPLES OF RIVER AUGMENTATION

During dry periods river flows may be augmented by using part of the large volume of water stored in aquifers. The objective is to modify the natural discharge from aquifers so that it occurs at a more even rate. Water is pumped from wells into the river whenever the flow falls below the level required to provide for the various demands on the river, whether for water supply, or the maintenance of adequate flows to dilute effluents, or to provide for irrigation or fisheries, or for general environmental amenities or a combination of these requirements.

Groundwater in an aquifer flows towards natural outlets, such as springs and seepages, which feed river flows. In view of this dependence of the river on groundwater, rational development of a resource for river regulation, or in conjunction with other water resources, requires an understanding of the basic principles behind the relationship between groundwater and surface water flow. This problem has been investigated by many authors including Oakes and Wilkinson[7], who specifically examined it in relation to river regulation schemes then under investigation in England. The seasonal variation in groundwater flow to a river is dependent upon the temporal distribution of infiltration and on a parameter which may be referred to as the aquifer response time, defined as T/SL^2 where T is the transmissivity, S is the storage coefficient, and L is the distance from the river to the impermeable boundary of the aquifer or to a groundwater divide parallel to the line of the river. Aquifers with a relatively fast response, for example highly permeable rocks with low storage coefficients, show a

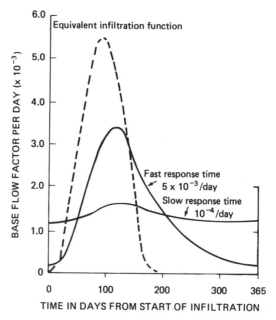

Fig. 14.2. Comparison of base flow variations in an average year from idealised aquifers with fast and slow response times and subject to a sinusoidal infiltration function (after Oakes and Wilkinson[7])

rapid change in groundwater discharge to a river in response to infiltration. A very fissured low porosity limestone is such an aquifer. In contrast, an aquifer with a slow response time has the effect of distributing seasonal infiltration more evenly, so that groundwater flow to the river is more nearly constant in time. The Triassic sandstones, with a high storage coefficient but relatively low transmissivity, tend to behave in this way. Seasonal variation in base flow of a river in response to a given infiltration distribution is illustrated for the two extreme types of aquifer in Fig. 14.2.

Aquifer response time is a principal factor in determining the effect of pumping from wells on river flow. The imposition of different abstraction regimes on an idealised river/aquifer system was considered by Oakes and Wilkinson[7].

A groundwater scheme which involves continuous abstraction from wells directly into supply will lead to a progressive reduction in the natural groundwater flow to the river that will ultimately equal the groundwater abstraction rate. The time taken to reach equilibrium depends upon the aquifer response time and the position of the well in relation to the river. It also depends upon a third factor, the permeability of the river bed. For simplicity, three cases may be recognised:

(a) the river bed is permeable and the river is in intimate hydraulic connection with the aquifer;

(b) the river bed is impermeable but groundwater can flow from the aquifer to the riparian zone, allowing effluent groundwater seepage to the river but not influent seepage from the river to the aquifer;

(c) the river bed is semi-pervious so that while groundwater may freely flow to the river, the reverse flow to the aquifer is retarded. This is the most common situation.

The three cases are illustrated in Fig. 14.3. An indication of which situation obtains may be provided by examining the sites of springs in relation to the distribution of alluvial deposits. If springs rise at the outer margin of the alluvium it implies that the river bed is impermeable or semi-permeable[5].

Fig. 14.4 illustrates the reduction in natural groundwater flow to a river with a permeable bed due to pumping from (a) wells in an aquifer with a slow response time and at some distance from the river, and (b) wells in an aquifer with a fast response time and close to the river. In the former case groundwater abstraction depletes the river flow only by an amount equivalent to the abstraction after many years, while in the second case the river is almost immediately affected.

A common misconception is that if groundwater abstraction reduces river flow, then river water is being drawn into the aquifer from the river and will eventually appear at the well. This occurs only if wells are close to the river or if abstraction rates are particularly high and the groundwater flow gradient at the river is reversed. This will occur, of course, only where the river bed is permeable.

In a river regulation scheme, groundwater is pumped into the river at times of low flow and abstracted at a downstream intake. Groundwater pumping is intermittent and the amounts and duration depend upon the demands to be met and the hydrology of the surface water system.

As already discussed, pumping from the aquifer will reduce the natural discharge to the river. Thus, all the groundwater that is pumped into the river is not available to meet the demand at the intake as some is required to make good the reduction of the base flow component. Some wells may also directly induce influent seepage from the river. The amount by which natural river flows are augmented by pumping groundwater is referred to as the *net gain*, commonly expressed as a percentage of the pumped quantity:

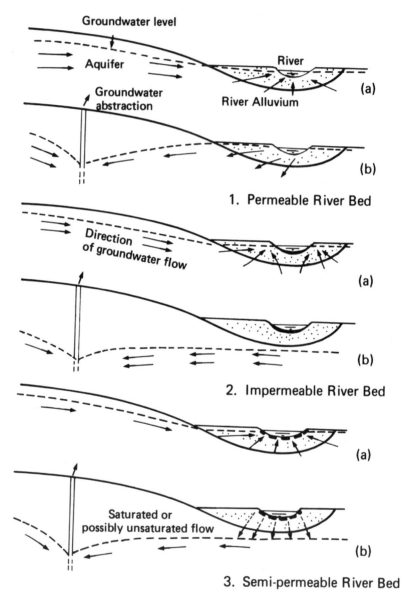

Fig. 14.3.   Three cases to illustrate differing degrees of hydraulic connection between an aquifer and a river for (a) natural and (b) groundwater abstraction conditions (after Downing *et al*[5])

$$\frac{G - (I + R)}{G} \times 100$$

where G is groundwater discharge to the river,
    I is natural groundwater discharge intercepted by the wells,
    and R is recirculation of water from the river into the aquifer by river bed leakage.

The net gain would be close to 100 per cent in a highly successful scheme, but in most schemes it is likely to be less than this, not least because of the relatively small size of river catchments in Britain and the difficulty of siting wells to avoid affecting surface water flows.

The minimum net gain acceptable depends upon the cost of the water yielded by the scheme compared with other schemes. In many schemes it will be essential to ensure that a high net gain is maintained until the end of the period during which the river is regulated by groundwater but, if the net gain in river flow is to be used in conjunction with pumped storage reservoirs in the lower reaches of a river system, then the overall net gain is the important factor.

The net gain depends upon the transmissivity and storage coefficient of the aquifer, the permeability of the river bed, and the position of the wells relative to the river and aquifer boundaries[7,8,9]. The delay between the beginning of pumping

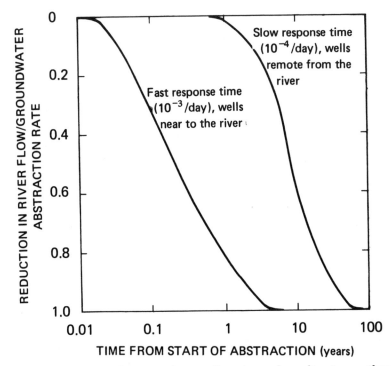

Fig. 14.4. Reduction in groundwater flow to a river due to continuous abstraction from wells when the hydraulic gradient is maintained towards the river (after Downing *et al*[5])

and the effect on the river is a function of the transmissivity and storage coefficient—that is, the diffusivity of the aquifer. The highest net gains in an unconfined aquifer, if the river bed is permeable, occur if the wells are sited some distance from the river; under these conditions the net gain would fall rapidly to zero if wells were sited adjacent to the river. For a given abstraction regime the net gain depends upon the response time of the aquifer, there being a tendency towards low net gains if the response time is fast and a high net gain if slow (Fig. 14.4). Fig. 14.4 emphasises that for aquifers with a slow or medium response time, the net gain in the early years of a continuously operated scheme is higher than the equilibrium value, which may not be attained for ten years or more. In actual practice, few schemes operate at levels approaching maximum capacity every year and in such circumstances the net gain will always exceed the equilibrium value. However, this is certainly not the case for fast response aquifers.

If the river bed is impermeable, it should be possible to develop underground storage within the aquifer below the river bed level. To develop this storage the abstraction rate must be sufficiently high so that the groundwater gradient at the river falls to zero and is reversed. Without this reversal the river behaves as though the river bed were fully permeable in the manner previously described. For a sealed river bed condition, dewatering must occur if the wells are located immediately adjacent to the river. From such an aquifer/river system high net gains may be obtained. The wells are ideally situated for river regulation in that only short lengths of pipeline are required to carry abstracted water to the river. For a particular abstraction regime, the equilibrium net gain may be attained only after a number of years. Again, the time taken to reach this equilibrium state, and the net gain values prior to and at equilibrium, depend upon the response time of the aquifer, the proportion of the natural recharge abstracted, and the geometry of the aquifer unit.

A semi-permeable river bed will give net gains intermediate between the two extreme cases. As the water level in an aquifer falls below the base of semi-permeable deposits forming the river bed, infiltration through the bed attains a maximum value dependent upon its permeability; thereafter it is independent of the abstraction rate.

In a groundwater river regulation scheme the degree of hydraulic continuity between the river and the aquifer is of prime importance in determining the disposition of wells, the resulting net gains and hence the yield of the scheme. It is important, therefore, to determine the permeability of beds of surface water courses by means of detailed river-flow gauging during pumping tests and by the analysis of water levels from piezometers in the alluvial deposits, during the planning stage of a scheme.

Successful operation of a river regulation scheme entails taking advantage of the low rate of groundwater flow and the large storage capacity of aquifers, which means that the effects of groundwater abstraction are only slowly transmitted to points of natural groundwater discharge.

During the winter following a period of pumping for river regulation, the river flow is actually less than would have occurred under natural conditions (Fig. 14.5) because infiltration preferentially restores the depleted aquifer storage.

If the object of the river regulation scheme is to provide additional water supply, then schemes can be developed along the following lines:

(i) A water supply can be obtained from a river intake, the flow of the river being supplemented by pumping from wells into the river at times of low flow. The river intake can be replaced by wells if the river is in hydraulic continuity with the aquifer, the wells deriving their yield from the river by induced recharge. This has the advantage that the water receives some degree of purification as it flows through the ground to the wells.

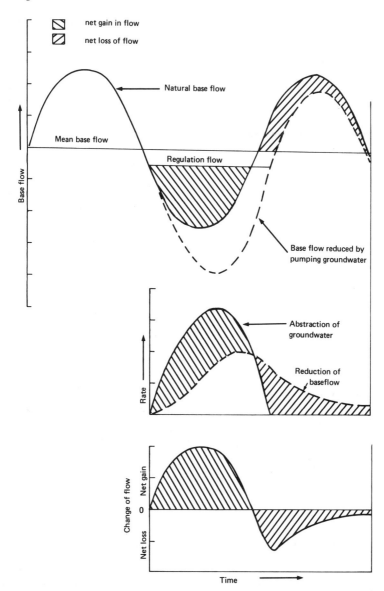

Fig. 14.5. Schematic diagram illustrating the regulation of river flow by pumping groundwater into a river (after Rodda, Downing and Law[83])

Note: With continuous seasonal regulation a new equilibrium would be attained ultimately and the winter base flow would then be reduced to a greater extent than shown

(ii) Groundwater can be pumped directly to supply continuously, but additional wells are required to pump compensation water into the river system to maintain acceptable flows.

(iii) Seasonal abstraction can take place from a river intake (or riverside wells if conditions are favourable) when the flow exceeds that required to meet non-water-supply demands on the river. At other times pumping is from wells at sites removed from the river. Some groundwater abstraction may be required to maintain acceptable river flows.

ASSESSMENT OF YIELD

The reliability of an assessment of both the surface water and groundwater resources of a catchment area and their capability of sustaining a yield for specified operating rules and failure criteria depends upon the availability and quality of the hydrological and hydrogeological data.

Estimating reliable yields from aquifers is more complex than a similar study for surface reservoirs due to a less precise knowledge of the natural recharge to aquifers, the volume of available water stored in aquifers and the complexity of the relationship between groundwater and river flows.

Natural Replenishment

The total water resources replenished annually are equivalent to the difference between rainfall and actual evaporation which represents total run-off. If ten or more years of river flow records are available, together with long-term rainfall data, a reasonable assessment can be made of both mean total run-off and mean groundwater flow, together with the temporal distribution over an annual period. Where a single aquifer crops out over most of the catchment, the groundwater discharge can be equated with infiltration into this aquifer. However, in many situations the geology of the catchment is more complex, including impermeable rocks and possibly several aquifers, and infiltration into the aquifers has to be determined by more subjective methods, including estimates from rainfall and actual evaporation data. Judgment is required prior to proposing the most likely range of values for the natural recharge rate to the aquifer.

Volume of Groundwater Storage

An estimate of the volume of water stored in an aquifer, potentially available for development, is obtained from the volume of saturated rock and the coefficient of storage. However, not all this water can be used for supply due to the difficulty of completely draining an aquifer and the imposition of restraints such as deterioration of water quality and reduction of permeability with increasing depth.

In the Chalk a limiting factor is likely to be a reduction of permeability with increasing depth. This aquifer has a low coefficient of storage of 1-5 per cent; water level drawdowns are large in relation to yield and specific capacity can decline significantly as groundwater levels fall.

The critical period for a groundwater reservoir is the time between the start of a significant artificial drawdown in groundwater levels and the maximum drawdown. The length of this period increases with the volume of storage developed and the extent to which the river flow is regulated. Fig. 14.6 illustrates the drawdown in groundwater levels that would occur in a typical Chalk catchment during an estimated drought of 1 in 50 years severity, for river flows regulated at 60-90 per cent of the mean. Many surface storage schemes use up to 50 per cent of total run-off, whereas in areas where groundwater represents a high proportion of the total flow it should be possible to regulate rivers by groundwater abstraction at up to 70 to 90 per cent of mean flow. As this percentage increases, the drawdown during the design drought becomes increasingly large, as does the length of time for recovery of water levels.

Unlike surface reservoirs, a groundwater reservoir is not readily emptied, and the yield is unlikely, therefore, to fall to zero even during droughts of greater severity than the design drought. Groundwater schemes rarely fail because of lack of storage, they fail because the well capacity is inadequate.

Conditions During a Design Drought

The groundwater resources, comprising the volume of water available in storage and the mean replenishment of the aquifer, have to be related to yields which can be sustained during the design drought period. Water resource schemes are frequently based upon design droughts of 1 in 50 or 1 in 100 years severity, although the limitations of this useful and relatively simple failure criterion have been indicated by Jamieson and Sexton[10].

Estimates of conditions likely to occur during design drought periods have to be made from available hydrological records and also if possible from models of the system[10].

Conjunctive use schemes are closely related to river flows, and some estimate must, therefore, be made of flows during the design drought. If at least 15 or 20

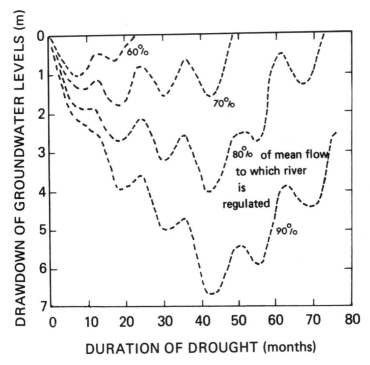

Fig. 14.6.   Typical drawdown of groundwater levels in the Chalk during a 2 per cent drought at specified levels of river regulation (after Downing *et al*[6])

years of river flow data are available, then the time-series method of data generation is ideal for estimating drought flows of specified frequency[11]. Alternatively, probability plots of requirements from groundwater storage can be obtained from existing river flow records over consecutive periods of, for example, 6 to 30 months[12]. This normally provides a useful guide to conditions during the 1 in 10 year drought, but flow records in the UK generally cover too short a period to reliably estimate conditions during the 1 in 50 year drought.

Probability plots of base flow, derived by hydrograph analysis of either actual or generated data, provide estimates of infiltration during droughts of specified duration and severity. In catchments with insufficient data, rainfall and flow records of adjacent catchments can provide additional information.

It may be possible to relate mean monthly groundwater levels to mean monthly base flow by either linear or exponential equations. From such equations, or from a model of the system, an estimate can be made of natural groundwater levels during the period of the design drought and of the levels resulting from groundwater abstraction necessary to support the design yield.

An assessment must also be made of the effect on natural groundwater discharge of pumping from the aquifer. This can be obtained from a knowledge of the aquifer properties after the positions of wells have been determined.

From all this information the volume of groundwater to be abstracted to maintain river flows at various percentages of the mean flow can be assessed, and with a knowledge of the coefficient of storage these volumes can be converted into actual drawdown. The reduction in the yield of the wells during the design drought period can be assessed from a knowledge of the vertical variation in hydraulic conductivity and the decline in transmissivity as water levels fall in the aquifer. Thus, the number of wells required to support a given yield during the design drought can be estimated and the cost of the scheme calculated.

It is important to appreciate that large-scale abstraction of groundwater during a summer period will lower river flows below natural levels in the winter period following pumping, due to both reduced groundwater flow to the rivers and, in some cases, reduced direct run-off. If in these circumstances river flows were below the prescribed flow it would be necessary to continue pumping groundwater into the rivers until they recovered to acceptable levels. River flows would recover, due to increased groundwater discharge as aquifer storage was replenished by winter infiltration or as direct run-off increased. Pumping would be reduced in stages to match this recovery.

An allowance should be made for pumping to cover this need when estimating the yield of a scheme. It could affect operational costs because longer periods of pumping are necessary.

Summary of Stages in Yield Assessment

The various stages in the assessment of yield may be summarised as follows:

(1) Assess mean total resources replenished annually; subdivide into mean direct run-off and mean infiltration.
(2) Assess groundwater storage available to augment river flows.
(3) Assess storage available in surface reservoirs, or underground storage available for artificial recharge.
(4) Determine during the design drought period the river flows, infiltration, and minimum groundwater levels.
(5) Assess the effect of pumping from the proposed well field on natural river flows.

(6) Determine the volume of groundwater to be pumped according to selected operating rules, such as that required to maintain the river at different percentages of the mean flow, and convert into drawdown of groundwater levels.

(7) Determine the number of abstraction wells required to support a given yield.

Complex Water Resource Systems

The sequence just summarised illustrates the basic principles that must be followed in assessing yields and can be readily applied to relatively simple water resource developments. The use of simulation techniques is more appropriate to more complex systems which incorporate several sources. The input of groundwater abstraction data to a surface water simulation model may be determined from a mathematical model of the groundwater flow in the aquifer. The effects of pumping groundwater on an aquifer system can be readily examined by mathematical models, as described in Chapter 6.

Assessment of the Efficiency of River Regulation Schemes

High rates of groundwater abstraction for river regulation disturb the natural hydrological regime. To assess the efficiency of a scheme and its consequences on both river flows and groundwater levels, natural values for both of these time-dependent variables have to be estimated, either by correlation with rivers and wells that are outside the pumping area or from models.

A direct method of assessing artificial changes in river flow involves the use of flow regression equations to estimate natural river flows based on data from one or more adjacent river gauging stations[13]. The extent of artificial changes can be determined by comparing measured flows with estimated natural flows. The advantage of the method is that it does not rely upon knowledge of the aquifer properties or the nature of the stream bed.

Ideally the flow regression equations should be applicable over a wide range of flows and for all meteorological conditions. But two conflicting criteria are involved—general applicability and accuracy. As accuracy is important, a compromise can be reached by basing the equations upon the lower range of naturally occurring flows. This is usually acceptable as it is particularly important to be able to assess the consequences on river flow during the summer and autumn when relatively low flows usually prevail. Accuracy is increased further if data from flow recession periods only are used in deriving the regression equations. A period of flow regression may be considered to occur when the flow does not change by more than 10 per cent on consecutive days[13].

Flow regression equations were used to assess the effectiveness of the groundwater schemes to regulate the rivers Thames and Great Ouse[13]. Experience indicated that two factors were of importance—the rate of groundwater abstraction, (P), and the standard error of estimate of the regression equation (S). If the ratio of P/S is too small then it may not be possible to assess the effects of pumping on river flow. Ideally, the rate of pumping P should be arrived at after S has been determined from *at least* 2 years of historic river flow data. The ratio of P/S should be 5 or more to ensure that reliable estimates of the change in river flow can be made but meaningful interpretations have been made with values as low as 3.5.

Understanding of the relationship between groundwater storage and river flows under natural conditions and during periods of groundwater abstraction was increased appreciably in the Upper Thames catchment by developing models of the physical processes involved[14].

With operational schemes where groundwater in upland catchments is pumped into the tributaries of a large river, the increase in flow in the main river cannot be measured directly. In this circumstance greater reliance must be placed on indirect analysis and modelling techniques[15,16,17]. Recent advances in groundwater modelling have made it possible to predict interactions between groundwater and surface water flows. It is possible to derive seasonal variations in the head distribution over an aquifer in response to an actual or proposed abstraction regime. Birtles and Reeves[17] described the concepts underlying the development of computer programs for simulation of groundwater flow in regional aquifer systems, emphasising the importance of modelling physical processes as precisely as possible, particularly when predictions are required outside the scope of natural hydrological events. Complex models are expensive to develop and operate. Areal and temporal variations in the various input parameters are often incompletely known and the inter-relationships of parameters may be incompletely understood. In these circumstances complex models are not always justified. Interpretation of complex causes and effects can often be obtained from lumped parameter models—that is, no account is taken of the spatial distribution of the input variables or the spatial variation of factors influencing the physical processes. Birtles and Reeves[18] described the application of such a model to the interpretation of river regulation schemes.

Factors Affecting Design Criteria

Effective Aquifer Thickness

Extensive studies of the hydrogeology of the Chalk during the last 10 years, involving geophysical borehole logging and statistical studies of the variation of specific capacity with depth of aquifer penetrated, have shown that, although the

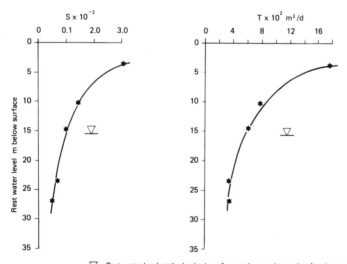

▽   Rest water level at the beginning of groundwater abstraction for river augmentation

Fig. 14.7.   Vertical variation of transmissivity (T) and storage coefficient (S) in the Chalk of the Upper Thames Valley (after Owen and Robinson[24])

formation attains thicknesses of up to 300 m, the effective thickness, in the sense of the thickness of the aquifer through which most of the flow occurs, is limited to about 50 m below maximum groundwater levels in unconfined situations[19-25] and the same distance below the base of confining strata under confined conditions[24,26]. The aquifer displays subdued karstic weathering, which is a dominant factor controlling the vertical distribution of permeability. The thickness of the effective aquifer is obviously related to a base level of erosion and, particularly near coastlines and along the lower reaches of major rivers, late Pleistocene base levels probably acted as controls[21,26,27]. In these situations the effective thickness may approach 100 m.

In the Upper Thames Valley, separate pumping tests of individual wells, starting with different thicknesses of saturated Chalk, indicated that the storage coefficient, as well as permeability, decreases with depth (Fig. 14.7 and Owen and Robinson[24]). This has also been demonstrated by relating volumes of water abstracted during extended well-field pumping tests to the volumes of aquifer drained.

These vertical changes in transmissivity and storage coefficient are superimposed on the well-established areal pattern of permeability, which is closely related to topography[28]. Transmissivity values are high (of the order of $2\,000$ m^2/d) along the lines of valleys, decreasing rapidly below the interfluves to less than 100 m^2/d. Studies of many wells in the Upper Thames Valley have shown that the storage coefficient displays a similar pattern, declining from 0.02 along the valleys to about 0.001 below the high ground. As a result of these lateral changes, there is a complex three-dimensional variation in each of the parameters.

As well as being very variable, the storage coefficient in the Chalk is low, and as a consequence seasonal water level fluctuations in response to recharge are large (up to 20 m or 30 m). Coupled with a relatively small effective thickness of aquifer, this results in a large seasonal variation in the volume of storage in the Chalk. In the Upper Thames Valley, the volume of storage under drought conditions only equals the average annual recharge. At the peak of the recharge season, when water levels are much higher, the volume in storage may be doubled, due to the substantially increased saturated thickness and storage coefficient. The low value of the storage to recharge ratio is a constraint on yield, in that a certain volume of water must be left in storage at the end of a period of extended river augmentation.

In the Chalk of the Candover catchment of the Itchen Basin (Fig. 14.1), the natural groundwater level fluctuations are unusually small for this aquifer, as they are only 3 to 4 m per year[29]. A relatively high storage coefficient as well as high permeability is necessary to account for variations in groundwater levels and groundwater discharge from the aquifer. On the other hand, analysis of drawdown data from test pumping individual wells and from the decline of water levels in the well-field as a whole gave values for the storage coefficient of between 0.008 and 0.013. An interpretation of these facts, supported by mathematical modelling, is that there is a thin, very permeable zone at the top of the saturated aquifer which has a high storage coefficient of about 0.03 to 0.05. This is underlain by, and is in hydraulic continuity with, the main part of the aquifer, which has a storage coefficient of about 0.01. After extensive pumping, storage in the main aquifer is replenished preferentially by winter recharge, and it is only when this has taken place that river flow recovers and returns to normal[25].

In an aquifer of limited effective thickness, which also has a low storage coefficient, drawdown in and around the pumped well may become a large proportion of the saturated thickness. In the Chalk of the Upper Thames Valley, vertical and lateral variations in transmissivity and storage coefficient result in an accelerating rate of drawdown in a pumped well for a fixed pumping rate, unless the latter is so low as to be impractical. Hence, limited effective thickness, particularly if combined with downward deteriorating aquifer properties, can be an important constraint on individual well yields and is a criterion in well-field design. Wells remote from a river will yield significantly lower quantities of water under drought conditions than under average water level conditions.

Although the upper 50 m of saturated Chalk is the main aquifer, significant quantities of water can be obtained in some areas from greater depths, particularly from the principal rock beds such as the Melbourn Rock and the Totternhoe Stone, which are at the base of the Middle Chalk and within the Lower Chalk respectively. Several wells in the Great Ouse Pilot Scheme derived up to 65 per cent of their total yield from below 45 m. In East Anglia, where the Chalk is overlain by glacial deposits, the upper 10 to 15 m consist of small fragments of chalk in a fine chalk matrix which is soft and plastic when saturated with water. This layer, formed by frost action during the glacial period, must be lined out in wells and drilling continued to firmer Chalk at greater depths.

In contrast to the Chalk, the effective thickness of the Triassic sandstones is not a constraint on development; the aquifer yields water from depths of 200 m or more[30]. The storage coefficient is higher and of the order of 15 to 20 per cent and does not reduce significantly with depth up to 150 m below surface, which is the normal depth range from which groundwater is obtained from these strata. In the upper 50 m of the saturated aquifer, exploitable water storage amounts to about 10 m, which is some 20 times the average annual recharge. In addition, because of the high storage coefficient, the natural water-level fluctuation in response to recharge is small (of the order of 1 to 2 m), and consequently the volume of storage changes little with season or even under drought conditions. Transmissivities are of the order of 200 to 500 m^2/d, and exceptionally as high as 1 000 m^2/d. The higher values are due to secondary fissure permeability which is variably developed through these aquifers[30-33]. In contrast with the Chalk, there is no obvious topographic control to variations of transmissivity. Clearly these properties emphasize the value of these and similar sandstones for river augmentation schemes.

Confined Conditions

The purpose of river augmentation schemes is to develop storage in an aquifer in the short-term, and obviously a large storage coefficient is an advantage. Under confined conditions the storage coefficient is small, generally of the order of 10^{-4}, and the decline of the piezometric surface around a well or well-field, in response to pumping, expands rapidly until a recharge (or a discharge) area is intersected. The hydraulic gradient between the abstraction centre and the margin of the confined area increases (or decreases in the case of a discharge zone) and the base flow of the river system is quickly reduced.

In England, confined conditions are not uncommon; for example, the Chalk may be confined by the London Clay, the Triassic sandstones by the Mercia Mudstone, and both by glacial clays. Because of reduced yields and/or a decline of groundwater quality as the thickness of confining clays increases, abstraction wells have to be sited relatively close to the margin of the confining bed. Under these conditions net gain may be expected to decline rapidly with time[7,34]. As the storage coefficient is relatively constant under confined conditions at about 10^{-4}, the rate of decline depends upon transmissivity and the distance of the abstraction centre from the margin of the confined area. As an example, if the transmissivity is $1\,000$ m^2/d and the storage coefficient 10^{-4}. then the net gain from wells sited about 10 km from the outcrop will decline to about 10 per cent after 3 months and to zero after 6 months.

However, actual values depend very much upon local aquifer properties and pumping rates. For example, the Thames Groundwater Scheme includes a group of 6 wells east of Reading, which penetrate the Chalk where it is confined by the Eocene. The wells are 4 to 8 km from the Chalk's outcrop and the regional transmissivity of the aquifer is about 350 m^2/d and the coefficient of storage 4 to 5 $\times$ 10^{-4}. The use of these wells for river regulation has been examined with a digital model[35]. Simulating pumping for 2½ months at 25 Ml/d, under conditions of the 1976 drought, gave a net gain of 50 per cent at the end of the period. If the abstraction rate were to be increased to 100 Ml/d, the gain would decline to 30 per cent after 2½ months.

In the Vale of York (Fig. 14.1), where Triassic sandstones are extensively overlain by glacial clays, the net gain from one group of wells declined rapidly to less than 40 per cent in 25 days but increased once unconfined conditions were created[36]. Similarly, in the Upper Wylye Valley (Fig. 14.1), pumping from the Upper Greensand where it is confined by the Lower Chalk rapidly intercepted groundwater discharge from the Upper Greensand and reduced the net gain to low values[20].

The Chalk and Pleistocene sands are overlain by thick boulder clays in East Anglia and the Waveney Groundwater Scheme (Fig. 14.1) is intended to assess the feasibility of using groundwater for river augmentation under these conditions. The presence of a soft, plastic layer of Chalk at the top of the aquifer in this area has already been referred to. Although this acts as an aquiclude, the Chalk and Pleistocene sands are in general a composite aquifer, confined by the boulder clay over much of the area, but unconfined in the lower reaches of the valleys. The transmissivity of the Chalk is about 300 m^2/d in the area of the groundwater scheme and the storage coefficient about 2×10^{-3}. From the areal drawdown after pumping five wells for 4 months at a total rate of up to 510 l/s, an overall coefficient of storage of 0.04 was obtained, reflecting leakage to the Chalk and the higher storage coefficient of the Pleistocene sands. The leakage factor for the semi-confining layer is of the order of 210 m, hydraulic resistance 150 days and vertical permeability 0.1 m/d. Recharge is limited by the boulder clay to 50 mm/year and additional recharge is unlikely to be induced by pumping. Consequently natural equilibrium can be restored only at the expense of spring discharge. In the groundwater scheme the wells were situated 1 to 4 km from the natural groundwater discharge points along the river. The change in hydraulic gradient at these outlets due to pumping was small and complete restoration to natural water levels was protracted. Within the abstraction area the average drawdown following 2 months pumping in 1975 and 4 months in 1976, with a total abstraction of 5.93 $\times$ 10^6 m^3, was 1.2 m. After 15 months recovery, the average water level was still 0.45 m below the natural level (P. L. Ashford, personal communication).

Where such semi-confined conditions exist and a high proportion of the natural recharge is to be pumped from wells remote from natural outlets, average groundwater levels will be lowered substantially below natural levels and recovery will be slow. This emphasises the value, where watertight river beds prevent reversal of flow, of siting wells close to natural outlets, eliminating natural discharge and lowering the water table below the river bed. In this situation, less disturbance of natural groundwater contours is necessary to reduce natural discharge and a quicker return to natural levels can be expected. Clearly, frequent use of groundwater in East Anglia for river augmentation depends upon eliminating confined conditions and taking advantage of the higher storage coefficient in the Pleistocene sands.

Water Quality Aspects

Any study of the potential of river basins for conjunctive use development must pay particular attention to water quality aspects for two reasons. Firstly, an understanding of variations in water quality determinands, when interpreted with other hydrogeological data, can give valuable information about the zones of recharge and natural discharge of groundwater and thus help in a subjective assessment of likely net gains. Secondly, water quality characteristics must be understood in order to plan the operation of a groundwater development scheme and ensure that it will fit into the total water resource system. Two groundwater developments considered for the Triassic sandstones of the English Midlands have shown how groundwater quality variations may both be advantageous and disadvantageous for conjunctive use of groundwater[37]. A proposal for intermittent abstraction of groundwater from the Triassic sandstones of Nottinghamshire, primarily for direct supply alternating with river abstraction, met difficulties because of possible incompatibility of the two different waters in the distribution system. It is believed that the aggressive effects of sandstone groundwater may be accentuated by regular switching with river water. This problem may be overcome only by using the groundwater to regulate river flow at greater capital and operating costs. In contrast, a scheme in Shropshire in the Severn catchment, mentioned in more detail later, is designed to allow mixing of groundwaters of different quality in the well-collecting mains before discharge to the river system so that acceptable groundwater quality can be achieved by blending. The Shropshire area has local pockets of groundwater where chlorides, iron and nitrate levels are higher than would be acceptable for direct continuous groundwater supply. The river regulation scheme, which allows these waters to be mixed, and later re-mixed with river water from an upland impermeable catchment, provides a means of using these groundwater resources which would not be possible by traditional means without expensive treatment.

Environmental Aspects

The development of regional groundwater schemes for river augmentation occurred at the time when world-wide interest in environmental matters was materialising and concern was expressed about possible consequences of pumping on the environment. The pilot studies were drawn up with an awareness of the problems and one objective was to avoid any undesirable environmental consequences that have on occasions been associated with previous groundwater development. To provide answers to the problems arising from the relationship of groundwater to other parts of the hydrological cycle and hence the environment, extensive programmes, including aerial surveys incorporating remote sensing techniques, have been carried out to study seasonal changes in soil moisture, the chemistry of river waters, the overall ecology of rivers and the factors affecting crop yields in areas in which large volumes of groundwater were being abstracted[12,19,38-42].

The greatest area of concern was the possible effect of reducing the amount of soil moisture available to vegetation, particularly crops and trees. The Chalk Downs of southern England have no glacial and little superficial cover and the loamy soils are generally no more than 1 m thick. Except along the relatively narrow valley tracts, the water table is normally between 10 m and 100 m below ground level. On the other hand, in parts of eastern England, for example East Anglia where the Great Ouse Groundwater Scheme is being developed, the topography is more subdued and water levels are nearer the surface but glacial tills overlie large areas of the Chalk. Extensive measurements of soil moisture during the Great Ouse Groundwater Scheme showed that over the greater part of the area the lowering of water levels by pumping did not affect soil moisture in the root zone of plants and trees. Vegetation was affected only along the river valleys or near spring lines where the water table was at depths of no more than 2 to 3 m. In fact, lowering the water table proved a benefit in some localities by reducing waterlogging and improving the drainage of alluvial soils.

The situation is similar in the relatively flat topography of the Shropshire plain. Areas exist where lowering of groundwater levels could affect plant growth and the design of groundwater development schemes must pay special regard to this problem by distributing abstraction wells so as to spread the effect of pumping over a larger area, and thus minimise drawdowns along river valleys.

The unique character of Chalk streams—clear and fast-flowing, with abundance of aquatic life—has focused attention on the possibility of groundwater schemes upsetting the natural ecological balance. An intensive coordinated programme of biological and fisheries investigations has been carried out since 1971 on many Chalk streams in southern England. These have involved detailed surveys of dominant macrophytes and selected invertebrates, and of fish growth, population and migratory habits. The results show that changes in the balance between the main macrophyte species resulting from river augmentation are likely to be within the changes which would be experienced naturally. A similar picture is emerging for the fish population, although a correlation does appear to exist between the number of young fish found in October and flows the previous Spring when the fry hatch. This may mean that on occasions groundwater may have to be discharged to rivers for short periods to enhance fish hatching.

Many of the rivers draining the Chalk in southern England are important fisheries. A good example is the River Wylye which, as already mentioned, drains a catchment exploited for groundwater. River augmentation is necessary to preserve the fisheries, and, because different rates of flow in the river are necessary at different times of the year, the flow is maintained on a sliding scale decreasing from May to September[43].

In confined aquifers the water may be de-oxygenated, and if discharged into a fishery river in which the volume of discharge is large compared to the natural flow, can have a deleterious effect on fish life. For this reason, water pumped from the confined Chalk in the Upper Thames Valley is aerated before discharge to rivers.

One of the most obvious effects of regional groundwater schemes is the possible failure of existing groundwater supplies, and all the authorities have arranged alternative supplies, deepened boreholes or constructed new ones or lowered pumps as appropriate. In the Candover Scheme, about 6 per cent of the total cost is attributable to such remedial measures, and similar figures apply to other schemes. In the Thames scheme, it was necessary to carry out remedial works at about 130 existing sources. Some public supply sources were protected by links from river augmentation pipelines to the raw water side of the public supply system. A similar number of private water sources will be affected by the proposed Shropshire development. In Hampshire, a particular problem has been the large number of commercial watercress farms which rely on artesian flows from springs and boreholes. Generally located near the perennial heads of Chalk streams, they are particularly vulnerable to the effect of catchment-wide lowering of groundwater levels. In the Candover Scheme, provision was made for installation of temporary electrical pumping plant to overcome any effects of the scheme when it was tested during the drought of 1976. In the event, the heavy rain of the winter of 1976/77 obviated this need.

Springs and seepages of groundwater, which discharge from aquifers at the margin of alluvial tracts and support wet-land environments with specialised ecosystems alongside rivers, are important to naturalists and biologists. The groundwater commonly discharges from many diffuse sources and the preservation of these environments can be difficult. Production wells must be sited to avoid interference with the natural hydrology of such areas or, alternatively, small diameter boreholes may be drilled from which groundwater is pumped to replace the natural flow. Small, low dams may also be constructed to maintain the water level in the wet-land environment. An assessment of the cost of such remedial works focuses attention on the intrinsic value of individual environmental sites and helps to determine priorities.

Design of Well-fields

The design criteria for well-fields required for river augmentation are influenced by many factors and some have been discussed in previous sections. The overall objective of well-field design is the optimisation of yield (that is, the net gain) while bearing in mind the ultimate unit cost of the water supply made available by the development, and the cost of the less tangible social and environmental impacts of the scheme. It is important to appreciate that a well distribution designed to give highest net gains does not necesssarily do so at the lowest total cost[44]. Well positions that lead to lower costs are closer to the river than those that give maximum net gains. This is because, at sites that maximise net gains, water levels are generally deeper and drawdowns greater.

Factors controlling the net gain have been reviewed and the importance of the nature of the river bed has been emphasised. Clearly, if wells have to be sited away from a river, then the cost of the scheme increases because:

(a) longer pipe-lines are needed;
(b) drilling costs are greater as water levels are deeper;
(c) running costs are higher because pumping water levels are lower; and
(d) more wells are needed for a given abstraction rate because permeability decreases away from the river.

However, the total volume of water to be pumped will be less from a site remote from a river because of the less direct effect of pumping on river flow.

The factors listed above, which affect the cost of schemes where wells are remote from a river, are not of equal concern in every aquifer. They are all important in the Chalk, but because of the more homogeneous nature of the Triassic sandstones and the more subdued topography, items (b) and (c) are of less significance and (d) rarely applies. But one fact is clear—the cost of pipelines is the over-riding influence on costs when it is necessary to site wells away from a river.

Ideally, a well-field should comprise a small number of large wells sited in the most permeable areas; this minimises construction and maintenance costs. Such a policy has to be relaxed in river augmentation schemes if the river is in hydraulic continuity with the aquifer and if the aquifer is relatively thin and the saturated thickness decreases significantly in a drought. In this situation, a larger number of smaller yielding wells are required to reduce water-level drawdowns and maintain an adequate saturated thickness and hence transmissivity.

Because of the low permeability below the upland areas of the Chalk outcrop, it is difficult to develop the storage. Pumping from wells situated on the flanks of the uplands tends to draw water preferentially from the more permeable parts of the aquifer in the direction of groundwater outlets, and steep hydraulic gradients develop between the wells and the low permeability areas[45]. Many small wells would be needed to develop adequately the aquifer in such areas, although there are indications from pumping small diameter boreholes that yields in these areas under drought conditions are often negligible[24].

The relationship between cost and well-field design was examined[46] for a typical Chalk catchment in eastern England, where river beds tend to be impermeable. In this situation, riverside abstraction is attractive in terms of both capital and running costs. However, as bed permeability increases above 10^{-2} m/d, this strategy becomes steadily less attractive. Recirculation from the river to the aquifer increases and greater volumes of water must be abstracted to regulate the river. Capital costs rise because more wells are needed and running costs increase because overall a larger volume of water must be abstracted. With a more even distribution of wells, necessary to minimise the effect of pumping on the river, capital and operational costs would be about twice that for riverside wells. The most significant cost factor is pipelines, but total costs of wells, pumps and switchgear are also important.

A similar comparison between riverside and high ground well distributions for the Triassic sandstones in Shropshire revealed smaller differences between the two approaches. The cost of a scheme with wells remote from the river was 20 per cent greater than for wells adjacent to the river, and if use could be made of natural channels to transport water from the wells to the main river, the costs were very similar. Total costs were not sensitive to well yields or pumping costs. This reflects the compensating effect of higher net gains from sites more remote from the river but with similar yields to riverside sites. The homogeneous nature of the aquifer and the relatively subdued topography are also important factors in arriving at these conclusions.

A number of general conclusions can be drawn about well-field design for river augmentation. Where the aquifer is the Chalk and the river bed impermeable, there are considerable cost benefits in developing at riverside sites and taking advantage of the high permeability along the valleys in this aquifer. The overall objective of river augmentation schemes is to develop storage in the aquifer and this can be achieved, with economic advantages, by concentrating wells in limited areas and pumping at high rates; if feasible, more than one well should be drilled at individual sites. This limits the extent of interference effects and sites can be selected to avoid principal outlets of groundwater discharge.

If the river bed is permeable, wells must be sited away from the river and a larger number of smaller yielding wells are necessary. An overriding influence in this situation is the thickness of the aquifer and the relationship of transmissivity to saturated thickness in a drought.

The Triassic sandstones do not exhibit the close relationship between permeability and topography that exists in the Chalk and, although the same principles apply to the sandstones, a similar number of wells would be required when wells are sited both near and remote from rivers. Water-level fluctuations under drought conditions are not critical as the storage coefficient of the sandstones is high, of the order of 0.2.

The obvious economic advantages in developing groundwater for river regulation at riverside sites led to proposals for sealing permeable river beds. Feasibility studies have been made in the case of the Chalk using puddled chalk, compacted chalk, and butyl rubber lining[47]. The use of compacted chalk was particularly encouraging and it would appear that lining of at least limited stretches of streams is practicable using compacted chalk where the Chalk forms the stream bed. In situations where the Triassic sandstones form stream beds, possibly a light loam mixed with coarse sand or fine gravel[48] could be used. Any decision requires consideration of the advantages of developing at riverside sites (for example, higher yields, lower pumping costs, no pipelines) against the cost of sealing and the alternative of developing at sites more remote from the river. In practical and economic terms, river beds are only likely to be sealed along limited tracts of small streams where maintenance of the environment is of paramount importance.

Before final decisions are made about well locations, various well-field designs and pumping programmes should be studied with aquifer simulation models which can be linked into resource allocation and cost optimisation models in complex water resource systems.

Factors affecting cost optimisation of groundwater schemes developed for river regulation were examined[49], using data for the Vale of York scheme. It was concluded that the capital costs exceed the total present value of operating costs by a factor of 5 if the discount rate is 5 per cent and by 10 if it is 10 per cent. This implies that optimising well yields could be based only on capital costs with a risk of incurring a maximum cost penalty of 20 per cent. A previous study showed that boreholes selected to minimise capital costs also come near to minimising operating costs[44].

STAGES OF DEVELOPMENT

Although the principles of groundwater/surface water relationships and the consequences on river flow of developing groundwater resources are now more fully understood, the actual field response of an aquifer/river system to development cannot be forecast in detail. Field relationships have been studied by pilot schemes in a number of areas of England and, as experience has accumulated, the controlling influence of local geological variations has been revealed in a number of cases.

Groundwater development schemes generally proceed in well-defined stages, this being one of the main advantages of using groundwater in water resource developments. However, because of the difficulties of forecasting the detailed consequences of development, it is necessary, particularly in the case of schemes involving river regulation with groundwater, to prove the reliability of each stage to meet the desired objective. Thus a number of wells for a particular stage should be agreed initially. The wells should be drilled and tested for yield in the order in which they are expected to give maximum benefit to the objective. In this way the number of wells originally planned may be reduced. Each well is tested to assess yield/drawdown relationships and well efficiencies, the hydraulic properties of the aquifer and the relationship of the aquifer to overlying and underlying deposits and to hydrologic boundaries, particularly rivers. With these data a mathematical model of the system can be constructed. The well-field should then be tested to establish the effect of pumping on the aquifer and on river flows and how these change with time. This involves comparing actual conditions during pumping with natural conditions that would have obtained had pumping not occurred. Natural river flows and natural groundwater levels are estimated from regression equations, relating flows at river gauging stations and water levels in observation wells outside the development area with stations and wells inside the area. This requires data about natural conditions for several years prior to the onset of extensive pumping from the well-field. To understand the system fully, the abstraction rate must obviously be high enough for the effect on river flow to be measurable (in the proving stage of the pilot scheme in the Chalk of the Great Ouse Basin the abstraction rate was some three times the average infiltration rate). To obtain reliable estimates of changes in river flow, the rate of abstraction should be greater than four times the standard error of estimate of the flow regression equation used to estimate natural flow. If this criterion is not met, considerable difficulty could be experienced in estimating the efficiency of a group of wells. The objective is to understand how the system responds to the total abstraction and, if possible, how each individual well responds, for the scheme will ultimately be controlled from a remote centre. For efficient operation the controller needs to understand the consequences of pumping individual wells or certainly small groups of wells. Actually the need for very fine control depends to a large extent upon whether groundwater storage is being developed in combination with some surface storage. If surface storage is available in the development scheme any over-pumping of groundwater can be recovered and stored in the surface reservoir, otherwise it is lost from the system. To prevent this, river gauges are necessary to monitor and control the output from individual well-fields[50].

Where well-fields are being developed for regulation of a large river, the consequences of pumping on river flow cannot be reliably determined until several well-fields have been completed and the pumping capacity is sufficient to cause measurable effects on the river. In these circumstances the efficiency of individual stages has to be assessed from the behaviour of the aquifer alone and mathematical models. The sequence of stages may be summarized as follows:

(i) Install observation wells, river gauging structures and collect hydrological data under natural conditions for at least two years. Derive regression equations from which natural river flows and groundwater levels can be estimated.

(ii) Estimate the number of wells required, making use of preliminary mathematical models.

(iii) Drill and test wells, revising the estimate of numbers required as data become available.

(iv) During tests determine aquifer properties etc.

(v) Test well-field to determine consequences on the hydrological system.

(vi) Refine mathematical model and use to determine management policy.

(viii) Decide whether further wells are required.

In southeast England many of the smaller rivers are supported by discharge from one aquifer—the Chalk—but in the Midlands and north of England, although the Permo-Triassic sandstones are the principal aquifers, less important aquifers generally contribute to river flow, and there are fewer river systems supported by one aquifer. River flows are therefore less dependent upon the main source of groundwater for supply and this gives greater flexibility in developing these sandstones.

3. CASE HISTORIES OF RIVER REGULATION SCHEMES

GREAT OUSE SCHEME

Introduction

The Great Ouse Basin can be divided into two regions, a western region made up mainly of impermeable Jurassic rocks and an eastern region underlain by the Chalk (Fig. 14.8). The aquifer crops out in the valleys but it is obscured by glacial deposits, principally boulder clays, on the higher ground. Groundwater in the Chalk is under artesian pressure below much of the boulder clay area.

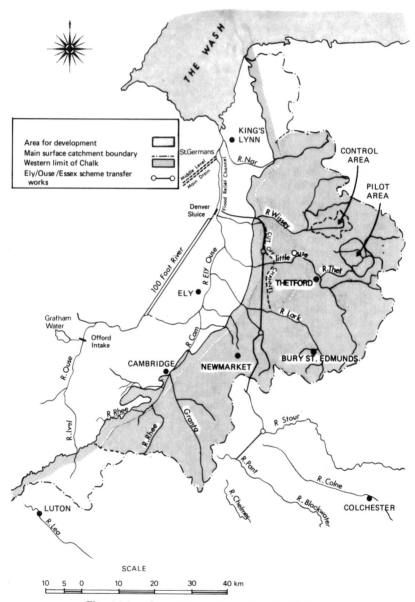

Fig. 14.8.   Great Ouse Groundwater Scheme

A major surface water scheme existed in the Great Ouse Basin prior to the groundwater scheme—that is, the Ely Ouse-Essex Scheme, involving transfer from the Ely Ouse river at Denver of up to 450 Ml/d by tunnel, pipe-line and river channels to the adjacent Essex river system (Fig. 14.8). The Chalk is drained by several tributaries of the Ely Ouse and it was proposed[4] that the yield of the scheme could be increased considerably by pumping groundwater from the Chalk into the tributaries to maintain higher flows in the Ely Ouse at Denver. This water would also be pumped from the river and transferred to the Essex river system by existing natural and artificial aqueducts. It is important to appreciate that the water is transferred from the Great Ouse Basin at a point very near the tidal limit. The water has, therefore, met all requirements in the Great Ouse Basin, including water supply and irrigation, before it is pumped to the adjacent river system.

As the use of groundwater storage for river regulation had not been attempted previously, the feasibility of the proposal was tested by a pilot study. The Great Ouse Pilot Scheme is described in some detail as an example of a pilot study, but a similar approach has been adopted in other areas.

The area selected for the study, in the River Thet catchment (Fig. 14.8), covered an area of 72 km^2 (Backshall et al.[50]; Great Ouse River Authority[12]). A control area was defined in the adjacent Wissey Valley so that comparisons could be made between groundwater levels and river flows in the pilot area and those in a similar area where abstraction of groundwater was not taking place.

The average annual rainfall in the region is about 600 mm/yr, spread fairly evenly throughout the year, but actual evaporation accounts for about 450 mm/yr. The difference of 150 mm/yr infiltrates into the Chalk almost entirely in the winter, but where the aquifer is overlain by boulder clay infiltration is reduced to about 50 mm/yr.

Objectives of the Pilot Scheme

The objectives of the pilot study were to determine:

(1) The yield characteristics of production wells.
(2) The hydraulic properties of the Chalk and overlying drift deposits.
(3) The extent to which groundwater levels fluctuate during a normal year.
(4) The extent to which groundwater level changes may be artificially induced by pumping groundwater.
(5) The minimum groundwater level likely to result from a once in 50 years drought.
(6) The effect of artificially induced groundwater level changes on existing water users.
(7) The effect on river flows of abstracting groundwater from the production wells, either individually or collectively, and discharging it into the river system.
(8) The optimum density of production wells commensurate with yield characteristics and effectiveness of groundwater level control.
(9) The optimum yield (for supply and river regulation) commensurate with costs and effects on existing water users.
(10) The application of the results of the pilot scheme to large scale development of groundwater resources of the Chalk in the Great Ouse Basin.

Hydrometric Network and Engineering Works

The first stage of the engineering works necessary for the study was concerned with establishing an extensive hydrometric network. Although some data existed prior to the scheme, it was necessary to augment this considerably if the scheme was to be adequately interpreted. As a result the following measurements were made regularly, in general beginning two years before any significant groundwater abstraction occurred in the pilot area:

(a) Streamflow at the three inflow points and at the one outflow point from the pilot area, and also at two subsidiary gauges, within the area.

(b) Rainfall at 25 gauges in the pilot area and the surrounding region.

(c) Evaporation, calculated from climatological data, crop patterns and soil types. A climatological station was installed in the pilot area.

(d) Groundwater levels in more than 130 observation boreholes in the pilot area and the surrounding region.

(e) Water levels at Fowlmere and Ringmere (2 small lakes) to check for any artificial influence due to pumping groundwater.

(f) Soil moisture (estimated by the neutron scatter technique) at 20 sites in the pilot area. The readings obtained using this technique were calibrated by field sampling.

(g) Surface water quality and temperature at 8 sites in the pilot area, including the river gauging stations.

(h) Groundwater quality from analysis of samples collected from production wells during pumping.

In addition to the measurements listed, individual surveys were made of soil types, land use, irrigation use and spring flows. Aerial surveys were carried out to record land use changes and to locate areas of vegetation, including crops, showing visible variations in growth. An ecological study of the rivers was also made. This extensive measurement programme was necessary not only to prove that the scheme was feasible but also to ensure that no undesirable consequences would result.

During the second stage of the engineering works, 18 production wells were drilled in the Chalk using percussion drilling rigs. The diameter of the wells was 450 mm and average depth about 100 m. The wells were developed by injecting 20 tonnes of hydrochloric acid into each well, followed by surge pumping. Generally this treatment more than doubled the specific capacity of the wells. Each well was tested to assess its yield characteristics and to determine the aquifer properties and the relationship of the Chalk to overlying deposits and boundaries, such as rivers.

The scheme involved the use of the river system as an aqueduct for groundwater and the 18 production wells were connected to the nearest watercourse by some 13 km of PVC pipeline ranging in diameter from 150 to 400 mm. Finally about 50 boreholes, 75 mm in diameter, were drilled in groups to different depths around selected production wells to study local changes of groundwater level and flow patterns in the vicinity of the wells, and the relationship between the river and the aquifer. Of 18 production wells, 10 were drilled near the river system and 8 at sites more remote from the river; the latter being referred to as "high ground" wells.

In an experiment on the scale envisaged it was essential to obtain a definite answer as to whether the scheme was feasible. In a hydrological experiment under field conditions there are so many variables that cannot be controlled that the artificial stress induced on the aquifer/river system has to be great enough to override natural variables. It was for this reason that 18 wells were drilled. Their average yield was expected to be at least 25 l/s to give a total yield of 450 l/s, sufficient to produce a measurable effect at the outflow gauging station, the key gauging station for assessing the success of the scheme. As it turned out, the total yield from the wells was 900 l/s, more than adequate to meet the principal objective. It enabled studies to be made of operating the scheme either with a lower density of wells than originally envisaged or pumping wells only when off-peak electricity tariffs were available.

Reference has been made to a "control area" established in an adjacent river catchment. The objective was to correlate river flows and groundwater levels between the control and the pilot areas so that natural river flows and groundwater levels could be estimated in the pilot area when the natural system had been disturbed by pumping. The establishment of such relationships was essential for adequate interpretation of the scheme. A good relationship was obtained between mean groundwater levels in the control and pilot areas by regression analysis but natural river flows were eventually estimated from a relationship between the inflow gauging stations and the outflow gauging station in the pilot area.

In addition, water levels in individual observation boreholes in the pilot area were correlated with wells outside the area affected by pumping, and this enabled the preparation of estimated natural groundwater level maps for the pilot area. These could be compared with actual groundwater level maps due to pumping, so that a regional pattern of the drawdown in groundwater level could be obtained.

Pumping Programme and Assessment of the Results

The experimental pumping programme covered a period of four years. The objectives of the various stages are summarised below:

1st year (1968): Individual production wells were pumped for 14 days to obtain their yield characteristics and to calculate aquifer properties.

2nd year (1969): The riverside wells were pumped for 65 days. After a recovery period of 1 month the high ground wells were pumped for 90 days. The objective was to compare the consequences of pumping from the two groups of wells.

3rd year (1970): All 18 wells were pumped at maximum rates for 250 days. The pumping rate was three times the average annual infiltration to the area. Such a high rate was necessary to obtain an understanding of the factors controlling the hydrological system.

4th year (1971): Wells were pumped as required to maintain a pre-determined flow in the river at the outflow gauging station. The object was to gain experience of operating the scheme under conditions that would obtain during a permanent development scheme. The wells were operated as required from May to October but pumping was limited to 15 hours per day to take advantage of off-peak electricity tariffs. The maximum abstraction rate during the period was about 500 l/s.

The mean groundwater levels in the pilot area in the years 1969 to 1971, together with estimated natural levels, if pumping had not taken place, are shown in Fig. 14.9. The effects of pumping, together with the recovery of levels following it, can be clearly seen. Fig. 14.9 also shows that groundwater levels had not completely recovered during the periods between pumping tests, even though river flow appeared to have recovered to its natural rate. For example, until the end of March 1970 the drawdown included the residual effects of the previous pumping test in 1969. The spatial distribution of groundwater levels in the pilot area towards the end of the 1970 tests is shown in Fig. 14.10.

Soil moisture studies indicated that pumping from the Chalk affected soil moisture only in the riparian zone and within this zone any effect depended upon the nature of the superficial deposits overlying the Chalk. These deposits vary considerably but with the usual disposition near the rivers of peat, peaty silts and clays, soil moisture changes were more closely related to changes in river stage than to fluctuations of water level in the underlying Chalk.

The drawdown of water levels during a drought requiring maximum development of groundwater storage can be considered to comprise:

(i) the natural drawdown which would have occurred during the drought; and
(ii) the artifical drawdown due to pumping.

Probability plots of natural groundwater levels in the Chalk of the Great Ouse Basin led to the conclusion that the average natural decline during a drought would be about 2½ m. As a safeguard it was considered that an additional 4 m could be artificially developed although as experience is gained in operating the scheme this could be increased, possibly to as much as 7 m.

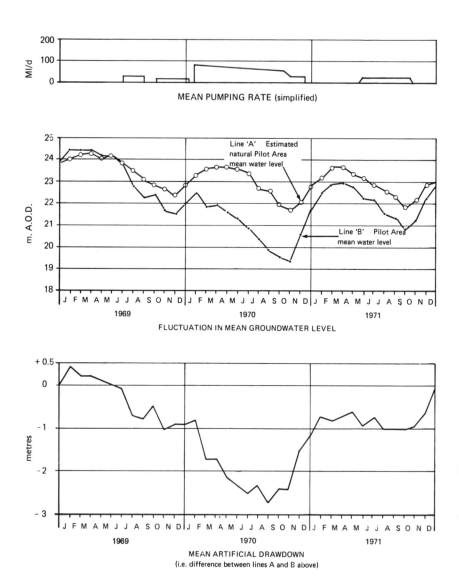

Fig. 14.9.   Effect of pumping on groundwater levels in Great Ouse Pilot Area

The annual infiltration into an aquifer over an extended period can be plotted on probability paper to obtain the infiltration likely to occur in a 1 in 50 year drought. In the Chalk of the Great Ouse Basin this would amount to about 28 per cent of the average infiltration and the annual infiltration during a drought sequence could be:

	Infiltration (per cent of mean)
1st winter	28
2nd winter	70
3rd winter	77
4th winter	85

The volume of groundwater that has to be pumped to maintain river flow at various percentages of the mean flow can be assessed and, from a knowledge of the storage coefficient, the drawdown of water level in the aquifer can be calculated.

The number of production wells depends upon the output required to meet peak summer requirements during a drought and the average reliable yield from a well during the drought, when it may be assumed that all natural groundwater discharge will be intercepted by wells and the entire flow in the river system will be maintained by pumping groundwater from wells.

After successful completion of the Pilot Study, a Parliamentary Order was issued in June 1977 for Stage 1 of the scheme for developing the Chalk in the Great Ouse Basin. This first stage involves development of the Pilot Area itself together with the Little Ouse catchment and also the Rhee, Cam and Granta catchments in the south of the basin (Fig. 14.8). By the end of 1981, 21 production boreholes had been drilled and tested in the three southern catchments (P. R. Dodge, personal communication). Ultimately a yield of 220 to 440 Ml/d from about 300 wells could be expected[12].

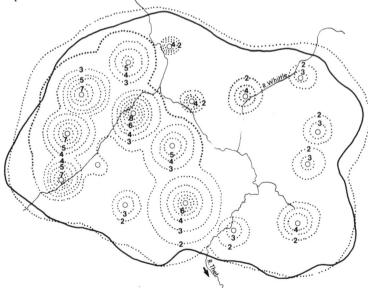

Fig. 14.10.   Drawdown of groundwater levels in Great Ouse Pilot Area in 1970 after pumping for 8 months

THAMES GROUNDWATER SCHEME

The purpose of this scheme is to augment the flow of the River Thames during periods of severe drought with groundwater from the Chalk (and perhaps eventually the Jurassic limestones), and thereby secure the water supply for London, which is at the downstream end of the river system. Groundwater is to be used in conjunction with pumped storage reservoirs which had previously been the main security for London's water supply. When an additional source of water was required for London, groundwater storage was selected as the most appropriate means of increasing the yield of the Thames system, not only because of difficulties in finding acceptable reservoir sites but also because of:

(1) lower units costs;
(2) facility for staged development;
(3) early availability of water from a first stage development; and
(4) limited environmental impact.

The groundwater scheme has been described[24,51] and discussed[52]. Only the main features are reviewed here.

As with the Great Ouse Scheme, the first stage was a pilot study to assess, *inter alia*, the validity of the proposals and to determine the ideal position of well sites for optimum yields[3]. The Chalk crops out in the upper part of the Thames basin in the main development area. It is overlain by thin, generally permeable, superficial deposits below the river beds. For the pilot study 5 wells were sited adjacent to perennial streams and 4 at some distance from perennial streams, mainly in dry valleys. Test pumping showed unequivocally that pumping from riverside sites under these conditions induced recirculation and reduced net gains to low values in a matter of days. To obtain adequate net gains it was necessary to site wells some distance from perennial streams. However, the permeability of the Chalk is closely related to topography, with zones of high permeability following the lines of valleys, and low permeability occurring below higher ground[28]. In these circumstances it has been necessary, when developing Stage 1 of the scheme, to site wells in dry valleys or valleys that contain intermittent streams which would, of course, not be flowing at times when the scheme was operational.

Although most of the production wells are, or will be, on the Chalk outcrop of the Berkshire Downs, a number are in the confined area east of Reading. As the aquifer is isolated from the river system by the confining beds, wells have been sited alongside the rivers and discharge directly into them. However, pumping from these wells reduces the flow of springs and rivers from the Chalk outcrop at the margin of the confined area and, therefore, the net gain does not equal the volume of groundwater pumped into the rivers.

On the basis of the results of the pilot study the first stage of the operational scheme was designed and has been commissioned in the Lambourn and Pang catchments, where the Chalk is unconfined, and also in an area between Reading and Newbury where the aquifer is confined (Fig. 14.11). Thirty-three production wells have been drilled in 7 well-fields, 5 in the unconfined area (27 wells) and 2 in the confined area (6 wells). Most of the water from wells in the unconfined aquifer is discharged from pipelines into the Lambourn or Pang rivers and two of the main discharge points are at the perennial heads of these rivers. The objective is to ensure that as far as possible lengths of flowing streams are the same while the scheme is operating as under natural conditions, thereby preserving the amenities and the environment.

The sustained yields from wells in the confined aquifer are between 5000 and

9000 m³/d but in the unconfined area are generally 2000 to 5000 m³/d. Geophysical well logging and test pumping of the production wells have thrown much light on the nature of the Chalk aquifer. The water enters wells from horizontal fissures, mainly restricted to the upper 50 m of the saturated aquifer both in the unconfined and confined zones. Both the transmissivity and storage coefficient decline non-linearly with depth (Fig. 14.7). This, together with the reduction of both these properties away from the valleys, restricts the total storage available for development. It also affects the response of the wells to pumping[51,53] in the unconfined area. The reduction in these properties is most accentuated under drought conditions when water is required from storage. Because of this the gross yield of Stage 1 of the scheme[3] has been reduced from 230×10^3 m³/d to 113×10^3 m³/d.

The Stage 1 scheme was operated during the drought of 1976 and high net gains of the order of 90 per cent were obtained[3] from the wells in the unconfined area, indicating that interception of base flow and recirculation were small. Model studies suggested that the gain from the wells in the confined aquifer declined to 50 per cent after operating for 2½ months and would probably become negligible after 6 months operation[35]. There is thus clearly a distinct advantage in developing the Chalk where it is unconfined.

Because of the non-linear decline of the transmissivity and storage coefficient with depth, small increases in production rates from wells induce large increases in

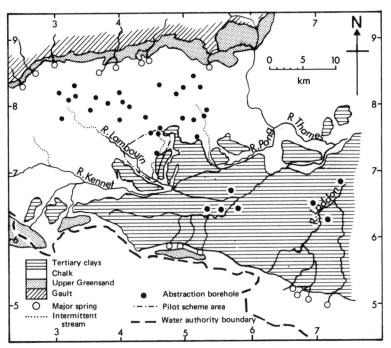

Fig. 14.11. Stage 1 of the Thames Groundwater Scheme (after Owen and Robinson[24])

drawdown. Excessive drawdowns occur in the pumped wells but declines in regional groundwater storage are small. The implication is that full development of storage in the unconfined Chalk will be accomplished most effectively by a higher density of smaller yielding wells[35].

The development of Stage 1 of the groundwater scheme and its successful operation during the 1976 drought confirmed that the Chalk can be developed for river augmentation in the typical extensive downland areas where it outcrops. Full

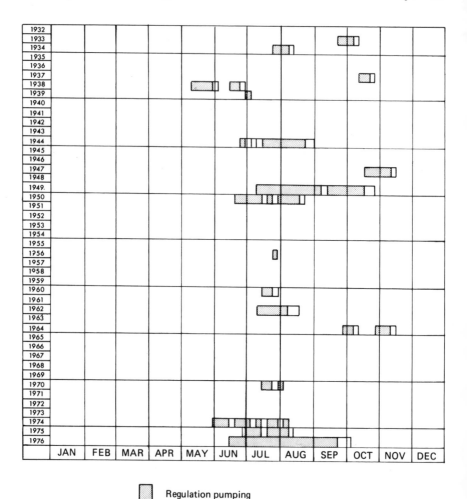

Fig. 14.12. Frequency and use of groundwater in Shropshire for river augmentation (after Severn-Trent Water Authority[41])

Note: The Fig. illustrates the use to meet demands for water at the end of the century during the years 1932 to 1976.

operation of the scheme is expected to be required once every 30 years with partial operation once every 7 years. Numerical models[3] suggest that the ultimate yield from full development of the Chalk could be at least 300×10^3 m^3/d.

The first stage of an augmentation scheme for the River Itchen has also been completed in a similar geomorphological and hydrogeological setting to the Thames Scheme[25,29]. The average net gain from testing 6 wells was between 60 and 70 per cent and ultimately the full scheme is expected to provide an additional yield of 90×10^3 m^3/d.

SHROPSHIRE GROUNDWATER SCHEME

The Triassic sandstones comprise the major aquifer of the English Midlands and over extensive areas groundwater licensed for abstraction exceeds the average annual infiltration[37]. The only area with substantial reserves is in north Shropshire, in the Severn Basin.

The River Severn is the main component of water resource strategy in the west Midlands. The demands for water supplied from the river are supported by releases of water from Clywedog Reservoir in central Wales. During the 1975/76 drought, the rapid decline in the storage in the reservoir led to restrictions on the consumption of water and a relaxation of the need to maintain a specified flow in the lower part of the Severn. In view of this apparent need for further storage, it was decided to develop groundwater in the Triassic sandstones in north Shropshire to regulate the river, a proposal which had been under investigation since 1971[41].

The average infiltration to the aquifer in the proposed development area is 200 Ml/d, of which 80 Ml/d were used to meet local needs in the late 1970s. Although local demand will no doubt increase, there is still a healthy surplus for river regulation.

The Triassic sandstones cover an area of some 800 km^2 and attain thicknesses in excess of 200 m. The feasibility of developing the aquifer was initially investigated in localised areas, each area representing different hydrogeological characteristics, such as different types and thicknesses of glacial deposits. Wells were drilled and tested to establish typical yields from the aquifer and assess the consequences of pumping from them to regulate river flow. Typical average yields were 3 Ml/d. If wells are sited to limit their impact on river flow, net gains of the order of 65 to 70 per cent over the pumping periods can be anticipated, ample to allow for economic operation of the scheme. In practice, the wells will be evenly distributed over a development area, about 1 km apart and not adjacent to main rivers.

The first stage of the scheme has been designed to provide a yield (i.e. a net gain) of 225 Ml/d from a pumping capacity of 330 Ml/d. Abstraction will be intermittent and take place only one year in three for periods varying from 3 to 19 weeks (Fig. 14.12). The long-term average demand on the aquifer to achieve the yield of 225 Ml/d is only 7 Ml/d which is less than 9 per cent of the residual resources available for development, after allowance has been made for continuous direct supply from the aquifer. It is anticipated that about 80 wells will be required. Under operational conditions the average drawdown of water levels in the development area at the end of the maximum period of pumping to produce 225 Ml/d will only be 1.5 m, less than the natural decline in water levels that can take place over a period of dry years.

Groundwater will be used in conjunction with storage in Clywedog Reservoir and the probable mode of operation will make maximum use of groundwater in years when dry weather begins early in the year as it is more advantageous to conserve surface storage against the possibility of a long sustained drought. In actual fact the extent to which groundwater is used will depend on the volume of water in Clywedog Reservoir at any particular time of the year (Fig. 14.12).

The present design proposals are conservative and it seems probable that ultimately yields of 340 Ml/d will be feasible at similar unit costs to those for the first stage. Theoretically, yields of at least 600 Ml/d are possible (Fig. 14.13) but, while this figure indicates the potential of such river regulation schemes, it may not prove possible to achieve this figure, which would require a pumping capacity of up to 750 Ml/d.

The first stage of the scheme should be operational by 1985, when it is anticipated that the net increase in river flow will be 29 Ml/d as a result of abstraction of 47 Ml/d from about 11 wells.

VALE OF YORK SCHEME

It has been realised for some years that the Triassic sandstones in the Vale of

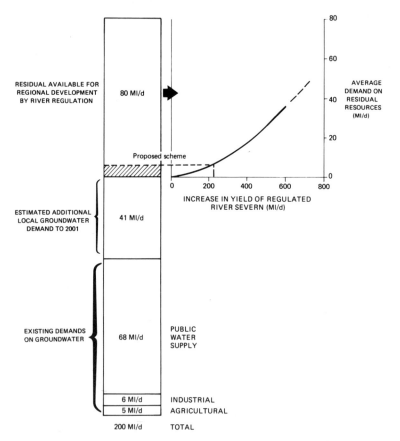

Fig. 14.13.   Use of groundwater in North Shropshire and possible increased yields by using groundwater for river regulation (after Severn-Trent Water Authority[41])

York contain appreciable reserves of groundwater[54] and in the early 1970s the Yorkshire River Authority began investigations to assess the feasibility of regulating the River Ouse with groundwater from the sandstones. The average annual recharge to the aquifer, which crops out over some 800 km², much of it overlain by glacial deposits, is 70 Ml/d. Licensed abstractions in 1974 amounted to 22 Ml/d, leaving a residual of some 50 Ml/d for development—a considerable resource when considered in conjunction with the River Ouse[36].

As in other areas, the feasibility was examined by pilot studies; in this case, in two areas some 20 km to the north-west of York. Three production wells were drilled in one area and two in the other, and extensive pumping tests carried out[36]. The reductions in groundwater discharge to the rivers as a result of the tests were very small in relation to river flows. This is not an uncommon problem in assessing the consequences of groundwater abstraction, and it was overcome by mathematical modelling, data derived from pumping tests and their effect on groundwater levels and local stream flows being used to verify the model of the aquifer system. A main conclusion of the pilot studies was that after pumping for 100 days at 28 Ml/d the net gain was about 65 per cent. About 20 Ml/d of the annual recharge is derived from leakage through overlying superficial deposits. Under development conditions when the hydraulic gradient increased this would rise significantly, the increase representing a reduction in natural discharge to the river system.

Mathematical models were invaluable for predicting the behaviour of the aquifer under conditions of more extensive development. Three types of models were used[17,36]:

(a) A stochastic model of flows in the River Ouse to generate sequences of synthetic flows from the limited historical records.

(b) A simple component model of the River Ouse Basin to identify short critical sequences from the synthetic flows when demands on the groundwater system would be particularly heavy.

(c) A detailed distributed parameter groundwater model to simulate the behaviour of the aquifer during critical drought sequences and to devise a system for operational management. This model was supported for extensive simulation of the system with a lumped parameter model[18].

Groundwater development in an aquifer such as the Triassic sandstones is unlikely to fail because of insufficient storage. It has a high storage coefficient of 10 per cent and a thickness of 150 to 250 m and contains some 4×10^6 Ml, at least 200 times the average recharge rate. The average transmissivity is 100 to 200 m²/d. However, failure could occur because:

(i) abstraction locally exceeds recharge and mining of groundwater occurs with water levels progressively falling;

(ii) installed pump capacity is too low;

(iii) individual well yields decline because high local drawdowns reduce the saturated aquifer thickness; and

(iv) wells have to be taken out of service because heavy pumping has induced the ingress of poor quality groundwater. This could be an important constraint.

In planning a major scheme these possible consequences of pumping have to be taken into account and it is necessary to define the objectives clearly. Maximising net gains may not be the optimum solution, for economic factors are likely to be overriding as well as, for example, protecting local environmental amenities.

How groundwater will actually be developed in the Vale of York is for the future but a study[36] considered that a scheme could yield 350 Ml/d while preserving a residual flow in the river of 950 Ml/d from an average recharge to the aquifer of 46

Ml/d. The maximum abstraction capacity necessary would be about 400 Ml/d although this could be reduced if, for example, some form of rationing were acceptable in a severe drought. After such a major scheme had been operating for a

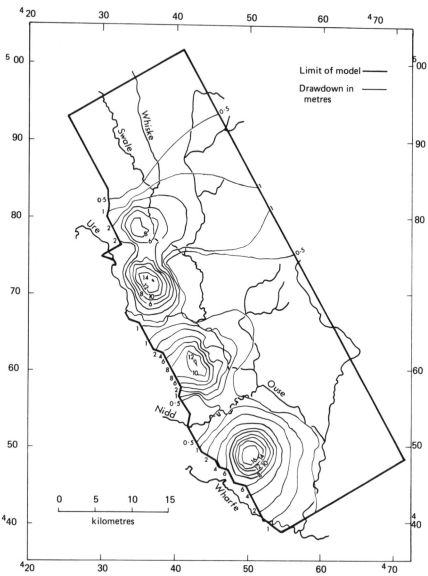

Fig. 14.14. Computer prediction of regional water level drawdowns due to large-scale groundwater development in the Vale of York (after Reeves et al[36])

number of years a new set of mean groundwater levels would obtain[36]. The regional drawdown of water levels under operational conditions would be more than 10 m below average natural levels in the proximity of well-fields (Fig. 14.14).

4. CONJUNCTIVE USE OF SURFACE WATER AND GROUNDWATER

INTRODUCTION

The optimal development of the water resources of a river basin requires integrated or conjunctive use of surface and groundwater resources. It involves determining the most economic method of developing different sources of supply within the constraints that apply to the system as a whole, including social costs and political realities. By adopting this approach the yields of surface resources and groundwater resources, as estimated independently, can be increased when the two are regarded as a single combined resource. In its simplest form the concept advocates the use of surface water when this resource is plentiful, reserving groundwater for periods of below average rainfall when surface resources cannot meet all the demands. During times of above average rainfall, surface water resources in excess of requirements may be used for artificial recharge to replenish depleted groundwater storage.

The traditional method of developing groundwater in England has been to abstract water at a rate that is a fraction, often a significant fraction, of the annual rate of recharge. The groundwater resources of a river basin or groundwater unit were assessed and licences granted as demand increased until the average abstraction rate approached the estimated resources. This approach, which incorporated the limiting constraint that average abstraction never exceeds average replenishment, makes very little use of the large volumes of water stored in groundwater reservoirs. To make use of this storage, the resources must be integrated with surface resources and must be more heavily pumped in dry periods, thereby causing a much greater range of groundwater levels in the reservoir than occurs naturally, and thus making better use of the water in storage.

In practice the operation of a conjunctive use scheme is more complex than the simplified form discussed above. Information is required about:

(1) Surface water resources—
    (*a*) total available
    (*b*) distribution in time
    (*c*) individual storage volumes
    (*d*) quality of the water
    (*e*) possible future methods of storage.
(2) Groundwater resources—
    (i) dimensions of aquifer(s), i.e. area, thickness
    (ii) nature of aquifer, i.e. lithology
    (iii) recharge—from infiltration and from streamflow
    (iv) total storage available in aquifers
    (v) nature and distribution of aquifer properties i.e. storage capacity and transmissive characteristics
    (vi) volume and location of natural discharges
    (vii) quality of water and distribution in space
    (viii) position and nature of aquifer boundaries.
(3) Current water use—location and purpose
(4) Future demands.
(5) Water distribution system.
(6) Waste water disposal system.

Many of these items are inter-related and deriving the optimum development scheme requires the use of mathematical models to assess the advantages and cost benefits of alternative schemes from which the most appropriate scheme can be identified. Models are then used to monitor the development of the selected scheme, produce operating rules and subsequently assist in management of the scheme.

The various schemes for regulation of rivers with groundwater, discussed in the previous section are, of course, conjunctive use schemes. They may involve the use of groundwater resources with a direct river intake or combined use of surface and groundwater reservoirs. This section is concerned with the combined use of groundwater and surface water, where river regulation is not a factor. The principles will be illustrated by case histories. In such situations development of groundwater still requires consideration of the impact of abstraction on river flows

Fig. 14.15.   Principal elements of the Lancashire Conjunctive Use Scheme

and as the proportion of groundwater abstraction to total infiltration increases, discharge to the river system may become necessary to maintain the flow.

LANCASHIRE CONJUNCTIVE USE SCHEME

The opportunity for conjunctive use of diverse sources of water arising from the juxtaposition of upland reservoirs in the Bowland Forest of Lancashire and the Triassic sandstones in the lowlands of the Fylde to the west, was appreciated by Law[55], who conceived a scheme that later developed into the Lancashire Conjunctive Use Scheme.

Law's proposals[55] involved the integrated use of surface reservoirs, river intakes and groundwater. In its present form, as developed by the North West Water Authority, the surface water component incorporates the Stocks and Barnacre reservoirs and the groundwater component is a well-field in the Triassic sandstones between Broughton and Garstang (Fig. 14.15). Water is also abstracted, when needed and available, from the lower reaches of the River Lune near Lancaster and pumped about 12 km through a pipeline and tunnel to the upper reaches of the River Wyre at Abbeystead, where it augments the river flow. After flowing 15 km downstream, an intake at Garstang transfers the water to a treatment works, whence it is pumped into supply (Fig. 14.15). Up to 280 Ml/d may be abstracted from the Wyre at Garstang and when the natural flow is too low to provide this, supplies are transferred from the Lune via the link referred to above. The available storage of the Stocks and Barnacre reservoirs is 14 250 Ml. The yield from this storage, considered as an independent source, is very much less than when incorporated in a conjunctive use scheme.

The Triassic sandstones extend across the Fylde from the River Ribble to Morecambe Bay and are generally overlain by superficial deposits, up to about 30 m thick, mainly of glacial origin and of variable composition. In the vicinity of the well-field the sandstones are 150 m thick but thicken rapidly to the west. Seasonal fluctuations of groundwater levels in the sandstones are very small, and generally no more than 1 or 2 m, so total storage in the aquifer is relatively constant. Average recharge to the aquifer is some 28 Ml/d, mainly derived from sub-surface flow from the Carboniferous rocks to the east (Oakes and Skinner[16]). Heavy abstraction from the aquifer increases this flow to more than 50 Ml/d. The transmissivity of the aquifer is generally between 250 and 500 m^2/d but values as high as 1 500 m^2/d occur when flow through the rock is primarily by fissures[32].

The aquifer has been developed by 41 wells drilled at 14 sites between Broughton and Garstang (Fig. 14.15). Individual wells are generally about 150 m deep and yield between 1 and 6 Ml/d. The effect of pumping on groundwater levels is monitored in 68 observation boreholes.

The maximum licensed abstraction rate from the well-field is 195 Ml/d but this could only be sustained for relatively short periods. It is considered that the abstraction should not exceed the natural average recharge rate over a 3 year period[56] but, as already mentioned, recharge is increased by pumping groundwater.

Fig. 14.16 illustrates how the objective of the conjunctive use scheme, namely to take water from the source best able to satisfy the demand at any given time, is achieved during a drought. Water may be drawn from existing impounding reservoirs and continue to be treated at source or alternatively water may be abstracted from the Wyre at Garstang in quantities of up to 280 Ml/d, subject to licence constraints. At times there is insufficient water in the Wyre and generally on these occasions water is available for transfer from the River Lune via the Lune-Wyre link. Finally during dry periods water may be drawn from the well-field with additional supplies from the reservoirs.

It is anticipated that optimum use of these resources will yield an additional 130 Ml/d and replace supplies to central and south Lancashire, enabling bulk supplies from the Lake District aqueducts to be relinquished and passed southwards.

HARDHAM CONJUNCTIVE USE SCHEME

The Hardham Basin is a small geological basin, 7 km long and 2 km wide, lying on the north side of the South Downs, in Sussex (Fig. 14.1). The basin comprises between 50 and 70 m of Folkestone Beds, overlain in the centre of the basin by up to 50 m of Gault Clay. Both are of Cretaceous age, the Gault Clay being a grey over-consolidated clay and the Folkestone Beds a clean, unconsolidated fine to medium-grained sand with occasional sandstone, ironstone and clay bands. The River Rother flows eastwards across the northern margin of the basin, and joins the River Arun before the latter turns south towards the sea.

Since 1954, the Southern Water Authority and its predecessor water undertaking have abstracted and treated water from the River Rother at Hardham Treatment Works (H. G. Headworth, personal communication). Currently 72 Ml/d can be abstracted and treated at Hardham. Groundwater abstraction from the Folkestone Beds commenced in 1964 and some 25 Ml/d can be abstracted from 6 wells to help meet demand when flows in the river are inadequate. By the late 1960s groundwater abstraction had reached 7.2 Mm^3/a, while only 3.8 Mm^3/a were abstracted from the river. As a consequence, groundwater levels in the centre of the basin fell considerably. Planned expansion of the treatment works led to a re-appraisal of the role of groundwater, which is now seen as fulfilling the secondary role to that of river supply, with wells being used to meet flow deficiencies, and not as a basic component of day-to-day requirement. By 1976/77, as a result of this change in emphasis, groundwater abstraction had fallen to 3.3 Mm^3/a, while river abstraction had risen to 8.2 Mm^3/a.

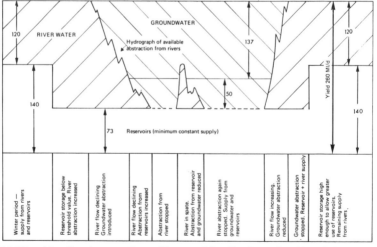

Fig. 14.16. Idealised operation of Lancashire Conjunctive Use Scheme over a period of one year to give a yield of 260 Ml/d (after North West WA)

Artificial recharge experiments were carried out between 1968 and 1974 with untreated river water recharged experimentally into five lagoons, up to 163 m by 14 m in size, purpose-built and dug into exposed Folkestone Beds[57]. These experiments showed the feasibility of this type of recharge. Further experiments have been carried out using a well 915 mm in diameter which is suitable for abstraction as well as recharge. It is drilled through the Gault Clay into Folkestone Beds and incorporates a well screen opposite the aquifer. Trials in 1981 showed that the well was capable of recharging under gravity over 4.5 Ml/d of fully treated river water with no significant build-up in head losses in the aquifer and no detrimental reaction with the receiving groundwater.

The Hardham abstraction and treatment works is an important strategic supply source in Sussex and is capable of phased expansion for the foreseeable future to meet growing demand around Crawley. As abstraction from the river increases to meet supply needs, so the ability of river flows to meet demand decreases and, in consequence, progressively more groundwater will be needed over the years to meet these deficiencies. It is envisaged that at anticipated full development of 170 Ml/d a total of some 20 wells will be required to meet flow deficiencies and cope with emergency closures of the river intake because of pollution. A two-dimensional finite difference mathematical model, constructed by the Water Research Centre, has shown that even at this level of development, under such low recharge and low groundwater level conditions as occurred between 1972 and 1976, the Folkestone Beds aquifer is capable of meeting the demand placed upon it without the need for artificial recharge, although the artificial recharge/abstraction well, already constructed, will be used to even out throughput at the treatment works and prevent groundwater levels becoming too depressed in the vicinity of the works.

The numerical aquifer model has been used to determine the minimum spacing for the additional 10 wells needed for subsequent stages of development, allowing for the effects of interference between them and for preventing excessive drawdown of pumping levels. In addition, the model is being used to assess the pumping regime which will minimise aquifer drawdowns and minimise pumping costs from the well-field (H. G. Headworth, personal communication).

CONTROL OF SALINE INTRUSION BY CONJUNCTIVE USE

Saline intrusion has occurred in Britain mainly where the Chalk and Triassic sandstones are extensively exploited for water near coastlines and estuaries (Fig. 14.17). This constraint on the full development of aquifer resources can be partially overcome by conjunctive use of individual groundwater sources or of groundwater with surface water. Abstraction of groundwater from a coastal aquifer reduces the freshwater head and, therefore, the flow of freshwater to the sea. This results in a movement inland of the saline interface (Fig. 14.18). The management of a coastal aquifer is concerned with fixing the ultimate landward extent of the saline water and calculating the amount of natural discharge necessary to maintain the interface in this pre-determined position. The difference between this discharge and infiltration represents the amount of water that can be developed. The wells used for development are sited inland of the ultimate position of the toe of the interface. As an aquifer is steadily developed the average volume of fresh water in storage is permanently reduced (Fig. 14.18).

Despite the inland movement of the saline interface in response to lowered water levels, because of the Ghyben-Herzberg relationship, the considerable volumes of fresh water stored below sea level must be displaced before extensive saline

Fig. 14.17.   Main areas of seawater intrusion in England and Wales

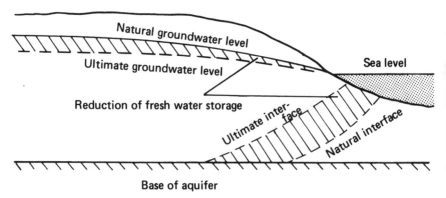

**Fig. 14.18.   Reduction of freshwater storage following groundwater
development in a coastal aquifer** (after Santing[78])

intrusion occurs. This delayed response can be relied upon in an aquifer where flow is by intergranular movement but, in a fissured aquifer, field evidence indicates that, in at least some locations, intrusion by fissure flow can be rapid[27].

Controlling the extent of saline intrusion requires overall control of well distribution and the pumping regime of each well and introduction of conjunctive use of well and surface sources if this is possible.

The problem of saline intrusion has been of concern for many years along the South Coast where the groundwater resources of the Chalk are intensively developed for water supply for about 90 km between Chichester and Eastbourne (Fig. 14.19). The aquifer forms a range of hills, the South Downs, dissected into five "blocks" by rivers that cross the outcrop of the Chalk from north to south; these blocks are effectively independent resource units.

Saline intrusion has been a particular problem in the Brighton Block, where the average abstraction of some 77 Ml/d represents about 33 per cent of the average annual recharge. Although the wells are evenly spread over the area of the block, except over the higher parts of the Downs, abstraction from wells near the coast has caused saline intrusion up to 2½ km from the coast[58]. Over the last 20 years abstraction from individual wells in the Brighton Block has been determined by seasonal variations in the amount of water stored in the Chalk. This has involved pumping from wells situated near the coast and rivers during the winter, to reduce the natural loss of water from the aquifer when this is high, and pumping from inland wells during the summer while at the same time limiting abstraction from coastal wells. During the summer, abstraction from coastal wells is controlled by the chloride content. This approach has increased the volume of water stored in the aquifer as a whole and considerably increased the annual volume of water that may be pumped from individual wells[58,59]. The optimum yield depends to a large extent on the well distribution. The extent to which this policy can be applied is currently limited by the number of wells available and the need to meet peak summer demands for water. Mathematical models have been used to examine possible well distributions for an extension of the policy[45,60]. A limiting factor to the development of storage from wells remote from the coast is likely to be the tendency for high permeabilities to occur towards the coast. This would result in a preferred development of storage in that direction and consequent saline intrusion. Field studies are required to determine whether this would be the case and to determine the extent to which the policy can be developed. Nevertheless, the conjunctive use of wells has obviously much to recommend it in the South Downs as a whole and in other areas where conditions are similar.

An important variable in development of a coastal aquifer is the total storage in the aquifer above sea level at the end of a summer period. The model studies suggested that saline intrusion may set a limit to development in the South Downs when storage above sea level in October of the final year of a severe drought (say, 1 in 50 occurrence) is 30 per cent of the natural value[61].

Groundwater resources of the five Chalk "blocks" of the South Downs have been developed to different extents. If the aquifer is to be exploited to its full potential and still avoid significant saline intrusion, the levels of development of each block should be more uniform and facilities introduced for the transfer of water between blocks; in other words, the aquifer of the South Downs should be treated as a single aquifer unit[61].

Theoretically, conjunctive use of groundwater sources in this region could be extended by incorporating surface water resources from the rivers of the Weald (Fig. 14.19) and also by using surplus surface water to recharge the Chalk[45,61]. The

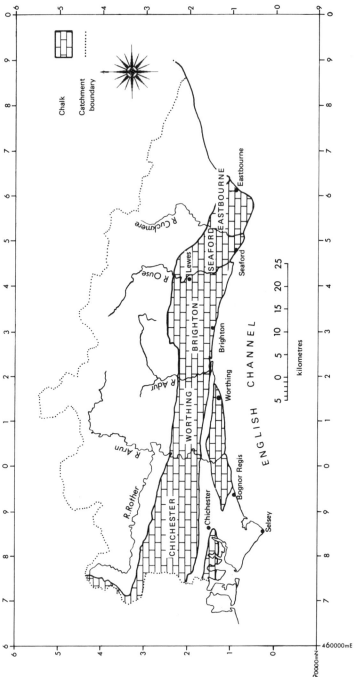

Fig. 14.19.   The Chalk aquifer of the South Downs showing the various Chalk "blocks"

important constraint that the volume of storage in an aquifer at the end of a summer period has on development has already been emphasised. Model studies[62] have suggested that artificial recharge into the Chalk of the South Downs at sites remote from the coast at rates as low as 10000 m^3/d over 6 months, would increase the minimum storage above sea level at the end of a summer recession by about 10 per cent or 10 Mm^3.

Conjunctive use of surface and groundwater in the South Downs is still in the future and at present water resource management concentrates on efficient operation of groundwater sources. In addition to aquifer models, a numerical operational model is being evaluated for use on a day-to-day basis to guide engineers operating the system as to the quantities of water that have to be pumped each day to fill the service reservoirs to meet anticipated demand (H. G. Headworth, personal communication). Decisions are required about which sources to use to provide water at a minimum cost. Abstracting groundwater on a daily least-cost basis could violate the mode of operating the wells to guard against saline intrusion, which seeks to conserve aquifer storage and maximise the use of groundwater flow to the sea when this is high, particularly in the winter. To meet both the minimum cost and minimum saline intrusion objectives, aquifer models will be used to test the impact on storage in the aquifer of projected minimum cost pumping regimes; if necessary, the actual pumping programme will be modified. In this manner the aims of aquifer management and source management can be reconciled.

5. ARTIFICIAL RECHARGE

Principles and Design Criteria

Artificial recharge is a means of supplementing the natural infiltration to an aquifer. An established technique in water management, it involves storing water in aquifers at times when it is surplus to requirements, for use at times when supplies are less plentiful, the aquifer being used in the manner of a surface pumped storage reservoir. It may be regarded as the final stage in development of an aquifer, being introduced when natural groundwater resources have been fully developed either by conventional means or in conjunction with surface water. Artificial recharge is necessary to derive full benefit from the storage available in aquifers as a greater range of water level fluctuations can then be induced. Apart from the important aspect of making more effective use of aquifer storage, artificial recharge can also play a role in water quality control, either by purifying surface waters or by improving the quality of waste waters; in some situations this is the primary purpose. It is also a recognised means of controlling saline interfaces and disposing of effluents. The source of water for recharge is usually surface run-off, treated effluents or cooling water.

Artificial recharge may be carried out through basins or wells or more simply by a system of ditches or controlled flooding. The methodology has been reviewed by Blair[63]. Wells are necessary when the aquifer is covered by impermeable deposits. In the UK basins and wells are the methods most likely to be favoured.

Artificial recharge is used to only a limited extent in the UK, but during the 1970s a series of experiments was promoted by the Water Resources Board in cooperation with several river authorities to gain experience of the technique[64,65]. The results of this programme, together with the experience gained in many parts of the world where the method is applied, allow the identification of general design criteria. These have been summarised by Edworthy and Downing[64] and the following paragraphs are based on that paper.

A suitable depth for a recharge lagoon is about 3 m with sides sloping at 1:2. This allows recharge under a maximum head of about 2.5 m. An artificial filter about 0.5 m thick on the floor of the basin protects the aquifer and extends the time before the infiltration capacity of the system is reduced below acceptable levels by accumulation of silt and clay and microbial growths. Basins have to be drained periodically so that the top 100 mm of the filter can be removed or the floor broken up by light ploughing or scarification to maintain high infiltration rates. The length of the recharge and cleaning cycle depends upon the nature of the aquifer but experience at sites in England suggests that a recharge period of about 30 days, followed by 7 days for draining and cleaning, is appropriate.

The diameter of a recharge well should be as large as possible and fully penetrate the aquifer. The design factors to be considered have been reviewed[66]. In the UK diameters are usually 600 or 900 mm and, in the Chalk, about 50 m of saturated aquifer are penetrated, although in sandstones more than this is usual. Unless the aquifer is extensively fissured and compact, well screens and gravel packs are necessary to stabilise it. Maintaining the recharge capacity of a recharge well is a major operating problem. Wells ultimately clog because of suspended solids, even with high quality water. The pack removes some of the suspended solids but most of the clogging occurs at the pack/aquifer interface[67]. During rehabilitation of wells this material has to be removed. The thickness of the pack should not exceed 200 mm, to allow redevelopment of the well and removal of the solids that accumulate in the pack and at the pack/aquifer interface. If the aquifer is a semi-consolidated sandstone and the screen and pack are used as insurance against possible collapse of the well, then a thin, coarse gravel pack may be appropriate, thereby allowing more ready access to the face of the formation in the well. Such a pack should be about 75 mm thick, with a uniform grain size of about 5 mm in diameter.

A high quality water is generally required for well recharge. Water quality is a primary factor in determining whether a project will be successful. At Clipstone, Nottinghamshire[68], the water contained less than 1 mg/l silt, with a particle size of less than 1 micron, but the recharge rate declined significantly after recharge had continued for about a year. In the Lee Valley, where recharge is into a fissured limestone, 5 mg/l silt have had no effect on recharge performance.

Recharge water must be chemically compatible with the native groundwater; insoluble compounds can precipitate by reactions between chemically dissimilar waters. For example, care must be taken to avoid precipitation of iron hydroxide, calcium carbonate or silica in the well or aquifer. The permeability of an aquifer can be reduced by air or gas entrainment and means of avoiding this should be incorporated in the design. The presence of oxygen in recharge water can lead to precipitation of iron oxides and hydroxides in the well. Recharge water must also be chlorinated to prevent microbial growths in the well.

With a well recharge scheme, rehabilitation of wells will be necessary but the frequency depends upon conditions specific to individual sites. Under operational conditions frequent redevelopment is favoured to avoid irreversible clogging. The actual frequency must be determined by practical experience but it may be daily and at rates several times the recharge rate.

It will be clear that avoiding premature clogging of a well, basin or aquifer is a very important factor in designing a recharge scheme. For this reason some form of pretreatment is usually necessary to remove suspended solids from the water. If the water to be used for recharge is of low quality, such as an effluent, then additional treatment would be needed, involving chemical coagulation, filtration, chlorination and possibly activated carbon. In some situations additional stages may be necessary[69]. In basin recharge, pretreatment can often be limited to settlement and aeration.

LEE VALLEY

The only major artificial recharge scheme in the UK is in the Lee Valley in east London, in a catchment which drains 1415 km^2 to the River Thames (Fig. 14.1). Both surface and groundwater resources have been extensively developed and river intakes, wells and surface reservoirs provide an average yield of 320×10^3 m^3/d, a figure approximating to the mean flow of the river.

The Lee Valley lies in the London Basin where the Chalk is the principal aquifer. In the central part of the basin, including the lower part of the Lee Valley, this aquifer is overlain by sands and clays of the Lower London Tertiaries which in turn are overlain by the London Clay.

During the nineteenth and early part of the twentieth century the groundwater resources of the confined region of the London Basin were extensively exploited. Water levels fell by as much as 75 m and the Chalk and overlying Tertiary sands were dewatered over 900 km^2. In the Lee Valley itself, the water level fell by as much as 60 m and the volume of dewatered storage now amounts to at least 150 Mm^3, four times the reservoir storage in the Lee Valley and 72 per cent of the surface storage in the entire Thames Basin[70]. Most of the storage is actually in the Tertiary sands overlying the Chalk.

Artificial recharge of the Chalk in the Lee Valley using wells was carried out between 1953 and 1968 by the Metropolitan Water Board whenever water treatment capacity exceeded demand[71]. The potential for artificial recharge in the London Basin as a whole was examined by the Water Resources Board in a series of reports[26,72,73] and one of the four most favourable areas was the lower Lee Valley.

The scheme in the Lee Valley involves recharging 12 wells, 6 existing public supply wells (5 of which have extensive adit systems in the Chalk) and 6 new wells (Fig. 14.20). All are fitted with pipework for both recharge and abstraction. A seventh new well is used for abstraction only[70]. The new wells have diameters of 720 mm, are 100 to 120 m deep and penetrate about 70 m of Chalk. They are cased and cemented into the top of the aquifer, which is left open. In new wells recharge water is injected below the rest water level but in existing wells water cascades into the wells from the surface.

Only 60 per cent of the water used for recharge is derived from the River Lee. The remaining 40 per cent is taken from the River Thames and pumped to the recharge area along the Thames-Lee Tunnel, an aqueduct some 30 km long. The water is treated to potable standards before recharge. Water pumped from the aquifer may be discharged either to the River Lee, or to nearby surface reservoirs or pumped directly into supply.

The total potential recharge rate at the beginning of a recharge period is about 75 Ml/d and the reliable yield after recharge is about 80 Ml/d for a 150 day period. This provides an additional yield of 60 Ml/d over the drought yield of 20 Ml/d available from the supply wells incorporated in the scheme. Modelling studies indicate that 70 to 80 per cent of the recharge water can be reabstracted at the recharge sites, with the balance moving down the hydraulic gradient towards the groundwater low below central London.

The scheme has been incorporated in the Thames Water Authority's regional resource system and is likely to be operated according to the following rules:

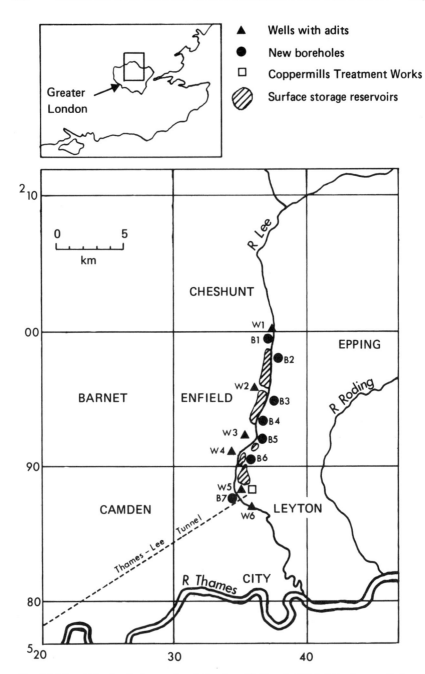

Fig. 14.20.   Principal elements of the Lee Valley Artificial Recharge Scheme

(1) When excess river flows are available, fill surface storage first and then recharge the aquifer.

(2) If river flow cannot meet demand, augment supplies from surface storage until a storage threshold, say 80 per cent full, is reached and then abstract groundwater until the volume of water recharged has been abstracted.

(3) Revert to supply augmentation from surface storage in a particularly severe drought and exploit the aquifer for a second time when surface storage has been reduced to a lower threshold, say 50 per cent of full capacity.

There is still considerable scope for expansion of artificial recharge in the Lee Valley and a scheme is currently being considered[70] that would yield an additional 200 Ml/d.

NOTTINGHAMSHIRE

The Triassic sandstones form a prominent aquifer in the Midlands and crop out over extensive areas in Nottinghamshire. During the early 1970s the Water Resources Board and the Trent River Authority carried out experiments to recharge the sandstone using basins and wells.

TABLE 14.I. Changes in Concentration of Selected Constituents during Pretreatment and Recharge in a Recharge Basin at Edwinstowe during 1971
(*from Satchell and Edworthy*[74])

	River	Settlement basin	Recharge basin	8 m depth†
Total organic carbon (filtered)	9.8	11.2	10.2	2.4
Permanganate value (4 hr @ 27°C)	7.5	6.4	6.1	1.0
Ammonia	7.2	7.2	5.7	0.1
Nitrate (NO_3)	38.2	35.0	38.4	52
Phosphate	1.3	1.3	1.25	0.2
Viruses (PFU)*	32	ND**	10	Nil
E. coli (in 100 ml)	100	9	2	Nil

Notes: Units are mg/l unless otherwise stated.
  *Plaque-forming units per litre.
  **ND Not Determined.
  † Collected from perched-water table in shallow borehole.

The object of the basin experiment was to examine the effect of artificial recharge on the quality of a polluted river such as the Trent[74]. The recharge source, the River Maun at Edwinstowe, was of similar quality to the Trent. Water was pumped from the River Maun to a settlement lagoon (minimum retention time 8 hours) and then to a 30 m² basin, 3 m deep. The water was aerated before recharge by cascading it into the basin. Higher recharge rates that declined less rapidly were achieved when the floor of the basin was covered by a filter 0.5 m thick with median grain size 0.5 mm and uniformity coefficient less than 3. The average recharge rate was 0.36 m/d. The recharge process considerably improved water quality. Suspended matter was removed, organic compounds significantly reduced, by adsorption or biodegradation, ammonia oxidised, phosphorus largely eliminated and detergents, pathogenic bacteria and viruses removed within 8 m of the bottom of the basin (Table 14.I). Because of the object of the experiment, care was taken to ensure that infiltration into the aquifer was by intergranular processes. This necessitated sealing fissures in the floor of the basin. If this had not been a prerequisite and recharge via fissures had been permissible, recharge rates of up to 100 m/d would have been possible.

The recharge well experiment in the Triassic sandstones was at Clipstone[68]. The objectives were to determine recharge rates and any change with time, any changes in chemical quality because of recharge and to monitor the formation and decay of the recharge mound.

The recharge well, 65.8 m deep, penetrated about 27 m below the rest water level

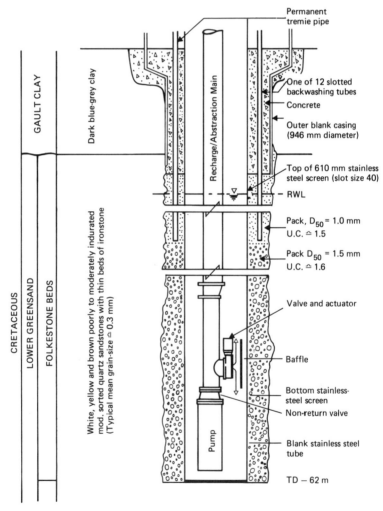

Fig. 14.21.   Section of a recharge borehole at Hardham, Sussex

at the time of drilling. The diameter was 915 mm and the well contained a well screen of 508 mm diameter and a gravel pack. The well was surrounded by 11 observation boreholes at distances of between 1.5 and 60 m. The recharge source for the experiment was chlorinated groundwater from a well 4 km distant.

The recharge well yielded 12.6 l/s for a drawdown of 9.4 m but this low yield was caused by the well's inefficiency because of mud-cake on the walls. The maximum recharge rate achieved during the experiments was 3500 m³/d. Over a period of 257 days the rate declined by 15 per cent from 2800 m³/d when the applied head was maintained at a nearly constant value of 34 m above rest water level. The conclusion from the experiments was that it should be possible to recharge treated water at a rate of 5000 m³/d for an extended period with a fully efficient well.

HARDHAM, SUSSEX

At Hardham, near Pulborough, the Folkestone Beds of the Lower Greensand have been intensively developed for a public water supply as already described. The aquifer, which is a fine to medium-grained sand 50 to 70 m thick, was being progressively dewatered until the abstraction rate was reduced in 1975. Experiments were begun in 1968 to assess the feasibility of increasing the yield of the aquifer by artificial recharge.

Experiments were conducted recharging partially treated and raw water from the River Arun into five basins up to 163 m long, 14 m wide and 2.5 m deep. The infiltration rate was different in each lagoon but maximum rates were about 2.2 m/d and up to 10000 m³/d were recharged. The detailed results are complex and have been reported in detail[57] and summarised[64,65]. The overall conclusion was that artificial recharge of the Folkestone Beds by means of basins could be successfully incorporated into a water resource system. However, the availability of land for basins would be a constraint and, if the river source and the aquifer at Hardham were to be used ultimately to their maximum extent, recharge through wells would be necessary.

With this in mind experiments are being carried out into the feasibility of well recharge. A well 62 m deep with a diameter of 915 mm has been drilled into the Folkestone Beds, fitted with a 610 mm screen and gravel pack (Fig. 14.21). Back-washing tubes are included in the pack to facilitate redevelopment of the well[64,65], which has been recharged with treated river water for up to 30 days at an average rate of about 50 l/s under a maximum head of 16 m. During this period there were no problems from clogging of the aquifer or changes in chemical quality (H. G. Headworth, personal communication 1981).

6. MINING OF GROUNDWATER RESOURCES

Groundwater management in the UK is concerned with using the resource in a manner that does not produce undesirable consequences. The extent of development is limited by the average annual recharge, although overdevelopment of an aquifer's resources over short periods forms a necessary part of the use of groundwater in conjunction with surface water. While this approach is appropriate in climatic regimes where rainfall is adequate to replenish groundwater storage on a regular basis, it is clearly not applicable to semi-arid or arid regions. Groundwater only has a value as a resource if it is used and, in regions where replenishment is not significant, development requires mining the resource in a manner similar to the extraction of oil or any other mineral resource. However, mining of groundwater does take place in more temperate regions and this may be unplanned or planned, as for example in the latter case, to delay commitment of capital for an alternative water supply scheme.

The control of groundwater abstraction, introduced in parts of England after the Water Act 1945, was a direct result of the overdevelopment or mining of groundwater resources. Groundwater levels had fallen by 40 to 75 m in and around Birmingham[75], saline intrusion was extensive on Merseyside[76] and in Grimsby[77], and reference has already been made to the decline of water levels in the central part of the London Basin by as much as 75 m.

The development of the central part of the London Basin may be taken as a case study of the use of a confined aquifer by mining the resource. Abstraction from the Tertiary sands below the London Clay began in the eighteenth century and in 1823 the first wells were sunk to the Chalk in Chiswick and Hammersmith. The number of wells drilled steadily increased and reached 50 to 60 per year in the 1930s when abstraction attained the peak rate of about 237 Ml/d. As a result of the demand from the well-field in the confined aquifer, the hydraulic gradient increased and more water began to flow through the Chalk from the outcrop towards the centre of the basin (Fig. 14.22). Further, less acceptable, consequences were greater pumping lifts as water levels declined (and hence increased costs), reduction of

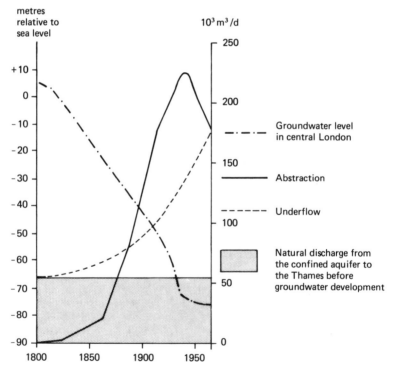

Fig. 14.22.   Relationship between groundwater level, groundwater abstraction and groundwater flow (underflow) through the Tertiary sands and Chalk below the London Clay

flows in rivers draining the Chalk's outcrop, saline intrusion along the Thames, and limited surface subsidence through consolidation of the overlying London Clay[26].

It has been estimated that up to 1965 5680 Mm³ were abstracted from the confined aquifer. About 80 per cent was derived from an increase in flow through the aquifer and 18 per cent from the reduction in groundwater storage. Theoretically in such situations, water levels can be lowered until storage is exhausted or until the changes in hydraulic gradients produce adverse effects (for example, a deterioration in water quality) or until abstraction is no longer economic because of increased pumping lifts. For a given abstraction rate, a new equilibrium will eventually be established, with the yield provided almost entirely from the outcrop. In the London Basin equilibrium conditions were attained in the 1950s at an abstraction rate of 180 Ml/d, probably as a result of economic factors related to increased pumping lifts and reduction of yields as water levels declined. Over the period 1800 to 1965, the average yield from the aquifer was 90 Ml/d and, as discussed earlier, part of the Tertiary sands and Chalk dewatered by the decline in water levels (Fig. 14.23) is now being used for artificial recharge.

The extent of the mining of groundwater in the London Basin (Fig. 14.23) represents the use of over 1000 Mm³ of water once only (generally referred to as a "one-time reserve"), and was the outcome of the need to increase flow through the aquifer to the well-field. In a similar manner, reduction of the hydraulic gradient in a coastal zone to reduce the loss of fresh water to the sea and create new equilibrium conditions that allow limited intrusion from the sea (Santing[78] and Fig.

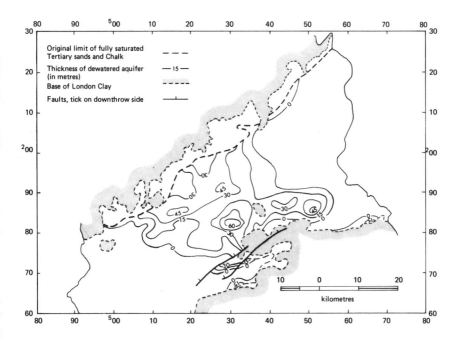

Fig. 14.23.   Thickness of dewatered Tertiary sands and Chalk in the central part of the London Basin

14.18) also releases a "one-time reserve". The development of aquifers in semi-arid and arid areas, although similar in that mining is involved, differs as the resource is essentially non-renewable and finite and has a limited life dependent on the rate of abstraction.

The initial problem in developing a major aquifer in an arid or semi-arid region is assessment of the total resource—that is, the total storage. Exploration wells provide information about the thickness and nature of the aquifer and its properties, from which a preliminary estimate of the total resource can be made. One of the advantages of developing groundwater is that it can proceed in stages as the demand arises. Capital need not be invested before the resource is required. The consequences of developing each stage can be studied before proceeding to the next stage. With this in mind, and following the usual practice in planning the exploitation of a mineral resource, the total resource can be divided into the following categories:

(a) Proven reserves.
(b) Probable reserves.
(c) Possible reserves.
(d) Additional resources—not exploitable in total.

The reserves are the proportions of the total resource that can be developed with differing degrees of certainty and usually at increasing cost. The values assigned to each category are functions of the extent of exploration, available drilling technology and the economics of development; a subjective element inevitably enters into the assessments. Proven reserves are the most reliable and represent the proportion of the total resource that, on the technical information available, can be recovered with reasonable certainty under current economic conditions using current operating practices. The designation of proven, probable and possible reserves may be regarded as present and future development targets or totals, within which resource exploitation schemes can be planned. As staged development proceeds, the volumes of water in the various categories are constantly revised and the optimum development plan of the aquifer modified, as appropriate, to changing conditions with the help of mathematical models. Observation wells may be necessary to monitor aquifer conditions and guard against undesirable changes.

Development of groundwater from major aquifers in arid zones commonly requires abstraction from confined areas of the aquifers. As the coefficient of storage of confined aquifers is small, the cone of depression around a well-field expands rapidly and ultimately intersects the unconfined area when the rate of decline reduces to a level commensurate with the reduction of storage necessary to meet the abstraction rate. Most of the water is derived from storage in the unconfined area, where the coefficient of storage is highest, and only relatively limited amounts are obtained by lowering the water level in the confined area, although in major aquifers these "relatively limited amounts" can be appreciable. Where aquifers are deep or thick, the constraint of maximum economic pumping lifts may mean that only a small proportion of the total available resource can be abstracted economically (Fig. 14.24).

The large volumes of water required in some areas involve abstraction from many wells distributed in well-fields. Ideally the wells in such fields should be arranged at right angles to the direction of flow, to intercept the maximum possible amount of flow through the aquifer, but, where a large number of wells are involved, grouping in two or more lines is necessary. Well-field design in these circumstances is concerned with well spacing and the ideal distance between wells is greater in confined aquifers than in unconfined aquifers because the storage coefficients are smaller. The objective is to avoid unnecessary interference between wells, bearing in mind the cost of linking them. Increasing the spacing reduces operating costs but increases the cost of a collector pipeline network between wells. Clearly there is an optimum relationship which can be investigated by computer modelling[79].

Well design is intended to produce the required output for the smallest capital and operating costs. This has been studied[80] for different types of water wells, including the deep wells necessary in some overseas countries, where resources are mined. Capital costs depend on depth of well, diameter, depth to rest water level and drawdown of water level. Diameter and screen length can be optimised for a given yield. Annual operating costs depend upon rate of discharge, pumping lift and duration of pumping or load factor. How these various factors are related to economic considerations and to the design of an optimum programme for mining groundwater is complex and has been discussed by Burt[81] and Domenico et al[82].

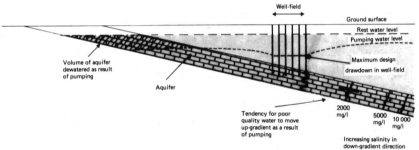

Fig. 14.24.   Some factors in the mining of groundwater in a confined aquifer

7. POSTSCRIPT

Early in the 1960s attention was beginning to be focused on the conjunctive use of groundwater and surface water sources. Since that time major advances have been made in understanding the methods needed to develop groundwater on a regional scale. The feasibility of using storage in aquifers and yet maintaining river flows under drought conditions in the small catchments typical of England, has been successfully demonstrated in a number of regions and with different rock types. Artificial recharge experiments, which were followed by the first operational scheme in the Lee Valley, have shown that the technique is applicable in the main aquifers of the UK, using either wells or basins. There are many areas where it could be applied on both a small and large scale[64].

In recent years the need for additional water supplies has receded and long-term forecasts of demand are uncertain. However, this is a situation where groundwater can be developed with advantage, for it can be readily phased to meet expanding demand as it arises, without the need to commit capital before this is necessary.

The volume of water stored in aquifers, particularly sandstones, is considerable. The upper 50 m of saturated Bunter (Sherwood) Sandstone over the 1000 km^2 outcrop in Nottinghamshire alone contains 10000 Mm^3 of available water, a figure that may be compared with the 1800 Mm^3 of storage that existed in 1970 in surface reservoirs used for water supply in the UK[83].

To use aquifer storage to the full, water levels must be lowered artificially in times of need to a much greater extent than has been the case in the past, both to balance uneven variations in the long-term and short-term distribution of rainfall and to store surplus surface run-off by artificial recharge. Emphasis in the future will be placed on the use of aquifers as storage reservoirs. The overall objective will be the optimum use of this storage in conjunction with surface resources in the context of the need for efficient river basin management.

8. ACKNOWLEDGEMENTS

This chapter summarises the progress made in the UK, during the last 20 years or so, towards understanding the methodology of developing groundwater within the context of the water resources management of entire river basins. The knowledge acquired is the result of the cooperative efforts of many individuals, who worked principally in the Water Resources Board, the Central Water Planning Unit, the Water Research Centre, the river authorities and their successors, the regional water authorities. Many of those involved are referred to through their publications quoted in the text but only the principal references are quoted. However, these publications themselves include references to most of the relevant literature.

9. REFERENCES

1. Ineson, J. and Rowntree, N. A. F. 1967 *J. IWE.*, 21, 275, Conservation projects and planning.
2. Ineson, J. and Downing, R. A. 1964 *J. IWE.*, 18, 519, The groundwater component of river discharge and its relationship to hydrogeology.
3. Hardcastle, B. J. 1978 "From concept to commissioning, in Thames Groundwater Scheme", Institution of Civil Engineers, London.
4. Binnie and Partners 1965, "Report on the water resources of the Great Ouse basin", Ministry of Housing and Local Government, London.
5. Downing, R. A., Oakes, D. B., Wilkinson, W. B. and Wright, C. E. 1974 *J. Hydrol.*, 22, 155, Regional development of groundwater resources in combination with surface water.
6. Downing, R. A., Ashford, P. L., Headworth, H. G., Owen, M. and Skinner, A. C. 1981 'The use of groundwater for river regulation' in "A survey of British hydrogeology 1980", The Royal Society, London.
7. Oakes, D. B. and Wilkinson, W. B. 1972 "Modelling of groundwater and surface water systems, I-Theoretical base flow", Water Resources Board, Reading.
8. Glover, R. E. 1960 "Studies of groundwater movement", Tech. Mem. 657, US Bureau of Reclamation.
9. Hantush, M. S. 1964 *J. Geophys. Res.*, 69, 2551, Depletion of storage, leakage and river flows by gravity wells in sloping sands.
10. Jamieson, D. G. and Sexton, J. R. 1972 Proc. Int. Symp. Wat. Res. Planning, Mexico, "The hydrological evaluation of regional water resource systems in the United Kingdom".
11. Bloomer, R. J. G. and Sexton, J. R. 1972 "The generation of synthetic river flow data", Water Resources Board, Reading.
12. Great Ouse River Authority 1972 "Great Ouse Groundwater Pilot Scheme—Final Report".
13. Wright, C. E. 1975 *J. Hydrol.*, 26, 209, The assessment of regional groundwater schemes by river flow regression equations.
14. Mander, R. J. and Greenfield, B. J. 1977 *Memoires Int. Assoc. Hydrogéol.*, 13, D42, Storage and discharge: Unconfined aquifers.
15. Oakes, D. B. and Pontin, J. M. A. 1976 "Mathematical modelling of a chalk aquifer", Tech. Rpt. 24, Water Research Centre, Medmenham.

16. Oakes, D. B. and Skinner, A. C. 1975 "The Lancashire Conjunctive Use Scheme groundwater model", Tech. Rpt. 12, Water Research Centre, Medmenham.
17. Birtles, A. B. and Reeves, M. J. 1977 *J. Hydrol.* 34, 97, Computer modelling of regional groundwater systems in the confined-unconfined flow regime.
18. Birtles, A. B. and Reeves, M. J. 1977 *J. Hydrol.*, 34, 77, A simple effective method for the computer simulation of groundwater storage and its application in the design of water resource systems.
19. Great Ouse River Authority 1971 "Groundwater Pilot Scheme, 4th Progress Report".
20. Avon and Dorset River Authority 1973 "Upper Wylye Investigation".
21. Foster, S. S. D. and Milton, V. A. 1974 *Bull. Hydrol. Sciences*, 19, 485, The permeability and storage of an unconfined Chalk aquifer.
22. Price, M., Robertson, A. S. and Foster, S. S. D. 1977 *Water Services*, 81, 603, Chalk permeability—a study of vertical variation using water injection tests and borehole logging.
23. Headworth, H. G. 1978 *Q. J. eng. Geol.*, 11, 139, Hydrogeological characteristics of artesian boreholes in the Chalk of Hampshire.
24. Owen, M. and Robinson, V. K. 1978 "Characteristics and yield of the fissured Chalk, in Thames Groundwater Scheme", Institution of Civil Engineers, London.
25. Headworth, H. G., Keating, T. and Packman, M. J. 1982 *J. Hydrol.*, 55, 93, Evidence for a shallow highly permeable zone in the Chalk of Hampshire, UK.
26. Water Resources Board, 1972 "The hydrogeology of the London Basin".
27. Monkhouse, R. A. and Fleet, M. 1975 *Q. J. eng. Geol.*, 8, 291, A geophysical investigation of saline water in the Chalk of the south coast of England.
28. Ineson, J. 1962 *J. IWE.*, 16, 449, A hydrogeological study of the permeability of the Chalk.
29. Southern Water Authority 1978 "Final report on the Candover Pilot Scheme, 1972-1976".
30. Reeves, M. J., Skinner, A. C. and Wilkinson, W. B. 1975 *J. Hydrol.*, 25, 1, The relevance of aquifer-flow mechanisms to exploration and development of groundwater resources.
31. Williams, B. P. J., Downing, R. A. and Lovelock, P. E. R. 1972 24th Inst. Geol. Cong., Montreal, Section 11, 169, "Aquifer properties of the Bunter Sandstone in Nottinghamshire, England".
32. Brereton, N. R. and Skinner, A. C. 1974 *Water Services*, 78, 275, Groundwater flow characteristics in the Triassic sandstones in the Fylde area of Lancashire.
33. Lovelock, P. E. R. 1977 "Aquifer properties of Permo-Triassic sandstones in the United Kingdom" Bull. 56 Geol. Surv. G.B. Institute of Geological Sciences, London.
34. Birtles, A. B. and Wilkinson, W. B. 1975 *Wat. Res. Res.*, 11, 571, Mathematical simulation of groundwater abstraction from confined aquifers for river regulation.
35. Morel, E. H. 1980 *Q. J. eng. Geol.*, 13, 153, The use of a numerical model in the management of the Chalk aquifer in the Upper Thames Basin.
36. Reeves, M. J. *et al* 1974 "Groundwater resources of the Vale of York", Water Resources Board, Reading.
37. Skinner, A. C. 1977 *Memoires Int. Assoc. Hydrogeol.*, 13, A1, Groundwater in the regional water supply strategy of the English Midlands.
38. Great Ouse River Authority 1974 "Some aspects of the ecology of the River Thet".
39. Brereton, N. R. and Downing, R. A. 1975 *Water Services*, 79, 91, Some applications of thermal infra-red linescan in water resources studies.
40. University of Reading 1975 "Ecological study of the River Lambourn".
41. Severn-Trent Water Authority 1977 "Shropshire groundwater. Report of the investigation and proposals for development".
42. Central Water Planning Unit 1978 "Recent developments in ecological studies of chalk streams", Appendix A, Annual Report for 1977-78.
43. Kenyon, W. J. and Hibbert, J. A. 1974 *Water Services*, 78, 154, The Upper Wylye investigation.
44. Birtles, A. B. 1977 *Memoires Int. Assoc. Hydrogéol.* 13, D32, Siting of groundwater abstractions for river regulation.
45. Nutbrown, D. A., Downing, R. A. and Monkhouse, R. A. 1975 *J. Hydrol.*, 27, 127, The use of a digital model in the management of the Chalk aquifer in the South Downs, England.
46. Reeves, M. J. 1974 "A preliminary study of the relationship between cost and well-field design in the Great Ouse Chalk groundwater development", Tech. Note No. 4, Central Water Planning Unit, Reading.
47. Eastwood, J. C., Kenyon, W. J. and Wilkinson, W. B. 1977 Seminar on Ecology and Management of Chalk Streams, University of Reading, "Sealing river beds and its relevance to the development of groundwater resources—with particular reference to the Gussage stream".
48. Hadfield, C. 1968 "The Canal Age", David and Charles, Newton Abbot, Devon.
49. Birtles, A. B. and Morel, E. H. 1980 *J. Hydrol.*, 48-197, Factors affecting cost optimisation of groundwater development schemes for river regulation.
50. Backshall, W. F., Downing, R. A. and Law, F. M. 1972 *Wat. and Wat. Eng.*, 76, 215, Great Ouse groundwater study.

51. Owen, M. 1981 'The Thames Groundwater Scheme' in J. W. Lloyd (Ed), "Case-studies in groundwater resources evaluation", Clarendon Press, Oxford.
52. Institution of Civil Engineers 1978 "Thames Groundwater Scheme" Institution of Civil Engineers, London.
53. Connorton, B. J. and Reed, R. N. 1978 *Q. J. eng. Geol.*, 11, 127, A numerical model for the prediction of long-term well yield in an unconfined Chalk aquifer.
54. Gray, D. A., Allender, R. and Lovelock, P. E. R. 1969 "The groundwater hydrology of the Yorkshire Ouse River Basin", Hydrogeological Report No. 4, Inst. Geol. Sci., London.
55. Law, F. 1965 *J. IWE.*, 19, 413, Integrated use of diverse resources.
56. Walsh, P. D. 1976 *J. Hydrol.*, 28, 215, Investigation into the yield of an existing surface reservoir and aquifer system.
57. Southern Water Authority 1979 "Lagoon recharge experiments at Church Farm, Hardham, Sussex".
58. Warren, S. C. 1962 *Proc. Soc. Wat. Treat. Exam.*, 11, 38, Some notes on an investigation into sea water infiltration.
59. Green, F. N. 1964 *Proc. Soc. Wat. Treat. Exam.*, 13, 4, A method of water conservation and automation.
60. Nutbrown, D. A. 1976 *J. Hydrol.*, 31, 271, Optimal pumping regimes in an unconfined coastal aquifer.
61. Nutbrown, D. A. 1976 "Optimum development of combined resources", Central Water Planning Unit, Reading.
62. Nutbrown, D. A. 1976 *J. Hydrol.*, 31, 57, A model study of the effects of artificial recharge.
63. Blair, A. H. 1970 "Artificial recharge of groundwater", Tech. Pub. 75, Water Research Association, Medmenham.
64. Edworthy, K. J. and Downing, R. A. 1979 *J. IWES*, 33, 151, Artificial groundwater recharge and its relevance in Britain.
65. Edworthy, K. J., Headworth, H. G. and Hawnt, R. J. E. 1981 'Application of artificial recharge techniques in the UK' in "A Survey of British Hydrogeology 1980", The Royal Society, London.
66. Monkhouse, R. A. and Phillips, S. 1978 "The design, construction and maintenance of recharge wells", Technical Note No. 25, Central Water Planning Unit, Reading.
67. Bichara, A. F. 1974 University of Strathclyde, PhD Thesis, "An experimental study of long-term artificial recharge of groundwater into confined aquifers using wells".
68. Edworthy, K. J. 1978 "Artificial recharge through a borehole", Tech. Rep. 86, Water Research Centre, Medmenham.
69. Zoeteman, B. C., Hrubec, J. and Brinkman, F. J. 1976 *J. IWE.*, 30, 123, The Veluwe artifical recharge plan. Water quality aspects.
70. Hawnt, R. J. E., Joseph, J. B. and Flavin, R. J. 1981 *J. IWES*, 35, 437, Experience with borehole recharge in the Lee Valley.
71. Boniface, E. S. 1959 *Proc. ICE*, 14, 325, Some experiments in artificial recharge in the lower Lee Valley.
72. Water Resources Board 1973 "Artificial recharge of the London Basin, III Economic and engineering desk studies".
73. Water Resources Board 1974 "Artificial recharge of the London Basin, IV Pilot recharge works in the Lee Valley".
74. Satchell, R. L. H. and Edworthy, K. J. 1972 "Artificial recharge: Bunter Sandstone". Water Resources Board, Reading.
75. Land, D. H. 1966 "The hydrogeology of the Triassic sandstones in the Birmingham-Lichfield district". Hydrogeological Rep. No. 2, Geol. Surv. Gt Brit.
76. Mersey and Weaver River Authority 1969 "First Periodical Survey".
77. Gray, D. A. 1964 "Groundwater conditions of the Chalk of the Grimsby area, Lincolnshire", Research Rep. No. 1, Water Supply Papers, Geol. Surv. Gt Brit.
78. Santing, G. 1957 "The groundwater in the coastal plain as a source of water supply", Pub. No. 23, Water Planning for Israel Ltd., Tel Aviv.
79. Bostock, C. K., Simpson, E. S. and Roefs, T. G. 1977 *Wat. Res. Res.*, 13, 420, Minimising costs in well field design in relation to aquifer models.
80. Stoner, R. F., Milne, D. M. and Lund, P. J. *Q. J. eng. Geol.* 12, 63, Economic design of wells.
81. Burt, O. R. 1967 *Wat. Res. Res.*, 3, 45, Temporal allocation of groundwater.
82. Domenico, P. A., Anderson, D. V. and Case, C. M. 1968. *Wat. Res. Res.*, 4, 247, Optimal groundwater mining.
83. Rodda, J. C., Downing, R. A. and Law, F. M. 1976 "Systematic Hydrology", Newnes-Butterworth, London.

Chapter 15

GROUNDWATER POLLUTION AND PROTECTION

1. INTRODUCTION

THE TERMS "pollution" and "contamination" are often used in a confusing manner. In this chapter "pollution" is defined as a degree of contamination with respect to a certain constituent, beyond which the use of groundwater for a given purpose is unsuitable. The limiting degree of contamination or the standard used, may be fixed for drinking[1], for irrigation or possibly for industrial use. This chapter covers both contamination and pollution; the identification and measurement of undesirable changes in physical, chemical, microbiological, or radiological properties both below and above the relevant standard.

For a surface water body, it is often easy to identify deterioration in quality; there may be an effect on the biota, or possibly some other clear visual indication. Furthermore, because the effects are often quickly identified, countermeasures may be rapidly applied. Groundwater differs from surface waters in a number of important respects which make changes in quality much more difficult to identify and measure and far more difficult to control.

Groundwater is not easily accessible, causes of quality change are often not clear even under natural undisturbed conditions and, because of the relatively large storage capacity of aquifers, the time lapse between cause and effect may extend to decades. A further obstacle to understanding groundwater quality changes is the natural variability of aquifers, which is comparable to that found in other natural systems. Recognition of the natural quality variations, or baseline quality, of an aquifer is an essential prerequisite to assessing the degree of contamination.

The principal recharge to aquifers in the British Isles is from rainfall. In pre-industrial times, the rainfall contamination would have been largely limited to traces of salts of marine origin. Today however, observations show that a much larger range of potential groundwater contaminants—for example, organic pesticides, can be identified in atmospheric water[2]. These are most abundant in the developed countries, but there is increasing evidence that atmospheric circulation is capable of effecting world-wide distribution. It is clear therefore that this form of contamination has no respect for international boundaries and is not amenable to easy or effective control. For this reason, it is sensible to regard this part of the groundwater contamination load as the practical baseline against which local pollution should be identified, measured and assessed.

As a further example, the compound trichloro-fluoromethane, which is entirely man-made, has been identified and used as a groundwater tracer in the USA. The use of this compound as an aerosol propellant started in 1943; between 1955-1975 the production of the chemical doubled every 4 years. A proportion of the chemical is taken up by atmospheric water and because it is entirely man-made, and extremely resistant to degradation, its distribution and concentrations can be a useful form of chemical label for groundwater[3]. Particulate matter, which too may be slightly soluble, is also abundant in an industrial environment and this 'fall-out' may make yet another contribution to the dissolved solids load in infiltrating water.

During infiltration, the dissolved solids in water may be concentrated as a result of evapotranspirative losses and also undergo chemical and possibly biological reactions before reaching the water table. The nature of these changes in glacial deposits over the Bunter Sandstone in the Vale of York has been reported[4]. In this instance numerous chemical processes were identified, with evaporative concentra-

TABLE 15.I.   Water Quality Changes during Infiltration
(from Spears and Reeves[4]; in mg/l)

	Rainwater (Leeds) median	Porewater median (mean)	Groundwater median (mean)
Na^+	2.3	15 (19)	13 (38)
K^+	0.5	4 (5)	2 (4)
Ca^{2+}	2.7	71 (71)	89 (152)
Mg^{2+}	1.0	18 (27)	22 (37)
SO_4^{2-}	12	170 (193)	76 (256)
Cl^-	5.3	33 (58)	22 (42)

tion affecting the levels of chloride, sodium and possibly potassium (Table 15.I).

At the water-table, recharge water moves along smooth flow-lines down the hydraulic gradient to the point of discharge. Under natural conditions the rate of groundwater flow is normally extremely slow; in the typical Bunter Sandstone, for example, an intergranular flow rate of 30 mm/day would be typical. In a fractured aquifer, however, the rates of flow may be at least an order of magnitude higher. The continuous and long-term interaction between the groundwater and aquifer means that a condition of dynamic chemical equilibrium is set up. Between recharge and discharge a pattern of groundwater quality develops, which is mainly determined by the nature and complexity of the aquifer and the rate of groundwater flow. Examples of the type of pattern which develops have been found in the study of the Lincolnshire Limestone and other aquifers[5].

The concept of chemical facies in groundwater is covered in Chapter 3 and only briefly touched upon here to illustrate the intrinsic natural variability of groundwater quality. An established chemical facies pattern can be sustained, provided natural flows are not interrupted or distorted. The pumping of groundwater may cause serious disturbance to flow with locally accelerated movement of groundwater and the inducing of vertical flow around and beneath the well. The interplay of pumping rate, well-depth and construction, and existing water quality distribution may lead to variations within a small area. Groundwaters from a number of public supply wells in the Lower Greensand near Cambridge illustrate this phenomenon (Fig. 15.1). Over a period of time, the distortions due to pumping may extend deep into an aquifer, leading to complete disruption of the natural water quality pattern, which may be a serious problem if saline or brackish water is drawn upwards. Hence, the rate of change of groundwater quality with time can also be a significant factor and must be carefully considered in the analysis of sets of chemical data.

Groundwater resource development may completely reverse hydraulic gradients, so that rivers or other surface water may become influent instead of receiving groundwater. Where the rivers are of poorer quality, contamination of ground-water can occur. Such contamination is, however, incidental in the sense that it is principally due to poorly planned groundwater development. The most serious

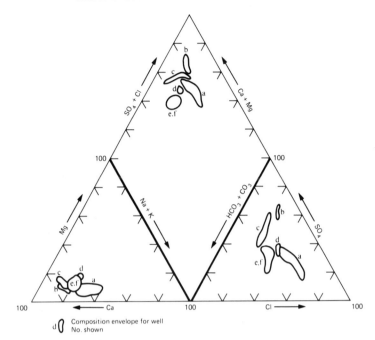

Fig. 15.1.   Local variation in groundwater quality in the Lower Greensand at a pumping station near Cambridge (all wells within 200 m radius)

groundwater contamination in the developed world results from other forms of bad planning outside the sphere of water resource development, such as uncontrolled waste disposal, accidental spills and discharges, large-scale land-use changes, or atmospheric fall-out.

Finally, the distinction is made in this chapter between point and diffuse (also known as dispersed or non-point) sources of pollution. The former sources are those discrete areas such as landfills, areas of effluent disposal or large-scale accidental spills from which contamination may be assumed, or demonstrated, to originate. Diffuse sources are those in which potential contaminants are derived from large, ill-defined areas, the principal example being the loss of nutrients and agrochemicals from farming. The distinction between the two classes is not always rigid. For example, on the regional or large catchment scale the multiplicity of small point sources such as leaking sewers, spillages at industrial premises etc, which are characteristic of established urban areas, may be considered as a type of diffuse pollution.

2. GROUNDWATER QUALITY MONITORING

Monitoring System Design

It is the rule rather than the exception that arrangements for monitoring groundwater quality are inadequate[6]. The number of observation holes is either too small or has been established on a grid-pattern which bears no relationship to the need for information from different areas. The most serious underlying deficiency in the planning process has frequently been an inadequate understanding of the hydrogeology, whether for a small site evaluation or for regional surveillance. A step by step approach to planning a monitoring system on the following lines is recommended. Whenever possible hydrometric and quality networks should be devised and operated as one and the following points refer to both:

(1) Agree on the objectives of the monitoring.
(2) Define hydrogeological regime in response to current use.
(3) Obtain groundwater use data in terms of pumping rates and distribution, particularly public water supplies.
(4) Identify actual and potential pollution sources and potential pollutants (rates and quantities).
(5) Evaluate pollution hazards vis-à-vis the existing pattern of groundwater use.
(6) Establish basic monitoring network and sampling and water-level measuring schedule.
(7) Periodically review the effectiveness of the basic system, amend network density and sampling and measurement schedules and frequencies.

It is not practicable to monitor all possible sources of pollution; the strategy should concentrate on defining the most important ones. The emphasis placed on each of the above steps will vary from place to place, depending on hydrology, population, density, geology, industrial activity etc. The geologist, hydrogeologist, well engineer, chemist, data manager, and modeller may be ultimately concerned with the use of data and their needs should be incorporated at an early stage.

The economic value of groundwater also varies, but is often considerable if replacement costs are considered, and there is a need to consider the balance between these costs and those of establishing and operating a monitoring network.

The operating costs of a monitoring network, including the sampling, measuring, analysis, and archiving, also need to be reviewed regularly in the light of any amended objectives for the scheme. Ideally the review should also be multi-disciplinary. Occurrence of pollution may require specific analysis at a much increased frequency, for example. A comparison which includes the operating costs of a network has been considered[6].

Monitoring System Operation

During the initial assessment period, sampling should be relatively frequent and a wide range of analyses carried out. This period should last for at least a year although other factors may dictate a different period. At the end of this time the data should be reviewed critically to assess both seasonal and random variations in quality parameters in space and time. When the range of variations has been established, it may prove possible to reduce the frequency of sampling and the range of analyses carried out, so that a relatively small number of determinations are made on a regular basis. However, it would be recommended that a more complete analysis be carried out on an annual basis, to include the following determinands:

Calcium	Iron	Chloride
Magnesium	Manganese	Sulphate
Sodium	Cadmium	Nitrate
Potassium	Chromium	Carbonate/Bicarbonate
	Copper	
	Lead	
	Zinc	

$$\left.\begin{array}{l} \text{pH} \\ \text{Temperature} \\ \text{Electrical Conductivity} \\ \text{Dissolved Oxygen} \end{array}\right\} \text{Field Analyses}$$

Where specific contaminants are known to exist these should be identifed, and then quantified. In many cases an 'indicator' constituent is adequate; for example, boron may be used to indicate sewage and total organic carbon to indicate other organic chemical contamination.

Because of the errors associated with emplacement and use of sampling equipment, and then with the processes of sampling and storage, a call for high accuracy in routine analysis is seldom justifiable. It must be borne in mind that precision is costly; to ask for twice the precision may more than double the cost. In any event change is what is looked for, so comparability rather than absolute accuracy should be the aim.

The frequency of long-term monitoring and the distribution of sampling points has to be geared to specific conditions but for public supplies or near known major pollution hazards weekly or even daily analysis may be appropriate.

3. GROUNDWATER POLLUTION EVALUATION

Groundwater pollution investigations differ from resources studies in that only a small volume of aquifer is normally involved, rather than a large catchment, although this may not be the case when a diffuse source of pollution is implicated. In general the investigation, evaluation or monitoring of groundwater pollution is focused on specific pollution incidents or potential areas of pollution within a larger area. In all cases, drilling plays an important role in recovering samples of rock and groundwater[7] but a whole range of geophysical methods and other remote techniques are also applicable in many cases (Chapters 8 and 9). In the following section the main techniques of evaluation and investigation are described.

When pollution of groundwater is discovered the main question to answer concerns the origin of the pollutant. In an urban setting it may be difficult to identify without determining groundwater flow direction and mapping the volume of polluted aquifer in more detail.

Three wells drilled in a triangular configuration, preferably to the same level in the aquifer, will allow the local groundwater gradient and flow direction to be estimated. In anisotropic aquifers, considerable distortion of flow lines from the theoretical distribution may occur[8], especially in the vicinity of abstraction points.

The following additional questions then may have to be answered:

(a) What is the pattern of the pollution both with respect to area and depth?
(b) How will the problem develop and how long will it last?

A complete investigation to evaluate the pollution may require additional boreholes to allow cores, depth samples or geophysical logs to be taken. Drilling is comparatively expensive and careful preplanning to optimize data acquisition is essential.

EXPLORATORY DRILLING

Depending on the strata, cores may be taken by percussion or rotary equipment. If samples of porewater or of the rock itself are to be subjected to chemical analysis, there are clearly restrictions on the type of drilling medium which can be used (Table 15.II). If laboratory determinations of physical properties of the rock or the chemical composition of porewaters are to be made the use of water or mud as a drilling medium is generally not acceptable. Air-drilling is more generally acceptable for coring to obtain samples for physical, hydraulic or chemical analysis of the rock, or chemical analysis of groundwater (porewater), and is widely used where sampling is important.

TABLE 15.II.   Summary of Suitability of Various Drilling Methods for Core Sampling

Drilling medium	Types of core analysis required		
	Whole rock chemical/ mineralogical	Physical and hydraulic	Porewater
Mud	B[1]	C	C
Water	B[1]	C	C
Mist	B	C	C
Air	A	A	A[2]
None	A	B[3]	A

Suitability of samples
A—Suitable   1. Core invaded by clay
B—Of restricted value   2. Some isotopic determinations not valid
C—Unsuitable   3. Compaction can cause problems

Boreholes of 150 mm diameter are adequate for most purposes; details of the methods of drilling and construction of such holes are given in Chapter 13.

If automatic water-level recording is to be carried out then 150 mm diameter would be a minimum; in an accurately vertical borehole this would allow float and counterbalance to operate without restriction. To allow for deviation from the vertical, a larger diameter is desirable, especially where the water table is deep. Pressure transducer equipment which has no moving parts avoids this problem.

Acquisition of core samples from the unsaturated zone is subject to some special difficulties. To facilitate drilling, and avoid overheating, a fluid may have to be used which introduces contamination by penetrating deeply into the dry or only partly saturated strata. Even with the use of a drilling fluid, shallow strata may be too poorly consolidated to sample. However, if the unsaturated zone is relatively thin (say less than 5 m) and the strata are not hard, inexpensive rock sampling by hand-augering may be feasible[7].

GROUNDWATER SAMPLING

Traditionally, groundwater has been sampled by bailing from the upper part of the water column in the borehole, or alternatively by using the pump discharge which effectively gives a composite sample from the full saturated depth. There are other methods however (Fig. 15.2) which should be considered for pollution evaluations. Some of the salient features of these other techniques are compared with the above, in Table 15.III.

Depth Sampling

The simplest types of depth sampler are cylinders which allow restricted throughflow during emplacement. The spring-loaded end-caps are then triggered mechanically or electrically from the surface and the sample recovered. A one-way valve allows water to flow into the "gas-ejection" type depth samplers and pressure

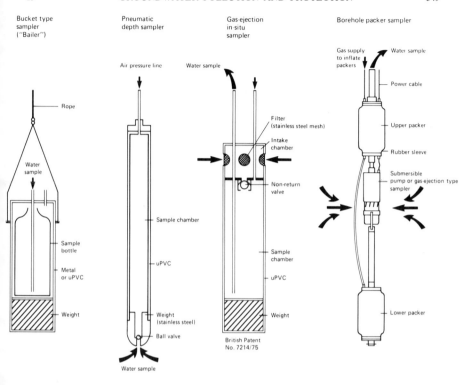

Fig. 15.2. Groundwater sampling methods (after Naylor *et al*[7])

is applied to one tube to evacuate a sample through the other. Chemical changes can be induced in the water sample by pressure during ejection and by the inadvertent escape of gas through the sampler into the aquifer. The extent and nature of such changes depend on many factors but mainly on the gas used.

Pumped Water Samples

For regional groundwater appraisal pumped samples provide a form of 'integrated' sample from the full thickness of the aquifer penetrated. Under stagnant conditions in the water column, chemical changes may take place due to the interaction of groundwater with the screen or casing, with cement or bentonite exposed to contact with groundwater, or with the atmosphere. When pumping starts (or an artesian well is uncapped), two main processes occur; the various parts of the aquifer are forced to attain a new equilibrium with the new water level or piezometric pressure, and the 'stagnant' water in the well is discharged. Samples taken soon after discharge begins may not, therefore, reflect accurately the quality of active water present in the aquifer. Examples of this effect in the Lincolnshire Limestone have been described[9]. With precautions, however, it is possible to obtain reliable continuous measurements of quality parameters from pumped supplies.

TABLE 15.III. Comparison of Groundwater Sampling Methods

	Ease of use (a)	Relative cost (b)	Advantages	Drawbacks
Bailed	1	2	Easy operation.	Samples only the top of the water column, which is subject to change. Interpretation difficult or impossible.
Depth sample ("messenger")	2	2	Allows some depth discrimination in water column.	Disturbs water column; samples artificial regime in borehole, at best.
Depth samples (pneumatic, electrical or gas-injection)	3	3	Allows some depth discrimination in water column.	Minimal disturbance; also samples artificial regime in borehole. Pressure can affect samples.
Pump discharge	2	1	Composite sample gives a type of regional value of quality.	Composition of sample a function of heads of contributing aquifers.
Pore-water	4	4	Detailed and specific in terms of narrow depth intervals.	May not be typical sample where fracture flow is important.
In situ	2	2-3	As above.	Requires good knowledge of profile to allow accurate and most useful location.
Inflatable packer	3-4	3	As above. Also hydraulic testing is possible.	As above. Uncertainty over inflatable seal.

Notes: (a) 1. Simple   3. Fairly difficult   (b) 1. Very cheap   3. Significant cost
          2. Fairly simple   4. Difficult   2. Not expensive   4. Very expensive

Inflatable Packer

Single or double packer devices are available, in a range of sizes and several different types of pump for sampling between the packers are available[7,10]. Using detailed information from the borehole, a packer sampler can be placed against an aquifer interval or against a fracture zone. This sampling method is of course not suitable for use in screened holes. Accurate placement is clearly essential and the seal between the packers and the borehole face has to be good. Boreholes which are unlined are normally irregular, and often extremely irregular with cavities and other small-scale roughness; the reliability of the seal should if possible be checked or downhole TV survey carried out prior to emplacement.

Where the sampled interval is thin (3-5 m), a low rate of pumping is sufficient and an adaptation of the gas-ejector depth-sampler has been found suitable[7]. An added benefit of using inflatable packers is that both sampling and aquifer testing can be done at the same time.

Porewater Sampling

The technique of centrifuging water from saturated rock is now well established, partly as a result of the methods and procedures developed by Edmunds and Bath[11] and partly due to the wider use and availability of high-speed centrifuges. Specially designed containers allow water spun from rock to be collected, albeit in relatively small volumes, for analysis.

As indicated in Table 15.III it is possible to obtain very detailed information from porewater but it is necessary to obtain good core samples to start with. The full process is involved, time-consuming and expensive and is neither appropriate nor necessary for most site evaluations.

Other methods for obtaining porewater include squeezing, leaching with deionized or distilled water, and displacement by compressed gas; these methods are best considered as research techniques.

In situ Samples

Prevention of groundwater movement within a borehole can contribute substantially to the acquisition of better samples. An adaptation of the gas-ejection sampler can be installed and sealed at one or more depths in a borehole. It is possible to obtain discrete samples on demand simply by pressurizing one of the connecting tubes. Experience in the use of this technique and a number of variants of it are given by Edworthy and Baxter[12]. Its use avoids the dangers of interaction of groundwater, particularly when polluted, with the atmosphere or of mixing within a borehole. It therefore allows depth-specific sampling and is easily adaptable for automatic operation.

THE UNSATURATED ZONE

The zone above the water table is often referred to as the unsaturated zone, zone of aeration or the vadose zone. It can vary in thickness from a metre or less, to many tens of metres and is an interval within which many important hydro-geological processes occur. When pollution occurs some of the natural processes that occur may be overloaded and become saturated while some may be accelerated greatly. The unsaturated zone is, however, a very important physical and chemical "buffer" protecting groundwater in the saturated zone. The storage capacity available is an important property which can retain potential contaminants for long enough to allow degradation to occur, or to reduce peak concentrations which reach the water table. Adsorption and ion-exchange capacity may be beneficial in some situations, while calcium carbonate may serve to neutralize acidic pollutants.

The early warning value of taking samples from the unsaturated zone may be very high in the vicinity of a landfill or other concentrated waste storage. Equally it may also be high where the groundwater is for public supply.

Conditions of saturation vary both as a function of depth to the water table, pore size distributions and rates of infiltration. The ease with which samples of infiltrating water can be obtained depends on the grain-size, sorting and many other features of the strata but there are some methods which are available. In fine-grained strata such as the Chalk, the level of saturation is normally such that samples can be obtained by centrifuging[11]. Porous ceramic suction-cup tensio-meters, as commonly used in soil-science studies, have been employed successfully in many pollution investigations. There are drawbacks, however, in that bacteria and viruses may be "strained out" or adsorbed by the ceramic element, or some of the chemical constituents subjected to change by passage through the porous cup. Although samples are continuously available in principle, the rate of flow may be very small and it is often difficult to obtain samples of the required volume fast enough to avoid deterioration before analysis. Furthermore, the suction which has to be applied, which must contribute to the chemical problems referred to above, is normally limited to -0.8 atmospheres.

The composition of pore gases within the unsaturated zone also changes in response to infiltration of polluting matter. Oxygen is consumed, and carbon dioxide, carbon monoxide, nitrogen and methane may be produced. Regular monitoring of these gases is a potentially valuable method for use above the water table.

GEOPHYSICAL METHODS

The use of geophysics for general groundwater applications is described in Chapters 8 and 9. All of these techniques can be extremely useful for defining geological features and helping to indicate how a pollutant might move in relation to local anisotropy due to stratification, faulting or facies changes. Polluted groundwater may affect the electrical or physical properties of an aquifer but the only practically detectable effects are those due to a substantial increase in conductivity, temperature or radioactivity.

Geophysical techniques permit the repeated measurement of certain properties of the aquifer and groundwater at costs far below those incurred by repeated drilling and sampling. They should therefore be applied where possible, as methods of monitoring the movement of polluted groundwaters. It is strongly recommended that a geophysical specialist should be consulted at the planning stage of all groundwater contamination investigations.

4. GROUNDWATER POLLUTION BY POINT SOURCES

POINT SOURCES OF POLLUTION

The principal potential source of pollution to water resources arises from the landfill disposal of wastes. Approximately 100 million tonnes of controlled wastes, that is household, industrial and commercial wastes as defined in Section 30 of the Control of Pollution Act 1974, are produced annually in the United Kingdom, of which over 90 per cent are deposited in landfills[13]. Of this total, about 22 million tonnes are composed of the mixture of household and commercial wastes collected by local authorities and sometimes referred to as municipal solid wastes and 74 million tonnes are of industrial origin, but are not classified as dangerous or intractable. It is estimated[14] that 4.4 million tonnes of hazardous industrial wastes arise annually in England and Wales, of which 1.7 million are in such a form as to require special handling and disposal procedures as defined in Section 17 of the Control of Pollution Act 1974. The disposal route for 85 per cent (3.7 million tonnes) of the hazardous wastes is to landfill, the remainder being subjected to chemical treatment, solidification, mineshaft disposal, incineration or disposal to sea. The hazardous waste arisings in Scotland are estimated to be about 200 000 tonnes annually.

In 1984, disposal of controlled wastes was to a total of 4 200 licensed landfills in England and Wales, of which 1 145 were authorised for the receipt of hazardous wastes. In Scotland, 17 sites were licensed for hazardous wastes. The great majority of sites licensed to accept hazardous wastes are operated by private contractors.

As well as the consented discharge of effluents to surface waters, approximately 150 000 m^3 of sewage effluents are discharged daily to soakaway systems in the Chalk aquifer, 128 000 m^3 to the Triassic Sandstone aquifer and 78 000 m^3 to minor aquifers[15]. Disposal of sewage sludge to landfills amounts to about 250 000 tonnes per year.

In addition to the main point sources outlined above, localized pollution may arise from the accidental loss of liquids, often hydrocarbons or other organic compounds, as the result of spillages in transit, from pipelines or from leaking storage facilities. The total annual loss is difficult to quantify, but it has been estimated[16] that at least 1500 m^3 of oil products are released annually into the environment in the United Kingdom.

Besides the controlled wastes, a further 70 million tonnes of mine and quarry wastes and iron and steel slags, which are not subject to the Control of Pollution Act 1974, arise annually in Britain. In many cases these wastes are deposited, or stored within the curtilage of the quarry or foundry, or employed as civil engineering fill.

CHARACTERISTICS OF POLLUTION FROM POINT SOURCES

Introduction

The threat of solid wastes to water resources arises from the formation of polluting liquors, known as leachates. Leachates are formed by liquids, principally water, which percolate through the wastes and which become charged with potential pollutants by the direct solution of certain compounds and by soluble degradation products resulting from chemical and biochemical reactions within the wastes. The total quantity of potential pollutants in a given mass of wastes is finite and progressive leaching gives rise to changes in leachate composition as the wastes age. At the same time, the rate of production of leachate may vary, both in response to seasonal variations in infiltration rates, and to changes in the infiltration resulting from landfill site management practices, such as the progressive capping of completed sections of fill.

A high proportion of the 74 million tonnes of industrial waste produced annually is composed of relatively inert materials (including building rubble) which contain only small amounts of soluble inorganic substances or degradable components. By contrast, the annual 22 million tonnes of municipal solid waste contain both soluble and readily degradable substances and may give rise to a highly polluting leachate. This section therefore considers the ranges in leachate composition which may be anticipated from:

(i)   solid municipal waste disposal;
(ii) the co-disposal of industrial wastes with solid municipal wastes;
(iii) leachates from sites receiving only industrial wastes; and
(iv) direct disposal of effluents to aquifers, and accidental spills.

Finally, because leachates are characterized by both strength and volume, the problem of estimating leachate production rates is considered.

Leachate from Municipal Solid Wastes

The composition of municipal solid wastes reflects the changing lifestyle of the society producing the wastes. Table 15.IV illustrates the changes which have occurred during the 30 year period since the mid-1950s. The principal changes to be noted are:

(1) A decrease in the proportion of fine screenings, which would include a high proportion of the ash from solid fuel heating. The first two columns of the table illustrate the significant difference in ash content between wastes collected during the summer and winter periods.

(2) An increase in the proportion of cellulosic materials (paper and cardboard), reflecting the increase in pre-packaging of many products.

(3) The appearance of plastics as wastes. By comparison, the proportion of vegetable and putrescible material, metals, glass and textiles has remained essentially constant.

TABLE 15.IV. Comparative Composition of Municipal Solid Wastes
(as percentages by weight)

Description	Sept 1955	Jan 1956	1974	1980
Screenings below 2 cm	28	56	20	6
Vegetable and putrescible	24	18	21	22
Paper and cardboard	19	13	27	36
Metal	7	4	9	7
Textiles	2	1	4	5
Glass	8	6	10	12
Plastics	nil	nil	6	4
Bone and cinders	7	trace	—	—
Non-combustile debris	2	2	} 8	} 8
Combustible debris				
Source	MHLG[17]		DoE[18]	Barber, Maris and Johnson[19]

TABLE 15.V. Stages of Putrescible Waste Decomposition

Stage	Principal reactions	Landfill gas/leachate	Duration of stage
Aerobic	Breakdown of proteins, carbohydrates and liquids to aminoacids, simple sugars, glycerol and long-chain volatile acids by aerobic bacteria.	Reducing oxygen, increasing carbon dioxide, nitrogen relatively constant. Leachate production limited.	Generally short; weeks or few months.
Acetogenic (anoxic)	Production of short chain volatile acids, hydrogen, carbon dioxide by anaerobic breakdown of products of first stage. Solubilization of metals.	Significant carbon dioxide increase, displacing nitrogen. Gaseous hydrogen and ammonia. Strong leachate with high concentration of volatile acids, ammonia, chloride, sulphates, certain metals.	May be prolonged, depending on moisture content.
Acetogenic (anoxic)	Reduction of short chain volatile acids to acetate by anaerobic bacteria.	Continued high strength leachate, acidogenic stage.	Overlaps and may co-exist with acidogenic stage.
Methanogenic (anaerobic)	Breakdown of acetate to methane and carbon dioxide.	Atmosphere principally methane and carbon dioxide. Leachate reduced in organic strength.	Probably relatively long term (years) once achieved.

Although direct solution of inorganic compounds and elements (chloride, sulphate, sodium, potassium etc.) may occur from the ash and other solids present within the wastes, the principal pollutant load arises from the microbial degradation of the putrescible components, and the interactions between the leachate so produced and the other components of the waste. The stages through which such wastes may pass is summarized in Table 15.V. During the first stage, which may have commenced prior to final disposal of the wastes to landfill, the readily degradable components of the waste are attacked by aerobic micro-organisms, which may multiply rapidly, consuming the atmospheric oxygen trapped within the wastes. The metabolism of the aerobic bacteria raises the temperature of the wastes and this, together with the carbon dioxide respired by the bacteria, gives rise to weakly acidic conditions which encourage solution of certain materials in the wastes.

Due to the slow rate at which atmospheric oxygen can diffuse into the wastes from the surface, the aerobic phase of decomposition is generally of short duration and is essentially completed when the atmosphere within the waste mass consists of residual atmospheric nitrogen and carbon dioxide from microbial respiration. The subsequent stages take place under anoxic conditions. Anaerobic bacteria supersede the aerobic forms, breaking down the large organic molecules into simpler components. The first stage of anaerobic degradation is marked by the continued production of carbon dioxide, accompanied by hydrogen and ammonia, the latter resulting from the breakdown of proteins, and the production of large quantities of volatile fatty acids (acetic, propionic, butyric, valeric and caproic acids). It is the high concentrations of these acids which give municipal solid waste leachate its high pollution potential and which further encourage the dissolution of metals and other components of the wastes. This period of volatile fatty acid production is known as the acidogenic phase and is superseded by an acetogenic stage in which the bacteria further degrade the higher molecular weight acids to acetate.

The anaerobic decomposition of waste is sensitive to moisture content and, particularly in dry landfills, the acidogenic and acetogenic phases may persist for up to 10 years after disposal of the wastes[20]. The final phase of anaerobic digestion is that of methanogenesis, during which strictly anaerobic bacteria convert the previously formed acetate to methane and carbon dioxide, to produce a leachate relatively low in organic strength. Methanogenic bacteria are inhibited by acidic conditions and are therefore suppressed during the acid-forming stages. In turn, the speed at which degradation of wastes proceeds towards methanogenesis is influenced by the moisture content of the wastes. Wastes as received for landfill often contain between 25 and 35 per cent by weight of water, whereas optimal methane production takes place at between 50 and 60 per cent water content. It is possible that landfills to which ingress of water is restricted by suitable site engineering works (see Section 6) may remain in the acidogenic/acetogenic stages and not reach fully methanogenic conditions.

The progressive changes in leachate composition which take place with increasing time since deposit of the waste (ageing) were first examined in detail in experiments carried out in the mid-1950s by the MHLG[17]. Table 15.VI[20] compares the leachate from freshly placed wastes (column 1), in which the wastes are in the acidogenic phase, with leachate from an aged waste (column 2), from which a great proportion of the organic load has been removed by leaching, but in which the high levels of ammonia reflect continued biological activity.

The absolute decrease in organic strength, as measured by BOD and COD values, is also normally accompanied, during ageing, by an increase in the COD:BOD ratio, indicating that a higher proportion of the remaining dissolved organic compounds are of types relatively resistant to microbial degradation. Column 3 of Table 15.VI contrasts the leachate produced by wastes with a high water content, in the fully methanogenic phase. The low values of organic contaminants (COD, BOD, TOC, volatile acids) indicate efficient conversion to landfill gas (methane and carbon dioxide) whilst the high ammonia levels result from intense anaerobic biological activity.

In the majority of landfills, wastes at different points in the ageing process coexist

TABLE 15.VI.   **Composition of Leachates from Municipal Solid Wastes**
(from DoE[20]; in mg/l except pH value)

Determinand	Fresh wastes	Aged wastes	Wastes with high moisture content
pH	6.2	7.5	8.0
COD (Chemical oxygen demand)	23 800	1 160	1 500
BOD (Biochemical oxygen demand)	11 900	260	500
TOC (Total organic carbon)	8 000	465	450
Volatile acids (as C)	5 688	5	12
NH_3-N	790	370	1 000
NO_3-N	3	1	1
Ortho-P	0.7	1.4	1
Cl	1 315	2 080	1 390
Na	960	1 300	1 900
Mg	252	185	186
K	780	590	570
Ca	1 820	250	158
Mn	27	2	trace
Fe	540	23	2
Ni	0.6	0.1	0.2
Cu	0.1	<0.1	—
Zn	22	0.4	0.5
Pb	0.4	0.1	—

and the overall quality of the leachate reflects a mixture of fresh and aged wastes, often modified by dilution with surface run-off from the landfill surface. A survey of the quality of leachate from 23 municipal solid waste sites[21] showed organic strength ranging from 11 600 mg/l COD, 7 250 mg/l BOD from wastes at a one year old landfill, to 125 mg/l COD, 4 mg/l BOD from a 12 year old site. In both cases dilution by surface waters was suspected.

Estimates of the total polluting load which may be leached from solid municipal wastes were made by the MHLG[17] for crude wastes tipped under both wet (saturated) and dry (normal infiltration with under-drainage) conditions (Table 15.VII).

TABLE 15.VII.   **Removal of Pollutants in Leachate from Municipal Solid Wastes, over a Two Year Period**
(from MHLG[17]; in kg/tonne waste)

Determinands	Dry conditions	Wet conditions
BOD	2.3	4.6
TOC	1.5	3.1
NH_3	0.3	0.5
Cl	0.9	1.3
SO_4	1.1	0.8

Concentrations of organic contaminants (BOD, TOC and ammonia) during the final year of the experiment were very low compared with those of the earlier years and it was concluded that a very high proportion of the available contaminants had been removed. By comparison, chloride and sulphate values did not show such a rapid decrease. Theoretically, both the vegetable and putrescible and cellulosic fractions of wastes (paper and cardboard) may be microbially degraded to add to the organic loading. However, newsprint and cardboard frequently appear to retain their integrity in dry tips, even after periods in excess of a decade, suggesting that under conditions of low moisture content they remain resistant to degradation and only contribute slightly, but over a long time span, to the pollution load. Under these conditions the principal organic pollution is derived from the rapid breakdown of the vegetable and putrescible fraction. In contrast, cellulosic materials in wet tips appear to be degraded rapidly, adding to the organic pollution load (compare columns 1 and 2, Table 15.VII). It has also been reported[21] that leaching experiments on shredded (pulverized) refuse released a total mass of COD, TOC and total solids twice that of crude wastes, over a 2 year period. The more rapid degradation of shredded waste may be attributable to the greater surface area exposed to bacterial attack and to the greater homogeneity of the wastes permitting more effective compaction and exclusion of air.

Leachates from Co-disposal Sites

The co-disposal of industrial wastes with municipal solid refuse has been the subject of both experimental studies and field investigation[22]. The objective of controlled co-disposal is to make use of the chemical and biochemical reactions occurring within the municipal waste substrata to degrade or immobilize specific components of the industrial wastes. As examples, 3 year leaching experiments of selected industrial wastes co-disposed with municipal wastes in 6 m^3 test cells and field investigations of sites receiving similar industrial wastes indicated[22]:

(a) The metals in an hydroxide sludge, rich in nickel and chromium, were not significantly mobilized, with evidence of the precipitation of insoluble sulphides and carbonates under anaerobic conditions.

(b) Spent cutting oil/water emulsion added at a rate sufficient to bring the test cells to field capacity led to only an initial increase in oil leaching, compared with control cells. Subsequent sampling of the experiments indicated that the oil had been adsorbed into and retained by the solid wastes, without significant degradation to soluble products.

(c) Less than 3 per cent of cyanide added as heat treatment waste was removed in leachate during the 3 year experiment. A further 3 per cent could be accounted for as residual cyanide within the wastes at the end of that time, together with thiocyanate loss in leachates. The remaining 94 per cent was postulated to have been removed as other nitrogenous compounds by leaching and volatilization loss as hydrogen cyanide gas.

In each of the cases, the associated field investigations produced results consistent with the findings from the experimental studies.

Comparison of leachate from co-disposal sites with the range of values for different constituents found in municipal waste leachate (Table 15.VIII) shows that the leachates from certain sites (columns 2 and 3) do not differ significantly from those formed from municipal wastes. Generally, the organic strength and metal concentrations were found to be similar, although high chloride concentrations at Rainham may be attributed to spent pickling acid disposals. However, major differences were recorded in the case of a site (column 4) at which very large volumes of liquid acidic wastes had been deposited into a lagoon.

Leachate from Industrial Waste Disposal Sites

Industrial wastes are potentially as varied as the industries from which they stem. The leachates which they may form are equally varied. Two examples (Table 15.IX) illustrate the potential range[24]. The landfill at Coatham Stob, Cleveland, is situated in a quarry excavated from a dolerite dyke cutting the Triassic Sandstone aquifer. Sludges resulting from the processing of chromium ore had been deposited in the quarry since 1947, and it was estimated that by the date of the investigation of

TABLE 15.VIII.   Comparison of Leachates from Municipal Solid Wastes and Co-disposal Sites
(from Barber[23]; in mg/l except pH value)

Determinand	Municipal	Pitsea (43% industrial)	Rainham (mixed industrials)	Eastfield (large volume of acid wastes)
pH	5.8-7.5	8.0-8.5	6.4-8.0	2
COD	100-62400	850-1350	ND	ND
BOD	2-38000	80-250	ND	ND
TOC	20-19000	200-650	77-10000	3500-11000
Volatile acids	ND-3700	20	600-10000	ND
NH_3-N	5-1000	200-600	90-1700	ND
Org-N	ND-770	5-20	ND	ND
NO_3-N	0.5-5	0.1-10	8.0	ND
Ortho-P	0.02-3	0.2	ND	ND
Cl	100-3000	3400	400-13000	6100-8800
SO_4	60-460	340	150-1100	500-146000
Na	40-2800	2185	2000	1150
K	20-2050	888	50-125	0.9-1700
Mg	10-480	214	ND	4900-7700
Ca	1-165	88	ND	ND
Cr	0.05-1.0	<0.05	<0.5	2
Mn	0.3-250	0.5	ND	800-1500
Fe	0.1-2050	10	0.6-1000	10000-36200
Ni	0.05-1.7	0.04	<0.5	20
Cu	0.01-0.15	0.04	<0.5	50
Zn	0.05-130	0.16	1-10	ND
Cd	0.005-0.01	<0.02	ND	ND
Pb	0.05-0.6	0.1	<0.5	ND

ND = not determined

the site (1975) approximately 7850 tonnes of hexavalent chromium had been deposited in the wastes. The Villa Farm site, near Coventry, is located on the Quaternary sands and clays, in a shallow sand pit. Municipal refuse and builders' rubble was deposited during the years 1945 to 1967, after which the site was used for the disposal of a wide range of industrial liquids and sludges, of which metal sludges and oil/water mixtures formed important components. Tipping ceased in 1982. The total quantities deposited are unknown, but during the 2 year period 1978-1980 approximately 48000 tonnes of liquids and sludge were deposited in the 2500 m^2 lagoon.

Although the organic strength of the Villa Farm leachate fell within the range measured at municipal waste sites (Table 15.VIII) the leachates at Villa Farm and Coatham Stob contained significantly greater concentrations of metals, in particular nickel and chromium respectively.

Effluent Discharges and Accidental Spills

Primary and secondary sewage effluents, containing a substantial proportion of industrial effluents, and comminuted sewage, are discharged via trenches and tile-drain soakaways to aquifers[15]. Disposal areas range in size from a few thousand square metres to nearly one square kilometre, with mean daily flows between 700 and 20000 m^3, indicating infiltration rates of between 10 and 400 mm/day.

The strength of sewage effluent is generally about one-tenth of that of typical municipal waste leachate. The principal differences lie in the higher concentrations, both absolutely and proportionally compared with organic contaminants (BOD, CD, TOC), of phosphorus in sewage effluent than in municipal waste leachate, and

TABLE 15.IX. **Leachate from Industrial Waste Sites**
(from Barber et al[24]; in mg/l except pH value)

Site	Coatham Stob	Villa Farm	
Type of Waste	Chromium ore wastes	Mixed industrial sludges and liquids	
Sampling Point	Leachate lagoon	Leachate lagoon	
Date	1975	1975	1982
Determinands			
pH	ND	7.5	7.3
Dissolved oxygen	ND	0	0
TOC	ND	2800	1400
Phenol	ND	110	26
Na	6400	1460	2500
K	38	340	300
Ca	390-1300	50	207
Mg	ND	40	1
Cl	ND	1120	2960
SO_4	3430—9300	1750	200
NO_3	ND	1	185
NH_3	ND	ND	39
Fe	33	20	4
Mn	<0.1	4	0.06
Cu	0.4	1	1
Cd	0.3	1.5	0.06
Ni	1	4	8
Zn		1.5	1
Pb	<2	0.15	ND
Cr	2610-11000	8	0.15

ND = not determined

in the higher concentrations of oxidized nitrogen in nitrified secondary effluents, and some primary effluents. In addition, by nature of their origin, sewage effluents characteristically contain high counts of pathogenic indicators. Examples of the quality of effluents discharged to aquifers are given in Tables 15.X and 15.XI.

The pollution threat from accidental spills or leakages varies with the liquid which is lost. It is unlikely that anyone in the United Kingdom would be faced with the problem described from France[25], where the rupture of a 25 m³ storage tank deposited 12 m³ of white wine into a shallow alluvial aquifer. The degradable organic load imposed on the aquifer gave rise to an increase in the nitrate and dissolved iron content of waters abstracted from a nearby well, which was only partially eradicated after pumping to waste at a rate of 10 m³/day for a 12 month period. Similar changes in groundwater chemistry could occur due to the loss of fermented liquors, such as cider, onto shallow aquifers with low buffering capacities, for example alluvial gravels. Spills of mineral acids (nitric, sulphuric etc.) may also locally overwhelm the buffering capacity of the soil and underlying strata, possibly giving rise to high dissolved concentrations of iron and manganese.

Most commonly, accidental spills are associated with the loss of organic liquids in transit or storage, in particular hydrocarbon products and organic solvents. The solubilities of these compounds in water are generally low (Table 15.XII) and, if sufficient of the liquid is released at the surface to overcome the retentive properties of the soil and underlying strata, the liquid may form an immiscible layer in the groundwater zone. Hydrocarbon products (oils) are lighter than water and float as a surface layer, whilst many solvents used for industrial and commercial degreasing operations are denser than water and may sink below the water table to form a discrete perched layer within the aquifer. The behaviour of both types of

TABLE 15.X.   Quality of Sewage Effluent Discharge to Aquifers

Site Type of effluent		Whittington Primary	Winchester Primary	Royston Primary	Whitchurch Comminuted	Caddington Secondary chlorinated
Dates of samples		1975-77	1976-80	1976-78	1976-80	1977-78
Infiltration rate (mm/d)		12	26	12	80	220
Aquifer		Triassic Sandstone	Chalk	Chalk	Chalk	Chalk
Determinands						
pH		7.0	7.6	—	—	7.2
BOD	as mg/l	64	183	—	721	—
COD	„	194	283	—	—	—
TOC	„	—	48	—	47	14
Suspended solids	„	104	160	—	—	—
NO₃-N	„	17	0.4	—	0.7	35
NH₃-N	„	13	31	—	22	—
Total phosphorus	„	7	5	—	7	15
Cl	„	111	75	—	57	105
SO₄	„	—	—	—	—	43
Alkalinity, as CaCO₃	„	—	368	—	—	—
Na	„	—	67	—	—	74
K	„	—	15	—	—	19
Ca	„	—	120	—	—	—
Fe	„	—	—	37	—	237
Mn	„	—	—	<30	—	11
Mg	„	—	3	—	—	—
B	„	—	—	—	2	—
Ba	„	—	—	—	—	<0.3
Phenols	„	2.5	—	—	—	—
Cr	as µg/l	35	—	—	—	7
Cu	„	95	—	33	—	35
Ni	„	48	—	<10	—	15
Zn	„	578	—	—	—	75
Cd	„	11	—	<30	—	4
Pb	„	104	—	—	—	45
Co	„	—	—	—	—	14
Ag	„	—	—	<30	—	—
Halogenated hydrocarbons	„	—	—	—	—	589

organic liquids in aquifers has been described in detail[26]. In general, the aqueous solubility of oils, and solvents, decreases with increasing molecular weight, with aromatic hydrocarbons being more soluble than aliphatic forms. Phenols, which may be present in oils used for cooling metal machining equipment (cutting oils), are highly soluble and even when present in waters at very low concentrations give rise to objectionable tasting chlorphenols, after chlorination.

Estimation of Leachate Volume

When municipal solid wastes are deposited in a landfill they typically possess a moisture content in the range 25 to 35 per cent by weight. At these moisture contents the water is effectively absorbed into the wastes and little or no free draining leachate is produced. However, the addition of moisture, from infiltration from rainfall and, possibly, the disposal of aqueous waste solutions to the site, is likely to raise the moisture content to the point where free drainage of leachate starts (between 50 and 60 per cent by weight). Prediction of the time at which leachate is first produced after deposit of wastes and the variations in flow rate during the active life of the landfill are important factors in assessing the potential impact of the leachate on water resources.

Estimation should be made by the water balance method, using the general relationship:

TABLE 15.XI.   Concentrations of Pathogens in Sewage Effluent
(from Baxter and Clark[15])

Site	Effluent type	E. coli Median No/100 ml	Faecal streptococci Median No/100 ml	Viruses Median No PFU/1
Whittington	Primary	1300000	12000	2924
Winchester	Primary	ND	ND	1440
Alresford	Secondary	10000	ND	44
Whitchurch	Comminuted	6110000	32000	400
Caddington	Secondary	3000	9400	3464
Ludgershall	Secondary	10000	ND	192

ND = not determined
PFU = plaque forming units

TABLE 15.XII.   Aqueous Solubilities of Organic Liquids

Compound	Density	Solubility at 10°C (mg/l)
Light heating oil/diesel fuel	Lighter than water	3-8
Paraffin, jet fuel, petrol	„ „	150-300
Crude oils	„ „	up to 25
Phenol	„ „	66600
Trichloroethylene	Heavier than water	1070
Tetrachloroethylene	„ „	160
1,1,1, trichloroethane	„ „	1700
Methylene chloride	„ „	13200 (at 20°C)
Chloroform	„ „	8200 (at 20°C)
Carbon tetrachloride	„ „	785 (at 20°C)

Leachate production rate = Inputs (precipitation plus liquid disposals) − runoff + change in storage of moisture in wastes − actual evaporation/evapotranspiration;
where the parameters are measured in consistent units.

At the simplest level, estimates may be made by employing long-term average rainfall and evaporation figures appropriate to the location of the landfill, and by assuming that over a 1 year time step the net change in moisture storage is zero. The estimate thus becomes:

Average annual leachate production = Infiltration (average annual rainfall − average annual evaporation) × area of landfill.

Slight sophistication may be introduced by applying appropriate runoff factors to sites which have been completed with clay or soil capping layers, and by employing evapotranspiration estimates of the appropriate root length constant to those sites which have been revegetated following completion. However, such calculations are unable to estimate the changes with time in leachate production which occur as a result of progressive filling of a site and associated activities and are only useful as crude predictions.

It is preferable to compute the dynamic water balances based on shorter period (month, week or day) records of precipitation and evaporation, taking account of the changes in available moisture storage which accompany continued waste disposal and compaction and changes in the rates of runoff and evapo-transpiration due to progressive completion, capping and revegetation of a site. Detailed examination of meteorological and leachate production and storage data from a site in south Essex[27] have demonstrated that a good estimate of the infiltration to a landfill site may be gained by use of data provided by the Meteorological Office's MORECS model. At the site in question the solid wastes, with an average depth of 6.0 metres, covered an area of about 135 hectares, with an additional 25 hectares being filled annually.

At many sites a far greater final thickness of waste is deposited in successive layers and progressive changes in available moisture storage must be taken into account, particulary if estimates are required of the time at which leachate would be continuously produced. Although the volume of water that can be retained within a given mass of waste appears superficially similar to the concept of field capacity in soil studies, it is not strictly comparable. Even on arable soils, subjected to regular cultivation, the field capacity value remains essentially constant over long periods of time. By contrast, the volume of water that can be stored in a unit mass of wastes before continuous drainage occurs changes with time, as a result of the progressive compaction and degradation of the wastes (waste stabilization). As an example[20], it is reported that crude domestic wastes emplaced at a density of 0.7 tonne/m^3 were able to absorb 100 litres/tonne (wet weight) of water, but that this capacity reduced to 24 litres/tonne as the wastes compacted to a density of 1.0 tonne/m^3.

In those cases where it is desirable to provide detailed estimates of the probable changes with time of leachate production rates it may be necessary to construct a simple multi-layered mathematical model in which it is possible to vary the hydraulic characteristics (absorption capacity etc.) of each successive layer, in order to account for these progressive changes.

MOVEMENT AND ATTENUATION OF LEACHATE IN AQUIFERS

Classification of Hydrogeological Environments

The extent to which leachates from waste disposal sites, or liquids from accidental spills, directly threaten groundwater quality depends on the hydro-geological environment into which the discharge occurs. Discharges onto perme-able strata permit the potential contaminants to percolate downwards to the water table, whereas those onto essentially impermeable formations (often taken as strata with *in situ* permeability of 10^{-7} cm/sec or less) result in the accumulation of the polluting liquid at the surface. The former class of sites are conventionally known as dilute and disperse (or simply dilution) sites, whilst the latter are referred to as collect and contain (or containment) sites[28]. Dilution sites vary considerably in the ease with which leachate escapes, with potentially very rapid movement away from sites on coarse gravels or highly fractured hard rock, and more gradual migration from sites on sands or porous limestones. The potential rate of migration of leachate is an important factor in assessing the suitability of a site to receive wastes and is further considered later. A continuum can be found between those sites from which very rapid leachate movement, with minimal attenuation of pollutants, occurs and those at which leachate is effectively contained (Table 15.XIII), due to the variations in hydraulic properties of different lithologies. Vertical and lateral variations in lithology are found at many sites and it is normal to classify the natural strata of the site on the basis of the most permeable strata identified. In general, sites permitting rapid leachate movement with minimal attenuation are not considered suitable for waste disposal. However, it is possible by suitable site

TABLE 15.XIII.   Classification of Hydrogeological Environments

	Dilution Sites ◄─────────────────────────► Containment Sites				
	Rapid leachate movement, minimal attenuation.	──►	Slow leachate movement, significant attenuation.	──►	No significant leachate movement.
Examples of typical lithologies	Coarse, clean gravels Highly fractured hard rocks Karstic limestones	Fissured sandstones Fissured limestones	Consolidated sandstones Porous limestones Sands Sandy gravels	Silty sands Fractured mudstones	Consolidated clays and marls Non-fractured igneous rocks

engineering to reduce or eliminate leachate escape from such sites, so that waste disposal becomes possible.

Movement of Leachates through Strata

Leachates are aqueous solutions and their movement through permeable strata therefore obeys the basic physical laws of groundwater flow (Chapter 4). The rate of progress of a particular pollutant may, however, be different from that of the water in which it is dissolved due to physical, chemical or biochemical interactions with the strata (Chapter 3). In general, such reactions tend to retard the progress of a pollution front. It is only in the case of persistent, mobile pollutants, such as chloride, that the rate of progression of a pollution front is the same as the velocity of groundwater movement.

Groundwater, and leachate, movement may be by intergranular or fissure flows. In the former case the flow takes place through interconnected pores between the grains comprising the rock matrix and is characteristic of movement in unconsolidated gravels and sands, and many consolidated sandstones and granular limestones. In the latter case, flow takes place through fissures, and occurs in its most developed form in the conduits in karstified non-porous limestones, or fractured igneous rocks. Both intergranular and fissure flow may be present in fissured sandstones and fissured, porous limestones, often with the principal flows occurring via the fissure sytems, but with the main storage being provided by the slower intergranular flow component.

In the unsaturated zone, through which leachate may have to pass before reaching the water table, the pore spaces, and fissures, are partially occupied by liquid and partially by gas, which has the effect of reducing the hydraulic conductivity. The basic relationship for flows in the unsaturated zone is given by:

$$v = -k\lambda \left(\frac{d\phi z}{dz} + 1 \right)$$

where v = flow rate

k = saturated hydraulic continuity

λ = unsaturation term which relates decrease in conductivity to decreasing saturation

$d\phi z/dz$ = change in suction (matric potential) measured by tensiometer, with depth.

When the rock is saturated, the matric potential is zero and $\lambda = 1$, at which point the relationship transforms to the familiar Darcy equation for saturated flow (Chapter 4). In aquifers dominated by fissure flows, such as the Carboniferous

Limestone or parts of the Jurassic Limestones, very rapid movement through the unsaturated zone may take place[29], with fast response to recharge events and corresponding short term fluctuations in pollutant inputs. All intergranular flow aquifers are able to retain a certain level of saturation without vertical flow taking place (below field capacity). In the coarser-grained types, unsaturated permeability increases relatively smoothly, although not linearly, from field capacity to full saturation, but in the finer-grained examples rapid changes in permeability over restricted ranges of matric potential are characteristic. The extreme example is provided by the Upper Chalk, where it has been shown by field measurements[30] that very little change in unsaturated permeability occurs between -950 and -50 cm water matric potential, but that between matric potentials of -50 and 0 cm water the permeability increases by 2 orders of magnitude (5 mm/day to 500 mm/day). These figures imply that a high proportion of infiltrating water, and dissolved contaminants, move slowly downwards by intergranular flow, and that rapid flow via fissures can only take place when the pores of the blocks of aquifer between the fissures are essentially saturated, corresponding to times of high infiltration. The proportion of total infiltration, and pollution, which moves slowly downwards to the water table and that which moves rapidly via fissures is therefore dependent on the relationship between unsaturated permeability and degree of saturation and variations in the rate of infiltration.

Although nearly all flows in both the unsaturated and saturated zones of aquifers are laminar, dispersion of dissolved constituents is commonly observed. Dispersion is recognized by the progressive reduction in strength of the pollutants (dilution) with distance from the source of pollutant inputs and may arise from the action of two mechanisms:

(i) molecular diffusion of solutes from areas of high concentration towards those of low concentration, and

(ii) convective dispersion due to variations in the length of individual flow paths, their tortuosity and flow velocities between grains or fracture bounded blocks of aquifer. The effect of this mechanism is to spread out the dissolved constituents both in the direction of flow (longitudinal dispersion) and normal to the flow direction (transverse dispersion).

Molecular diffusion is normally only important in essentially static groundwater systems—for example, within the water retained in very fine porous rock matrices. In general, dispersion refers to the effect of convective mixing in flowing groundwater systems.

It has been shown[31] that the dispersivity of a porous medium is a property of the geometric arrangement of pores within the medium, and is related to the dispersion coefficient as follows:

$$D = \alpha u$$

where D = dispersion coefficient (L^2/T)
       α = dispersivity of the medium (L)
       u = mean pore velocity (L/T)

Dispersion is, therefore, a function of the groundwater flow velocity and, also of the distance over which dispersion is estimated. The latter is because changes in lithology, including grain size and fracture density variations along a flow path, lead to variations in the dispersivity of the media. The effects of increasing distance over which dispersivity is estimated on the value of dispersivity has been confirmed by field experiments on gravel aquifers in Bavaria[32], which have shown the dispersivity to increase from a value of 1 m over a flow path of 5 metres, to over 50 m over a flow distance of 1 000 m. On an even greater scale, recent experiments on the partially karstic Carboniferous Limestone of the Chepstow area[33], over a flow path of 7 km, provided a dispersivity of 720 m. The greater the dispersion coefficient due to any combination of high dispersivity, increased porewater velocity and length of flow path, the greater is the observed reduction in concentrations of pollutants by dilution.

The effect of dispersion on a conservative contaminant, such as chloride, derived at an essentially constant rate from a point source of pollution, is to progressively decrease the concentration of the contaminant in the direction of groundwater flow[34]. At a certain distance from the point source the concentrations become indistinguishable from the natural levels in the host groundwater (background values), thereby defining the plume of pollution. Velocities of groundwater flow are likely to vary seasonally in response to the annual recharge/discharge cycle, giving rise to parallel changes in the dispersion coefficient. A dynamic equilibrium therefore exists and has been well described[35] from a landfill on the Lower Greensand in Kent, where the 50 mg/l isochlor, which defined the pollution plume, was found to extend up to 1 700 m in the direction of groundwater movement during the late summer, but to be reduced to 1 200 metres under the increased groundwater gradients of late winter.

Attenuation of Pollutants

The reduction in concentrations of both conservative and labile pollutants along groundwater flow paths is referred to as attenuation. In the case of conservative contaminants the effect is due entirely to dilution resulting from dispersion. For other contaminants, attenuation occurs through the action of various chemical, biological and physical processes, including dilution, which reduce the concentrations.

The principal chemical and biochemical reactions which may change the strength or composition of groundwater contaminated by pollutants have been described in Chapter 3, but are here briefly recalled:

(1) **Complex Formation** takes place where two or more ions in solution link to form a new complex which may be more or less mobile than the constituent ions. Examples of the former case are heavy metal ions which when complexed with chloride or certain organic compounds may be less affected by precipitation or adsorption processes and thus be present at high concentrations and in more mobile forms. On the other hand, complexation with humic organic compounds and hydrous metal oxides, which become adsorbed to the aquifer matrix, reduces their mobility.

(2) **Neutralization.** Many compounds and elements, especially cations, are more soluble in low pH (acid) conditions. The principal buffering capacity of many aquifers is the dissolved carbonate system, which in turn depends upon the presence of carbonate minerals in the aquifer. Buffering of strongly alkaline solutions (pH >9) is provided by alumino-silicate minerals. Aquifers of mixed lithology, containing both carbonate and silicate minerals, provide the maximum buffering capacity. In contrast, clean silica sands or quartzites may possess very limited neutralization capacity, so that acid or alkaline conditions persist.

(3) **Oxidation-Reduction Processes** may be important for those elements which can exist in more than one oxidation state. Groundwater in unconfined, recharge areas is normally aerobic, whilst that present in fully confined conditions tends to be anoxic. The presence of dissolved organic components in leachates frequently leads to anoxic conditions both in the underlying unsaturated zone and in the groundwater in the immediate vicinity of the source of pollution. Assuming an initially aerobic groundwater, the following sequence of reactions would be expected as the water

becomes increasingly anoxic: reduction of dissolved oxygen and its total disappearance—denitrification—appearances of dissolved ferrous iron and Mn^{2+}—reduction of sulphates to sulphides, carbon dioxide to methane and nitrogen to ammonia. Increased oxygen content of initially anoxic groundwater leads to the following sequence: oxidation of dissolved organics—conversion of sulphides to sulphates—conversion of ferrous (Fe^2) to ferric (Fe^3) iron, with the precipitation of ferric oxide—oxidation of ammonium to nitrate—oxidation of dissolved manganese and precipitation of an hydrous oxide form.

(4) **Precipitation-Dissolution Reactions** may decrease or increase the solution strength. The presence of high concentrations of anions, such as carbonate, phosphate, hydroxide, sulphide or silicate, may lead to the precipitation of insoluble cations, especially the multivalent heavy metals. However, if the precipitation reaction has involved a change in the valency of the cations, dilution, or a general change in the oxygen status of the solution, may return some of the constituents to solution.

(5) **Sorption Reactions.** The process of ion exchange (adsorption) takes place when cations, and to a very limited extent anions, in solution displace other cations from clay minerals. The removal of heavy metals by this process releases equivalent quantities of lighter, alkaline metals (Na, K, Ca) into solution. A change in the chemical conditions, for example a reduction in pH or leaching of the clay minerals by more dilute solutions, may lead to some of the adsorbed materials returning to solution (desorption).

(6) **Biochemical Processes.** The anerobic breakdown of organic compounds to methane, carbon dioxide and water within landfills has been described earlier. The same reactions may continue within aquifer materials, subject to the continuation of anaerobic conditions and the presence of nutrients. Further, aerobic, degradation may take place within groundwater systems around the edges of pollution plumes. In addition, the growth of microbial populations requires N, C, P and S and some minor elements for cell syntheses, removing them temporarily from solution.

It is clear that an aquifer of mixed mineralogy, with a substantial buffering capacity, such as the Lower Greensand, would offer the optimum site for many of the attenuating processes. Detailed, long-term experimental studies of the migration of pollutants through the unsaturated zone of the Lower Greensand[36,37] have been carried out on large (60 m^3) undisturbed lysimeters. The lysimeters were irrigated at 700 mm/year for nearly 4.5 years with synthetic leachates containing high concentrations of organic compounds (pH 7.0), anions (pH 7.5) and heavy metals (pH 5.0)[38], with regular measurements being made of moisture content profiles, pore suction potentials, gas composition and drainage volume and composition. The results indicated extensive degradation of phenol, dichlorophenol, aniline and acetate, without adsorption, within the upper 250 mm of the lysimeter, under conditions of a decreased oxygen status.

As anticipated, persistent anions, such as chloride, passed directly through the lysimeters without attenuation, but there was evidence of removal of ammonia and phosphorus by microbial assimilation and of limited denitrification. The alkali metals, Li, K, Na all showed evidence of cation exchange with calcium, in the approximate ratios 3.4:1.3:1. The heavy metal leachate contained metal concentrations some ten times those normally encountered in leachates, and was strongly acidic (pH 5.0). The high buffering capacity of the Greensand, due to the presence of carbonate minerals (calcite and aragonite) rapidly neutralized the leachate to pH 7.5, releasing calcium and some magnesium into solution. Significant attenuation of the heavy metals by co-precipitation with hydrated ferric oxides, as poorly soluble carbonates and by cation exchange retarded their progress and significant concentrations were not recorded below 400 mm depth. The order of mobility determined was Ni>Cd>Zn>Cu>Cr>Pb; with lead being the most strongly and nickel the least attenuated species. Subsequent irrigation with an acidic leachate (pH 5) not containing heavy metals leads to limited remobilization of the metals. Even so, it was estimated[37] that it would have required 11 years of continuous irrigation by the acidic leachate to remove the most mobile metal, nickel, from the upper 400 mm, and that it would not have been detectable below 2 metres depth.

More recently, preliminary results from a field experiment in which a 6 metre thick layer of remoulded lower Greensand has been placed as an artificial unsaturated zone beneath a domestic waste landfill in Kent[38] have indicated immobilization of chromium and zinc in the artificial layer, with reduction in ammonia by cation exchange and progressive biodegradation of volatile fatty acids.

Comparative experimental studies of the effectiveness of unsaturated Lower Chalk, Plateau Gravels and Triassic Sandstone in attenuating leachate components, compared with Lower Greensand, have been reported[39]. The monoliths were irrigated with the same heavy metal, acidic, synthetic leachate employed in the lysimeter experiments described above. Efficient retention of the heavy metals was reported from all four rock types. Comparison of the concentrations of metals immobilized onto the sediments with background values for the same sediments indicated retention of all metals, except minimal nickel, within the first 700 mm of the Lower Greensand, Lower Chalk and Plateau gravel monoliths, and within the first 950 mm of the Triassic Sandstone. Again, with the exception of very low nickel concentrations, porewater concentrations of heavy metals below 450 mm depth in all four lithologies fell below detection limits. It was concluded that the efficient metal retention by the Lower Chalk and Lower Greensand resulted from their high buffering capacity due to elevated calcite content, and high cation exchange capacities related to their clay mineral contents. By comparison, the low buffering capacity and reduced cation exchange capacity of the Triassic Sandstone permitted greater mobility of the metals. The apparently effective immobilization of metals by the Plateau Gravels was attributed to the presence of layers of sand containing calcite, which were not present in the original sediments, but introduced for experimental purposes.

These experiments did not estimate the efficiencies of the different rock types in encouraging attenuation of organic components of the leachate. However, from the lysimeter studies, it would be anticipated that the less reactive character of the Triassic Sandstone, compared with the Lower Greensand, would be reflected in not only less attenuation of heavy metals, but also in less effective degradation of organics. Field investigations of two domestic waste landfills on the Triassic Sandstone near Nottingham[40,41] have revealed the presence of organic pollution fronts, measured as TOC, moving slowly downwards (at between 1 and 2 m/year) through the unsaturated zone with no significant attenuation apparent. A zone of low pH, which would inhibit microbial degradation, was found to be associated with the organic fronts and it was postulated that the low buffering capacity of the formation contributes to the lack of organic degradation.

Although the effectiveness of unsaturated zones in attenuating all leachate components has been brought into question for certain lithologies, it appears that the general conclusions reached by the DoE[22] as the result of the examination of 20 landfill sites were valid. In those cases where slow, intergranular flow through the zone occurred, substantial attenuation of metals by neutralization and immobilization was noted, with significant decreases of organic compounds and persistent contaminants such as chloride by dilution in the porewaters. An example is provided by a site of approximately 2 hectares on the Chalk in Suffolk (Fig. 15.3) at which, between 1968 and 1973, solid and liquid wastes of industrial origin, including paper, sawdust, egg packing wastes, synthetic latex, general factory

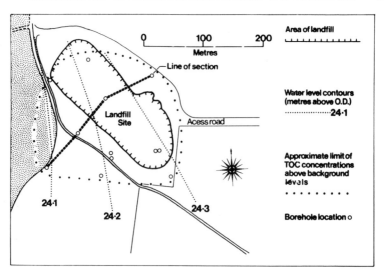

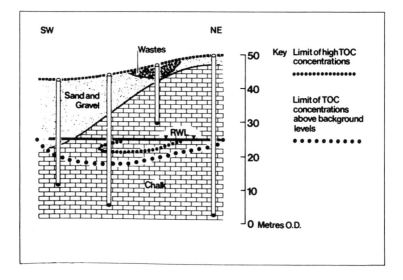

Fig. 15.3.   Plan and section of landfill site on Chalk near Bury St. Edmunds, Suffolk (after Stiff and Young[42])

rubbish and oily aqueous liquids were deposited. High TOC concentrations (maximum 24 000 mg/l) were recorded in the Chalk immediately beneath the wastes at the southern end of the landfill where substantial lagoon disposal of liquid wastes had occurred, decreasing to 14 000 mg/l 5 metres above the water table. By contrast, TOC concentrations decreased from 10 000 mg/l at the top of the Chalk at the northern end of the site, to 4 mg/l above the water table. TOC concentrations above background levels were not detected in groundwater at distances of greater than 50 m in the direction of flow.

5. GROUNDWATER POLLUTION BY DISPERSED SOURCES

INTRODUCTION

The dividing line between point and dispersed sources of pollution is not rigid, but dependent, to some extent, on the scale of the problem. Although a large landfill site or effluent discharge would inevitably be viewed as a point source, at the regional scale a large number of small sources may be viewed as a dispersed source, as for example the leaching of lead from pottery glaze wastes in the Po Valley of Italy[43] or chromium from small plating works in the Chalk of northern France[44]. However, the principal identified source of dispersed pollution within the United Kingdom, and many other countries, is the loss of agrochemicals from farmland, and in particular nitrate and pesticides.

The problem of increased nitrate concentration in regional groundwater supply sources has been recognized since the early 1970s[45-48]. In 1976 it was estimated[49] that approximately 100 public supply sources in England and Wales produced water which persistently or intermittently exceeded the guideline value of 11.3 mg N/l (50 mg NO$_3$/l). By 1984 the number of sources in this category had risen to about 140, with a licensed yield of approximately 500 Ml/d out of a total groundwater use of about 5400 Ml/d in England and Wales. Following recommendations by the Seventh Report of the Royal Commission on Environmental Pollution[50], the national situation was reviewed by the Standing Technical Advisory Committee on Water Quality[51]. The worst affected region was identified as the Anglian Water Authority, but with local difficulties apparent in the Southern, Severn-Trent and Yorkshire areas. Long-term data on the nitrate levels in 75 groundwater sources were examined and it was found[51] that 65 per cent showed increasing trends, the remainder appearing essentially stable, but subject to substantial fluctuations.

Information on the occurrence of pesticide residues in groundwater supplies has only recently started to become available and is far less complete than in the case of nitrates. However, a recent survey of ground and surface waters of the Anglian region[52] has shown the presence of both phenoxyalkanoic acid residues and atrazine in groundwaters at very low concentrations, often in areas associated with increased nitrate levels. The former group of compounds (phenoxyalkanoics) are typical of pesticides in current agricultural usage, whilst atrazine is now used only minimally in agriculture, but is employed widely as a total weed control to roads, railways etc.

SOURCES, MOVEMENT AND ATTENUATION

Agriculture in the United Kingdom has become increasingly intensive since the 1950s. During the period 1939-46 a substantial enlargement took place of the agricultural land devoted to arable crops, especially in the southern and midland counties where, in some cases, the arable area nearly doubled[53]. The resulting high proportion of agricultural land used for arable crops has persisted, with crop yields being maintained and improved by selective plant breeding and the intensive use of fertilizers. The greatest increase in fertilizer applications of major nutrients has been nitrogen, rising steadily from an UK total of 200000 tonnes in 1950 to 1400000 tonnes in 1983.

As a result of an extensive programme of field investigations during the 1970s[54,55] a clear relationship was established between farming practice and nitrate leaching losses. High rates of loss, often equivalent to between 50 and 70 kg N/ha/yr, were found to be characteristic of intensively cultivated, fertilized arable soils. The nitrate losses were attributed not to direct leaching of applied fertilizer, but to the release of nitrate by microbial mineralization from the enlarged crop residues and weeds after harvest and ploughing. In contrast, low rates of leaching loss, often below 5 kg N/ha/yr, were found to be typical of permanent grassland and woodland[56]. Examples of the vertical distributions of nitrate in the unsaturated zone, under different farming usages, are shown in Fig. 15.4[57].

Field-scale experimental studies[58] have shown that releases of nitrate of the order of 200 kg N/ha could be attributed to the ploughing up of established grassland, due to the microbial mineralization of the accumulated soil organic residues. Although the earlier studies[54] suggested that leaching losses from normally fertilized grassland were minimal, recent work[59] has shown that losses comparable with those from arable soils may occur from intensively grazed grassland, but that losses from heavily fertilized grass cut for hay or silage are low. Repetitive drilling and

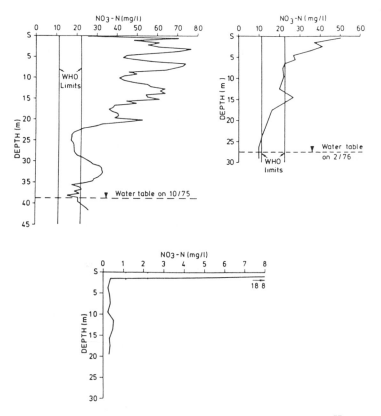

Fig. 15.4.   Nitrate depth profiles (after Young and Hall[57])

measurements of nitrate profiles after a 3 year time lapse at a number of sites[56] indicated that a high proportion of the nitrate moves slowly downwards through the unsaturated zone. The rate of movement has been found to be dependent on the local infiltration rate and the hydraulic characteristics of the aquifers, often in the range 0.5–1.5 m/year in the Upper Chalk and perhaps twice as fast in the Triassic Sandstone.

The unsaturated and saturated zones of the recharge zones of aquifers are characteristically aerobic, under which conditions nitrate may persist as a stable ion. Although bacteria potentially capable of attenuating nitrate by denitrification have been found to depths of 50 metres in the Chalk[60], no unequivocal evidence of removal of nitrate by this process has been recorded and it seems probable that attenuation occurs principally by dilution in the saturated zone. Simple mathematical models to predict the future concentrations of nitrate in groundwater catchments have been developed[61] and applied to areas of the Chalk, Triassic Sandstone and Lincolnshire Limestone aquifers.

Direct knowledge of the sources and routes by which pesticide residues enter and move through aquifers is sparse, but the coincidence of residues in groundwaters with increased nitrate levels suggests that similar transport mechanisms may apply. By their nature pesticides are generally resistant to rapid microbial degradation and attenuation may be limited to dilution by dispersion.

6. AQUIFER PROTECTION AND REHABILITATION

INTRODUCTION—BACKGROUND TO AQUIFER PROTECTION

Water authorities are charged under Section 10 of the Water Act 1973 with the duty of conserving and securing the proper use of water resources in their area, which includes water in underground strata. About one-third of the UK's public water supply is derived directly from wells and boreholes, and its quality is usually extremely good, requiring the minimum amount of treatment. The quality of groundwater is outstanding considering that it has percolated through from the surface, where there may be large quantities of decaying organic vegetable matter and faecal matter spread as manure containing large numbers of bacteria. The ground is therefore an excellent purifying medium.

In view of the large quantity of groundwater used for public supply it is surprising that there has been little legislation concerned directly with protection of groundwater[62]. In the past the number of activities that may have given rise to groundwater pollution was perhaps fewer than today. Much of the early legislation that concerned groundwater protection in the late 1800s was to protect wells, from which many households drew their supply, from pollution from burial grounds. Pollution of wells in urban areas arose from the disposal of wastes into middens, ash pits or cesspits which could be near to a dug well providing the water supply. Pollution of this nature was no doubt considerably reduced by the widespread introduction of public piped water supplies and sewerage. The Water Act 1945 allowed for byelaws to be made to prevent pollution of the water of a water undertaker, and also gave powers to acquire land for the purpose of protecting against pollution any water which the water undertaker was authorized to take. Although there was little statutory legislation regarding protection of groundwater against pollution, there was protection afforded to owners under Common Law and also by various Planning Acts which would not allow works to take place that would be likely to interfere with water supplies.

The Water Resources Act 1963 gave river authorities power to control discharges into underground strata, but not discharges to the surface. This was because, though incidents of groundwater pollution were known to have occurred from such as silage liquor or discharges onto open rock strata in old quarries, it was generally the case that pollution was less likely to reach the groundwater from material spread on the surface than if it was introduced into an aquifer by a well or borehole. Although the statutory controls to prevent pollution of underground water were small there were few case histories of public underground water supplies becoming contaminated to such a degree as to render them unfit for drinking. This was no doubt due to the vigilance of many water undertakings in protecting their sources of supply.

Further proposals for the protection of underground water have been introduced in the Control of Pollution Act 1974, of which Part II (COPA II) has recently come into operation. Part I of the Act, covering waste disposal, established new responsibilities for collection and disposal of controlled waste, chiefly by means of a site licensing system for waste disposal sites.

Before issuing a site licence, which may have conditions stipulating the type, manner and means of waste disposal, as well as site preparation, control and monitoring, the waste disposal authority has a statutory duty to consult the water authority. If the water authority objects to the granting of a licence, because of the risk of water pollution, the licence must be withheld and the disagreement resolved by appeal to the Secretary of State. It is also the duty of the waste disposal authority to revoke a site licence should it appear that continuation of the operation to which the licence relates would cause water pollution.

It was recognized by the DoE that close collaboration should take place to overcome the difficulties of potential conflict between the interests of water authorities to protect the quality of underground water, and of the waste disposal authorities to provide a sufficient number of waste disposal sites. The development of aquifer protection policies or guidelines has contributed to an understanding of the problems involved, although each proposed waste disposal site must be considered on its merits.

Part II of the Control of Pollution Act, covering the pollution of water, makes it an offence to cause any poisonous, noxious or polluting matter to enter any stream or controlled water or specified underground water unless it is done in pursuance of a disposal licence issued by a disposal authority, or a consent issued by the water authority or the Secretary of State. Certain defences are provided to this offence including "good agricultural practice". Specified underground water is defined as underground water in the water authority area which is specified in a document available for public inspection as water which is used or expected by the authority to be used for any purpose. Most water authorities have specified all underground water throughout the whole of their area.

The Control of Pollution Act also enables water authorities to undertake remedial work where pollution is likely to occur or has occurred from an unconsented discharge, and to recover the costs incurred from the person who made the discharge.

The Secretary of State may also designate areas within which prescribed activities which are likely to result in pollution of underground water can be prohibited or restricted, although no such regulations have been made as yet.

The EEC has also issued a directive on protection of groundwater against pollution caused by certain dangerous substances (80/68/EEC). The DoE noted that present legislation contained in the Water Act 1973 and the Control of

Pollution Act 1974 provided adequate measures for the protection of groundwater.

PHILOSOPHY OF AQUIFER PROTECTION

The development of UK legislation on groundwater quality protection outlined above has followed on the increasing awareness of the vulnerability of groundwater to pollution from human activities, and that the risk of pollution has been increasing. Similar developments in many other countries have led to the formulation of groundwater protection policies, though the philosophy and administration of such policies may differ considerably.

Aquifer protection involves both the legislation to control possible polluting activities and also an assessment of the vulnerability of the groundwater to pollution and hence the degree of protection that is required.

Types of Aquifer Protection Policy

The basic aim of all aquifer protection policies is to protect groundwater from contamination, but the method by which protection is afforded and the degree of protection may vary. There are two main approaches to groundwater protection, a statutory approach or a strategic approach.

In a statutory approach, groundwater protection zones have been established by legislative procedures, as for example in West Germany[63] and in the USSR and certain states of the USA. Specific activities may be prohibited, such as solid waste disposal, within a specified distance of a public water supply source. The distance may vary from system to system, and may not have regard to the nature of the wastes disposed or the local hydrogeological conditions. In West Germany a detailed and specific enquiry must be undertaken before a groundwater protection zone can be established. Protection zones can only be applied to existing or proposed public supplies but once established they ensure legal prohibition of potentially polluting practices. In the West German system there are three encircling zones: zone III the whole of the groundwater catchment supplying the borehole, but rarely applied with stringent control beyond a 2 km radius; zone II the zone in which the time for movement of groundwater towards the borehole is less than 50 days; zone I a small inner zone of 10-50 m radius around the borehole.

The problems perceived in a statutory approach are either:

(*a*) The system is rigid and a protection zone can only be established after a detailed hydrogeological investigation. It may also only be possible to establish protection zones around existing public supply sources. It should be noted however, that the provisions of the EC Directive on Groundwater (80/68/EEC), require that prior investigation of waste disposal sites should be carried out before licensing.

(*b*) The system has arbitrary restrictions, that are not related to the hydrogeology.

(*c*) A statutory aquifer protection policy may be difficult to change, in the light of advancing knowledge.

(*d*) A statutory policy is largely based upon prohibition, and in most cases will not allow the establishment of an optimum balance between conflicting interests.

The alternative to a statutory approach is the strategic approach. Generally this method seeks to provide protection on an aquifer-wide basis to protect future resources as well as present supplies. The degree of hydrogeological input to the policy varies, but it demands less time and resources to prepare a policy document of this type, than to carry out the investigation for a statutory protection zone.

In the UK those RWAs that have an aquifer protection policy have adopted the strategic approach. This approach is to some extent a result of English legislation whereby the statutory framework is laid down by central government, but the actual control is delegated to an authority operating at regional or local level—which in the case of water pollution control is the RWA[64].

Objectives of an Aquifer Protection Policy

Although the ultimate aim of an aquifer protection policy is to protect the quality of the groundwater, the adoption of a strategic approach by most UK authorities to cover all the groundwater resources within their area means that an aquifer protection policy document may have several objectives.

Those objectives common to both the Severn-Trent and the Southern WA aquifer protection policies are:

(i) Development and adoption of a uniform approach throughout the RWA to all matters relating to aquifer protection.
(ii) To form a basis by which the RWA will judge individual issues.
(iii) To provide a guide to the local authorities and other bodies on the RWA's attitude to aquifer protection.

The RWAs have inherited different codes of practice or guidelines on aquifer protection from their predecessor statutory water undertakings. The objectives of these may have been similar but their details may differ. Each RWA area covers a number of county councils and district councils and an aquifer protection policy provides a means of indicating the WA's interests, at an early stage in the development of strategic planning and in preparing waste disposal plans and also in providing a guide to the likely response of the water authority on consultation on individual waste disposal sites and planning applications.

TECHNICAL BASIS OF AN AQUIFER PROTECTION POLICY

In considering the technical basis for an aquifer protection policy regard must be given to the hydrogeology of the aquifers, the nature of pollutants and factors controlling their migration and persistence.

The hydrogeological controls relate to the properties of the aquifer:

(1) lithology;
(2) type and amount of permeability and porosity;
(3) size and direction of the hydraulic gradient;
(4) volume of the aquifer; and
(5) thickness of the aerated zone.

The physical and chemical properties of the aquifer, the groundwater and the pollutant are important, as are the processes by which they can change:

(a) density;
(b) viscosity of the groundwater and pollutants;
(c) solubility;
(d) chemical reactions;
(e) oxidation/reduction;
(f) production and diffusion of landfill gases; and
(g) adsorptive and ion-exchange properties of the pollutant and aquifer.

Biological factors must also be considered:

(i) the presence of an aerobic/anaerobic regime;
(ii) biodegradation processes; and
(iii) bacterial action.

The interaction of all the many factors involved may be very complex and difficult to assess when considering any one actual or potential case of groundwater pollution. Ideally each groundwater abstraction should have a protection zone drawn around it related to the detailed hydrogeology etc. but in practice there are normally insufficient data, and insufficient manpower time to collect the data. It is also a practical advantage if a readily described and delineated standard protection zone can be drawn around all the abstractions. As well as delineating a protection zone around a groundwater source, consideration must also be given to delineating the activities that the authority may regard as liable to cause pollution and so would wish to object to those activities in particular areas, or ensure that adequate safeguards were agreed. In a strategic aquifer protection policy, the extent and importance of the aquifer will be taken into account in defining protection zones other than those immediately around a groundwater source.

Inner Protection Zone (Zone 1)

A common feature of most protection policies is an area immediately around the abstraction to give a high degree of protection. This should be large enough to afford adequate protection but not needlessly large. A 3 km radius quoted in the Ministry of Health Memorandum of 1948 was widely adopted by the UK water industry. An alternative is the 50 day residence period used in Europe. The distance required for a 50 day residence period will vary accordingly to hydrogeological conditions, which, as already noted, may not be known sufficiently accurately, and also results in varying sizes for protection zones, even where boreholes may have the same abstraction rate. Southern WA have made a series of theoretical calculations for a variety of aquifer conditions and pumping rates and have shown that for granular aquifers the distance required for 50 days' protection is less than 1 km and for rates less than 5 Ml/d is usually less than 0.5 km. For a Chalk aquifer an upper limit of about 1.5 km is required for abstraction rates up to 20 Ml/d but this does not allow for problems with extremely fissured Chalk. The width of inflow to the abstraction and the distance down hydraulic gradient to the stagnation point are generally greater than the distance required for 50 days' residence time.

As no single size zone is appropriate for all sources and all aquifers a semi-arbitrary standardization of zones is required. A number of different situations must be considered:

(1) Granular aquifers.
(2) Fissured aquifers.
(3) Natural springs.

Granular aquifers, such as the Triassic Sandstone, generally behave on a macroscale as though they were homogeneous. Cones of depression are approximately circular around major abstractions, and it is, therefore, easy to define a protection zone with a circle of appropriate radius. The radius may be proportional to the abstraction rate. In the Severn-Trent and Southern WA aquifer protection policies, a radius of 1.0 km is chosen for major abstractions, though this includes a 0.5 km buffer zone in the case of Southern WA.

Abstraction rates in fissured aquifers may be much higher than in granular aquifers. A larger radius protection zone is therefore appropriate to allow for the higher abstraction rate and faster groundwater flow through the aquifer. Further protection may be afforded by extending the protection zone up the hydraulic gradient. Many old sources in the Chalk were constructed with adits and these must be included in the protection zone.

There may be local circumstances at an abstraction point that will modify the size of the proposed protection zone, for example in minor aquifers, where there is a succession of aquifers and aquicludes, the catchment for a groundwater abstraction may not be immediately around the borehole, and there may be an aquiclude overlying the aquifer immediately around the borehole. In this case a 1 km protection zone is inappropriate and could be reduced to a size sufficient to protect the headworks.

The presence of glacial drift materials overlying the aquifer may also provide protection to a groundwater abstraction, but because of the variability and sometimes lack of information on the drift it may still be appropriate to draw a protection zone, though in this case activities within the protection zone will need to be treated on the basis of information available. In some fissured strata—for example in certain Chalk catchments, and in Carboniferous Limestone, boreholes and springs may be known to respond quickly to specific swallow holes that may be several kms from the abstraction. These connections have been ascertained from past events and it is clearly necessary that to afford protection to the abstraction a protection zone must be drawn around the swallow hole/s.

Springs are important sources of supply, especially in the fissured aquifers, and protection zones must also be drawn up for them. It is unlikely that there will be any risk of pollution to a spring from down hydraulic gradient. The protection zone may be defined as a semicircle with its centre at the spring, or as a circle with the spring on the circumference on the down hydraulic gradient. The protection zone may be extended up hydraulic gradient as fissure flow may be increased in the vicinity of a spring.

It is estimated that zone 1 areas cover 1 per cent of the Severn-Trent WA area and 15 per cent of the Southern WA. The total quantity of groundwater abstracted in the two authorities is very similar, though Severn-Trent is twice the area of Southern WA.

The larger area of zone 1 in Southern WA indicates the importance of groundwater which provides 80 per cent of the public water supplies compared to 39 per cent in Severn-Trent.

Major Aquifers (Zone 2)

The inner protection zones immediately around the boreholes (zone 1) protect the borehole against the risk of imminent pollution but to provide longer-term protection the resources of the major aquifers must also be protected from pollution. A second protection zone is, therefore, required covering the outcrop of all the major aquifers, excluding the zone 1 areas already delineated. The protection afforded must be such that it would prevent any unacceptable pollution, though activities that may present a low degree of risk may be acceptable according to local conditions.

It is estimated that in Severn-Trent WA 25 per cent of the authority's catchment is defined as zone 2 and in Southern WA 18 per cent. Within any authority's policy the aquifers that are included within zone 2 and whether there is in effect a subdivision of this group is often a reflection on the aquifers present within that authority and their importance for water supply. Yorkshire WA is the only authority in which both the country's major aquifers occur, but no specific aquifer policy has been formulated by this authority. The existing aquifer protection policies have, therefore, been drawn up in authorities where there is one major aquifer (the Triassic Sandstone in Severn-Trent and the Chalk in Southern WA) and this is reflected in the protection zones that have been drawn up. In Southern WA a distinction is drawn between the Chalk and the more important granular formations (primarily the Lower Greensand). The range of objectionable activities in each zone is similar, but a distinction is drawn to take account of the pre-eminence of the Chalk as a water-bearing formation and its importance in the authority's resources, whereas the granular formations generally have slower groundwater movement, and more dispersion and delay of any contaminants.

Minor Aquifers

Within each authority there are minor aquifers which may locally be important for water supplies. Generally they do not have any potential for yielding major additional water supplies, but they require protection to safeguard existing abstractions and possible future local use. In geological formations such as the Carboniferous Coal Measures and Millstone Grits there are numerous minor sandstone aquifers.

Other Areas

The areas within an authority that are not covered by the major and minor aquifers vary from one authority to the next. In the south-east of the UK these will be mostly the Clayey formations such as the Kimmeridge, the Gault Clay, the Weald Clay and London Clay, and in the Midlands the Keuper Marl and Lias. Although all these formations are predominantly clayey there may be minor discontinuous aquifers that are utilized for local supplies, and it is important that these sources are protected from pollution.

Potentially Polluting Activities

In drawing up an aquifer protection policy the water authority must attempt to delineate the activities which it would regard as liable to produce pollution. An identical activity arising in two different locations may not present the same risk of groundwater pollution. The risks of pollution are obviously greatest in the zone 1 areas immediately around sources of supply and in these areas the strictest controls will be required on activities that may potentially cause pollution. The following list indicates some of these activities and the general attitude toward them in zone 1 areas, as included in the Severn-Trent and Southern WA aquifer protection policies.

(a) **Waste disposal**
   No waste disposal, except clean demolition rubble.
(b) **General development**
   (i)   No residential or industrial development that could not be connected to a public sewer.
   (ii)   No burial grounds.
   (iii) No oil pipelines.
   (iv)   No main foul sewers, except in approved materials.
   (v)   No industrial development involving the use, production or storage of oil, chemicals or fertilizers unless adequate protective measures agreed.
(c) **Mineral working and mining**
   (1)   No mineral working to within a specified height above the maximum local water table.
   (2)   No backfilling with imported fill.
   (3)   Strict control on mining and mining waste.
(d) **Agriculture**
   No development of intensive agricultural activities, including:
   (i)   intensive animal rearing units;
   (ii)   large manure heaps;

(iii)   silage clamps;
(iv)   farm drainage by soakage; or
(v)   excessive application of fertilizers unless proper measures agreed for collection
        and disposal of effluent.

(e) **Sewage and drainage**
(1)   No disposal of sewage sludge to land.
(2)   No storm overflows by soakage.
(3)   No discharge of surface water run-off to the aquifer if there is a risk of the water
       being polluted.
(4)   Soakaways for drainage to be of an approved design appropriate to the
       conditions.

In zone 2, the major aquifers, authority attitudes may differ with regard to activities that are permissible—for example, Southern WA would permit the disposal of domestic and commercial non-hazardous waste, whereas it would be more likely that Severn-Trent would oppose such disposal.

There is generally less constraint in the zone 2 area on the activities listed as being unacceptable than in the zone 1 area. For example septic tanks with sub-surface soakage are generally acceptable and there is less constraint on agricultural activities and disposal of sewage sludge to land though in many instances the details of any particular activity will be subject to consultation with the authority.

In the minor aquifers any activities that would result in a major source of pollution would generally be opposed. In this zone and the zone 4 category of other areas the authorities' main aim would be the protection of all licensed and known unlicensed sources.

POSSIBLE AREAS OF CONFLICT BETWEEN AQUIFER PROTECTION POLICIES AND OTHER ACTIVITIES

An aquifer protection policy will highlight the areas of potential conflicting interests between the water authorities' duty of protecting the water resources and other activities such as those of waste disposal authorities, agricultural activities, or in some instances the water authorities' policy of sewage sludge disposal to land.

Mineral Extraction and Waste Disposal

A large proportion of mineral extraction takes place from aquifers (sand and limestone) or from alluvial deposits (sand and gravel) that may themselves be an aquifer or may directly overlie an aquifer. These excavations provide an obvious choice for landfill sites, but a number of reports have indicated that landfill is a source of possible groundwater pollution[65] and these have been substantiated by the more recent DoE sponsored co-operative programme of research[22]. The DoE research programme was orientated towards the disposal of hazardous waste and as a result many of the problems associated with the disposal of domestic waste are still open to question. In recent years there have also been changes in waste disposal practice, both in the manner of site management, controlled tipping and compaction, capping and lining to control leachate generation etc., but also changes such as pulverizing and baling that may in turn produce significant changes in the nature of the leachate generated and also the move towards much larger waste disposal sites. Experience gained from the nationally based research programmes, and studies carried out by RWAs and WDAs, together with greater interchange of experience between the water and waste disposal industries, has led to a growing consensus of views on the best practicable method of disposing of waste without damage to the aquatic environment, as exemplified by the reports of the Landfill Practices Review Group[13].

In some instances planning authorities have encouraged the development of mineral excavation in a specific locality. This has resulted in some areas in which a locally large proportion of the outcrop of a minor aquifer has been quarried—for example, the Upper Magnesian Limestones in North Yorkshire near Ferrybridge. Planning consents may have been granted in the past with the conditions limited; the depth of working and excavation may have been taken to below the highest water table level during dry years, or dewatering may be used to allow working to well below the water table. With West Yorkshire County Council having difficulty in finding suitable waste disposal sites to keep pace with the volume of waste the Yorkshire WA comes under increasing pressure to allow the utilization of such a large series of excavations for waste disposal. Because of the size of the excavation, the proposed tipping of baled refuse, and a minimal saturated thickness of aquifer and the absence of guidelines and data, it would appear that waste disposal on such a large scale must result in major pollution of the aquifer.

Agricultural Activities

There is increasing evidence that the rise in nitrate concentration in groundwater is primarily due to agricultural activities, such as the change of cropping regimes and the application of nitrogenous fertilizers at rates in excess of the take-up rate by crops. At present there is no effective means of controlling the rise in nitrates. The increase in the number of intensive livestock units has resulted in an increased risk of pollution from the storage and disposal of effluent from these units. The Yorkshire WA, in conjunction with the Agricultural Development and Advisory Service and the National Farmers' Union, has prepared guidelines for the storage and disposal of animal wastes from intensive livestock units. The guidelines were drawn up in response to the increasing number of intensive livestock units, particularly piggeries, in the East Riding of Yorkshire, many of which are situated on the Chalk. Similar guidelines will be incorporated in the technical memoranda of the Severn-Trent aquifer protection policy[66].

Sewage Sludge to Land

Where a water authority disposes of sewage sludge to land suitable guidelines may be drawn up for the operation which, as part of their recommendations, will include practices to prevent pollution of groundwater. These guidelines or their appropriate parts will also be included in an aquifer protection policy if the authority has formulated one.

REHABILITATION

Introduction

Good management of activities such as solid waste disposal, effluent discharges and agricultural chemical use, together with the effective implementation of groundwater protection policies, should enable groundwater pollution to be minimised. However, it is inevitable that incidents will continue, both from past practices of waste disposal etc. which still actively produce leachate, and from accidental spillages. This section deals with actions that may be taken to limit or remove the pollution source and to restore damaged aquifers to use. The extent to which a contaminated aquifer can be restored will depend on a large number of factors, and in particular the economic value of the resource. As an ultimate goal, the complete restoration of an aquifer may be desirable. Restoration implies a return of the affected aquifer to the state which it was in before contamination occurred. Even when technically feasible, such restoration is likely to be extremely lengthy and costly. Rehabilitation of the system to the point at which the water quality is sufficiently improved for it to be put back to its original use may be more practicable in the short or medium term.

Remedial measures, aimed at rehabilitating the system, may be directed at:

(a) the source of the pollution,
(b) the groundwater abstraction point, and
(c) the whole groundwater catchment, by aquifer management.

The measures may be applicable singly or in any combination, depending on the scale and nature of the pollution incident.

In general, methods are available, at a cost, to control or ameliorate pollution and to rehabilitate aquifer contamination by point source pollution, but both in terms of water management and engineering techniques and within the framework of UK legislation, there are few currently practicable long-term solutions to the problems of dispersed source pollution.

Remedial Measures at the Source of Pollution

Remedial measures that may be taken at the pollution point depend on the source and the timescale of the pollution:

(i)   removal of the source of pollution;
(ii) limited duration, such as accidental spillage;
(iii) longer term, such as landfill;
(iv) continuous, such as sewage effluent discharge.

In some cases of pollution a considerable investigation may be required before the source of pollution is identified, and to identify the degree and extent of pollution that has taken place. Such an investigation is demanding in time and skilled manpower, and may require a large number of observation boreholes. Considerable costs may have been incurred before any work has been done to abate the pollution.

In other instances the source of pollution may be obvious and little preparatory work may be required before remedial action can be taken to counter the pollution.

Removal of the Source of Pollution. The most obvious remedy is to remove the source of pollution, although in many cases this may not be practicable. Stockpiles of salt used for de-icing roads have been the source of a number of cases of groundwater pollution, as for example, the pollution of a supply borehole at Leamington where chlorides rose from 30 mg/l to 375 mg/l.

In this case the remedial measures considered were:

(1) removing the salt to another stockpile not on an acquifer;
(2) a concrete holding bay for the salt/and collection of leachate;
(3) covering the salt to prevent leachate generation; or
(4) abandoning the source.

Local groundwater contamination may result from agricultural activity, such as silage clamp liquor. In such situations a change in practice can remove the source of pollution.

Contamination of wells from sewage may frequently be traced to a broken sewer pipe or a badly maintained or constructed septic tank or cesspit. Remedial measures are to repair broken sewers, and possibly use ductile iron in areas where sewers pass close to boreholes, and to inspect and empty septic tanks/cesspits at regular intervals. Pollution from a source such as a broken sewer may occur without any warning, may be difficult to trace and may discharge directly into a saturated aquifer, by-passing the purification processes afforded by the soil.

Although legislation and site licensing have considerably improved the situation with regard to landfill there may still be instances of pollution arising from illegal tipping or as a consequence of past practices. In a few situations it may be feasible to excavate the polluting matter and transport it to a secure storage.

However, in many cases removal of the leachate producing wastes will not be possible and measures may have to be taken to collect and dispose of the leachate in an environmentally acceptable manner. In some circumstances direct disposal of the leachate to a sewer may be possible. When that is not possible due either to the lack of a suitable sewer reticulation in the area, or because the variable volumes and strengths of the leachate make it unacceptable at a sewage works, on-site treatment of the leachate may be necessary before discharge externally. The simplest method, which amounts to crude aerobic treatment, but which requires substantial adjacent areas of land, is that of irrigation. The method has been employed for some years in Cornwall[67] onto both grassland and woodland, at rates of up to 6 mm/day (34 Ml/day/hectare), with minimal effect on the waters of receiving streams.

The recirculation of leachate through landfilled solid wastes has been suggested as offering potential advantages in reducing liquid volume, by evaporation, and reducing leachate strength by crude anaerobic treatment within the wastes[68]. Barber and Maris[69] have reported the results of a 3 year full-scale experiment at a site near Scarborough, in which significant decreases in COD were noted in the recirculated area, when compared to a control area. However, it was concluded that recirculation by itself would not provide a permanent solution to leachate management, although useful reduction in volume and strength of leachate could be obtained by careful management. With this constraint in mind, laboratory-scale studies of the application of aerobic treatment processes suggested that aeration accompanied by nutrient balance corrections, especially phosphorus addition, could achieve substantial decreases in organic strength within relatively short periods. A 29 m^3 aeration tank pilot-scale plant in Essex has been operated over a 12 month period with retention times down to 10 days, with 99 and 96 per cent removal of BOD and COD respectively[70], whilst a 1000 m^3 aerated lagoon, with 10 days' retention time has achieved a mean reduction in BOD of 99.4 per cent over 18 months at a site in central Wales[71].

As a principle it is clearly better to limit and control the volume of leachate produced than to be faced with subsequent, remedial treatment, measures. It is becoming increasingly common for landfill licence consent conditions to include the provision of adequate, properly engineered liners to retain leachate within the site, and capping layers to limit the ingress of water and leachate formation[13,72].

Immediate Action after Accidental Spillage. Pollution from accidental spillage, as for example a road or rail tanker, provides an obvious source of pollution and one of which the RWA would expect notification, although there is no legal requirement to report a spill. The consequences of such a spill depend on the nature and quantity of the pollutant, the hydrogeology of the aquifer and locality of the spill. The immediate problem may be dealt with by neutralizing, diluting or washing away the spilled material.

If action can be taken sufficiently quickly the contaminated spoil can be removed and disposed of in a safe manner. This may be possible for perhaps hours after the spill or at the most a few days. The presence of underground services may make excavation impracticable. If the water-table is shallow, trenching may be used to prevent lateral migration of the pollutant, and also as a means of recovering the pollutant.

Oil products are the most likely source of accidental pollution. Blair[73] noted that more than one-third of the pollution incidents in Anglian WA are due to oil spills, the majority from small sources, leaks from storage tanks, or spills from careless handling. Major spills are more likely when oil is in transit, including pipelines and from refineries and bulk storage areas. Where oil installations are on aquifers, preventative measures such as bunding should be installed to contain spills, and underground storage avoided where possible.

From Switzerland Dracos[74] described measures taken to protect an alluvial aquifer below a new railway marshalling yard from pollution by accidental spillage of petroleum. The aquifer was covered by a drainage blanket with reduced permeability to allow sufficient containment time for removal of material contaminated by spillage but allowing natural infiltration to occur.

Containment of the Polluted Groundwater at the Pollution Site. Once the pollution has passed through the soil zone into the unsaturated zone it may not be possible to carry out any remedial work until the pollution has reached the water table and the character of the pollutant may have been modified as it passed through the soil and unsaturated zone. Detailed knowledge of the local hydrogeology of the aquifer and of how the pollutant will behave in the aquifer is required, to determine the best solution for preventing contamination once the pollutant reaches the water table. The pollutant may completely dissolve or disperse in the water, as for example landfill leachates, or, as with oil, some fractions may dissolve in the water and others float on the surface of the water. The removal of pollutants from groundwater may be a long operation, and the techniques often rather primitive.

The movement of polluted groundwater may be controlled by pumping at a sufficiently high rate to create a cone of depression large enough to draw the polluted groundwater towards the borehole. In the case of oil or other immiscible or partially immiscible liquids scavenge pumping may be required to remove the oil from the surface of the water. There may be problems disposing of the contaminated water pumped from the borehole.

Scavenge pumping was considered as a method of removing phenolic pollution in the Chalk in Essex[75], but not pursued because of the disposal problems with the pumped water and the fact that there was no guarantee of success.

Day[76] has described contamination of Chalk boreholes by organic solvents due to leaking underground drains, which necessitated the boreholes being shut down for a year, scavenging of contaminated water from eight dug pits, and the replacement of the underground drains by surface drains. £200000 was spent on new effluent arrangements and £50000 on scavenge pumping.

Some of the difficulties involved in attempting to recover aviation fuel spilled from a pipeline into the Chalk have been described[73]; a large number of observation boreholes were required to define the extent of pollution, a 2 km pipeline to discharge the pumped groundwater, and a rapid rise in water level from recharge by snow melt caused new fissure systems to change the behaviour of the aquifer. The cost of this work has been about £120000 (about £60000/m^3 of oil recovered).

Initial recovery rates may be encouraging but the rate is likely to diminish and pumping may be required for several years. The cost of these remedial measures is high and they may be in operation for an extended period.

Continuous Discharge to the Aquifer. In some parts of the country, effluent from sewage treatment works is disposed into an aquifer by soakaway. In some instances the flows are quite high, but only in one or two instances has there been evidence of groundwater pollution at boreholes in the vicinity[77]. In situations where effluents are causing groundwater pollution remedial measures may be expensive—for example:

(*a*) Upgrading treatment works.
(*b*) Piping effluent to a more suitable disposal point.

In the case of both sewage effluent and landfill leachates a considerable improvement in water quality may be effected where there is passage through a thickness of unsaturated aquifer[15], although in many cases the heavy loading of organic pollutants will create anaerobic conditions in the unsaturated zone.

Remedial Measures at the Borehole

In many cases groundwater pollution is not apparent until the pollution has reached an abstraction borehole. Once a borehole has become polluted remedial measures may be uneconomic and such measures as can be taken may not be able to return the water to its former quality.

The majority of cases of borehole pollution arise from the borehole drawing in polluted groundwater from the aquifer but pollution of the borehole may arise from the immediate environs of the borehole itself—for example, ingress of flood water or spillage of oil at the well head. Pollution may arise through faulty construction of the borehole—for example, faulty grouting, or faulty or failed lining tubes. Some of the remedial measures that can be used are more normally associated with maintenance and development of boreholes, discussed in Chapter 13.

The removal of oil from borehole walls and lining may require jetting, swabbing and the use of detergents. There is always difficulty in removing contaminants that float on the water surface. Foam drilling fluids may assist in removing oil materials.

Pollution may be responsible for the growth of iron deposits or encrustation on the borehole walls or screen, or causing clogging of the aquifer around the borehole. The techniques of surging the borehole with a plunge block, racking with stop/start pumping, acidization, chlorination/sterilization are generally familiar and may restore or partially restore the yield of a borehole. If the source of pollution causing the trouble is not stopped the remedial action may need to be repeated at regular intervals, or if full restoration is not achieved, at increasingly frequent intervals, until the borehole has to be abandoned.

If groundwater pollution is severe a water authority has the option of abandoning the source and considering alternative sources. A private abstractor is unlikely to have the option of an alternative source, and may be dependent on a supply of good quality water.

The remedial measures that can be considered at the borehole are:

(i)   water treatment;
(ii) modification of the pumping regime; and
(iii) modification of the borehole.

Water Treatment. Groundwater resources have generally been of good quality and frequently require no treatment other than chlorination, which will deal with most bacteria and viruses. The presence of ammonia may give rise to taste problems with chlorination, and an excessive chlorine demand. This may be the first indication of pollution if there is no analysis of raw water, or chlorination is carried out directly into the borehole.

Where groundwater has become polluted it may be possible to make the water suitable for use by more extensive treatment, depending on the nature and severity of the pollution and the standard of water required. The range of possible treatment processes is wide and they are generally considered as being more applicable to treatment of surface water rather than groundwater—for example, ion exchange, lime-soda treatment, activated carbon.

It has already been commented that pollution frequently arises from the presence of phenols and petroleum products. Only minute quantities are required to give rise to objectionable tastes, especially when the water is chlorinated. Experiments on treating polluted well water with 0.07 mg/l chlorine dioxide to remove 30 mg/l phenols produced a treated water in which phenols could not be detected by taste or analysis.

An alternative method is to use an activated carbon treatment plant. Where a sophisticated treatment plant has to be installed the unit-cost of water will increase appreciably over the cost of an unpolluted groundwater source.

Modification of the Pumping Regime. An improvement in pumped water quality may be obtainable by carrying out alterations to the borehole or pumping system. Detailed knowledge of the borehole construction, the pumping equipment and the hydrogeology of the borehole are required in order to plan such changes. Poor quality water may enter the borehole from one specific fissure or horizon in the aquifer and flow conditions within the aquifer may change due to river or tidal influences.

If poor quality water is gaining access to a borehole at one particular level then consideration may be given to the possibility of excluding that water by grouting or by inserting additional casing. These measures may not always be practicable.

The Essex Water Company[78] have described a situation at Canvey Island with two boreholes penetrating the Chalk beneath a cover of London Clay. One borehole was contaminating both the Chalk aquifer and a second borehole, through the ingress of saline water from superficial deposits via a damaged casing. Attempts to grout the damaged casing failed because of the construction of the borehole, with one set of casing tubes inside another. Water was, therefore, pumped to waste from the damaged borehole to protect the other borehole from contamination.

Scavenge pumping has been used in the Permo-Triassic aquifer of North Shropshire to control the ingress of saline water into the boreholes[79]. After an extensive hydrogeological investigation, including geophysical logging, small capacity scavenger pumps were installed in the boreholes below the main pump suction levels. It was shown that a yield of 45 to 60 Ml/d could be obtained by pumping 1 Ml/d to waste. The waste water, discharged to a stream, contained chlorides in the range 1000–1600 mg/l and the supply water had the chloride concentration reduced from 350 to 158 mg/l. Additional running costs, and disposal arrangements for the waste water, may lead to the rejection of a scavenge pumping arrangement on economic grounds. An alternative to installing the scavenge pump in the abstraction well is to construct a borehole designed solely for scavenging.

The simple expedient of a reduced yield may sometimes produce more acceptable water quality. Analysis of water samples at different pumping rates may

TABLE 15.XIV.   Pump Suction Levels and Water Quality
(mg/l)

Borehole	Pump suction depth (m)	Nitrate	Total hardness	Sulphate
Hatfield 1	63	7.4	120	55
Hatfield 2	79.8	4.5	121	56
Hatfield 3	72.2	11	150	38
Hatfield 4	73	10.1	174	49
Heck 1	88	4.1	137	23
Heck 2	79	12.0	229	72

indicate a marked deterioration beyond a certain yield. The depth at which the pump suction is located may also have an important influence on pumped water quality. A number of Yorkshire WA pumping stations in the Triassic Sandstone exhibit different water quality from different boreholes on the same site. In some cases the boreholes on one site have different depths and lengths of casing and also pump suctions set at different levels. At the Hatfield Pumping Station there are four boreholes with depths between 137 m and 152 m, and casing between 30 and 36 m. Pump suction levels and nitrate levels are shown in Table 15.XIV. Generally, the shallowest pump has highest nitrate levels, except No. 1 borehole which though higher than the other pumps, has a lower pumping rate. A simpler case at the Heck pumping station, with two similar boreholes 115 m and 120 m deep, but with pump suction at 79 m and 88 m respectively, also shows a marked difference in nitrate levels. At Heck there is a marked contrast in the total hardness of the water from the two boreholes, with the high nitrates associated with lower hardness. The water quality at all these boreholes has been very stable for several years. The two Heck boreholes act in the manner of scavenge pumps, advocated above, but in this case by blending the two outputs an acceptable nitrate level has been achieved.

Modification of the Borehole. Pollution of a borehole may arise through poor construction, or subsequent failure of the casing—for example, in situations where aquifers containing poor quality water have been cased out. The most satisfactory solution is to carry out work to remedy the defect in the borehole, but this may be difficult and there may be no guarantee of success. Grouting up failed casing or installing and grouting in new casing may be considered but much depends on having adequate details of the original borehole construction, knowing the location and nature of the failure, and having sufficient diameter in the borehole to be able to carry out any modifications.

A careful hydrogeological investigation of a pumping station with problems may result in modifications or redevelopment that can improve the situation. Pollution of a source at Nutwell in the Triassic Sandstone in South Yorkshire was recorded by Nicholls[80], who considered that the source of pollution could be either infiltration from a colliery waste tip, or infiltration into the aquifer from a stream that carried mine drainage water, adjacent to the pumping station. Two original boreholes 760 mm diameter and 150 m deep with 15 m and 33 m of casing were constructed in 1925. The boreholes showed a slight increase in hardness, chlorides and sulphates but the iron content increased to above acceptable levels. Investigation showed the poor quality water to be due to infiltration from the stream, with access of contaminated water to the borehole past the lining tubes. As an additional problem the original boreholes also pumped sand at moderate to high abstraction rates. Two new boreholes were constructed as far from the stream as practicable, with 60 m of casing and 60 m of wellscreen and gravel pack. Pumping tests indicated that water quality from the new boreholes was similar to that of the original boreholes when sunk. A number of factors were considered in designing the new boreholes:

(1) The increased length of casing
  (a)   giving a longer travel path for contaminated water; and
  (b)   producing lower drawdowns, and hence leakage, in the sandstone/sand immediately below the stream because of the contrasts between vertical and horizontal permeability of the sandstone.
(2) By increasing the pumping rate, the proportion of flow drawn from the polluted stream would be reduced, leading to greater dilution.
(3) Gravel packs and well screens were required to allow high abstraction rates without sand pumping.

Aquifer Management

Many of the remedial measures considered above are suitable for cases of point-source groundwater pollution. However, the character of dispersed-source pollution, such as nitrate from agriculture, renders these methods ineffective, or successful for only a short period of time. In the cases considered a more acceptable quality of water could be obtained by blending the output from several boreholes at one site. The same procedure of blending can be extended to cover several pumping stations, so that water from one pumping station failing in one criterion, such as high nitrates, is mixed with water from another station that has low nitrates but which may fail on some other criterion. The feasibility of such a scheme depends on adequate knowledge of the hydrogeology of the aquifer, and whether different qualities of groundwater occur sufficiently close to allow blending to be carried out with relatively short lengths of main.

In the Triassic Sandstone of Southern Yorkshire many of the older pumping stations situated on the recharge zone of the aquifer have nitrate levels above the recommended level of 11.3 mg N/l. The aquifer is covered in places by thick drift deposits which include boulder clay. Under these deposits the groundwater in the Sandstone is sometimes of very good quality, with exceptionally low levels of chlorides, sulphates, and nitrates, but because of the reducing conditions iron and/or manganese may be unacceptably high. At Carlton an existing pumping station with nitrate levels of 10.0 to 13.0 mg N/l has been complemented by a new station 2 km away with nitrates less than 0.1 mg/l but manganese levels of 0.25 mg/l. By controlling the output from the two stations nitrate levels are reduced though care must be exercised to ensure that manganese does not become troublesome.

A more familiar problem that demands aquifer management as a solution is saline water intrusion, as has occurred in a number of aquifers such as the Bunter Sandstone along the Mersey, the Chalk along the Thames Estuary, the Humber Estuary at Hull and Grimsby, and along the south coast of England, and the Magnesian Limestones at Sunderland and Hartlepool.

It may be more difficult to design an acceptable programme of aquifer management in the situation where a large number of private abstractions are involved compared to the situation where the RWA is the major abstractor.

There are a number of methods for reducing or controlling saline intrusion:

(i)   Reducing the total abstraction.
(ii) Pumping from a larger number of lower yielding boreholes.
(iii) Pumping from shallow wells and adits.

(iv) Pumping from coastal stations in the winter and inland stations in the summer.

Examples of methods (iii) and (iv) can be found in the Chalk in the Southern WA area[77]. In the Chalk of the Isle of Thanet extensive use of adits only 3 m below the groundwater level has been instrumental in reducing the extent of the saline intrusion.

In the Chalk of the Brighton area a system was established in 1945 of pumping coastal stations in the winter to abstract surplus recharge water that would otherwise be lost to the sea, and as chloride levels rose to approximately 100 mg/l switching to inland stations in the summer. As a result of this controlled abstraction groundwater levels in the Brighton area have risen by up to 5 m in the last 20 years, despite an overall 25 per cent increase in abstraction. With an increase in demand of 50 per cent forecast by 1991 an extensive investigation has been made of the aquifer, including infra-red aerial surveys, drilling and logging of boreholes and mathematical modelling.

An example of saline pollution from a somewhat different cause is the contamination of the Chalk aquifer in East Kent by mine drainage[77,81]. This case is instructive in that the pollution was caused by mine drainage discharging 318000 tonnes of salt into the aquifer between 1906 and 1973, the majority of it between 1955 and 1973. Although the pollution was recognized in 1930 it took 30 years to abate the pollution. An extensive investigation was made to assess the extent of pollution (27 km^2) and whether clearance pumping could be used to rehabilitate the aquifer in a shorter time. It was concluded that clearance pumping would not significantly shorten the time of 30 years that was required for natural clearance to reduce chloride levels to 200 mg/l. This example is salutory in the light of hindsight:

(1) Much of the pollution was caused when the problem had been recognized but legal powers were not available to stop the pollution in the timescale required for rehabilitation of the aquifer; and

(2) Little could be done to speed up the natural processes.

7. REFERENCES

1. Commission of the European Communities 1980 "Council directive relating to the quality of water intended for human consumption (80/778/EEC)".
2. Tarrant, K. R. and Tatton, J. O. G. 1968 *Nature, London*, 219, 725, Organochlorine pesticides in rainwater in the British Isles.
3. Thompson, G. M. and Hayes, J. M. 1979 *Wat. Res. Res.*, 15, 546, Trichlorofluoromethane in groundwater—a possible tracer and indicator of groundwater age.
4. Spears, D. A. and Reeves, M. J. 1975 *Q. J. eng. Geol.*, 8, 255, The influence of superficial deposits on groundwater quality in the Vale of York.
5. Edmunds, W. M. 1977 'Groundwater geochemistry—controls and processes' in Wilkinson, W. B. (Ed.) "Groundwater quality—measurement, prediction and protection". Proceedings, Water Research Conference, Reading. WRC, Medmenham.
6. Wilkinson, W. B. and Edworthy, K. J. 1981 'Groundwater quality monitoring systems—money wasted?' in van Duijvenbooden, W., Glasborgen, P. and van Lelyveld, H. (Eds.) "Quality of groundwater", Proceedings, International Symposium, Netherlands, 1981, "Studies in environmental science 17", Elsevier.
7. Naylor, J. A. *et al* 1978 "The investigation of landfill sites", Water Research Centre, Technical Report No. TR 91, WRC, Medmenham.
8. Brereton, N. R. and Wilkinson, W. B. 1977 'Flow mechanisms governing the movement of a pollutant in a groundwater system' in Wilkinson, W. B. (Ed.) (see ref. 5).
9. Marsh, J. M. and Lloyd, J. W. 1980 *Ground Water*, 18, 366, Details of hydrochemical variations in flowing wells.
10. Price, M. Morris, B., and Robertson, A. 1982 *J. Hydrol.*, 54, 401, A study of intergranular and fissure permeability in Chalk and Permian aquifers, using double-packer injection testing.
11. Edmunds, W. M. and Bath, A. H. 1976 *Environ. Sci. Tech.*, 10, 467, Centrifuge extraction and chemical analysis of interstitial waters.

12. Edworthy, K. J. and Baxter, K. M. 1981 "Virology of waste water recharge of the Chalk aquifer; Part 1, hyrogeology and sampling". Proceedings of Conference on Viruses and Waste Water Treatment, University of Surrey, Guildford, UK, pp. 53-58. Pergamon Press, London.

13. Department of the Environment 1985 "Landfilling wastes", Draft synopsis of the report of the Landfill Practices Review Group, HMSO, London.

14. Department of the Environment 1985 "Hazardous waste management, an overview", First report, the Hazardous Waste Inspectorate, HMSO, London.

15. Baxter, K. M. and Clark, L. 1984 "Effluent recharge—the effects of effluent recharge on groundwater quality", Water Research Centre, Technical Report No. TR 199, WRC, Medmenham.

16. Hoare, M. J., Eastwood, J. W. and Brown, S. 1979, Surveyor, 24.5. '79, 12, Groundwater contamination: combatting problems on site.

17. Ministry of Housing and Local Government 1961 "Pollution of water by tipped refuse", HMSO, London.

18. Department of the Environment 1980 "Digest of environmental pollution and water statistics, No. 3", HMSO, London.

19. Barber, C., Maris, P. J. and Johnson, R. G. 1980 "Behaviour of wastes in landfill sites: study of the leaching of selected industrial wastes in large-scale test cells, Edmonton, N. London", WLR Technical Note No. 69, WRC, Medmenham.

20. Department of the Environment 1984 "The selection of landfill sites", Landfill Practices Review Group, WLR Technical Note No. 64, HMSO, London.

21. Robinson, H. D. and Maris, P. J. 1979 "Leachate from domestic waste: generation, composition and treatment: a review", Water Research Centre, Technical Report No. TR 108, WRC, Medmenham.

22. Department of the Environment 1978 "Co-operative programme of research on the behaviour of hazardous wastes in landfill sites", Final report of the Policy Review Committee, HMSO, London.

23. Barber, C. 1982 "Leaching of hazardous wastes in landfills", Proceedings, IPHC Conference, University of Nottingham.

24. Barber, C. et al 1981 'Groundwater contamination by landfill leachate: distribution of contaminants and factors affecting plume development at three sites, UK' in van Duijvenbooden, W. et al (see ref.6).

25. Aubic, J. 1981 'Accidental water pollution caused by 16000 bottles of Sauternes' in van Duijvenbooden, W. et al (see ref. 6).

26. Schwille, F. 1981 'Groundwater pollution in porous media by fluids immiscible with water', in van Duijvenbooden, W. et al (see ref. 6).

27. Holmes, R. 1984 Q. J. eng. Geol., 17, 9, Comparison of different methods of estimating infiltration at a landfill site in south Essex with implications for leachate management and control.

28. Department of the Environment 1976 "Waste management paper No. 4—the licensing of waste disposal sites", HMSO, London.

29. Fox, I. A. and Rushton, K. R. 1976 Ground Water, 14, 21, Rapid recharge in a limestone aquifer.

30. Wellings, S. R. 1984 J. Hydrol., 69, 259, Recharge of the Upper Chalk aquifer at a site in Hampshire, England. 1. Water balance and unsaturated flow.

31. Oakes, D. B. and Edworthy, K. J. 1977 'Field measurements of dispersion coefficients in the United Kingdom' in W. B. Wilkinson (Ed.) (see ref. 5).

32. Behrens, H. and Seiler, K-P 1981 'Field tests on propagation of conservative tracers in fluvioglacial gravels of Upper Bavaria' in van Duijvenbooden, W. et al (see ref. 6).

33. Clark, L. 1984 "Groundwater development of the Chepstow Block: a study of the impact of domestic waste disposal on a karstic limestone aquifer in Gwent, South Wales", Proceedings of International Groundwater Symposium, Quebec, Canada, II, 300.

34. Oakes, D. B. 1977 'Use of idealised models in predicting the pollution of water supplies due to leachate from landfill sites' in W. B. Wilkinson (Ed.) (see ref. 5).

35. Millbank, P. 1976 Surveyor, 6.8 '76, 28, Results of long-term monitoring of industrial wastes at a site in Kent.

36. Ross, C. A. M. 1980 Q. J. eng. Geol., 13, 177, Experimental assessment of pollutant migration in the unsaturated zone of the Lower Greensand.

37. Campbell, D. J. V. et al 1983 Waste Man. Res., 1, 31, Attenuation of potential pollutants in landfill leachate by Lower Greensand.

38. Robinson, H. D. and Lucas, J. L. 1984 Wat. Sci. Tech., 17, 477, Leachate attenuation in the unsaturated zone beneath landfills: instrumentation and monitoring of a site in southern England.

39. Newman, J. R. and Ross, C. A. M. 1985 "Mineralogical and geochemical controls on heavy metal pollution in monolith lysimeters", Fluid Processes Research Group, British Geological Survey Report 85-5, BGS, Keyworth.

40. Harris, R. C. and Parry, E. L. 1982 'Investigations into domestic refuse leachate attenuation in the unsaturated zone of Triassic Sandstones' in Perry, R. (Ed.) "Effects of waste disposal on groundwater and surface water", Proceedings of Symposium, 1st Scientific General Assembly, IAHS, Exeter, UK. (IAHS Publication No. 139).

41. Harris, R. C. and Lowe, D. R. 1984 *Q. J. eng. Geol.*, 17, 57, Changes in the organic fraction of leachate from two domestic refuse sites in the Sherwood Sandstone, Nottinghamshire.
42. Stiff, M. J. and Young, C. P. 1977 'Factors affecting the transport of pollutants within and away from landfill sites' in Wilkinson, W. B. (Ed.) (see ref. 5).
43. Pellegrini, M. and Zavatti, A. 1980 'Lead pollution in the groundwater of the Modena alluvial plain, Po Valley, Italy' in Jackson, R. E. (Ed.) "Aquifer contamination and protection", IHP Series, Studies and Reports in Hydrology No. 30, 305, UNESCO, Paris.
44. Caous, J. Y., Caudron, M. and Dumont, D. 1978 'Pollution industrielle de la nappe de la craie par le chrome hexavalent dans le Vimen (Somme)' in "Proc. Coloque Régional—Hydrogéologie de la Craie du bassin de Paris", pp 89-94, Rouen 1978, BRGM, Orleans.
45. Greene, L. A. and Walker, P. 1970 *Wat. Treat. Exam.*, 19, 169, Nitrate pollution of chalk waters.
46. Satchell, R. L. H. and Edworthy, K. J. 1972 "Artificial recharge: Bunter Sandstone", Trent Research Programme No. 7, WRB, Reading.
47. Foster, S. S. D. and Crease, R. I. 1974 *J. IWE.*, 28, 178, Nitrate pollution of chalk groundwater in East Yorkshire: a hydrogeological appraisal.
48. Greene, L. A. 1980 *Proc. ICE*, 69, 73, Nitrate in groundwater in the Anglian region.
49. Young, C. P., Oakes, D. B. and Wilkinson, W. B. 1976 *Ground Water*, 14, 426, Prediction of future nitrate concentrations in groundwater.
50. Royal Commission on Environmental Pollution 1979 7th Report, "Agriculture and pollution", HMSO, London.
51. Standing Technical Advisory Committee on Water Quality 1984 "Fourth Biennial Report, February 1981—March 1983", HMSO, London.
52. Croll, B. T. 1985 "The effects of the agricultural use of herbicides on fresh water", WRC/WHO Conference, Stirling.
53. Young, C. P., Hall, E. S. and Oakes, D. B. 1976 "Nitrate in groundwater: studies on the Chalk near Winchester, Hampshire", Water Research Centre, Technical Report No. TR 31, WRC, Medmenham.
54. Young, C. P. and Gray, E. M. 1978 "Nitrate in groundwater—the distribution of nitrate in the Chalk and Triassic Sandstone aquifers", Water Research Centre, Technical Report No. TR 69, WRC, Medmenham.
55. Oakes, D. B., Young, C. P. and Foster, S. S. D. 1981 *Sci. Total Environ.*, 21, 17, The effects of farming practices on groundwater quality in the United Kingdom.
56. Young, C. P. 1981 *Wat Sci. Tech.*, 13, 1137, The distribution and movement of solutes derived from agricultural land in the principal aquifers of the United Kingdom, with particular reference to nitrate.
57. Young, C. P. and Hall, E. S. 1977 'Investigations into factors affecting the nitrate content of groundwater' in Wilkinson, W. B. (Ed.) (see ref. 5).
58. Young, C. P. 1985 "Nitrate in groundwater and the effects of ploughing on release of nitrates", WRC/WHO Conference, Stirling.
59. Ryden, J. C., Ball, P. R. and Garwood, E. A. 1984 *Nature, London*, 311, 50, Nitrate leaching from grassland.
60. Whitelaw, K. and Rees, J. F. 1980 *J. Geomicrobiol.*, 2, 179, Nitrogen transforming bacteria in the unsaturated zone of the Chalk.
61. Oakes, D. B. 1982 'Nitrate pollution of groundwater resources—mechanisms and modelling' in Zwirnmann K-H. (Ed.) "Non-point nitrate pollution of municipal water supply sources; issues of analysis and control", International Institute for Applied Systems Analysis, Collaborative Proceedings Series CP-82-S4, 207, The Institute, Laxenburg, Austria.
62. Goodman, A. H. and Beckett, M. J. 1977 'Legislative aspects of groundwater quality' in Wilkinson, W. B. (Ed.) (see ref. 5).
63. Exler, H. J. 1977 'Groundwater protection in Germany' in Wilkinson, W. B. (Ed.) (see ref. 5).
64. Renshaw, D. 1980. *Wat. Qual. Bull.*, 5, 41 and 49, Water pollution control in England.
65. Ministry of Housing and Local Government and Scottish Development Department 1970 "Disposal of solid toxic wastes", HMSO, London.
66. Selby, K. H. and Skinner, A. C. 1981 'Management and protection of quality of groundwater resources in the English Midlands' in van Duijvenbooden, W. *et al* (see ref. 6).
67. Rowe, A. 1979 *Solid Wastes*, 69, 603, Tip leachate treatment by land irrigation.
68. Robinson, H. D., Barber, C. and Maris, P. J. 1982 *Wat. Pollut. Control*, 81, 465, Generation and treatment of leachate from domestic wastes in landfill.
69. Barber, C. and Maris, P. J. 1984 *Q. J. eng. Geol.*, 17, 19, Recirculation of leachate as a landfill management option: benefits and operational problems.
70. Maris, P. J., Harrington, D. W. and Chismon, G. L. 1984 *Wat. Pollut. Control*, 83, 521, Leachate treatment with particular reference to aerated lagoons.
71. Robinson, H. D. and Davies, J. 1985 *Surveyor*, 165, 7, Automatic answer to leachate treatment.
72. Hoeks, J. and Agelink, G. J. 1982 'Hydrological aspects of sealing waste tips with liners and soil

covers' in Perry, R. (Ed.) (see ref. 40).

73. Blair, A. H. 1980 *J. IWES,* 34, 557, Groundwater pollution by oil products.

74. Dracos, Th. 1974 'Protection of aquifers against petroleum pollution in Switzerland' in Cole, J. A. (Ed.) "Groundwater pollution in Europe", Proceedings, Water Research Association Conference, Reading. Water Information Center, Inc., Port Washington, New York.

75. Aspinwall, R. 1974 'Naphtha leakage at Purfleet and spillage of leaded fuel at South Stifford, Essex' in Cole, J. A. (Ed.) (see ref. 74).

76. Day, J. B. W. 1974 'A recent case history of groundwater pollution by organic solvents' in Cole, J. A. (Ed.) (see ref. 74).

77. Headworth, H. G. and Wilkinson, W. B. 1977 'Measures for the protection and rehabilitation of aquifers in the United Kingdom' in Wilkinson, W. B. (Ed.) (see ref. 5).

78. Essex Water Company 1974 'Saline pollution of two boreholes at Canvey Island' in Cole, J. A. (Ed.) (see ref. 74).

79. Tate, T. K. and Robertson, A. S. 1971 "Investigations into high salinity groundwater at the Woodfield Pumping Station, Wellington, Shropshire", Water Supply Paper of the Institute of Geological Sciences, Research Report No. 6.

80. Nicholls, G. D. 1974 'Pollution affecting wells in the Bunter Sandstone' in Cole, J. A. (Ed.) (see ref. 74).

81. Headworth, H. G., Puri, S. and Rampling, B. H. 1980 *Q. J. eng. Geol.,* 13, 105, Contamination of the Chalk aquifer by mine drainage at Tilmanstone, East Kent, UK.

Chapter 16

THE LAW RELATING TO GROUNDWATER IN THE UNITED KINGDOM

1. INTRODUCTION

THE LAW relating to groundwater in the United Kingdom is primarily to be found in the common law as enunciated by the judges in the course of litigation, and the legal rights and obligations as between private persons rest almost entirely on the common law. Except to the extent that Parliament by public or private legislation has expressly overridden the common law a statutory water undertaker is in no different position in relation to a private person than are private persons *inter se*.

Water authorities, statutory water undertakers and their predecessors over many years have obtained numerous private Acts and statutory orders having effect within defined areas. Such Acts and orders must not be overlooked in considering the rights and obligations of the undertakers, and the protection which may be afforded to the individual in those areas.

It is hoped that this chapter will assist the engineer and the hydrogeologist in understanding the common law relating to the abstraction and pollution of groundwater, support from groundwater, and the statutory provisions which have supervened as may be sufficient for their purposes. But a little knowledge may be a dangerous thing and, as some of the leading cases may turn on distinctions not always readily apparent, the engineer and the hydrogeologist should seek legal advice before getting out of their depth.

As shown in Chapters 2, 4 and 6 no valid scientific distinction can be made between groundwater flowing in a known and defined natural underground channel (flow in karst systems or fissure flow) and water percolating or oozing through underground strata (intergranular flow). But the courts in the case law for more than a century have held such a distinction to be of fundamental importance in relation to the rights and obligations of neighbouring owners of land in respect of abstraction of groundwater. The common law distinction will prevail unless and until the House of Lords, as the supreme judicial body, can be persuaded of the scientific view, although the regulation of "water rights" achieved through legislation, such as the Water Resources Act 1963, which applies in England and Wales, may make common law cases of less practical importance. Abstractions of water which are exempt from licensing will be wholly subject to principles of common law.

The common law (i.e. the case law) of England and Wales is generally followed in relation to Scotland and Northern Ireland, as indeed are Scottish and Northern Irish cases in relation to England and Wales. The statute law of England and Wales does not apply, however, to Scotland or to Northern Ireland, although it frequently happens that the statutes of England and Wales are shortly afterwards re-enacted by the respective legislatures in relation to Scotland and Northern Ireland with only minor amendments and modifications.

2. COMMON LAW

ENGLAND, WALES AND NORTHERN IRELAND

The courts have never been required to define groundwater, sometimes referred to as subterranean water, it being a question of fact. The meaning of "groundwater" under the Water Resources Act 1963 is defined later in this chapter.

Abstraction—Underground Channels and Percolating Water

In relation to abstraction of groundwater common law distinguishes between water flowing in a defined underground channel or subterranean stream and water which is oozing or percolating in the underground strata. It will be seen however, from *Chasemore v Richards* that as between a surface riparian owner and an owner of underground strata (but not as between two riparian owners) a surface river or stream may be regarded at common law as "groundwater" and the rights and obligations determined accordingly if the flow is primarily sustained by a spring or other groundwater source.

In *Chasemore v Richards (1843-60) All ER 77*, the appellant was the occupier of an ancient mill on the River Wandle about a mile from Croydon which for upwards of sixty years had been driven by water from the river. The flow in the Wandle upstream of the mill was partly maintained by springs fed by rainfall on Croydon sinking into the upper ground and flowing and percolating through the strata. The local Board of Health sunk a large well to a depth of 74 feet (22.5 m) for the purpose of supplying water and took some water which otherwise would have percolated through the strata and found its way to the river above the appellant's mill. The court held that the principle that a proprietor of land had the right to have water come to him in its natural state in flow, quantity and quality but must let it pass from him without obstruction (which applied to a surface stream) did not apply to water percolating through underground strata, which had no certain course and no defined limit, but oozed through the soil in every direction in which the rain penetrates. But now see Section 29 of the Water Resources Act 1963 (in Section 3 of this chapter). The owner of land under which there is water which is not in a known and defined channel can appropriate the water, even though in so doing he deprives an adjacent land owner of water which he has enjoyed for many years. That was so whether the diversion of the water was caused by the action of a private person in sinking a well for his domestic use, or the action of a public authority in taking the water from a large area of land owned by them and supplying it for the use of the residents of that area.

As was subsequently recognised in *Ballard v Tomlinson (1881-85) All ER 688*, *Chasemore v Richards* did not decide, as it is sometimes stated, that a person has no right to groundwater percolating under his land. Under common law, a person may abstract all the percolating groundwater which it is physically possible for him to take, but he has no right to complain if that water is diverted from his land by some interference by a neighbouring owner or by a water undertaker exercising statutory powers. Percolating water below the surface of the earth is a common reservoir or source of supply in which no-one has any property, but in which everyone has the right of appropriating the whole, so far as he is physically able to do so.

The principle in *Chasemore v Richards* was applied in *New River Company v Johnson (1860) 2 E&E 435* where it was held that no action would lie when water collected in a well was drained away by a sewer constructed under statutory powers. As Compton, J. observed, the only remedy of the owner was to sink his well deeper.

It was held in *R v Metropolitan Board of Works (1863) 3 B&S 710* that even when water was drained away by a sewer constructed under the Metropolitan Sewers Act, which provided for the payment of compensation to persons suffering injury from the construction of the authorised works, the plaintiff would not be entitled to compensation because compensation was only payable in respect of such works where, but for the statutory powers, the plaintiff would have had a claim for damages at common law, and it had been established by *Chasemore v Richards* that there was not such right to damages.

The distinction between percolating water and water flowing in a stream was affirmed and applied in *Grand Junction Canal Company v Shugar (1871) LR 6 Ch 483* where a landowner was restrained from drawing off subterranean waters flowing in a known and defined channel when the effect was to drain away water flowing in a defined surface channel on adjoining land. Hatherley, L. C., relying on *Chasemore v Richards*, said that if an owner is simply using what he has a right to use and leaving his neighbour to use the rest of the water as it flows on then the owner has a right to do so, but he must not appropriate that which he has no right to appropriate to himself. His Lordship did not consider that *Chasemore v Richards*, or any other case, had decided more than that an owner had the right to all the water which he can draw from the different sources which may percolate underground. But that had no bearing at all on what he may do with regard to water which is in a defined channel, and which he is not to touch. A person is not, by his operations or by any act on his part, to diminish the water which runs in a defined channel, because the water is not only for that person but for his neighbours also, who have a clear right to use it and have it come to them unimpaired in quality and undiminished in quantity.

An attempt was made to circumvent *Chasemore v Richards* in the case of *Bradford Corporation v Pickles (1895-99) All ER 984,* which went to the House of Lords. the plaintiffs sought to prevent the defendant diverting groundwater when he was doing so, not because he required the water himself, but maliciously to disrupt the plaintiffs' source of supply in the hope that they would then be compelled to pay him for the water which they were draining from under his land. A local Act provided that it would not be lawful for any person other than the water company (predecessors to the Corporation) to divert, alter or appropriate in any manner other than by law they may be legally entitled to, any water supplying or flowing from the springs, or to do any act matter or thing whereby the spring water may be drawn off or diminished. A subsequent section imposed a daily penalty if anyone did illegally divert or appropriate such water.

Hatherley, L. C. said that the words of the local Act contemplated that persons other than the water company "may be legally entitled" to appropriate water. He read the section as saying that the thing which was prohibited was taking or diverting water which had been appropriated and paid for by the water company; but the thing which was not prohibited was taking water which had not reached the company's premises, to the property in which no title was given by the section, and which, by the very act complained of, never could reach the company's premises at all.

The requirement that an underground channel must be known does not mean that it must have been revealed by excavation or exposure. Knowledge by reasonable inference from existing and observed facts in the natural or pre-existing surface of the ground will be sufficient.

In *Bleachers Association v Chapel-en-le-Frith RDC (1932) All ER 60*, Luxmoore, J., following two Irish cases, considered whether groundwater was percolating or oozing through strata, or was flowing in a defined channel or watercourse below ground. The headnote to the case states that the question of fact to be determined is whether the underground water appearing at a given point and then becoming a surface stream comes from subterranean percolation or oozing water or whether it flows in a defined channel or watercourse underground to the point where it appeared. To decide that question it lay on the party asserting his right to the flow to show affirmatively, not as a matter of fact, but as a reasonable inference from known facts, that the water came to the place of emergence, not by percolating or oozing, but in a defined channel; that the plaintiffs had failed to prove, and they were not entitled to the injunction they claimed.

As regards subterranean water flowing in a known and defined underground channel, the rights and liabilities at common law are the same as those relating to a surface water stream as enunciated in *Young & Company v Bankiers Distillery Company (1891-94) All ER 439*. There have been a number of cases relating to "extra ordinary and justifiable use" of surface water streams, but such cases are unlikely to have any practical application to underground streams. The licensing provisions of the Water Resources Act 1963 make the application of such cases even less likely, as an "extra ordinary and justifiable use" can only be enjoyed if authorised by a licence. It would appear, following the recent case of *Cargill v Gotts (1981) All ER 682*, that in considering the rights and obligations at common law as between individuals the court may take into account whether or not such rights and obligations have been the subject of a licence under the Water Resources Act 1963.

Support from Groundwater

Pumping or drawing groundwater and thereby lowering the water level or pressure in adjacent strata leads to an increase in effective stress in the strata causing it to compress, which may manifest itself as surface settlement. In most situations, particularly in hard rocks, such effects are very small and will go unnoticed, but where the abstraction is from compressible strata (e.g. aquifer with intermittent layers of thick clay), appreciable surface settlement may result, and in extreme cases damage to property or change in surface drainage patterns can occur.

Aquifer systems with a high compressibility are relatively uncommon in the UK. The withdrawal of hydrological support has been the subject of some litigation, and it is well established that there is no right of support from groundwater or subjacent support by water. In *Popplewell v Hodgkinson (1861-73) All ER* it was held that the plaintiff had no inherent right to subjacent support by water. It was also held that as it must have been contemplated that the adjacent land would be used for building purposes, there could be no implied undertaking not to put it to such purposes, or to carry out such work as was customary prior to the construction of a building. A right to support cannot be acquired by prescription, that is, by the enjoyment of the support over a period of time.

In *Jordison v Sutton Gas Company (1899) 2 Ch 251* the court decided that the case of *Popplewell v Hodgkinson (1861) 73 All ER 996*, which related to groundwater, did not apply to wet running silt, and held that the plaintiff had a right of support from such silt. The problem was again considered in *Fletcher v Birkenhead Corporation (1907) 1 KB 205* where the Corporation were, by a special Act incorporating the Waterworks Clauses Act 1847, authorised to construct a reservoir and take water from underground. After completion of the works and in the course of pumping water a bed of wet running silt was abstracted which resulted in subsidence. The Corporation contended that as the water was being taken under statutory powers they had no liability to anyone who suffered damage as a result, relying on the principle that there can be no liability in damages for any nuisance resulting from the exercise of statutory powers. But the Court of Appeal held that Sections 6 and 12 of the Waterworks Clauses Act 1847 provided for the payment of compensation in the event of damage caused by the use or maintenance of waterworks, and as the running silt was being drawn away in the course of the use of the reservoir, the plaintiff in accordance with the decision in *Jordison v Sutton Gas Company* was entitled to compensation because he had a right to support from the running silt. The relevant cases were reviewed by Plowman, J. in the recent case of *Longbrook Properties Limited v Surrey County Council and others (1969) All ER 1424*, where the several defendants concerned in various ways in the construction of a motorway made excavations in proximity to the plaintiffs' land, from which they had to pump water to keep the workings dry. It was alleged that the plaintiffs' buildings suffered some subsidence in consequence. The plaintiffs did not plead that they had a right to support, as clearly the precedents were against them on that, but they argued that the defendants must not use their property so as to cause a nuisance to a neighbour, and that the nuisance could have been avoided had they not also been negligent in that they pumped away water with the knowledge that damage would be caused to the plaintiffs' property and that they were negligent in failing to consider the safety of their neighbours.

Plowman, J. concluded that the authorities cited on behalf of the defendants established that a man may abstract from under his land water which percolates in underground strata to whatever extent he pleases, notwithstanding that that may result in the abstraction of water percolating under the land of his neighbour, and thereby cause him injury. There was no room for the law of nuisance or negligence to operate. If there were, it seemed to him highly probable that the courts would already have held so. In *Chasemore v Richards* the opportunity was there, as the water undertakers were aware of the natural and probable consequences of what they were doing, but there was no suggestion in the House of Lords that that was a relevant matter. Moreover, since it was not actionable to cause damage by the abstraction of underground water, even where that was done maliciously *(Bradford Corporation v Pickles)* it would be illogical that it should be actionable if it were done carelessly. A claim in nuisance could fare no better, since nuisance involved an unlawful interference with a man's use or enjoyment of land, but the authorities showed that the interference was not unlawful.

He suggested that the conclusion may be thought to be unsatisfactory having regard to the recent trend in cases in negligence. He said that if indeed the defendants could have avoided damaging the plaintiffs' property by the exercise of reasonable care, it might be asked why they should not be liable for their failure to do so. But so far as a court of first instance was concerned, it must be taken as settled that the restrictions which the law imposes on a landowner's freedom of action for the benefit of his neighbours were not such as to give the plaintiffs a cause of action in that case.

Pollution

Common law will restrain a person from polluting groundwater whether it percolates through an aquifer or flows in a known defined underground channel, although it appears that the principles under which it does so will differ according to whether the water is percolating or flowing.

The principle enunciated by the Irish Court of Appeal in *Ewart v Belfast Guardians (1881) 9 LR 172*, when considering *Chasemore v Richards*, that there can be no "property" in underground water may be misleading. It might appear inconsistent that common law holds that a person has no right to prevent a neighbour diverting percolating water from his well, but that he has a right to prevent a neighbour from polluting the water which percolates to that well. Although common law does not recognise any right to the water, it does impose on all persons a duty not to cause a nuisance to their neighbours.

As Blackburn, J. put it in *Hodkinson v Ennor (1863) 4 B&S 229*, "I take the law to be as stated in *Tenant v Goldwin (1704) 2 Lord Raymond 1089* that you must not injure the property of your neighbour, and that consequently if filth is created on any man's land, then in the quaint language of the report of that case 'he whose dirt it is must keep it that it may not trespass'".

In *Ballard v Tomlinson (1881-85) All ER 688* it was held that, while no one has at any time any property in water percolating below the surface of the earth even when it is under his land, yet every land owner has a right to appropriate that water while it is under his land, even by artificial means such as pumping, and he has a right to appropriate it uncontaminated by any act of any other person. That is to say, that although a person has no right to take percolating water, if he is able to take it then he is entitled to take it without any pollution by his neighbour.

The law as to the pollution of water flowing in a known and defined underground stream is the same as that applying to the pollution of a surface stream, and is encapsulated in the well-known judgement of Lord Macnaughton in *Young & Company v Bankiers Distillery Company (1891-94) All ER 439* which (in relating to pollution) may be summarised as follows:

"A riparian proprietor is entitled to have the water in a known and defined underground stream over which his land lies flow down to him as it has been accustomed to flow down to his property without sensible alteration in its character or quality"

COMMON LAW IN SCOTLAND

The right to abstract water from surface and underground sources in Scotland is founded in the common law, and on several statutes which govern abstractions for specific purposes.

Under the common law of Scotland, where a stream rises in and flows to the sea within the lands of one owner, he has absolute proprietary rights over it. In every other case, running water is not the subject of property, but a riparian owner is entitled, subject to the rights of opposite proprietors, to make use of the water in a stream in his lands provided he returns it unpolluted in quality and unaffected in force and quantity at or before the point where the stream leaves his lands, except insofar as the water has been consumed for 'primary purposes' such as domestic use for drinking, cooking, baking and washing etc. and for certain agricultural purposes (but not irrigation). Apart from resort to common law action, there is no means of preventing riparian owners from abstracting water from the stream. Such action may be taken only by a party having an interest in the water concerned.

3. STATUTE LAW

ENGLAND AND WALES

From time to time, local authorities and statutory water undertakers (or water authorities) promote private local legislation containing provisions relating to groundwater. When there is such legislation it must be referred to as it may affect the rights enjoyed at common law, although as has been seen from some cases referred to above (for example, *New River Company v Johnson*), legislation may have a more limited effect than may first appear. It was not until the Water Act 1945 that it became necessary for Parliament to provide some regulation and control throughout the country, and then only to a limited extent.

The Water Act 1945

Section 14 of the Water Act 1945 provided that the Minister of Health, if satisfied that special measures for the conservation of water in any area were necessary in the public interest, whether for the protection of public or industrial water supplies, may make an order defining the area as a "protected area". In a protected area, no persons could construct a borehole or abstract water except in accordance with a licence from the Minister, unless it was done by a person for the domestic purposes of his household, or was authorised by some enactment.

The licensing provisions in Section 14 were repealed by the Water Resources Act 1963 but, provided an application was made within three months, a licence which was extant at 31 March 1965 could be continued as a licence of right under the Water Resources Act in terms and subject to conditions corresponding as nearly as may be to those contained in the licence under section 14. Section 14(9) remains in force, and is no longer restricted to areas protected by orders made prior to 1965. It provides that no person shall cause or allow any underground water to run to waste from any well, borehole or other work, except for the purpose of testing the extent or quality of the supply, or of cleansing, sterilising, examining, or repairing the work. The sub-section also prohibits any abstraction in excess of a person's reasonable requirements. That prohibition is of value in so far as it might be invoked to prevent a person allowing artesian discharges to run to waste. But an abstractor who holds a licence may abstract water to the extent permitted by the licence, and an abstractor who is taking water for a purpose for which a licence is not required by reason of the exemptions in Section 24 of the Water Resources Act 1963 (see later) would lose the benefit of the exemption if he took more water than is permitted by it, and thus be in contravention of the 1963 Act. There is a proviso to the subsection, similar to that in 24(4) of the Water Resources Act, that where underground water interferes or threatens to interfere, with the execution or operation of underground works, whether water works or not, it shall not be an offence to allow the water to run to waste so far as may be necessary to enable the works to be executed or operated if no other method of disposing of the water is reasonably practicable.

A contravention of the sub-section is subject to a penalty on summary conviction of £200, and the court may make an order that the well shall be effectively sealed, or requiring other work to be carried out as may be necessary to prevent waste of water. If a person fails to comply with an order, the court may authorise the water authority to take such steps as may be necessary to execute the order and any expenses so incurred may be recovered summarily as a civil debt. The section also confers on a water authority specific powers of entry for the purpose of that section.

Section 15 of the Water Act 1945 enables a water undertaker to enter into an agreement with an owner or occupier of land or with a local authority, for the execution and maintenance of such works as the undertaker considers necessary for the purpose of draining the land, or for more effectively collecting, conveying or preserving the purity of water which the undertakers are authorised to take.

Section 21 makes it an offence for any person by his act or neglect to cause pollution, or a likelihood of pollution, of any spring, well, borehole or adit from which water is taken for human consumption or domestic purposes, or for the manufacture of food or drink for human consumption.   Section 22 of the 1945 Act enables water undertakers to acquire land for the purpose of protecting from pollution any water which belongs to the undertakers, or which they are authorised to take, whether it is on the surface or underground.

Under Section 34 a water undertaker may make a temporary discharge of water into any watercourse for the purpose of constructing, altering, repairing or cleaning any well or borehole.

Section 71 of the Third Schedule to the Water Act 1945 makes it an offence for any person manufacturing or supplying gas to cause any gas liquor to run, or be conducted into, any drain communicating with any spring, or into any depression in the ground in proximity to any spring or well belonging to a water undertaker, or wilfully to do any other act so as to foul any water of a water undertaker.

The Water Resources Act 1963

The Water Resources Act 1963 contains provisions whereby water authorities, as successors to river authorities, can in the public interest control the abstraction of groundwater.

"Water Resources" is defined as meaning water for the time being contained in any source of supply, and (in relation to groundwater) "source of supply" means any underground strata in the area. "Underground strata" is defined as strata subjacent to the surface.

For the purpose of the Act, water for the time being contained in a well, borehole or similar work (including any adit or passage constructed to facilitate the collection of water), or in any excavation into underground strata where the level of the water in the excavation depends wholly or mainly on water emerging from the strata, is to be regarded as water contained in the underground strata.

Thus, water contained in a gravel pit or quarry primarily fed by percolation or discharge through the sides or by artesian pressure through the base is groundwater, while water in a clay pit filled by precipitation or surface drainage is not.

Although water flowing in a surface water stream or river which is primarily sustained from a spring or other underground source is regarded at common law as groundwater for the purpose of determining the rights and obligations as between the owner of the underground strata and the riparian owners *(Chasemore v Richards (1843-60) 60 All ER 77* and *Bleachers Association v Chapel-en-le-Frith RDC (1932) All ER 60)*, a surface river or stream is always an "inland water" for the purpose of the Water Resources Act, even though the whole of the flow may be sustained by a spring or a discharge from underground strata.

But the Water Resources Act provides that any reference to "water in underground strata" includes water so contained otherwise than in a sewer, pipe, reservoir, tank or other underground works constructed in any strata, so that water flowing in an underground river or stream through some natural passage or cavity is to be regarded as "groundwater" for all purposes of the Act, even though at common law it may be subject to principles applied to surface water channels. A well is not a "reservoir, tank, or other underground work" in the concept of the Act.

The provisions in the Water Resources Act relating to groundwater primarily regulate the powers of the water authority and compulsorily modify the rights of the individual as an abstractor, or as a potential abstractor. Matters arising between individual owners remain subject to common law but see *Cargill v Gotts (1981) All ER 682*. The rights and obligations of a water authority in their capacity as statutory water undertaker, and in relation to the public generally, will be subject to common law except in so far as the Water Act 1945, the Water Resources Act 1963 or any local Act or statutory order otherwise provides. But a water authority in discharging their regulatory functions must take into consideration the interests of those who may be affected by any abstraction.

The point at which underground water emerging from the ground becomes an inland water for the purposes of the Act may give rise to difficulty. So far as is known, there have been no decisions on that, but it would seem that if water, which is drawn off by a pipe before, or at the point at which it emerges from the ground, is immediately collected in a tank then the water is groundwater. But once it has discharged to form a stream, however rudimentary it may be, then it is to be regarded as an inland water. The Act does not confer directly any rights, or impose any obligations, as between individuals, although it was held by the Court of Appeal in *Cargill v Gotts (1981) A11 ER 682* that the plaintiff in an action against a neighbour could not rely on an abstraction of water subsequent to the introduction of licensing control (30 June 1963) to establish an easement by prescription, as the court would not recognise an easement established by an illegal activity. The court also held that, although an easement established prior to the introduction of licensing control was not destroyed by the Act, it could not be lawfully exercised unless a licence was obtained as required by the Act. The plaintiff was entitled to an easement to take water by virtue of prescription prior to 30 June 1963, but he was only entitled to exercise that easement subject to his obtaining a licence under the Act.

Section 135 provides that the sections which restrict the abstraction of water, prohibit the pollution of groundwater, and relate to borings to prevent water in underground strata interfering with engineering operations shall not confer any right of action in civil proceedings, nor derogate from any right of action, or other remedy (whether civil or criminal) in proceedings instituted otherwise than under the Act.

Water Conservation

A water authority's functions in relation to groundwater fall within the general responsibility for water conservation. Section 10 of the Water Act 1973, re-enacting 4 of the Water Resources Act 1963, provides that it shall be the duty of each water authority to take all such action as they may from time to time consider necessary or expedient, or as they may be directed to take, for the purpose of conserving, redistributing or otherwise augmenting water resources in their area, of securing the proper use of water resources, or of transferring any such resources to the area of another water authority. The powers to discharge that duty are those contained in the Water Resources Act 1963, although para 2 of Schedule 3 of the Water Act 1973 confers a general power on water authorities "to do anything which in the opinion of the authority is calculated to facilitate, or is conducive or incidental to the discharge of any of their functions". In the event of a dispute it would, of course, be for the courts to determine the scope of that general power; and some think it would be wise to exercise it with caution. The duties imposed on river authorities under Part III of the Water Resources Act 1963 as to the assessment of water resources and related matters, including the express power to investigate water in underground strata, have for the most part been repealed by the Water Act 1973. But Section 24 of that Act then reimposes on water authorities the duty to carry out periodical reviews and prepare plans and programmes. In exercising their general powers, water authorities can investigate water in underground strata, and perform the other functions which were more specifically contained in Part III of the 1963 Act.

Section 23 of the Water Resources Act, subject to certain exceptions, prohibits, after 30 June 1963, the abstraction of water from a source of supply, unless the abstraction is authorised by licence, and is made in accordance with the conditions prescribed by the licence.

When a licence is required in respect of an abstraction from underground strata, the construction or extension of a well whereby water may be abstracted must also be licensed, and the installation or modification of any machinery or apparatus whereby an additional quantity of water may be abstracted must not be contrary to the provisions of the licence.

Section 24 contains the exceptions to the general requirement that abstractions must be licensed. An abstraction of a quantity of water not exceeding 1000 gallons (4546 l) which is not part of a continuous operation, or a series of operations whereby the aggregate exceeds 1000 gallons, is exempt. It was held in *Cargill v Gotts* that each abstraction from a source of supply to fill a bowser for an agricultural purpose was part of a series of operations the object of which was to meet the water requirements of the land, and the exception was not intended to authorise any one person to abstract from time to time as much water as he pleased from any one source provided that each operation did not exceed 1000 gallons.

A licence is not required for an abstraction from underground strata in so far as the water is abstracted by or on behalf of an individual as a supply for the domestic purposes of his household. As the exception applies to water abstracted "on behalf of an individual" it would include an abstraction to supply the domestic requirements of employees, and perhaps others taking water from a small private estate supply, but the courts have not hitherto had to consider the extent of that exemption.

A licence is not required in respect of an abstraction from underground strata made to prevent groundwater interfering with any mining, quarrying, engineering, building or other operation, or to prevent damage to works resulting from any such operation. The exemption is not lost if water abstracted is then used in connection with the operation (e.g. gravel washing) instead of being run to waste.

Section 24(9) provides that an abstraction of water, or the construction or extension of any well, or the installation or modification of machinery or apparatus is exempt from licensing if the purpose is to ascertain the presence or the quantity or quality of groundwater, or the effect of the abstraction on another well, provided that the consent of the water authority is obtained and any conditions which the authority may impose are complied with. Strictly a water authority may not be able to invoke that exception in so far as they cannot give themselves a consent, but there is no provision which requires the consent of the Secretary of State in respect of work undertaken by a water authority under that sub-section, and it appears that a water authority may be able to rely on their general powers under para 2 of Schedule 3 of the Water Act 1973.

Section 25 enables the Secretary of State by order to make further exceptions to the licensing requirement in a particular area, but no order has so far been made. A person who holds a licence to abstract water, or who may abstract water in circumstances in which he is exempt from the need for a licence, enjoys a "protected right" to abstract water to the extent authorised by the licence and in accordance with the provisions, or to the extent permitted by the exemption. That is to say, a protected right includes an abstraction which is licensed, and an abstraction for which no licence is required by reasons of the exceptions contained in Section 24.

A person may apply for a licence to abstract from underground strata if he is the occupier of land comprising the underground strata, or if the water is groundwater contained in an excavation in underground strata and he satisfies the water authority that he has, or at the time the licence may take effect, that he will have a right of access to land comprising the underground strata. It is sufficient if a person can satisfy the water authority that he has entered into negotiations for the acquisition of an interest in land, such as an easement.

A water authority must not grant a licence authorising an abstraction which would derogate from protected rights enjoyed by other licence holders, or by persons who are taking water for a purpose for which a licence is not required. When considering an application for a licence to abstract groundwater the water authority must take account of any protected rights in the groundwater, and in a surface water stream if the abstraction of groundwater could have an adverse effect on the flow of that stream. Furthermore, section 29(7) expressly imposes an obligation on a water authority when considering an application for a licence to abstract groundwater to have regard to the requirements of existing lawful uses of water abstracted from those strata, whether for agriculture, industry, water supply or other purposes. If the abstraction of groundwater is likely to affect the flow, level, or volume of inland water then the water authority must have regard to the criteria to be taken into account in relation to a working minimum acceptable flow, such as the character of the inland water and its surroundings, its natural beauty, the safeguarding of public health, and the meeting of general requirements and demands on the water.

There is no definition of "lawful uses", but the intention appears to be that a water authority must take full account of all the consequences which might result from permitting an abstraction. This reverses the position at common law in respect of an abstraction of percolating water in circumstances in which a licence is now required, as previously a person could take all the water he required, regardless of the effect that the abstraction might have on his neighbours (see *Chasemore v Richards*). The position remains as it was in respect of abstractions for which, by reason of the exceptions under Section 24, licences are not required. It must be noted also that in the case of an application for a licence of right a river authority was obliged to grant the application regardless of the effect the abstraction may have had.

A water authority may be under some disadvantage as regards the obligation to those who enjoy protected rights for which licences are not required, as the water authority may not be aware of their protected rights. If the water authority, be it deliberately or inadvertently, grant or vary a licence which does derogate from a protected right the licence is nevertheless valid, and in any action brought against the licence holder it would be a good defence for him to prove that the abstraction was in accordance with the licence. The existence of the licence does not absolve the licensee from liability for negligence or breach of contract.

If in breach of their duty a water authority do grant a licence which results in a derogation of a protected right the duty is not enforceable by criminal proceedings, or by any proceedings for prohibition or injunction, but the person entitled to the protected right may sue the water authority for damages for breach of statutory duty. At the time of writing it is believed that no such proceedings have been taken.

A holder of a licence of right will not have any remedy in respect of derogation if it is legally possible for him to carry out alterations which would avoid the derogation, such as the alteration of works, or the modification of machinery or apparatus within the terms of his licence. So it would seem that a holder of a licence relating to a well or borehole who can deepen it to obtain water, at least to any maximum depth which may be specified in his licence, or who can put in larger pumps, must do so before he can resort to litigation to protect his interests.

Under Section 50 the Secretary of State may direct a water authority to grant, or vary, a licence which may derogate from protected rights, but the water authority will nevertheless have a liability in damages to the holders of the protected rights for breach of statutory duty. The Secretary of State may, if he thinks fit, repay to the water authority the amount of the damages which have been paid and any costs which have been incurred.

It will be a good defence in an action for damages if the water authority can show that the derogation was wholly or mainly attributable to exceptional shortage of rain, or to an accident or other unforeseen act, or to an event not caused by and outside the control of the water authority.

A practice has been established in relation to protected rights which may be affected by major groundwater schemes undertaken by a water authority of including in the licence a general provision for compensation. The general provision is to the effect that if a protected person (i.e. a person enjoying a protected right) within a defined distance of the point of abstraction and the water authority as licence holder agree that there has been a reduction in the supply available to the protected person such that he is prevented from taking water to the extent permitted by the protected right at the time the licence is granted, then the water authority may afford an alternative supply of water at their expense on terms to be agreed or settled by arbitration, or may carry out alterations or extensions to the protected source as may be necessary to offset or dimish the effect of any diminution. It would appear that if the protected person and the water authority cannot agree that there has been a reduction in the water available the protected person can only pursue his remedy as provided in the Act, unless a statute or statuory instrument authorising the water authority's works provides otherwise.

Public Health Act 1936

By Section 124 all public pumps, wells and other works used for the gratuitous supply of water to the inhabitants of any part of a district are vested in the local authority, and are under their control, and they may cause the works to be maintained and supplied with wholesome water. If the local authority are satisfied that the works are no longer needed, or that the water is polluted and it is not reasonably practicable to remedy the cause of pollution, they may close the works. It was held in *South Devon Water Board v Gibson (1955) 2 All ER 813* that the section did not apply to a supply from a well to houses through pipes, and that such an installation was vested in the water board who had taken over from the local authority the supply of water, and could then make a charge for providing the same.

It was held in *Holmfirth LB v Shore (1895) 59 JP 344* that a stone trough fed by water from a spring was either a well or a reservoir. If it was a well then it would appear that the water must be groundwater.

Under Section 125 a parish council (or community council in Wales) may utilise any well or spring, provide facilities for obtaining water therefrom, and execute works of maintenance or improvement. The section was in part repealed by the Water Act 1973, but it is significant that the power remains with parish and community councils.

Section 140 provides that if a local authority are of the opinion that water from a well which is not vested in them is, or is likely to be, used in preparation of food or drink for human consumption, is or is likely to be polluted, or to be prejudicial to health, they may apply to a court of summary jurisdiction for a summons to be issued to the owner or occupier of the premises. The court may order that the well be temporarily or permanently closed, or be only used for purposes outside the section, or the court may make such other order as may be necessary to prevent injury or danger to health.

Control of Pollution Act 1974

The Control of Pollution Act 1974 extends the limited powers of control previously provided by Section 72 of the Water Resources Act 1963.   Section 3(1) prohibits the deposit of household, industrial and commercial waste on any land, or the use of any equipment for the purpose of disposing of such waste, unless it is authorised by and in accordance with a disposal licence held by the occupier of the land. Sub-section (3) provides for a higher penalty if the waste deposited is of a kind which is poisonous, noxious or polluting, its presence is likely to give rise to an environmental hazard, and it is deposited in circumstances which indicate that it was abandoned or disposed of as waste. The deposit of waste is to be regarded as an environmental hazard if it threatens the pollution of water, whether surface or underground. A waste disposal authority are not obliged to grant a disposal licence for a site in respect of which planning permission has been granted if they are satisfied that its rejection is necessary to prevent the pollution of water, or a danger to public health.

Where a disposal authority propose to issue a disposal licence they are required to refer the proposal to the water authority and to consider their representations. If the water authority requests the licence to be withheld, or seeks the imposition of conditions which are not acceptable to the disposal authority, the dispute must be referred to the Secretary of State for determination. A disposal licence may include conditions as to precautions to be taken in the disposal, including precautions for the protection of water.

Section 7 imposes a duty on the waste disposal authority to serve on a licence holder a notice modifying the conditions of a licence to the extent necessary for ensuring that the activities do not cause the pollution of water. Furthermore, where a disposal licence is in force and it appears to the waste disposal authority that continuation of the activities would cause pollution which cannot be avoided by a modification of the conditions then the licence must be revoked.   ·

Section 9 provides that while a disposal licence is in force it shall be the duty of the waste disposal authority to take such steps as are necessary to ensure that the activities do not cause pollution of water, and to ensure that the licence holder complies with any conditions prescribed.

If the disposal site is on land occupied by the disposal authority then the disposal authority are under a duty to ensure that the site is used in accordance with conditions calculated to prevent the disposal of waste causing pollution of water. Before using any such land for waste disposal the disposal authority must refer the proposal to the water authority, and consider any representations which may be received from them. If a water authority request the disposal authority not to proceed with the proposal, or if the water authority disagree with the proposed conditions, then the matter may be referred to the Secretary of State and the disposal authority shall not proceed except in accordance with the Secretary of State's decision.

The Control of Pollution Act 1974 does not apply to all underground water as did Section 72 of the Water Resources Act 1963, but only to "specified underground water".

"Specified underground water" means underground water which is specified as water which is used, or which is expected by a water authority to be used, for any purpose. The specification is to be contained in a document to be prescribed by regulations, which must contain prescribed particulars, and must be available for inspection by the public.   Whether or not water is used, or is expected to be used, is a decision for the water authority, and there is no provision for an appeal against such a decision.

Underground water which has been specified, together with streams and those parts of the sea that are controlled waters, are collectively referred to as "relevant waters", and subject to the pollution of water provisions in Part II of the Act (see page 572).

Statute Law in Scotland

The main statutory provisions relating to groundwater (as well as surface water) in Scotland are contained in the Water (Scotland) Act 1980, which consolidated previous water legislation, and in the Control of Pollution Act 1974.

In order to understand fully the position with regard to groundwater, a knowledge of the general position on water abstraction and the statutory procedures governing it is helpful.

The most notable innovation upon the Scottish common law is the special right given to water authorities (regional and islands councils) to abstract water for public supply. Since 1946 water authorities, without prejudice to their rights to promote private legislation, have been able to apply to the Secretary of State for an order either approving an agreement to acquire water rights, or authorising them to acquire water rights compulsorily. The current provisions are contained in Section 17 of the Water (Scotland) Act 1980.

Where application for such an order is made, the proposal must be advertised and notice served on a number of bodies including river purification authorities*. There can then follow, if objections are made, either a public inquiry into the proposals or, if the Secretary of State so decides, special parliamentary procedure.

The 1980 Act states that an order (known as a 'water order') is required when a water authority wishes to take water from "any stream or other source" and this has been interpreted as applying in the case of underground sources whether streams or not. There is, however, some doubt as to whether it should apply in the case of percolating groundwater if the authority is the owner of the land. In a particular case in late 1981, it was decided that an order should be made so that the water authority's rights would be firmly established. For landowners other than water authorities rights to abstract groundwater are governed by common law. There is no general system of licensing of abstractions as in England and Wales.

Section 68 of the Scottish Act of 1980 makes similar provisions to those contained in Section 15 of the Water Act 1945. Also similar are the provisions for making byelaws for preventing pollution of water sources, contained in Section 71 of the 1980 Act. The provisions of Section 21 and 22 of the 1945 Act, making it an offence to pollute springs, wells etc and enabling water undertakers to acquire land for the purpose of preventing pollution of water, are paralleled in Section 75 and 76 of the 1980 Act.

Section 25 of the 1980 Act permits a district council or a water authority to construct public wells for supplying water to inhabitants of their district or supply area. Section 26 allows these authorities to close down wells vested in them or constructed under Section 25 if the wells are no longer required or become

---

*In Scotland, while water supply is the responsibility of the water authorities, water pollution control is the responsibility of, in the mainland, 7 river purification boards and, in the island areas, of the island councils as river purification authorities.

polluted. Under Section 27 an islands or district council may seek an order directing the closure or restriction of use of any source of supply not vested in them if it has, or is likely to, become dangerously polluted.

Section 93 of the 1980 Act requires any person who proposes to sink a well or borehole to more than 50 feet (15 m) below the surface to give notice in writing to the Natural Environment Research Council and to keep a detailed journal of the work. Authorised representatives of the said Council are to be allowed access to the works and information and the Council are to be supplied with a copy of the complete journal together with particulars of any tests made of the flow of water.

Hitherto (with the exception of a local Act covering the area of the Clyde River Purification Board) there has been no statutory provision to control polluting discharges into underground strata, other than for the protection of public water supply. However, controls over water pollution contained in Part II of the Control of Pollution Act 1974 will, as in England and Wales, extend to "specified underground water". This is defined for Scotland as "such underground water as may be prescribed". It has been announced that the Secretary of State intends to prescribe all underground water in Scotland.

The waste disposal provisions in Part I of the 1974 Act in general apply in Scotland as they do in England and Wales.

STATUTE LAW IN NORTHERN IRELAND

The Department of the Environment for Northern Ireland (DoENI) is the sole water authority for Northern Ireland for all matters affecting water, except for matters of urban and arterial drainage and for provision of water recreational facilities: these exceptions being functions of the Department of Agriculture for Northern Ireland (DANI). DoENI exercises its functions through the Water Service, advised by the Northern Ireland Water Council. DANI exercises its functions through its drainage division in consultation with the Drainage Council for Northern Ireland.

The fundamental statutes governing the water functions of DoENI and DANI, in respect of groundwater, are outlined below.

The Water Act (Northern Ireland) 1972

This Act provides that:

(1) The DoENI shall promote the conservation of the water resources of Northern Ireland.
(2) The DoENI shall promote the cleanliness of water in underground strata (strata subjacent to the surface of any land).
(3) The DoENI shall have regard to the protection of public health.
(4) A consent must be obtained from the DoENI for the discharge into any underground stratum of any trade or sewage effluent, or any other poisonous, noxious or polluting matter. The DoENI has powers to review and vary any consent at intervals of not less than three years.
(5) The DANI shall have regard to the conservation of water resources and to the prevention of pollution. It is an offence, with penalties, to pollute any underground strata.

The Water and Sewerage Services (Northern Ireland) Order 1973

This Order states that it is an offence, with penalties, to pollute any water owned by or controlled by the DoENI unless the polluter can prove that reasonable care was taken to prevent the pollution.

The Pollution Control and Local Government Order 1978

This Order (No. 1049 (NI 19)) provides for a disposal licence system for controlled waste which takes into account water considerations.

The Order also permits the DoENI to take remedial measures to prevent potential polluting matter from entering underground strata, or to remove, dispose of or mitigate the effects of any pollutant in underground strata.

4. ARTIFICIAL RECHARGE OF GROUNDWATER

In so far as recharging is a relatively new development in water conservation it may create legal problems which have not previously arisen. But it would seem that established common law principles as to nuisance and negligence would apply in England, Wales and Northern Ireland, and in particular the principle in *Rylands v Fletcher (1868-73) All ER1* that is something is taken onto land which would become a "nuisance" if it escaped then the person who takes it on to the land has a duty to ensure that it is not allowed to escape. The Water Resources Act 1971 (England and Wales) enables the Secretary of State to make an order authorising a water authority to discharge water into underground strata, subject to such conditions as he thinks necessary, and provided that it appears appropriate to facilitate the performance of water conservation. Such an order would be a defence to any proceedings based on "nuisance" but not in the event of any "negligence".

The Act provides that any person who suffers damage attributable to any discharge of water under such an order shall be entitled to compensation, and any extra expenditure which is attributable to the discharge which may be incurred by a public authority in carrying out their statutory function shall be deemed to be damage and recoverable from the water authority.

As any artificial recharge will almost certainly be carried out by a statutory authority under *ad hoc* statutory powers, reference must be made to these statutory powers to ascertain any conditions—in particular, any provisions for compensation for those who may suffer injury.

5. EEC DIRECTIVES

On 4 May 1976, the Council of the European Communities published a directive (No. 76/464/EEC) on the "pollution caused by certain dangerous substances discharged into the aquatic environment of the Community". It applies to:

    (*a*) inland surface water,
    (*b*) territorial waters,
    (*c*) internal coastal waters and
    (*d*) groundwater

and seeks to:

    (i) eliminate pollution by certain of the more dangerous substances (List I)
    (ii) reduce pollution by other less dangerous substances (List II).

The directive provided for a separate directive on protection of groundwater.

An EEC directive of 17 December 1979 (No. 80/68/EEC) states that its purpose is to prevent the pollution of groundwater by certain prescribed substances, and to check or eliminate the consequences of any pollution which has occurred. Groundwater means all water which is below the surface of the ground in the saturation zone, and in direct contact with the ground or subsoil. Pollution is defined as meaning the discharge by man, directly or indirectly, of substances or energy into groundwater the results of which are such as to endanger human health or water supplies, harm living resources and the aquatic ecosystems, or interfere with other legitimate uses of water.

The directive does not apply to domestic effluents from isolated buildings situated outside an area protected for abstraction of water for human consumption, to trivial discharges, or to discharges of radioactive substances which are the subject of other directives. Member states are required to take steps to prevent the introduction of List I substances, and to limit the introduction of List II substances. The obligations of members states as to investigation, surveillance and procedures are expressed in some detail.

Any artificial discharge for the purpose of groundwater management must be authorised by the member state on a case by case basis, and authorisation may only be granted if there is no risk of polluting groundwater.

Guidance on the implementation of this directive has been issued by the Department of the Environment, the Welsh Office (for England and Wales) and by the Scottish Office (for Scotland). This guidance makes it clear that implementation is to be achieved within the framework of existing legislation (including, that is, Part II of the Control of Pollution Act 1974).

INDEX